Physical Science

by

DONALD S. ALLEN
Professor of Chemistry
State University College of Education
Albany, New York

and

RICHARD J. ORDWAY
Professor of Geology
State University College of Education
New Paltz, New York

D. VAN NOSTRAND COMPANY, INC.
PRINCETON, NEW JERSEY
Toronto · London · New York

D. VAN NOSTRAND COMPANY, INC.
120 Alexander St., Princeton, New Jersey (*Principal office*)
24 West 40 Street, New York 18, New York

D. VAN NOSTRAND COMPANY, LTD.
358, Kensington High Street, London, W.14, England

D. VAN NOSTRAND COMPANY (Canada), LTD.
25 Hollinger Road, Toronto 16, Canada

First Published April 1960
Reprinted August 1960, July 1961

PRINTED IN THE UNITED STATES OF AMERICA

Preface

This text has been written for the non-science major who has had little or no previous training in the sciences and no mathematical training beyond elementary algebra. It is an outgrowth of a year course in the physical sciences which has been developed at State University College of Education, New Paltz, New York, over a period of nearly fifteen years.

No introductory course today, whether in a single science or in a more comprehensive work in physical science, makes any pretense of "covering the field" of science; scientific knowledge is far too extensive. Rather, the attempt here is to limit the discussion to a selected few significant topics and to treat each with some thoroughness. Anecdotal and historical materials have been strategically interspersed to lend color and interest to what is frequently regarded by the student as the dull descriptive aspect of science.

It is the conviction of the authors that chemistry and physics cannot be adequately interpreted unless mathematical concepts are included. It is also their experience that students often come to college with too limited an understanding of basic mathematical concepts. These concepts have been incorporated into the text as needed, in the early chapters at a very elementary level. While the maturity of level progressively increases in later chapters, only algebraic concepts are employed. The authors anticipate that their emphasis on a gradual thorough understanding of simple arithmetic and algebraic processes will successfully lead the student into a reasonably adequate mathematical interpretation of the sciences. All too often interest is lost early in a course by plunging the student into a maze of intricate symbolism which he is ill equipped to understand. As an illustration, the solving of physics problems is little more than guesswork until the student understands the principle of consistent units. Considerable attention is given to understanding this principle.

The text has been written in two independent sections: chemistry and physics in Chapters 1-14, earth science (astronomy, meteorology, and geology) in Chapters 15-33. This should be a convenient flexible arrangement, since either section may be used first. The earth science section offers additional flexibility as it has been organized so that the astronomy, meteorology, and geology units may be taken up in any order. Furthermore, if it is necessary to shorten a course, one or more of the later chapters in geology (except Chapters 32 and 33) can be omitted or assigned to top students as independent study without seriously impairing the continuity.

Although the authors recognize the importance of integrating ideas from the different physical sciences, the integration in this text is somewhat more limited than in a number of other physical science texts. Our experience has been that a chemist will usually be willing to teach physics and a physicist chemistry. Many instructors, especially of lesser experience, hesitate to attempt to teach in more than one science outside their major area. The geologist will usually teach astronomy if at the same time he does not have to grapple with the intricacies of chemistry and physics. The experienced professor who can capably teach in all the areas of physical science will find this arrangement a convenient one in that it focuses on two sciences at a time.

The authors are indebted to many people for inspiration and assistance in bringing this book to completion. President Emeritus James B. Conant of Harvard University should receive a goodly share of credit for providing the inspiration to initiate this work. One of us (Allen) was fortunate enough to participate in a summer course at Harvard in which Dr. Conant took time out from his busy life to lend inspiration to a group of college science teachers. The influence of the Harvard case histories is obvious throughout this book. Any errors or shortcomings are obviously the responsibility of the authors.

Many others shared generously in the work of getting this book into the world. Floyd Parker and Richard Madtes have read and criticized Chapters 1-14. Betty Burns, Rosetta Einenkel, and Livia Tenedini have assisted in typing the manuscript. The photographs taken especially for this text by Neil Croom are appreciated. Special thanks are due also to Martin Harris, Jr., and to Christoph Parade for execution of the drawings. Our wives, Kay Allen and Mary Jane Ordway, have assisted with the reading of the proof. The patience and forbearance of our families who have forgone or shortened vacations or curtailed other interesting activities so that this work might be completed are hereby gratefully acknowledged.

DONALD S. ALLEN
RICHARD J. ORDWAY

Albany, New York
New Paltz, New York
January 1960

Table of Contents

CONTENTS

The Length and Breadth of Measurement

AT THE southeastern corner of Sicily, an island in the Mediterranean just touching the toe of Italy, lies the city of Syracuse (Fig. 1-1). Today it is a city of some 50,000 people—certainly not a great metropolitan center. Twenty-two centuries ago it was among the wealthiest and largest cities in Europe, a rival of Athens and Alexandria in the realm of the intellectual and cultural. It was founded by

Archimedes (287-212 B.C.). A modern artist pictures the moment when the aging geometrician, deep in thought in his study, is surprised by the Roman soldier who killed him. According to legend, his last words, as the intruder's footstep blurred the lines of geometric figures traced on the sanded floor, were, "Be careful! You are spoiling my figures!" The Roman victor had been delayed for months by defensive machines devised by this man of genius.

Greeks, and in it the physical sciences reached the peak of their development in Greek civilization. One of its most famous inhabitants, a man largely responsible for its pre-eminence in the physical sciences, was Archimedes (287-212 B.C.). He is probably best known to us for the role he played in solving King Hieron's problem about the honesty of the royal jeweler.

The king gave the jeweler a lump of gold and asked him to make a

Fig. 1-1.

This map of the Mediterranean region shows the location of Syracuse, a city founded twenty-seven centuries ago by Corinthian Greeks. When Archimedes lived there (third century B.C.) it was the greatest city of Sicily and an important center of Greek science and mathematics.

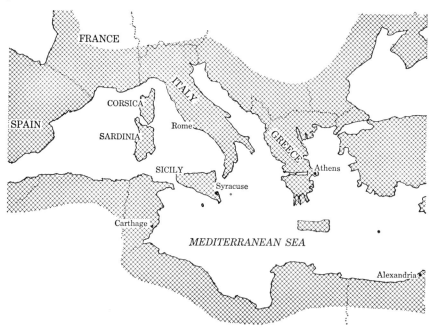

crown. When the job was finished, the king suspected that the crown did not contain all the gold he had given the jeweler; the weight of the crown was the same as that of the original lump of gold, but the king suspected that a less expensive metal had been substituted for some of it. Archimedes was brought in as a sort of scientific detective to find out if there was any reason to suppose that a substitution had been made. He was not to mar the crown in any way in his scientific sleuthing. The problem for a long time baffled even this astute mathematician. Then one day as Archimedes entered a local public bath, he watched how the water level rose higher and higher on the wall as more and more of his body became submerged.

What was unusual about such an observation? Anybody knows that the material substance of Archimedes' mortal frame could not occupy the same space as the water in the bath. Objects which are immersed in water push out of the way, or displace, an equal *volume* of water (Fig. '1-2). How could so commonplace an observation serve as the key to Archimedes' solution of so difficult a problem?

An object which is completely immersed in a liquid displaces a quantity of liquid equal to its own volume. An irregular object like a crown, whose volume could not be measured directly, is thus as easily measurable as a cube. In the kitchen the cook may use a similar method for making sure she has exactly half a cup of butter.

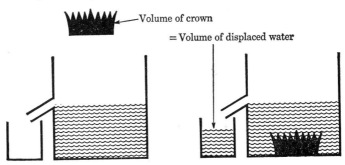

Fig. 1-2.

Every child has been asked the catch question, "Which is heavier, a pound of lead or a pound of cork?" Of course a pound is a pound: the difference between lead and cork is in the volume occupied, a pound of cork occupying a much larger volume than a pound of lead. In a word, lead is *denser* than cork. To understand the problem raised by the gold crown and its solution, we must first understand what is meant by density and the closely related quantity known as specific gravity.

The Concept of Density   If cubes of certain metals, each 1 centimeter on a side (2.54 cm = 1 in.), are weighed, their weights will be as shown in Fig. 1-3. Density may be practically defined as *weight per unit volume.* The density of gold is 19.3 grams per cubic centimeter.* (This may also be written 19.3 gm/cm³ or 19.3 gm/cc.) In order to calculate the density of an object, its weight must be divided by its volume. Density may also be expressed in other units of weight

Fig. 1-3.

Centimeter cubes of different metals have different weights. The weight of a unit cube is the density of the metal. Density is formally defined as mass per unit volume. It is numerically the same as weight per unit volume at sea level. Weight is distinguished from mass later in this chapter (See page 10, The Standard of Mass).

The specific gravity of a substance is the ratio of its density to the density of water. Since in the metric system the density of water is 1 gm/cc, the specific gravities of other substances are numerically the same as their densities: e.g., the density of gold being 19.3 gm/cc and the density of water 1 gm/cc, the specific gravity of gold = 19.3 gm/cc ÷ 1 gm/cc = 19.3.

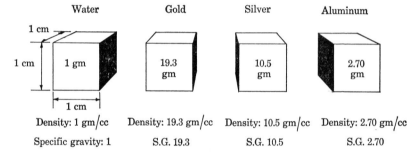

Water	Gold	Silver	Aluminum
1 gm	19.3 gm	10.5 gm	2.70 gm
Density: 1 gm/cc	Density: 19.3 gm/cc	Density: 10.5 gm/cc	Density: 2.70 gm/cc
Specific gravity: 1	S.G. 19.3	S.G. 10.5	S.G. 2.70

and volume, as for example in pounds per cubic foot. Water has a density of 1 gm/cc; this is equivalent to 62.4 lb/cu ft. The numerical value of the density depends, then, on the units used.

ILLUSTRATIVE PROBLEM

Determine the density of gold if the volume occupied by 4825 gm is 250.0 cc.

Solution

$$\text{Density} = \frac{\text{weight}}{\text{volume}}$$

$$\text{Density} = \frac{4825 \text{ gm}}{250.0 \text{ cc}} = 19.30 \text{ gm/cc}$$

The weight given, 4825 gm, is that occupying 250.0 units of volume

* The milliliter is often used in expressing liquid volumes. For all but the most precise measurements the milliliter and the cubic centimeter may be considered equivalent.

(250.0 cc). Density is numerically equal to the weight of a *single unit of volume.*

Specific Gravity   Specific gravity and density are closely related; in fact, the two may be identical in value. Specific gravity is defined as the ratio of the weight of an object to that of an equal volume of water:

$$\text{Specific gravity} = \frac{\text{weight of object}}{\text{weight of water, same volume as object}}$$

An overflow can filled with water (Fig. 1-2) is a very useful device for determining specific gravity because it provides a convenient means of obtaining a quantity of water whose volume is equal of that of the object.

Specific gravity may also be defined as the ratio of the density of the object to that of water.

$$\text{Specific gravity} = \frac{\text{density of object}}{\text{density of water}}$$

Specific gravity and the density are equal if the density of water is unity. Furthermore, the ratio of an object's density to that of water is equal to the weight ratio of similar unit volumes of these materials.

$$\text{Specific gravity} = \frac{\text{density of object}}{\text{density of water}} = \frac{\text{weight of 1 cu cm of object}}{\text{weight of 1 cu cm of water}}$$

$$= \frac{\text{weight of 1 cu ft of object}}{\text{weight of 1 cu ft of water}}$$

THE SOLUTION OF ARCHIMEDES' PROBLEM

In Fig. 1-3, we have taken equal units of volume of different metals and compared their weights: thus the density of gold is 19.3 gm/cc, the density of silver is 10.5 gm/cc, and the density of aluminum is 2.70 gm/cc. We might in the same way take equal units of weight of each metal and then compare their volumes: if gold weighs 19.3 gm/cc, then the volume of 1 gram of gold is

$$\text{Volume} = \frac{\text{weight}}{\text{density}} = \frac{1 \text{ gm}}{19.3 \text{ gm/cc}} = 0.0518 \text{ cc}$$

Similarly, the volume of 1 gram of aluminum is 0.370 cc. The number 0.370 is considerably larger than 0.0952, which is larger than

0.0518; thus the volume occupied by 1 gram of silver or by 1 gram of aluminum is larger than the volume occupied by 1 gram of gold. Since the crown had the same weight as the original gold, its volume must be greater if the jeweler substituted an equal weight of silver or aluminum (though he could not have done this: aluminum was not available in ancient Sicily) for the gold. What Archimedes suddenly realized as he plunged into his bath was that for a given weight, a metal of smaller specific gravity or density than gold would have a greater volume than gold and hence would displace a greater amount of water (Fig. 1-4). This gave him the solution to the king's problem,

The solution of Archimedes' problem. Equal weights of metals having different densities will displace unequal volumes of water. The greater the density, the smaller the volume displaced. The lump of pure gold balances the crown in a pair of scales, but the crown proves to be made of an alloy, for it displaces a larger volume of water than the lump.

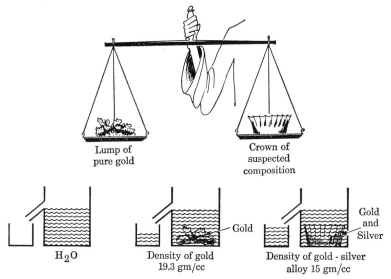

Lump of
pure gold

Crown of
suspected
composition

H_2O

Density of gold
19.3 gm/cc

Gold

Density of gold - silver
alloy 15 gm/cc

Gold
and
Silver

Fig. 1-4.

and this is why he raced home shouting "Eureka! Eureka!" (I have found it). Once home, he promptly filled a vessel with water to the brim, plunged the king's crown into it, and measured the overflow. Sure enough, the amount of water displaced by the crown proved to be greater than the amount displaced by a lump of pure gold that balanced the crown in a pair of scales. The king's jeweler was dealt with accordingly.

STANDARDS

The fact that Archimedes was able to solve the crown problem implies that he was able to make measurements of fair accuracy. The measuring devices available to him allowed him to discriminate between the weights of equal volumes of material, or between the volumes of equal weights of material.

One of the marks of the advance of civilization has been the ability to make comparisons between quantities with more and more accuracy. As long as linear measures depended on the span of a human hand or the length of a foot, there was opportunity for a wide margin of error; the standard could vary with the individual hand or foot. Progress in the sciences of physics and chemistry has been associated with ability to define ever more precisely our standards of quantitative measure and to make accurate comparisons with these standards. Modern analytical balances enable us now to measure weights to the nearest millionth of a gram. Such accuracy was unattainable even a hundred years ago. Before examining the scientific implications of standards, however, let us examine their impact on everyday life.

In your city, or perhaps in your county, if you live in a small community, lives a man called the Sealer of Weights and Measures. It is his responsibility to check the accuracy of devices for weighing and measuring in order to assure you of full measure when you purchase commodities, or even to protect merchants who may be overgenerous in dispensing their wares. You may have noticed the seals which the Sealer affixes to gasoline pumps in filling stations or to scales in grocery stores after he has made his inspection. He is the custodian of the local sets of standards. Once in about every five years he must take his sets of standard weights, standard measures, and standard tapes to the State Bureau of Weights and Measures for calibration. State standards in turn are checked at our National Bureau of Standards every ten years, and once in twenty years our national standards are checked against the international standards which are kept at the International Bureau of Weights and Measures near Paris, France. These standards are the ultimate standards for most of the countries of the civilized world today.

The Standard of Length The international standard of linear measure is the standard meter. It is simply the distance between two fine parallel lines ruled on a bar composed of an alloy of platinum and iridium. Since this alloy neither expands nor contracts to any appreciable extent with changing temperature, it is particularly valuable for maintaining constant dimensions. The standard meter is 39.37 inches long, i.e., some $3\frac{1}{3}$ inches longer than a yard. The yard is defined in this country as 3600/3937 meter.

When the meter was agreed upon as the international standard, several replicas were made up for use in the various countries. Our National Bureau of Standards in Washington obtained prototype meters numbered 21 and 27, which are the standards in the United States. Briefly, here are the events which led to the establishment of this length as a standard.

In the seventeenth century the French astronomer Mouton proposed that the length of a pendulum making a given number of swings in a certain period of time be regarded as linear standard. This length was remarkably constant for any given location. However, the suggestion had to be discarded when Richer, in 1671, discovered that the number of swings per second for a pendulum of given length changed with the latitude because of the differences in gravitational pull at different latitudes on the earth (see Chapter 4).

Late in the eighteenth century a movement was started in France

Fig. 1-5.

The distance surveyed during the eighteenth century in establishing the standard meter lay on the earth's meridian that passes near Dunkirk, France, and Barcelona, Spain.

to define the meter as one ten-millionth of the distance from the earth's equator to the pole, measured along a meridian (line of longitude). Since it was impractical to measure so long a distance, it was finally agreed to make a survey of the comparatively short distance between Dunkirk, on the northern coast of France, and Barcelona, Spain — cities which are located at sea level and on the same line of longitude (Fig. 1-5). The difference between the latitudes of these two cities gave the angle subtended at the earth's center corresponding to the measured distance between them along the earth's surface. The distance from the equator to the pole could then be calculated, since this distance was in the same proportion to the measured distance between the two cities as 90° was to the difference in degrees between their latitudes (see Fig. 1-6). The meter was established as one ten-millionth of this calculated distance. In later years, sad to say, the survey was found to be in error. Thus the standard meter is actually

Calculating the distance from pole to equator: $x/675.3$ mi $= 90°/9.79°$; $x = 6208$ mi. A cross section of a quadrant of the earth, showing Barcelona and Dunkirk and the distance used in determining the length of the standard meter. The meter was intended to be one ten-millionth of the arc between the North Pole and the equator. Despite the inaccuracy of the original survey, the meter is very nearly the intended length.

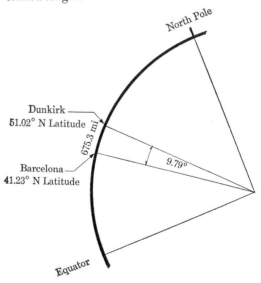

Dunkirk
51.02° N Latitude

675.3 mi

Barcelona
41.23° N Latitude

North Pole

9.79°

Equator

Fig. 1-6.

just an arbitrary length rather than one ten-millionth of the distance from equator to pole.

The standard meter may also be defined as a multiple of the wave length of the orange light emitted by krypton atoms of mass 86 (Kr^{86}). The concept of wave length is most readily understood if we consider the waves produced when a ball is dropped into a placid pool of water. A series of ripples is sent out which in cross section would appear as shown in Fig. 1-7. A wave length is simply the linear

A wave length is the distance between the corresponding parts of successive waves.

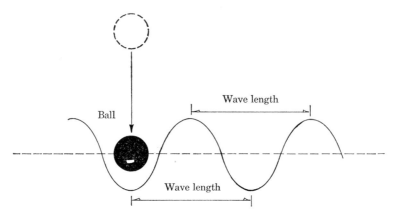

Fig. 1-7.

distance between the crests of any two successive waves. The lineai distance between the crests of waves sent out by Kr^{86} is exceedingly small—so small, in fact, that 1,650,763 successive wave lengths are needed to equal the length of the standard meter. Scientists at the International Conference on Weights and Measures held in Paris in October 1960 gave official recognition to the adoption of the krypton wave length as the primary linear standard.

The Standard of Mass   Mass may be described as the amount of matter in a body. It is not synonymous with volume, which is the amount of space occupied by the body. It is not the same as weight, although masses may be compared by weighing and the weights in a weight set are often referred to as either masses or weights.*

* The mass of a body can be measured by the resistance it offers to a change in motion— by its *inertia* (see Chapter 3) compared with the inertia of the standard kilogram.

The inertial effect of a kilogram mass (its resistance to the action of a force) is the same in different latitudes or at different elevations above sea level. However the kilogram mass suspended from a spring balance would *weigh* less on a mountain top than at sea level. Thus mass is independent of location on the surface of the earth. Weight on the other hand varies with location, decreasing as the object is moved farther from the earth's center.

The national standard of length in Washington, D.C. Prototype Meter No. 27 is a platinum iridium bar duplicating the international standard meter in Sèvres, France. Prototype Kilogram No. 20, the national standard of mass, duplicates the international kilogram. Both standards are made of an alloy of 90% platinum and 10% iridium. Adoption of the krypton wave length as the primary linear standard makes the meter bar a secondary standard. (Courtesy, National Bureau of Standards)

Fig. 1-8.

The international standard of mass is a platinum-iridium cylinder whose diameter and height are both approximately $1\frac{1}{2}$ inches. It is called the standard kilogram and is one of the primary standards housed at the International Bureau of Weights and Measures near Paris. Our national standards of mass, housed in the National Bureau of Standards in Washington, D.C., are replicas of this international standard, prototype kilograms numbered 4 and 20. The standard kilogram was originally intended to be the mass of a cube of water 10 centimeters on a side at 4°C, the temperature at which the density of water is a maximum. Subsequent refinements showed the original measurement of this mass to be in error, and hence the standard kilogram is, like the meter, an arbitrary standard.

UNITS OF MEASUREMENT

When we measure a quantity, we single out some property such as length or mass for comparison with some standard. If we describe the desk top as being 2 meters long, we mean that two meter sticks laid end to end would be equal to the length of the desk. If an object has a mass of 3 kilograms, this means that three standard kilogram masses are required to balance the object in the opposite pan of a balance.

The meter and kilogram are standards of measure, but these units would not be convenient for all measurements. A great many different units of measure are in use, the unit chosen for a particular measurement depending on the size of the object or distance to be measured. If the distance between cities is to be measured, the mile is used in this country, the kilometer (about 0.6 mile) in Europe and many other parts of the world. The unit of measure used in estimating astronomical distances is the light-year (the distance traveled by light in 1 year) which is almost 10,000,000,000,000,000 times as long as the meter. On the other hand, light waves are extremely small and are measured in angstrom units, which are only 1/10,000,000,000 as long as the meter. Through the years, then, different systems of units have been developed as needed for the measurements which were to be made.

By a simple operation, either multiplication or division, any linear unit may be converted into the corresponding number of linear units of a different size. But linear units can never be converted into units of mass. Units of length and mass are known as "fundamental" units.

Units of area and volume are called "derived units," since two or three linear units must be multiplied to obtain them. Density, which is defined in terms of weight and volume and so involves more than one fundamental unit, is also derived.

Systems of Units   Two systems of units are in general use today in this country, the metric and the English. There are numerous other systems, of course, such as the Troy weights of the jeweler and type sizes in printing, which belong to particular trades and industries. The metric system is almost universal in scientific research, but the English system still prevails in the United States and Canada in business and commerce. Some people feel that life would be simplified if we were to discard the English system altogether and use only the metric system.

Table 1-1   METRIC TABLES, WITH ENGLISH EQUIVALENTS

LENGTH	VOLUME
1 kilometer (km) = 1000 m	1 kiloliter (kl) = 1000 liter
1 hektometer (hm) = 100 m	1 hektoliter (hl) = 100 liter
1 dekameter (dkm) = 10 m	1 dekaliter (dkl) = 10 liter
1 meter	1 liter
1 decimeter (dm) = 0.1 m	1 deciliter (dl) = 0.1 liter
1 centimeter (cm) = 0.01 m	1 centiliter (cl) = 0.01 liter
1 millimeter (mm) = 0.001 m	1 milliliter (ml)^a = 0.001 liter

1 m = 39.37 in.   1 liter = about 1.06 U.S. liq qt
1 km = 0.62 mi

WEIGHT

1 kilogram (kg)   = 1000 gm
1 hektogram (hg) = 100 gm
1 dekagram (dkg) =   10 gm
1 gram
1 decigram (dg)   =   0.1 gm
1 centigram (cg) =   0.01 gm
1 milligram (mg) =   0.001 gm

1 kg   = 2.2 lb
453.6 gm = 1 lb

^{a} For all practical purposes, 1 milliliter = 1 cubic centimeter

One of the advantages of the metric system is that the conversion from measurements in one metric unit to those in another (e.g., meters to centimeters) is performed entirely by multiplying or dividing by powers of 10—by moving a decimal point. This is far simpler than multiplying or dividing by such numbers as 12, 16, and 5280 as in the English system. The following problem illustrates this difference.

ILLUSTRATIVE PROBLEM

A distance of 2542 ft (775 meters) is what part of 1 mile (or what part of 1 kilometer)?

Solution: English System

$$1 \text{ ft} = \frac{1}{5280} \text{ mi}$$

$$2542 \text{ ft} = \frac{2542}{5280} \text{ mi}$$

$$2542 \text{ ft} = 0.481 \text{ mi}$$

$$
\begin{array}{r}
0.481 \\
528)\overline{254.200} \\
211\,2 \\
\hline
43\,00 \\
42\,24 \\
\hline
760 \\
528 \\
\hline
232
\end{array}
$$

Solution: Metric System

$$1 \text{ m} = 0.001 \text{ km}$$
$$775 \text{ m} = 0.775 \text{ km}$$

Compare the ease of computing this problem in the metric system with the more cumbersome arithmetic in the English system. Our adoption of the metric system as the sole system of weights and measures would also eliminate altogether the many conversions now necessary from one system of units to another—yards to meters, miles to kilometers, and so on. However, the issue is a controversial one. There are good arguments on both sides. The English system has been adequate, the change would cause untold confusion, and converting or replacing all our measuring devices would be enormously costly.

Since we do in fact have and use the two systems now, problems involving a conversion from one unit to another are common. The point which should always be kept in mind in any conversion of units is that if the new unit is larger than the given unit, then we must have a smaller number of converted units; if the new unit is smaller than the given unit we must have a larger number of converted units. If we are changing inches to centimeters, we must end up with more centimeters than we had inches because the centimeter is a smaller unit (Fig. 1-9). If we are changing yards into meters, we must end

Fig. 1-9.

The centimeter is a smaller unit of linear measure than the inch. In a given length there will always be a larger number of centimeters than inches.

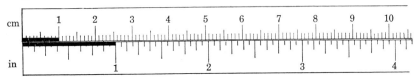

up with fewer meters than we had yards because the meter is a larger unit than the yard. If we change miles to kilometers, should we have a smaller or a larger number of kilometers?

APPROXIMATION: SIGNIFICANT FIGURES

For the scientist, 10 grams does not have the same meaning as 10.00 grams. The first measurement has two significant figures, the second has four. The former implies that the measurement is correct to the nearest gram—i.e., lies between 9.5 and 10.5 grams; the latter, that it is correct to the nearest 0.01 gram—i.e., lies between 9.995 and 10.005 grams. The number of significant figures which may be obtained in a given measurement depends on the measuring instrument used. A micrometer caliper will give a larger number of significant figures in measuring the diameter of a steel cylinder than will a ruler.

Suppose that we measure the length of a block of wood by means of a meter stick having only centimeter divisions as shown in Fig. 1-10.

Fig. 1-10.

This ruler tells us that the length of the block is between 5 and 6 centimeters. We estimate it to be 5.7 cm.

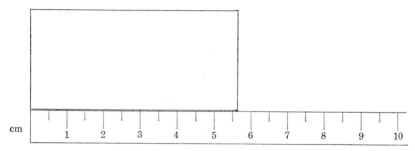

The length of the block is apparently between 5 and 6 centimeters. We imagine the distance between the fifth and sixth centimeter marks to be divided off into ten equal subdivisions. We estimate that the edge of the block would coincide with the seventh subdivision; so we record 5.7 cm as the length of the block. Other observers might judge it to be 5.6 or 5.8 cm. Tenths of centimeters are then said to be "doubtful figures," but are nevertheless included as significant figures.

Suppose that the block is measured by a ruler actually having ten subdivisions between each pair of centimeter marks, so that we no longer have to imagine them. The length is between 5.6 and 5.7 cm, as shown in Fig. 1-11. The edge of the block is estimated to be $\frac{2}{10}$ of the distance from the 5.6 to the 5.7 mark and the length is recorded as 5.62 cm. In this case we are certain of the 6, and the final 2 is the doubtful figure.

The most accurate possible measurement is sometimes of vital importance in scientific research. Near the end of the nineteenth century, the British scientist Sir William Ramsay noted that the density of the "nitrogen" produced by removing oxygen from air was 1.2572 grams per liter, whereas nitrogen prepared from ammonium compounds had a density of only 1.2505 grams per liter. The difference between the two was less than 0.007 gram per liter, but persisted even under the most careful possible measurement when the experiments were repeated.

Fig. 1-11.

Measuring the block with a ruler marked in millimeters indicates a length between 5.6 and 5.7 cm. We estimate it to be 5.62 cm.

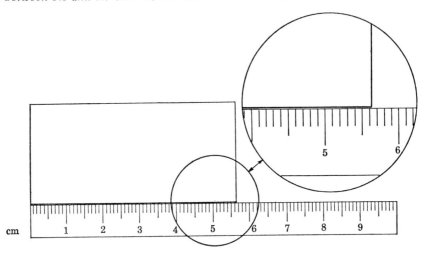

Several decades before, Bunsen and Kirchhoff in Germany had developed the spectroscopic method of identifying chemical elements. By obtaining the spectral lines emitted by these two kinds of nitrogen and finding their patterns to be quite different, Ramsay was finally able to demonstrate that the supposed nitrogen obtained from air actually contained a hitherto unknown gas, which he called argon. This discovery of a new element depended in the first place on the availability of measuring instruments capable of discriminating weights to the nearest 0.001 gram; a balance allowing only two-place accuracy would not have given Ramsay the hint he needed for the discovery of this new element. The discovery depended also, of course, on the availability of the spectroscopic method, which will be discussed in Chapter 8.

We think of the scientist as making always the most accurate possible measurements. This impression is not quite justified by the facts. Often he may be satisfied to obtain the weight of an object to two decimal places, say 12.13 grams, when he has available in the laboratory a balance capable of measuring its weight to the fourth decimal place, say 12.1327 grams. The larger number of significant figures, while indispensable for certain purposes, is frequently attained only with more time-consuming and painstaking operations and, in general, requires more expensive equipment. An industrial company simply cannot afford to have a man spend fifteen minutes on an extremely accurate weighing when an adequate though less precise one can be made in a few seconds. Occasionally the cost of equipment becomes the limiting factor.

There is also a mathematical reason for simplifying some measurements. The product of two or more numbers cannot have more significant figures than the smallest number of significant figures in its factors, and the quotient of two numbers cannot have more significant figures than the smaller number in its dividend and its divisor. There-

The burette is used for measuring liquid volumes. A burette reading is shown which should be recorded with four significant figures.

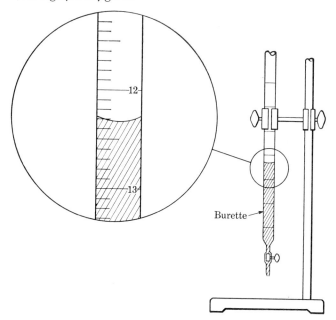

Fig. 1-12.

Burette

fore, if one factor of a product has only two significant figures, nothing is gained by making measurements to more than two significant figures for the other factor.

As an example, suppose we wish to determine the specific volume of water, defined as the volume occupied by a single unit of weight (usually the gram): specific volume = volume/weight. If the volume is to be determined by measuring the water in the burette shown in Fig. 1-12, we can obtain only four significant figures for the measure, and we record a volume of 12.32 cc. We might be able to measure the weight to six significant figures, but the quotient, specific volume, would still have to be rounded to four significant figures.

Specific volume = volume/weight = 12.32 cc/12.31 gm = 1.001 cc/gm, when rounded to four significant figures. If we had used the more accurate measure of 12.3089 gm for the divisor, we would have spent time both in measurement and in arithmetic computation and yet gained nothing in the accuracy of the result. Unusable accuracy is waste motion, experimentally and mathematically.

WEIGHTS AND MEASURES
IN THE UNITED STATES

Since most of the early colonists in what is now the United States were British, it was only natural that the English system of weights and measures should have been adopted. Use of the system persisted even after the country ceased to be a British colony. When the Constitution was written in 1787, a phrase in Section 8 of Article I authorized Congress to "fix the standards of weights and measures." This function, however, seems to have been handled for the most part by the individual states.

At the time of the French Revolution, France adopted what has come to be known as the metric system of weights and measures and proposed that the United States do likewise. In 1795 George Washington transmitted France's proposal to the Congress of the United States; but even though France had been our ally in the Revolutionary War, there was little disposition in this country to accept the suggestion.

The Office of Weights and Measures was established in Washington, D.C., by the Treasury Department in 1832. Four years later, Congress

The National Bureau of Standards buildings in Washington, D.C. (Courtesy, National Bureau of Standards)

directed this bureau to provide each state with a duplicate set of weights and measures in order to ensure uniformity. In many states these sets were adopted by the legislatures as the legal standards. By an act of Congress in 1866, it became legal to use the metric system in contracts.

Since 1870 the United States has been one of the members participating in the International Bureau of Weights and Measures with headquarters near Paris. In 1890 the United States received the prototype meters and kilograms mentioned above in the discussion of the standards of length and of mass. In 1893 the yard was legally defined as 3600/3793 meter and the pound avoirdupois as 1/2.2046 kilogram.

The National Bureau of Standards was established in the Department of Commerce in Washington, D.C., in 1901. It is the duty of this bureau to perfect and maintain correct working standards in all phases of measurement in the nation.

EXERCISES AND QUESTIONS FOR CHAPTER 1

1. The height of the column of mercury in a barometer is 760 mm. Calculate the corresponding height in inches.

2. The distance from New York City to Albany is 150 mi. Calculate the corresponding distance in kilometers.

3. One cubic foot of water has a weight of 62.4 lb. Calculate the corresponding weight in kilograms.

4. Find the number of grams in 1.00 oz (avoirdupois).

5. Find the weight of 75 cc of alcohol if its density is 0.79 gm/cc.

6. The density of mercury is 13.6 gm/cc. What volume is occupied by 100 gm of mercury?

7. Calculate the number of miles in a light-year.

8. How is density defined? What measuring instruments would you need in order to determine the density of a given object? Describe how you would carry out the measurements.

9. What is meant by specific gravity? Is the density of an object ever different from its specific gravity? Explain.

10. Standard meter bars may eventually be supplanted by the lengths of light waves. Why?

11. Describe the survey carried out in France in the late eighteenth century to determine the length of the standard meter.

12. Do you favor the adoption in this country of the metric system as the only system of weights and measures? Outline your reasons pro or con.

13. Why is a knowledge of significant figures important in scientific calculations?

14. Discuss the history of the development of a system of weights and measures in the United States.

CHAPTER 2

Forces Meeting Objects: Simple Machines

In PLUTARCH's *Lives* there is a vivid description of the reception accorded the Roman general Marcellus and his army as they stormed the approaches to Syracuse about 215 B.C. We are inclined to think of machinery as the creation of our modern age; yet more than 2000 years ago Archimedes struck terror in the ranks of the advancing Romans with the ingenious war machines he had devised. Huge beams with heavy boulders attached were swung out from the tops of the cliffs over the advancing boats, and the boulders were then smashed on the decks, making the ships toss as upon an angry sea. There were also huge beaks which were lowered to grasp the boats, lifting them up on end and tipping the hapless crews into the harbor.

All this was the work of Archimedes' machines, for which the motive power was supplied by the muscles of men or of animals. Archimedes would leave no written record of the work which he did as an inventor of machines, for it was beneath the dignity of a philosopher to write about such mundane matters. His published treatises dealt with subjects which he considered more profound. Everywhere in the world of Greece and Rome, society was based on a division between free men and slaves. Archimedes was among the free men who could use their leisure to be philosophers and theoreticians if their inclinations lay in that direction. Slaves were rarely educated and did all the manual work. Thus it was very hard for the world of Greece and Rome to understand that brain and brawn might be brought together to assist each other.

The simple machines—the lever, screw, pulley, wheel and axle, and inclined plane—are devices that allow a small force to be as effective as a large force applied without their aid. They certainly date from thousands of years before Archimedes, and in one form or another their origins must go back to prehistoric times. Men first devised gadgets to help in their work and take care of their needs; the explanations of how the gadgets functioned were developed later. In very ancient times implements were made of stone, later of bronze, and still later of iron and steel. Logs of wood were used to get the leverage necessary for moving bulky objects. How the Egyptians were able to set huge blocks of stone in place in the pyramids has always been a source of wonder and amazement, even for our modern world. It is possible that the blocks were pushed along on logs, which served as wheels, up a sloping road (inclined plane) to the top of the pyramid.

The great philosopher Aristotle (384-322 B.C.), contributor of so much to Greek science, wrote down an explanation of the machine which we call the lever. "The weight which is moved is to the weight which moves it in the inverse ratio of the lengths of the arms of the lever; always in fact a weight will move as much more easily as the weight which moves it is further from the fulcrum." Here is the germ of the idea which eventually became the law of moments.

Archimedes some 100 years later further elaborated and refined the Aristotelian statement. He stated seven postulates concerning levers which he regarded as being self-evident. From these he deduced fifteen propositions. It is doubtful, however, if Archimedes ever carried out experiments for the express purpose of either affirming or denying the validity of his propositions dealing with levers. He was a very keen observer, and it appears certain that he was able to deduce new facts and principles from observation alone.

In the early centuries of the Christian era, forces were abroad which stifled thinking, and civilization became enshrouded in the cloud known as the Dark Ages. Not for a thousand years was the cloud dispersed. At the time of the Renaissance, able men began once more to apply their talents to investigating the physical world. Such figures arose as Leonardo da Vinci (1452-1519), another important contributor to the understanding of the lever, during whose lifetime Christopher Columbus sailed on his famous voyage to the New World.

THE PRINCIPLE OF MOMENTS: THE SEESAW

Any youngster knows that when he climbs on a seesaw, if his partner has the same weight as he has, the two must sit at equal distances from the point of rotation (fulcrum) if the seesaw is to balance; also, the one who moves farther away from the fulcrum will have a greater tendency to cause rotation (downward) and his end of the seesaw will fall to the ground.

In Fig. 2-1, if boy A is so inconsiderate as to jump off, the seesaw will rotate in the clockwise direction and his partner B will hit the ground with a thud. If the two weights are unequal, then balance will be attained if the heavier boy sits nearer the fulcrum.

If a seesaw is to remain horizontal, the weight of one boy multiplied by his distance from the fulcrum must equal the weight of the other boy multiplied by his distance from the fulcrum. Each of these products (weight × distance) is called a *moment of force*. The principle of moments establishes the condition which must obtain if there is to be no rotation of the lever—in other words, if a state of equilibrium is to exist. It asserts that the moment tending to cause clockwise (right side down) rotation must equal the moment tending to cause counterclockwise (left side down) rotation. A moment of force that tends to cause rotation, as in this case, is called a *torque*. The clockwise torque

Fig. 2-1.

A seesaw balances when children of equal weights are seated at equal distances from the fulcrum; when the two weights are unequal, the lighter child must be seated farther from the fulcrum. The condition necessary for a seesaw to balance is that the rotational moments of force (the torques) shall be equal and in opposite directions.

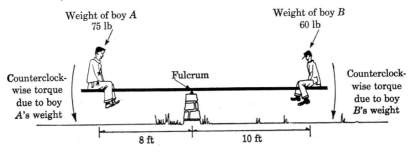

in Fig. 2-1 is the product of the weight of boy B (60 lb) and his distance (10 ft) from the fulcrum; the counterclockwise torque is the weight of boy A (75 lb) multiplied by his distance (8 ft) from the fulcrum.

When a condition of equilibrium exists, we may write an equality sign. The basic mathematical equation which represents the above equilibrium is

Counterclockwise moment = clockwise moment

Since in our example a moment of force is defined as the product of a weight and the distance from the fulcrum to the line of action of the weight (the lever arm), the above equation may be translated into the following equality:

$$(\text{Weight of A}) \cdot \left(\begin{array}{c}\text{distance of A} \\ \text{from fulcrum}\end{array}\right) = (\text{weight of B}) \cdot \left(\begin{array}{c}\text{distance of B} \\ \text{from fulcrum}\end{array}\right)$$

If the appropriate values for weight and distance (Fig. 2-1) are substituted in the equation above, it will be clear that the two opposing rotational tendencies are equal.

$$(75 \text{ lb}) \cdot (8 \text{ ft}) = (60 \text{ lb}) \cdot (10 \text{ ft})$$

In a problem situation, any three of the above quantities might be specified and the fourth be unknown. Solving an equation amounts to finding a value for the unknown quantity which will make the two sides of the equation equal. Occasionally this unknown quantity can be obtained by inspection; more often it is obtained by algebraic methods.

ILLUSTRATIVE PROBLEM

A boy weighing 100 lb sits 3 ft from the fulcrum of a seesaw. How many feet from the fulcrum must a 75-lb boy sit if the two boys are to balance?

Solution

Let $x =$ the number of feet required.

$$\text{Counterclockwise moment} = \text{clockwise moment}$$
$$100 \text{ lb} \cdot 3 \text{ ft} = 75 \text{ lb} \cdot x$$
$$300 \text{ lb-ft} = 75 \text{ lb} \cdot x \text{ ft}$$
$$x = 4 \text{ ft}$$

Solving this equation means finding the value of x which will make the right-hand member equal 300 lb-ft. This value of x is 4 ft: the seesaw will balance if the 75-lb boy sits 4 ft from the fulcrum.

THE PLATFORM BALANCE AND
THE ALGEBRAIC EQUATION

Every science laboratory makes use of a simple form of lever, the platform balance (see Figs. 2-2 through 2-5). Many platform balances

How the platform balance illustrates the principles of solving an algebraic equation.

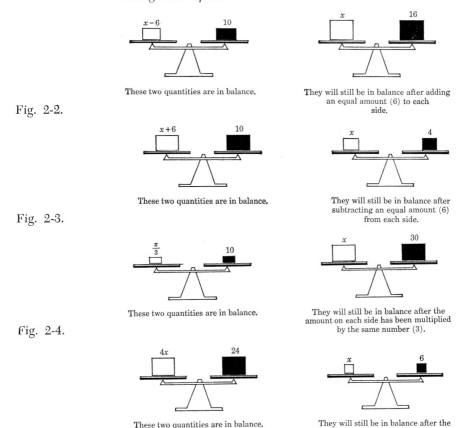

Fig. 2-2.

These two quantities are in balance.

They will still be in balance after adding an equal amount (6) to each side.

Fig. 2-3.

These two quantities are in balance.

They will still be in balance after subtracting an equal amount (6) from each side.

Fig. 2-4.

These two quantities are in balance.

They will still be in balance after the amount on each side has been multiplied by the same number (3).

Fig. 2-5.

These two quantities are in balance.

They will still be in balance after the amount on each side has been divided by the same number (4).

have the two arms of equal length. An object is weighed by placing it on one pan and weights on the other. Thus there are equal torques which act in opposite rotational directions. The fundamental relation governing such a balance is the principle of moments.

The platform balance may be used to illustrate the four axioms of algebra:

I *If equals are added to equals, the results are equal.*
II *If equals are subtracted from equals, the results are equal.*
III *If equals are multiplied by equals, the results are equal.*
IV *If equals are divided by equals (other than zero), the results are equal.*

The meaning of these axioms will be clearly understood if we consider them in relation to the platform balance. The quantities on the right and left of an equation represent the same thing; otherwise we would have no right to put in the equality sign. No operation performed on an equation must be allowed to upset this state of balance.

THE AXIOM OF ADDITION

Illustrative Problem

Solve the equation $x - 6 = 10$

Solving the equation means finding the value of x which will make the left side of the equation equal 10. If $x = 16$ the two sides will balance, and hence 16 is the correct answer. In solving equations the aim is to obtain x all by itself on one side of the equality sign. If 6 is added to the left side of the equation it will cancel -6 and x will be the only term on the left. The axiom says that if 6 is added to the left side it must also be added to the right side. If there is a balance with $x - 6$ on one pan and 10 on the other, this balance will be preserved if 6 is added to both sides. The secret to correct operation on algebraic equations is to treat the two sides of the equation the same. Never let one side down. (See Fig. 2-2)

THE AXIOM OF SUBTRACTION

Illustrative Problem

Solve the equation $x + 6 = 10$

It is clear that if 4 were put in place of x, the condition of equality would be satisfied. If 6 is subtracted from the left side of the equation, x will be alone on that side. According to the axiom of subtraction, 6 must also be subtracted from the right side of the equation. The two sides must be treated alike or the equilibrium of the pair of scales will be upset. (See Fig. 2-3)

THE AXIOM OF MULTIPLICATION

Illustrative Problem

$$\text{Solve the equation } \frac{x}{3} = 10$$

If 30 is substituted for x, the two sides of the equation will be the same. If a pair of scales is in balance, it will remain in balance if the weights on each side are tripled. (See Fig. 2-4)

THE AXIOM OF DIVISION

Illustrative Problem

$$\text{Solve the equation } 4x = 24$$

If x has a value of 6, the above expression is a true equality. If a pair of scales is in balance, it will remain in balance if the weight on each side is reduced to $\frac{1}{4}$ its value. (See Fig. 2-5)

If we visualize the platform balance when in doubt as to how to operate on an algebraic equation, we will have an unerring guide. We must always treat the two members of an equation the same, never letting one member down by failing to accord it the same treatment as the other.

THE MECHANICAL ADVANTAGE OF A LEVER

By means of machinery—levers, pulleys, and the like, either singly or in combination—we can move an object by applying a force much smaller than would be required if we tried to move it directly without the use of machinery. The *mechanical advantage* is often described as a measure of the "force-multiplying ability" of a machine. One formal definition is the ratio of the resisting force and the applied force.

$$\text{Mechanical advantage} = \frac{\text{resisting force}}{\text{applied force}}$$

On a seesaw the ratio of the weight suspended (resisting force) to the applied force required to hold it precisely in equilibrium gives us the mechanical advantage of the lever—for the seesaw is a lever. If a weight of 100 pounds is just held suspended by a 10-pound weight or its equivalent in exerted force, the machine has a mechanical advantage of 100 to 10, that is, of 10. In a highly efficient machine, where little friction impedes movement, the 100-pound weight would begin to rise if the slightest additional effort were applied to the 10-pound balancing weight.*

ILLUSTRATIVE PROBLEM

A force of how many pounds must be exerted 4 ft to the left of the fulcrum of a lever to balance a 100-lb weight suspended from the opposite end at a point 1 ft to the right of the fulcrum? Calculate the mechanical advantage of the lever.

Solution

Let $x =$ the number of pounds force required.

$$\text{Counterclockwise moment} = \text{clockwise moment}$$
$$(x) \cdot (4 \text{ ft}) = (100 \text{ lb}) \cdot (1 \text{ ft})$$
$$4x = 100 \text{ lb}$$
$$x = 25 \text{ lb}$$

A 25-lb force suffices to balance the 100-lb weight. The mechanical advantage is

$$\frac{\text{Resistance}}{\text{Effort}} = \frac{100 \text{ lb}}{25 \text{ lb}} = 4$$

Suppose that in the situation of the problem we want not merely to hold the 100-pound weight in balance, but to lift it, to make it move. The force required will be the equivalent of a weight of just over 25 pounds applied at the point 4 ft from the fulcrum. (For our calculations we can neglect the slight difference.) It turns out that the point at which the 25 pounds is applied will move 4 inches for every inch that the 100-pound weight rises. The 100-pound weight rises 1 inch in the same time that the 25-pound effort is moving the point at which it is applied a distance of 4 inches.

The distances through which the two forces act are in inverse proportion to the forces; thus

$$\frac{4 \text{ in.}}{1 \text{ in.}} = \frac{100 \text{ lb}}{25 \text{ lb}} = 4$$
$$\frac{\text{Effort distance}}{\text{Resistance distance}} = \frac{\text{resistance (weight)}}{\text{effort (force)}}$$

---

* Apart from overcoming the friction that can never be quite eliminated, the additional force is required to start the movement—in Newton's terms, to impart the initial acceleration to overcome inertia, as will be discussed in Chapter 3. The 10-pound force which just suffices to hold the 100-pound weight in balance will also suffice to keep it moving once it is in motion.

The ratio on the right side of this equation expresses the mechanical advantage; the ratio on the left side is called *velocity ratio*. The quantities are expressed without units, and are numerically equal. Both velocity ratio and mechanical advantage here are 4.

The Wheel and Axle Two wheels of different diameters which are bolted to each other, as in Fig. 2-6, exemplify the wheel and axle

Fig. 2-6.

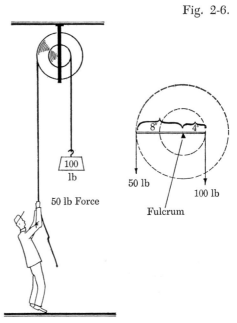

The wheel and axle may be considered a lever with arms of unequal length. Here a downward pull of 50 lb will hold a 100-lb weight in balance, and any increment to the pull will cause the weight to begin rising.

and may be regarded as a lever with arms of unequal length. The center of the axle about which the wheels turn may be considered to be the fulcrum. Suppose one wheel has a radius of 4 inches and the other wheel a radius of 8 inches. The problem of the relation between force and weight may be solved in the same manner as in any other lever problem. A 50-pound force applied to the radius of the larger wheel will be sufficient to balance a 100-pound weight suspended from the smaller. The mechanical advantage of this machine is 2. The weight of the object is twice as large as the force required to balance it.

The length of the crank (pedal arm) of a bicycle is larger than the radius of the geared wheel, known as the sprocket, to which it is attached. Hence the force exerted on the bicycle chain by the sprocket wheel will be larger than that exerted by the foot on the crank. The mechanical advantage will depend on the relation of the length of the crank to the radius of the sprocket. Once again the principle of moments is applicable.

SIMPLE MACHINES AND THE PRINCIPLE OF WORK

The problems considered above have all been based upon the principle of moments, which defines conditions for a balance of rotational tendencies. The equality signifies that an equilibrium exists, that several rotational effects balance one another.

There is another method which might have been used to solve these problems. It is based upon a *work principle* illustrated by the mountain climber. When you climb a mountain, you do the same amount of *work* in reaching the top whether you take a path which is short and steep or one which is long and gradual. Work, as defined by the physicist, is the product of a force and a distance, both measured in the same direction. In the case of climbing a mountain, the force is the weight of the person, and the distance is the vertical height which he rises.

This principle will be employed in the solution of problems involving several other simple machines. Of course, a method depending on equilibrium conditions could also be applied.

The Inclined Plane   A 300-pound box rests on the ground under the tailboard of a truck. If this box is lifted vertically against the pull of gravity, a force of just over 300-pounds will be required. If a 300-pound force acts vertically through a distance of 4 feet, 1200 foot pounds of work are said to have been done. If a plank 12 feet long has one end resting on the ground, the other on the tailboard, as shown in Fig. 2-7, the box may be pushed up the plank with a force much smaller than 300 pounds.

$$\left(\begin{array}{c}\text{Work done in lifting}\\ \text{box vertically}\end{array}\right) = \left(\begin{array}{c}\text{work done in pushing}\\ \text{box up plank}\end{array}\right)$$

The equality is based on the fundamental assumption that the same amount of work will be required whether we lift the box vertically or push it up the plank. Keeping in mind that work is the product of a force and a distance, the above equality may be expressed

$$\left(\begin{array}{c}\text{Weight}\\\text{of box}\end{array}\right) \cdot \left(\begin{array}{c}\text{height}\\\text{to be lifted}\end{array}\right) = \left(\begin{array}{c}\text{number of lb force } F \text{ needed}\\\text{to push box up plank}\end{array}\right) \cdot \left(\begin{array}{c}\text{length}\\\text{of plank}\end{array}\right)$$

$$(300 \text{ lb}) \cdot (4 \text{ ft}) = (F) \cdot (12 \text{ ft})$$
$$1200 \text{ lb} = 12F$$
$$F = 10 \text{) lb}$$

Thus anything over a 100-pound force will be sufficient to start a 300-

Fig. 2-7.

An inclined plane allows us to raise a heavy object by applying a force smaller than the weight of the object. In any actual case the total work done in moving the heavy object up the plane may be far greater than the work done in direct lifting, owing to the friction that must be overcome. Even so, it pays to use the inclined plane. With its help a much smaller force can raise the weight, even though it must also overcome friction.

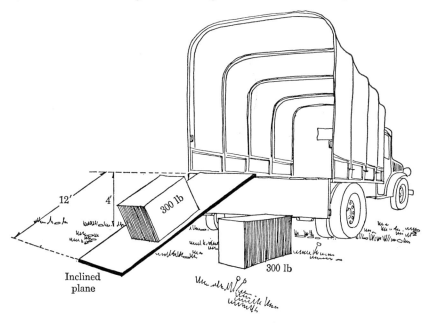

pound object up the plank. This inclined plane has a mechanical advantage of 300 lb/100 lb = 3. The weight moved is three times as large as the applied force.

This calculation assumes the plank to be a frictionless surface along which the box may slide; in any actual case, additional force would have to be applied to overcome friction.

The Jackscrew   In order to lift a very heavy object such as a building, it is necessary to use a machine with a very large mechanical advantage such as the jackscrew (Fig. 2-8). This is particularly impor-

The jackscrew is a simple machine which has a very large mechanical advantage—the ratio of the circumference to the pitch a in drawing (a). The screw can be considered an inclined plane wrapped round a cylinder.

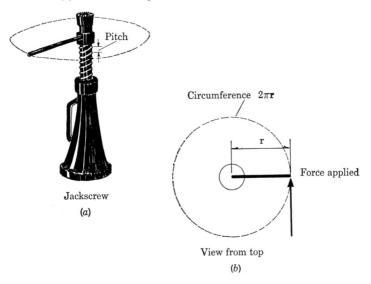

Pitch

Circumference $2\pi r$

r

Force applied

Jackscrew

(a)

View from top

(b)

Fig. 2-8.

tant if a single workman is to operate it. The work done on the heavy object is the product of the weight of the object and the vertical distance through which it is moved (note the similarity to the inclined plane). The workman applies the force at right angles to the handle of the jackscrew; the point of application of the force thus moves along the circumference of a circle. When the handle of the jackscrew moves through one revolution, the screw moves vertically a distance equal to the spacing between two successive threads (called the pitch of the screw). The basic pattern used in the solution of this problem is the same as for the inclined plane:

$$\left(\begin{matrix}\text{Work done in lifting}\\ \text{house vertically}\end{matrix}\right) = \left(\begin{matrix}\text{work done in pushing}\\ \text{the handle}\end{matrix}\right)$$

Keeping in mind again that work is force times distance, we may translate the equation above into the following:

$$\begin{pmatrix} \text{Weight} \\ \text{of} \\ \text{house} \end{pmatrix} \cdot \begin{pmatrix} \text{pitch} \\ \text{of} \\ \text{screw} \end{pmatrix} = \begin{pmatrix} \text{number of lb} \\ \text{force } F \text{ exerted} \\ \text{on handle} \end{pmatrix} \cdot \begin{pmatrix} \text{circumference of} \\ \text{circle through} \\ \text{which force moves} \end{pmatrix}$$

If the house in question weighs 4000 pounds, and if the pitch of the jackscrew is ¼ inch and its handle is 12 inches long, the following substitutions may be made in the above equation:

$W \cdot P_{IT}{}_{c}H = F \cdot C$

$$(4000 \text{ lb}) \cdot (\tfrac{1}{4} \text{ in.}) = (F) \cdot (2\pi \cdot 12 \text{ in.})$$
$$1000 \text{ lb} = 24\pi \cdot F$$
$$F = \frac{1000 \text{ lb}}{24\pi} = 13.26 \text{ lb}$$

Thus a force just over 13.26 pounds suffices to lift the 2-ton house. The mechanical advantage of this machine is 4000 lb/13.26 lb = 301.7.

Again it should be emphasized that idealizations have been assumed, as in the account of the inclined plane. Frictional effects in the jackscrew have been neglected, whereas in actuality they are quite

A single pulley wheel. This acts as a lever with arms of equal length, the radius R. No mechanical advantage results, but the "advantage of convenience" may be considerable, especially in changing the direction of the pull.

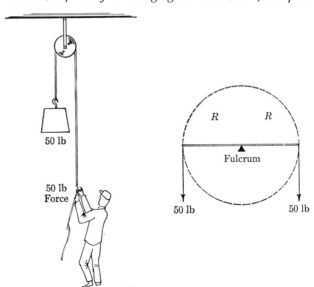

Fig. 2-9.

significant. Furthermore, the calculation assumes that force is constant as the workman turns the handle and that it is always applied at
right angles to the handle. In any actual case, we know that these
conditions would be very difficult of realization. It is certain that in a
practical case, a force substantially larger than 13.26 lb would be
required.

Pulley Systems   One more illustration of the work principle applied
to the solution of problems of simple machines: A pulley is simply a
grooved wheel, like that shown in Fig. 2-9. A single pulley wheel
has a mechanical advantage of 1; i.e., for equilibrium, the force exerted on the rope on one side must be equal to the weight on the
other, as explained on the basis of the lever principle.

If a second pulley wheel is supported by the first, as shown in Fig.
2-10, the lower block may be lifted by pulling on the rope at the

Fig. 2-10.

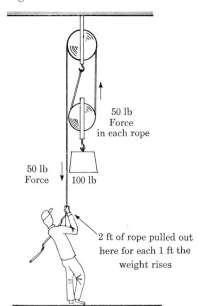

50 lb
Force
in each rope

50 lb
Force

100 lb

2 ft of rope pulled out
here for each 1 ft the
weight rises

*This double pulley offers a mechanical ad-
vantage of 2. Note that the wheels need not
be of the same size.*

extreme left. If the rope on the left is pulled out a distance of 8 feet,
each of the ropes supporting the lower pulley wheel will be shortened
by 4 feet; in other words, for each foot that the weight rises vertically
the rope must be pulled out a distance of 2 feet.

The work principle again applies, as shown in the equation

$$\begin{pmatrix} \text{Work done in lifting} \\ \text{the weight} \end{pmatrix} = \begin{pmatrix} \text{work done in pulling} \\ \text{on the rope} \end{pmatrix}$$

Substituting force times distance for work:

$$\begin{pmatrix} \text{Weight} \\ \text{lifted} \end{pmatrix} \cdot \begin{pmatrix} \text{distance} \\ \text{weight is lifted} \end{pmatrix} = \begin{pmatrix} \text{number of lb} \\ \text{force } F \text{ on rope} \end{pmatrix} \cdot \begin{pmatrix} \text{distance through} \\ \text{which force moves} \end{pmatrix}$$
$$(100 \text{ lb}) \cdot (1 \text{ ft}) = (F) \cdot (2 \text{ ft})$$
$$100 \text{ lb} = 2F$$
$$F = 50 \text{ lb}$$

Thus anything over a 50-pound force on the rope will suffice to lift a 100-pound weight. The mechanical advantage of this machine is $100 \text{ lb}/50 \text{ lb} = 2$.

Once again, idealizations are involved: friction between ropes and pulleys has been neglected, and the weight of the movable pulley has not been taken into consideration. Note that the mechanical advantage is the same even though the pulley wheels are of different diameters.

REDUCTION OF FORCE IS COMPENSATED BY INCREASED DISTANCE

Machines never save us any work; they merely make it possible for us to move bulky objects with forces which are less than the resistances of the objects moved. Each of the three illustrations above—the inclined plane, the jackscrew, and the pulley—has been based upon the principle that the work done will be the same in either of two alternative ways. If it is possible to move an object with a reduced force, the force must of necessity act through a correspondingly greater distance. In the problem illustrating the inclined plane, the effort had to move through three times as great a distance as the resistance was raised. In the illustrative problem dealing with the jackscrew, the end of the handle moved 301.7 times as far as the house was lifted vertically. In the pulley problem, the reduction of the effort to one-half the weight of the object was compensated by the necessity of pulling the rope out twice the distance that the object moved. In all cases, then, reduced force is attained at a cost. The greater the reduction of the effort as compared with the resistive force, the greater the distance through which the effort has to be exerted.

IDEALIZATION IN SCIENCE

It has been said that part of the genius of Galileo was his ability to see a simple principle in a complex interplay of forces. In discussing the principles of simple machines, we ignored frictional effects as if they were nonexistent and treated the barely moving system as if it were in equilibrium. In a succeeding chapter we will neglect the effects of air resistance on the acceleration of falling bodies. Simplifying assumptions are to be encountered frequently in the generalizations of science. They are a part of its very fabric, and unless this is clearly understood a very significant aspect of the nature of science will have been overlooked.

The question arises, "If the generalizations of science are never exactly true, why bother with them?" The answer is that generalizations make for economy of expression. One simple equation enables us to make predictions for large numbers of similar devices, each of which has its own distinctive features. One equation predicts the force relations for all inclined planes even though the frictional effects will be different in each. While the result is never exactly correct because of these frictional effects, the generalization does nevertheless make it unnecessary for us to work out a mathematical equation to fit the peculiarities of every inclined plane we wish to use. Furthermore, as we are able to refine our techniques and eliminate extraneous factors such as friction in the inclined plane, actual forces more nearly approximate those predicted by the generalization.

Some other idealizations will be pointed out as they appear in subsequent chapters.

Exercises and Questions for Chapter 2

1. A 500-lb barrel is rolled up a 15-ft plank to a platform whose vertical height above the ground is 3 ft. Neglecting friction, what effort is required?

2. The crank of a windlass is 2.5 ft long and the drum on which the rope winds is 5 in. in radius. Neglecting friction, what effort is needed to raise an object weighing 360 lb?

Fig. 2-11.

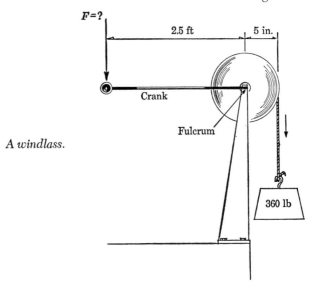

F = ?

2.5 ft   5 in.

Crank

Fulcrum

A windlass.

360 lb

3. The safety valve on a boiler is a horizontal metal bar 20 in. long which is hinged at one end. What force exerted by steam acting on the valve 3 in. from the hinged end will balance a weight of 2.5 lb suspended from the other end of the bar?

The safety valve on a boiler.

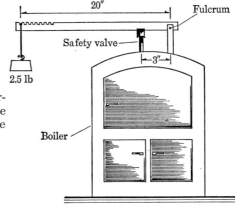

20″   Fulcrum

Safety valve

3″

2.5 lb

HINT: Clockwise and counterclockwise moments must balance even though the fulcrum is at the end of the lever.

Boiler

Fig. 2-12.

4. What force must be exerted (vertically) on the handles of a wheelbarrow 3.5 ft from the axle of the wheel in order to lift a weight of 200 lb which is concentrated at a point 2.2 ft from the axle?

A wheelbarrow.

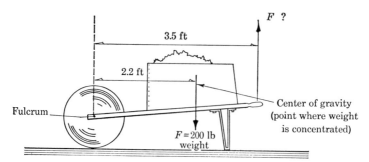

Fig. 2-13.

5. What force exerted on a hammer handle 12.0 in. from the fulcrum will pull out a nail whose resisting force is 500 lb, if the distance from the nail to the fulcrum is 1.6 in.?

The hammer.

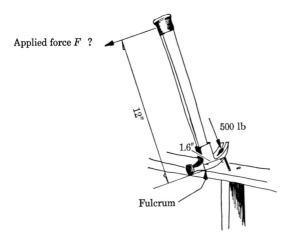

Fig. 2-14.

6. A plank 18 ft long weighs 124 lb. This weight may be considered to be concentrated at the mid-point of the plank. What is the minimum force which must be applied at one end of the plank in order to raise it (i.e., to cause it to rotate about the opposite end)?

7. Approximately how long has man been using the so-called "simple machines"? Discuss.

8. State the principle of moments. Illustrate its meaning by referring to the seesaw.

9. What is meant by "solving an equation"? Why are algebraic methods of solving equations usually preferred to those of inspection?

10. What is meant by (*a*) the mechanical advantage of a machine, and (*b*) the velo.ity ratio of a machine?

11. Do simple machines save us work? Explain.

12. If machines do not behave exactly as described in a generalization such as the principle of the inclined plane, why do we bother to state it?

13. Describe how the principle of work applies in (*a*) the inclined plane, (*b*) the jackscrew, and (*c*) the pulley.

14. Generalizations of science often imply certain idealizations. Illustrate.

REVIEW

1. Archimedes stated that a body which is completely immersed in water will weigh less than in air by an amount equal to the weight of the displaced water. If an object weighing 125 gm in air has an apparent weight of 80 gm under water, what is its specific gravity?

2. Calculate the number of liters in a cubic foot of water.

CHAPTER *3*

Forces, Changers of Motion

A<small>N OFT-REPEATED</small> story recounts that Aristotle, the famous Greek scientist and philosopher, believed that objects would fall with speeds which were proportional to their weights—that a 10-pound ball, for example, would fall ten times as fast as a 1-pound ball. Another story tells how Galileo disproved this idea some 1900 years later by dropping objects of different weights from the top of the Leaning Tower of Pisa. There is considerable doubt whether Galileo ever made measurements on freely falling objects, but he is known to have "diluted the motion" of falling objects by rolling them down inclined planes, and from these experiments to have discovered that different objects fall similar distances in the same time intervals irrespective of their weights.

Galileo Upsets Authority Greek men of science were essentially philosophers; most of them devoted effort to speculation and very few to experimentation. They were more concerned with *why* objects fall than with the observations which led to an understanding of *how* they fall.

In these discussions of the "why" of fall they were pondering a subject which is at best superficially understood even today; we still know little about the cause of gravitation. On the other hand the passage of time has shown that the "how" of falling bodies, that is, knowledge of the relations between distance, rate, and time of fall, would have been a much more fruitful aspect of falling bodies to investigate.

Aristotle was one of the intellectual giants of the age in which he lived. He contributed a pattern of logic (the syllogism) to the art of thinking and established a pattern of classification in biology. Unfortunately his stature as a physicist was not as great; he made no important discoveries in this area. His written works were lost to the Western World for many centuries. When they were finally recovered, during the Middle Ages, his name became authoritative in many fields of study. The view that the speed of fall of an object was proportional to its weight, usually attributed to him, became almost universally accepted. This erroneous concept still persisted when Galileo appeared on the scene in the seventeenth century. So Galileo was confronted not only with the problem of discovering the correct description of falling bodies but also with the task of convincing the world that the great authority, Aristotle, had been wrong.

Galileo was concerned, then, with a much simpler aspect of nature than that considered by the Greeks. He was more interested in an exact measurement of *how* objects fall than in a theory of *why* they fall. He described the fall of a body in terms of time, distance, and velocity. Aristotle had made chance observations on falling objects; it occurred to Galileo that he might speed up the tempo of observation by making phenomena recur at will, that is, by actually dropping stones of different weights. He also made the technique of studying free fall more manageable by observing the speeds of objects as they rolled down inclined planes, an illustration of his ability to devise crucial experiments to verify his hunches. The manner in which he deduced the nature of the motion of falling bodies by means of the inclined plane is discussed in his *Dialogues Concerning Two New Sciences,* a work considered by many to be the foundation of the modern science of mechanics.

By the end of the sixteenth century it was beginning to occur to men that they need not accept as correct every statement handed down to them by thinkers of the past. The essential message of Francis Bacon (1561-1626) was that men had been depending for too long on the authority of the great minds of the past and that they should rely more on their own resources in obtaining knowledge. The steps which Bacon suggested as representing the systematic manner for acquiring knowledge have developed in the course of 350 years into what is known as "the scientific method" (if we may speak of *the* method; today many scientists feel that there is not *a* scientific method but rather scientific methods, based on attitudes, habits, and skills). One of the important aspects of Bacon's method was the planning of *experiments.* There is no need to sit around waiting for a phenomenon worth observing to happen. Speed up the process by creating the situation you wish to investigate. In this way nature can be coaxed into divulging her secrets at an accelerated pace.

INERTIA: NEWTON'S FIRST LAW OF MOTION

It seems to be a universal truth that everything "resists being forced," as Aristotle stated it. If the motion of a speeding bicycle is suddenly halted, the rider is hurled unceremoniously over the handle bars. Bumps and bruises give testimony to the fact that once a mass is set in motion there seems to be a tendency for it to keep moving; it resists a change which would halt its motion. A locomotive with a long string of heavily laden freight cars tugs and pulls with very little effect at first, as it starts. But once in motion it is very difficult to stop; the engineer must apply the brakes far in advance of the desired stopping point.

Inertia is simply the property of a body which causes it to resist a change of motion. If the object is at rest, inertia will oppose its movement. If it is in motion, inertia will oppose its stopping. The principle might be described as one of contrariness: Try to set an object in motion and it prefers to stay at rest. Try to stop it while in motion, and it wants to continue to move at the same speed. There is a comparable principle in chemistry, the Le Châtelier principle, and another in electricity, Lenz's law. An alert mind will discover many other manifestations of this principle of resistance to change.

Kepler (1571-1630), one of the greatest of the early astronomers, thought that something must be pushing the planets in order to keep them moving in their orbits. Galileo was more incisive in his thinking; he grasped the idea that owing to inertia a planet tends to move in a straight line at uniform speed. Of course some other force was indicated. It modified this natural tendency and bent the planet's path into an ellipse. Isaac Newton (1642-1727) first clearly generalized the principle of inertia in his *first law of motion,* which says, in effect,

"Every body at rest tends to remain at rest; every body which is in motion tends to remain in uniform motion in a straight line."

An object is in uniform motion if it moves through equal distances in equal time intervals. The motion of an automobile, for example, is *not* uniform. When we say that a car traveled at 40 mi/hr over a certain period of time, we refer to average speed, even though in problems we treat it as if it were uniform: we realize that at any given time during that period the momentary speed may have been greater or less than 40 mi/hr.

The first part of Newton's principle, "Bodies at rest tend to remain at rest," squares with our experience: we are unaccustomed to having inanimate objects, such as stones and books, start moving of their own volition. But since it is the usual circumstance for moving objects to come to rest because of friction, the second part of the principle seems less in accord with our experience. There will be further discussion of this point later in the chapter.

CHOICE OF CORRECT UNITS: EQUATION FOR UNIFORM MOTION

There is an old and familiar formula, $d = r \cdot t$ (distance equals rate times time), used for many years by problem makers in algebra who set people to rowing boats up and down rivers and airplanes to bucking headwinds. Often their problems seem tricky enough in themselves without introducing the additional complication of consistency of units. However, a failure to realize that an equation must represent an equality of units as well as an equality of numbers has been the shoal upon which many a student has been shipwrecked in his study of physics.

ILLUSTRATIVE PROBLEM

How far does a car averaging 40 mi/hr travel in 30 min?

Solution

$$\text{Distance (miles)} = \text{rate} \left(\frac{\text{miles}}{\text{hours}} \right) \cdot \text{time (hours)}$$

$$\text{Miles} = \frac{\text{miles}}{\text{hours}} \cdot \text{hours}$$

$$\text{Time} = 30 \text{ min} = \tfrac{1}{2} \text{ hr}$$
$$d = 40 \text{ mi/hr} \cdot \tfrac{1}{2} \text{ hr} = 20 \text{ mi}$$

Note that hours will cancel from numerator and denominator, and then the units on either side of the equals sign will be the same.

Suppose the 30 min had been substituted directly into the equation:

$$\text{Distance (miles)} = \text{rate} \left(\frac{\text{miles}}{\text{hours}}\right) \cdot \text{time (minutes)}$$

$$\text{Miles} = \frac{\text{miles}}{\text{hours}} \cdot \text{minutes}$$

$$d = 40 \text{ mi/hr} \cdot 30 \text{ min} = 1200 \frac{\text{mi min}}{\text{hr}}$$

While theoretically we might designate the distance traversed as 1200 mi min/hr, this is a scrambled collection of units which would convey little meaning. Take care to look over the units given in a problem and make such conversions as lead to recognizable equalities, as illustrated in the first solution. It would obviously be incorrect if the above were written:

$$d = 40 \text{ mi/hr} \cdot 30 \text{ min} = 1200 \text{ mi}$$

In solving problems in physics, check the units being substituted and make sure that they lead to appropriate units in the answer. Indiscriminate substitution of just any units given in the problem will lead to incorrect results sooner or later.

BUILDING ALGEBRAIC EQUALITIES

The art of setting up algebraic equations to represent scientific problem situations is essentially one of discovering or building equalities. In lever problems, rotational tendencies are said to be *equal* if the lever is balanced. In the inclined plane, the amount of work done is assumed to be the *same* whether the object is lifted vertically against gravity or pushed up an inclined plank. Before starting to solve any such problem, first ask, "Under the conditions of the problem, what quantities are equal or can be made equal? What can we equate?"

Once again it must be emphasized that idealizations are involved. In a problem dealing with a rowboat on a river, to select a common example, it is often assumed that a boat starts at a certain point, rows up stream, and then returns to the original point *by an identical path* (Fig. 3-1). This is obviously impossible as a practical matter. However, it is this assumed equality of the distance up the river and the distance back which justifies our setting up an equation. Often in such problems we assume constant rowboat speeds or constant speed of flow of the river—further idealizations.

Fig. 3-1.

Before writing an algebraic equation we must discover, in the statement of a problem, two quantities which are equal, or which may be made equal. In many problems dealing with boats and rivers, the distance traveled upstream is assumed to be equal to that traveled downstream.

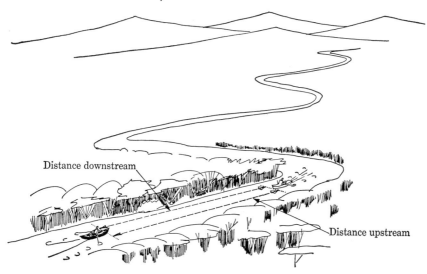

A few examples will illustrate the method of first seeking the basic pattern of equality before attempting to set up algebraic equations for solving the problem.

ILLUSTRATIVE PROBLEM

A man drove to New York at an average speed of 50 mi/hr, and then returned by the same route at an average speed of 40 mi/hr. If the round trip took 9 hr, how far did he drive?

Solution

What can we equate? We might let t = the number of hours driving to the city, let $9 - t$ = the number of hours returning, and equate the two distances ($d = r \cdot t$):

$$\text{Rate} \cdot \text{time (going)} = \text{rate} \cdot \text{time (returning)}$$
$$50 \text{ mi/hr} \cdot t \text{ hr} = 40 \text{ mi/hr} \cdot (9 - t) \text{ hr}$$
$$50t = 360 - 40t$$
$$90t = 360$$
$$t = 4 \text{ hr}$$

So distance going: $50 \cdot 4 = 200$ mi

distance returning: $40 \cdot 5 = 200$ mi

and round trip $= 400$ mi

Or if we let $d =$ the distance each way, we might equate the total time given (9 hr) with the sum of the times for the two trips ($t = d/r$):

$$\text{Time (going)} + \text{time (returning)} = 9 \text{ hr}$$
$$d/50 + d/40 = 9$$
$$4d + 5d = 1800$$
$$9d = 1800$$
$$d = 200;$$

so round trip $= 400$ mi

ILLUSTRATIVE PROBLEM

How much water must be added to 50 lb of a solution which is 60% alcohol (by weight) so that the resulting solution will be 25% alcohol (by weight)? See Fig. 3-2.

Changing the proportions of a solution. The addition of water to an alcohol-water mixture does not change the weight of the alcohol. The weight of the alcohol in the original solution is equal to that in the more dilute solution.

X = Alcohol molecules

O = Water molecules

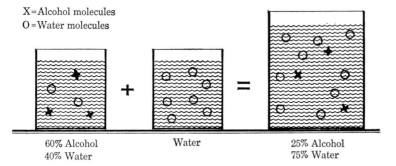

| 60% Alcohol | Water | 25% Alcohol |
| 40% Water | | 75% Water |

Fig. 3-2.

Solution in Outline

Adding water to this mixture does not in any way change the *weight* of the alcohol molecules which were present before the dilution. Hence the following will be a logical equality:

$$\frac{\text{Weight of alcohol}}{\text{in the 60\% solution}} = \frac{\text{weight of alcohol}}{\text{in the 25\% solution}}$$

If we add x lb of water, then

$$60\% \text{ of } 50 \text{ lb} = 25\% \text{ of } (50 + x)$$
$$x = ?$$

FORCE: NEWTON'S SECOND LAW OF MOTION

In Chapter 2, forces were discussed in connection with machines without describing their nature in any detail. They were merely assumed to be pushes or pulls exerted on objects. It is now appropriate to examine further some of the implications of the concept of force.

It is a common-sense observation that an object at rest has a natural tendency to remain at rest. The book on the table will remain where it is unless a force acts upon it. Though a railroad train which is running along a level track gradually slows down and eventually comes to a stop if the power is turned off, this happens because air resistance and friction in the wheels and motive machinery act as counterforces to oppose its inertial tendency to continue its uniform motion in a straight line indefinitely. Forces, then, are changers of motion. If a car is traveling at a rate of 30 mi/hr and it speeds up to 40 mi/hr, a force must be acting upon it; if a train is traveling at 60 mi/hr and it slows down to 25 mi/hr, forces must be opposing its motion.

Just as the lengths of objects may be measured in feet and their masses in kilograms, forces may be measured quantitatively in terms of such units as dynes, newtons, and poundals. These units of force are related to other measurements, with which we are familiar, by Newton's *second law of motion*. This law states the relationship between the acceleration imparted to a mass and the force imparting it. It can be most simply expressed in the form of an equation: $F = ma$, where F is the force, m is the mass, and a is the acceleration imparted to m by F. Thus we encounter a new concept, that of acceleration— the *rate of change in motion*.

Acceleration   If the velocity of a body changes by 10 ft/sec—for example, from 40 ft/sec to 50 ft/sec—during a time interval of 1 second, then it is said to have been accelerated by 10 feet per second per second, usually written 10 ft/sec/sec, or 10 ft/sec^2. The first part, 10 ft/sec, is the change in the velocity; the last "per second" is the time interval during which the velocity change takes place.

Here again we are considering uniform acceleration, just as in Newton's first law of motion we considered uniform motion. Uniform acceleration means equal velocity changes in equal intervals of time (Fig. 3-3). Thus an acceleration of 10 ft/sec/sec is the same as an

The velocity of an object whose motion is accelerating uniformly changes equal amounts in equal time intervals. The distance it travels in each time interval increases correspondingly.

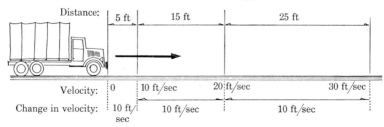

Fig. 3-3.

acceleration of 600 ft/sec/min. (The velocity change in a minute is 60 times that in a second.) When an object is accelerating uniformly, its velocity is never the same from one second to the next, or even from one instant to the next; the velocity is changing *continuously*.

The formula $F = ma$ reveals that in order to impart equal accelerations to each of two bodies of different masses, a proportionately larger force must be exerted upon the larger body. Ten times as much force is required to accelerate a 30,000-pound truck 20 ft/sec² as is required to increase the speed of a 3000-pound automobile by the same amount. It is a matter of everyday experience that it is easier to change the speed of a child's cart than that of an automobile.

Similarly, if different forces act upon each of two bodies having equal masses, the accelerations imparted will be proportional to the forces acting. Twice as much force will be required to accelerate an object 12 ft/sec² as will be needed to accelerate an object of equal mass 6 ft/sec². Freely falling bodies are accelerated 32 ft/sec². This acceleration, which is caused by gravity, is designated by the letter *g*. The force acting on a freely falling body—its weight—is thus its mass times the acceleration *g*:

$$W = m \cdot g$$

Consistency of Units: Newton's Second Law of Motion   The equation for uniform motion ($d = rt$) is likely to be familiar because it is usually studied in algebra. Distances, rates, and times are commonly used in algebraic problems. However, units of force (Fig. 3-4), mass,

A force of 1 dyne imparts to a 1-gram mass an acceleration of 1 cm/sec².
This definition is in ideal terms, since forces of friction and gravity are
assumed to be zero. In defining absolute units, a characteristic of mass
is chosen that does not change from one locality to another in space.
This is inertia. *In the figure, the velocity of the 1-gram mass rises to 1*
cm/sec in moving from rest at A to B in 1 second. If the illustration
were drawn to exact scale, the 1-gram mass would be shown to have
moved ½ centimeter.

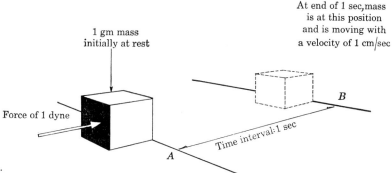

Fig. 3-4.

and acceleration are likely to be somewhat new and strange. The
tables which follow simply indicate sets of units which may be used
together in the same equation, that is, which are consistent.

ABSOLUTE UNITS

Force   = *mass · acceleration*
Dynes   = grams · cm/sec²
Newtons = kilograms · m/sec²
Poundals = pounds · ft/sec²

ILLUSTRATIVE PROBLEM

What force is needed to impart to a 10-lb *mass* an acceleration of
4 ft/sec²?

Solution

$$F = ma$$
$$F = 10 \text{ lb} \cdot 4 \text{ ft/sec}^2$$
$$F = 40 \text{ poundals}$$

From the table above it will be seen that when the mass of an
object is expressed in pounds and acceleration in ft/sec², the force
will be expressed in poundals.

Life would be much simpler if the matter could be dropped with
this single example. However, to limit the explanation to this situation

is to tell only half the story. Future confusion may be avoided by pointing out that the pound (or gram or kilogram) may refer to the *mass* of a body as in the problem cited, or to the *weight* of a body. If reference is made to the *weight* of a body, its mass may be calculated through division by g, the acceleration of gravity:

$$\text{Mass} = \frac{\text{weight}}{g}$$

GRAVITATIONAL UNITS

$Force$ $= mass \cdot acceleration$

$$\text{Pounds} = \frac{\text{pounds (weight)}}{g \ (\text{ft/sec}^2)} \cdot \text{ft/sec}^2$$

$$\text{Grams} = \frac{\text{grams (weight)}}{g \ (\text{cm/sec}^2)} \cdot \text{cm/sec}^2$$

$$\text{Kilograms} = \frac{\text{kilograms (weight)}}{g \ (\text{m/sec}^2)} \cdot \text{m/sec}^2$$

ILLUSTRATIVE PROBLEM

What force is needed to impart to a 10-lb *weight* an acceleration of 4 ft/sec²?

Solution

$$F = ma$$

$$F = \frac{W}{g} a$$

$$F = \frac{10 \text{ lb}}{32 \text{ ft/sec}^2} \cdot 4 \text{ ft/sec}^2$$

$$F = \tfrac{5}{4} \text{ lb}$$

Each of the two illustrative problems above concerns the same 10-pound object. One describes its weight; the other its mass. Since 1 pound of force in gravitational units is equal to 32 poundals of force in absolute units, the two answers are equivalent. This is to be expected since the amount of force required to impart an acceleration of 4 ft/sec² should be the same irrespective of the property by which it is described.

You should experience no difficulty with Newton's second law of motion if you use absolute units when the problem refers to *pounds mass* and gravitational units when it refers to *pounds weight*.

NEWTON'S THIRD LAW OF MOTION

It would hardly be appropriate to discuss two of Newton's laws of motion without mentioning the third. This law—"To every action there is always an equal and opposite reaction"—says in effect that forces always exist in pairs. If the wheel of an automobile pushes on the pavement, the latter must in turn push on the wheel. If two magnets are supported so as to float on water with opposite poles facing, each will attract the other; the effects are mutual. In a similar way, if the earth pulls on a falling body, the latter in turn pulls on the earth. The two forces are equal. Since the masses of the two are so vastly different, the effect on the earth is negligible.

EXERCISES AND QUESTIONS FOR CHAPTER 3

1. In the equation $d = r \cdot t$, if d is expressed in meters and t in seconds, in what units must r be expressed?

2. A car travels at an average speed of 45 mi/hr.
   (a) How far will it travel in 5.5 hr?
   (b) What is its speed in ft/sec?

3. A car has a *weight* of 4800 lb. What force will give it a horizontal acceleration of 16 ft/sec²?

4. Calculate the force necessary to impart to a 100-lb *mass* an acceleration of 20 ft/sec².

5. Calculate the force needed to impart to a 10-lb *mass* an acceleration of g

6. Explain what is meant by inertia.

7. How does uniform motion differ from uniformly accelerating motion?

8. State each of Newton's three laws of motion.

9. The pound may have different definitions. Illustrate.

REVIEW

1. Calculate the weight of water contained in a filled 2-gal can.

2. A crow bar is used to pry loose a heavy rock. The resisting force of the rock is 750 lb, the perpendicular distance from the line of action of this force to the fulcrum is 8 in., and the force applied at the other end of the crow bar is 4.5 ft from the fulcrum. Calculate the force needed. What is the mechanical advantage of the lever?

CHAPTER 4

The Force Called Gravity

Isaac Newton, whose laws of motion are the subject of Chapter 3, was one of the greatest geniuses science has ever known. He was born in England in 1642, the year in which Galileo died. In 1665, shortly after Newton's graduation from Cambridge University, a terrible plague visited England. Newton had been appointed to return to Cambridge as a Fellow, but because of the plague the university was closed; so he returned temporarily to the family estate at Woolsthorpe. Here, over a two-year period, he carried on work of world-shaking importance. It was during this time that he developed his method of fluxions, which anticipated the branch of mathematics known as the calculus. It was also here that he carried out the famous experiments by which he established the complex nature of white light (see Chapter 8). Here too, according to the traditional story, he was reclining in the family orchard when a falling apple launched him on his study of universal gravitation.

This story, like many others which have been frequently repeated, has accumulated details of doubtful authenticity. Apparently Newton's thoughts gravitated from falling apples to the "fall of the moon." It occurred to him that if this mysterious force could tug at the apple on the twig, it might even extend as far as the moon. During this time he made his first calculations on gravitation. According to one account, Newton used an incorrect number of miles for the distance on the earth's surface corresponding to one degree of arc, and conse-

Isaac Newton's birthplace and Cambridge, where he studied and taught. Science owes a great debt to the plague that visited England in 1665 and kept Newton "idling" at his father's Woolsthorpe estate.

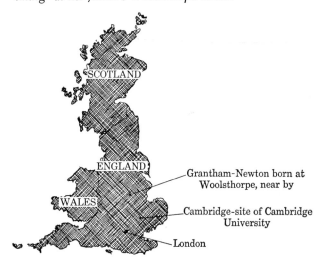

Grantham-Newton born at
Woolsthorpe, near by

Cambridge-site of Cambridge
University

London

Fig. 4-1.

quently he did not discover the hoped-for concordance between the known distance of fall in one second at the earth's surface and the corresponding "fall of the moon." Several different values for the number of miles in one degree of arc, including the correct value, 69 miles, were apparently available to Newton.* Had he made calculations with each one of these values he would have obtained the necessary concordance when using the correct value. At any rate, this early work on gravitation was put aside for about twenty years.

Edmund Halley, discoverer of Halley's comet, was a close friend of Newton. Halley and several colleagues were also interested in questions of gravitation. On one occasion Halley sought out Newton to ask him about certain details of a gravitational problem he was working on; he found that Newton had worked out the same problem years before, and he later received a written solution of the problem from Newton. It was only through Halley's urging that the report of Newton's work on gravitation ever reached the Royal Society. Halley at a later date assumed much of the expense of publishing what is perhaps Newton's greatest scientific work, the *Principia*.

Newton seems to have been a very sensitive man who felt criticism

* Florian Cajori, *A History of Physics*, Macmillan, 1924, p. 58.

deeply. On one occasion he had a bitter exchange with Robert Hooke concerning a problem in optics. He may have delayed publishing the third volume of the *Principia* out of a desire to avoid another such controversy.†

WHY IS GRAVITY A FORCE?

In Chapter 3, a force was described as a changer of motion. The speed of a falling object is increased 32 ft/sec during each second it falls; hence a force must be acting upon it. This force which causes all freely falling bodies to accelerate nearly 32 ft/sec² is called gravity. Let us now explore the effects of gravity further.

The Motion of Falling Bodies The three equations which follow summarize our knowledge concerning the free fall of objects which start from rest and are acted upon by gravity. ("Free fall" assumes that no forces are acting on a body other than the force of gravity.)

$$v = gt \quad \text{start from rest} \tag{4-a}$$
$$v^2 = 2gd \tag{4-b}$$
$$d = \tfrac{1}{2}gt^2 \tag{4-c}$$

where v = velocity of fall at a particular instant.
t = time of fall (usually expressed in seconds).
d = distance of fall.
g = acceleration imparted by the force called gravity. The numerical value assigned to g will depend on the unit of distance employed.

Equation 4-a enables us to predict the instantaneous velocity of an object which has started from rest and fallen freely for a specified length of time t.

ILLUSTRATIVE PROBLEM
What is the instantaneous velocity of a falling body exactly 3 sec after it starts to fall?

Solution
$$v = gt$$
$$v = 32 \,\frac{\text{ft}}{\text{sec}^2} \cdot 3 \text{ sec}$$
$$v = 96 \,\frac{\text{ft}}{\text{sec}}$$

† J. W. N. Sullivan, *Isaac Newton*. Macmillan. 1938, p. 90.

At the very instant that 3 sec have elapsed the velocity is 96 ft/sec. Note the consistency of the units in this equation:

$$v = g \cdot t$$

$$\frac{\text{ft}}{\text{sec}} = \frac{\text{ft}}{\text{sec}^2} \cdot \text{sec}$$

Equation 4-b makes it possible to predict the instantaneous velocity of a falling object at the instant it has fallen a specified distance d from rest.

ILLUSTRATIVE PROBLEM

How fast is an object falling at the instant it has fallen a distance of 49 ft?

Solution

$$v^2 = 2gd$$

$$v^2 = 2 \cdot 32 \frac{\text{ft}}{\text{sec}^2} \cdot 49 \text{ ft}$$

$$v^2 = 64 \cdot 49 \frac{\text{ft}^2}{\text{sec}^2} \qquad \text{(What is the square root of 64? of 49?)}$$

$$v = 56 \frac{\text{ft}}{\text{sec}}$$

When the object has fallen a distance of 49 ft its momentary velocity is 56 ft/sec. Both the distance d and the gravitational acceleration g involve the same linear unit ($d = 49$ ft, $g = 32$ ft/sec^2). The velocity squared has units of ft^2/sec^2, and hence the velocity is in ft/sec.

Equation 4-c makes it possible to predict the distance of fall of a body after any specified time t.

ILLUSTRATIVE PROBLEM

An object hit the pavement exactly 8 sec after it was dropped from a skyscraper window. How far (feet) did it fall?

Solution

$$d = \tfrac{1}{2} \cdot g \cdot t^2$$

$$d \text{ (ft)} = \tfrac{1}{2} \cdot 32 \frac{\text{ft}}{\text{sec}^2} \cdot 64 \text{ sec}^2$$

$$d = 1024 \text{ ft}$$

SUMMARY OF ASSUMPTIONS:
EQUATIONS DESCRIBING FREE FALL

As has been stressed, the quantity v in Equations 4-a, 4-b, and 4-c represents the velocity of a falling body at a particular instant. The letter v has been chosen to distinguish the instantaneous velocity of a falling body from r in the formula $d = r \cdot t$, in which r is a rate or a speed. While the two are dimensionally the same, it seems desirable to differentiate between them by means of this difference in symbolism: r will be used to represent a *constant* rate or speed; v will represent a *continuously varying* velocity.

Each of the three equations above assumes that the falling body starts from rest. If the body was already in motion when we started measuring time or distance, we would have to use a different set of equations.

Free fall is assumed in each equation. Each would be strictly valid only for a body falling in a vacuum. An object which falls through air must push aside millions and millions of tiny air molecules. Even though these are very minute individually, there are so many that a measurable amount of force is required to move them. Hence their effect is to retard the fall of a body. Over short distances of fall the effects of air resistance are negligible, but the continuing acceleration of a body will be accompanied by an increasing number of collisions with air molecules. The resisting force which results from these collisions gradually reduces the amount of acceleration and eventually prevents any further increase in velocity; a constant (terminal) velocity is eventually reached. The falling object is then traveling at a very great velocity, but there is no further *increase* in velocity. Problems dealing with falling objects assume air resistance to be negligible over the small distances usually given.

The value of g is assumed to be constant. Newton's law of universal gravitation (discussed later in this chapter) suggests that it should change slightly with changes in latitude or altitude; but for short distances of fall, this too is neglected.

Table 4-1 summarizes the information that may be obtained by means of Equations 4-a, 4-b, and 4-c, above. The first column gives the time of fall in seconds. The second column indicates the instantaneous

Table 4-1   FREELY FALLING BODIES STARTING FROM REST
AND UNDERGOING ACCELERATION OF 32 ft/sec²

Time of Fall	Instantaneous Velocity at End of Second	Average Velocity During the Last Second (Treated as Uniform Speed)	Distance Fallen During the Last Second	Total Distance Fallen from the Start
(sec)	(ft/sec)	(ft/sec)	(ft)	(ft)
0	0	0	0	0
1	32	$\dfrac{0+32}{2} = 16$	16	16
2	64	$\dfrac{32+64}{2} = \dfrac{96}{2} = 48$	48	$16 + 48 = 64$
3	96	$\dfrac{64+96}{2} = \dfrac{160}{2} = 80$	80	$64 + 80 = 144$
4	128	$\dfrac{96+128}{2} = \dfrac{224}{2} = 112$	112	$144 + 112 = 256$

velocity when the time indicated has elapsed. The third column, headed "Average Velocity During the Last Second," is obtained by dividing the sum of the velocities at the beginning and end of the particular second by two. This average velocity, so calculated, is treated as if it were a uniform speed during the entire second. If the average velocity during the third second is 80 ft/sec, then the distance fallen in this second is 80 feet. The values in the fourth column, then, are obtained by multiplying the average speed from column three, expressed in ft/sec, by the time, 1 second. Hence the values in column four, in feet, are numerically equal to the velocities in column three.

GRAVITATIONAL ACCELERATION AND GEOGRAPHICAL LOCATION

During the latter half of the seventeenth century, the Dutch scientist Christian Huygens (1629-1695) was making a study of the pendulum (see Chapter 5). A pendulum just over 39 inches long was a useful device for keeping a clock ticking off the seconds in equal intervals. In Paris this "seconds pendulum" required 1 second to make one complete swing from extreme to extreme. In 1671 Huygens suggested to the French astronomer Richer that Richer take the pendulum to French Guiana where he was going to observe an eclipse.* Richer discovered that in French Guiana the "seconds pendulum" took longer than 1 second to complete a swing.

The earth is a slightly flattened sphere;† it bulges at the equator (Fig. 4-2). The North Pole is a bit nearer the center of the earth than

The earth is a slightly flattened sphere (greatly exaggerated as shown). As we move from the equator along the surface of the earth, our distance from the center of the earth decreases slightly. A given object will weigh slightly more at Paris than at Cayenne.

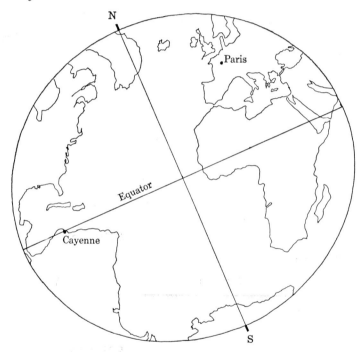

Fig. 4-2.

is the equator. In French Guiana (close to the equator) the pendulum was slightly farther from the earth's center than it was in Paris; the pull on the pendulum was less, and more time was required for a complete swing. The weight of the pendulum was reduced even though its mass remained unchanged. This was one of the earliest hints that there was a distinction between mass and weight.

* Henry Crew, *Rise of Modern Physics*, Williams & Wilkins, 1935, p. 126.
† Recent evidence indicates that the earth is slightly pear-shaped.

NEWTON'S LAW OF UNIVERSAL GRAVITATION

Every body in the universe attracts every other with a force which is directly proportional to the product of their masses and inversely proportional to the square of the distance between them. This is a statement of Newton's law of universal gravitation. It may be expressed mathematically by the equation

$$F = G\frac{m_1 m_2}{d^2}$$ (4-d)

where F = force of attraction.
   G = gravitational constant (not the same as g).
   m_1 and m_2 = masses of the two bodies.
   d = distance between (centers of gravity of) the bodies.

If the distance between any two bodies is constant, the force of attraction pulling the two bodies together is directly proportional to the product of the two masses. Consider masses of 50 kg and 100 kg which are 10 meters apart, and masses of 100 kg and 200 kg the same distance apart as shown in Fig. 4-3. The product of the masses is four times as large in the latter case, so the force pulling these bodies

The forces of attraction between spheres the same distance apart are proportional to the product of their masses. The force of attraction of the lower pair of spheres is four times that of the upper pair.

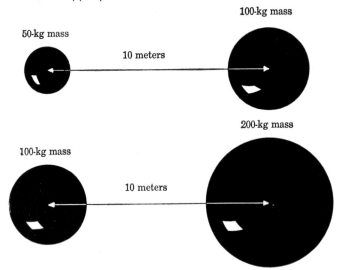

100-kg mass

50-kg mass

10 meters

200-kg mass

100-kg mass

10 meters

Fig. 4-3.

together will be four times as large as the force pulling the smaller bodies together.

Likewise, if the product of the masses of any two bodies is constant, then the force of attraction pulling two bodies together is inversely proportional to the square of the distance between them. Suppose the 50-kg and 100-kg masses which at first are 10 meters apart are moved so as to be 20 meters apart, as shown in Fig. 4-4. The distance has

The forces of attraction between masses are inversely proportional to the squares of the distance separating them. The force of attraction between the upper pair of masses is four times that between the lower pair.

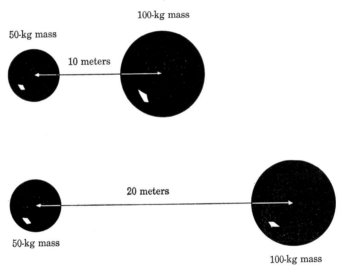

Fig. 4-4.

been doubled, so the force of attraction is now one-fourth of its previous value. Note in Equation 4-d that d is squared. If two objects are removed to three times their former distance apart, the force of attraction becomes one-ninth as large.

G, the gravitational constant is called in mathematics a proportionality factor; it is equal to 6.67×10^{-8} dyne cm^2/gm^2. It should not be confused with g, the acceleration imparted by the force of gravity on the earth's surface. G is not confined to the earth but is universal. It is also called the Newtonian constant, but its value was first actually measured by Henry Cavendish in 1798. Its meaning should become clearer after considering the following example.

ILLUSTRATIVE PROBLEM

Calculate the force of attraction between two 1-gm masses whose distance apart is 1 cm.

Solution

If the numerical value of G were omitted, it would appear that the force of attraction was 1 dyne.

$$F \text{ (dynes)} = \frac{\text{dyne cm}^2}{\text{gm}^2} \cdot \frac{1 \text{ gm} \cdot 1 \text{ gm}}{(1 \text{ cm})^2} = 1 \text{ dyne}$$

Experimental measurement of the force between these two masses actually gives a result of 6.67×10^{-8} dyne rather than 1 dyne. Introduction of this factor then brings the mathematical equation into accord with experimental results.

$$F \text{ (dynes)} = 6.67 \times 10^{-8} \frac{\text{dyne cm}^2}{\text{gm}^2} \cdot \frac{1 \text{ gm} \cdot 1 \text{ gm}}{(1 \text{ cm})^2}$$

$$= 6.67 \times 10^{-8} \text{ dyne}$$

ILLUSTRATIVE PROBLEM

Two spheres of mass 250 gm and 500 gm, are 25 cm apart. Find the force of attraction in dynes.

Solution

$$F = G \frac{m_1 m_2}{d^2}$$

$$F = 6.67 \times 10^{-8} \left(\frac{\text{dyne cm}^2}{\text{gm}^2} \right) \cdot \frac{250 \text{ gm} \cdot 500 \text{ gm}}{25^2 \text{ cm}^2}$$

$$= 6.67 \times 10^{-8} \cdot 200 \text{ dyne} = 1334 \times 10^{-8} \text{ dyne, or } 1.334 \times 10^{-5} \text{ dyne}$$

SCIENTIFIC NOTATION FOR WRITING VERY LARGE OR VERY SMALL NUMBERS

The numerical value of G is written 6.67×10^{-8} rather than 6.67/100,000,000. This notation, called *denary notation*, is nearly always used in print to express very large or very small numbers. It is much more economical of time and of space on the printed page. Because denary notation is so common in scientific literature, it is important to understand how to write and how to interpret numbers in this notation. The following table should be of assistance.

Table 4-2   POWERS OF 10

$$10^3 \ = 1000$$
$$10^2 \ = \ \ 100$$
$$10^1 \ = \ \ \ 10$$
$$10^0 \ = \ \ \ \ 1$$
$$10^{-1} = \ \ \ \ 0.1$$
$$10^{-2} = \ \ \ \ 0.01$$
$$10^{-3} = \ \ \ \ 0.001$$
$$10^{-4} = \ \ \ \ 0.0001$$

By analogy, it should be possible to write the equivalent number for any power of 10. Remember that, just as

10^3 has 3 zeros after the 1, so
10^{20} has 20 zeros after the 1; but
10^{-3} has just 2 zeros after the decimal point before the 1, and
10^{-20} has just 19 zeros after the decimal point before the 1.

Remember too that

to multiply by 10^3, we move the decimal point 3 places to the right;
to multiply by 10^{-3}, we move the decimal point 3 places to the left;

dividing by 10^3 is the same as multiplying by 10^{-3} $\left(\dfrac{1}{10^3} = 10^{-3}\right)$; and

dividing by 10^{-3} is the same as multiplying by 10^3 $\left(\dfrac{1}{10^{-3}} = 10^3\right)$

ILLUSTRATIVE PROBLEM

Express 0.0000035 in denary notation.

Solution

We wish to express the number as 3.5 times some power of 10. By what power of 10 must we multiply 3.5 to obtain 0.0000035 (to move the decimal point 6 places to the left)? When we multiply by 10^{-6} we move the decimal point 6 places to the left, so 0.0000035 $= 3.5 \times 10^{-6}$.

ILLUSTRATIVE PROBLEM

Express 602,000,000,000,000,000,000,000 in denary notation.

Solution

We wish to express the number as 6.02 times some power of 10. By what power of 10 must we multiply 6.02 to obtain 602,000,000,000,-000,000,000,000 (to move the decimal point 23 places to the right)?

Since multiplying by 10^{23} means moving the decimal point 23 places to the right, $602,000,000,000,000,000,000,000 = 6.02 \times 10^{23}$.

ILLUSTRATIVE PROBLEM

Multiply 6.25×10^{-27} by 8.4×10^{8}.

Solution

$$6.25 \times 10^{-27} \times 8.4 \times 10^{8} = 6.25 \times 8.4 \times 10^{-27} \times 10^{8}$$
$$6.25 \times 8.4 = 52.5$$

When we multiply 52.5 by 10^{-27} we move the decimal point 27 places to the left; when we multiply this by 10^{8} we move the decimal point back 8 places to the right, so the decimal point will end up 19 places to the left, and the answer will be 52.5×10^{-19} or 5.25×10^{-18}.

ILLUSTRATIVE PROBLEM

Divide 8.1×10^{15} by 2.7×10^{-4}

Solution

$$\frac{8.1 \times 10^{15}}{2.7 \times 10^{-4}} = \frac{8.1}{2.7} \times \frac{10^{15}}{10^{-4}} = 3 \times 10^{15} \times 10^{4} = 3 \times 10^{19}.$$

EXERCISES AND QUESTIONS FOR CHAPTER 4

1. (a) In the equation $v = gt$, in what units should v be expressed if g is 32 ft/sec^2 and t is expressed in seconds?
   (b) In the equation $v^2 = 2gd$, if v is expressed in m/sec, in what units should g and d be expressed?
   (c) In the equation $d = \frac{1}{2}gt^2$, if g is expressed as 9.8 m/sec^2 and t is expressed in seconds, in what units should d be expressed?

2. An object is dropped from a balloon which is at a height of 1600 ft. Calculate its velocity (a) at the end of 5 sec; (b) at the instant it strikes the ground.

3. Express the following in denary notation.
   (a) 2,500,000
   (b) 0.0000000137

4. Multiply 1.3×10^{7} by 3.8×10^{12}.

5. Divide 3.9×10^{23} by 2.6×10^{15}.

6. How many molecules are there in a pound of hydrogen gas if 2.02 gm contains 6.02×10^{23} molecules?

7. The average diameter of a red blood corpuscle is 8×10^{-5} cm. Calculate its area of cross section. ($A = \pi r^2$; π is approximately 22/7.)

8. The charge on 6.02×10^{23} electrons is 96,500 coulombs. How many electrons constitute 1 coulomb of charge?

9. Two spheres, each of mass 8 kg, have their centers 40 cm apart. Calculate the attractive force between them in dynes.

10. Why do we refer to gravity as a force?

11. State Newton's law of universal gravitation.

12. Gravitational acceleration varies with geographical location. Explain.

13. What is the difference between g in the equations for the motion of falling bodies and G in the mathematical expression of Newton's law of universal gravitation?

14. Two objects, one of 4-lb and the other of 16-lb mass, are allowed to fall freely. Each is accelerated 32 ft/sec/sec. How do the forces of gravity on these objects compare? Why?

REVIEW

1. Calculate the force needed to accelerate a 4-kg mass 10 m/sec².

2. Calculate the mass of a spherical lead ball (dens. = 11.4 gm/cm³) whose diameter is 2.5 cm. (Volume of sphere $= \frac{4}{3}\pi r^3$.)

3. Calculate the mechanical advantage of a jackscrew whose pitch is ⅛ in. and the radius of whose handle is 10 in. (Neglect friction.)

CHAPTER 5

Force and Work:
The Study of Energy

ALL through the ages men have been devising schemes for obtaining wealth: some have sought buried treasure, some have tried to convert inexpensive metals into gold, and some have been lured by the prospect of constructing a machine that will do more

Benjamin Thompson, Count Rumford, 1753-1814, in the portrait by Rembrandt Peale.

work than the energy supplied to it—the so-called perpetual-motion machine.

One of these would-be perpetual-motion devices was based on an invention attributed to Archimedes, the Archimedes' screw (Fig. 5-1).

A would-be perpetual motion machine based on a spiral tube used to raise water, the so-called Archimedes' screw. Water flowing out the top spills over the vanes causing the tube to turn. This pulls more water up the central spiral tube (an Archimedes' screw). Why does this model fail to operate?

Fig. 5-1.

The screw itself was a device for raising water. When it was rotated, the water was drawn up through the central corkscrew (helical) pipe. In the perpetual-motion machine based on this device, fins or vanes were rigidly attached to the exterior of the pipe. The water which issued from the top of the pipe poured over the vanes, causing further rotation and thus pumping more water. Once started, the machine was supposed to operate by itself, without the application of any energy from outside. Unfortunately the model never operated as the inventor hoped it would.

Leonardo da Vinci apparently understood the futility of such a quest; he is said to have chided those who speculated on perpetual motion for the will-o'-the-wisp machines they had devised.* Galileo likewise recognized the impossibility of such machines, for he understood that a pendulum bob which was pulled aside, and then released

* Charles G. Fraser, *Half Hours with Great Scientists*, Reinhold, 1948, p. 70.

could not rise higher at the far end of the swing than its original height. John Bernoulli, a Swiss doctor and mathematician, observed that the *vis viva* (live force) of a pendulum bob disappeared when it reached the top of its swing. Bernoulli also stated a principle which he called the "conservation of *vis viva*" which shows that he too was aware of the impossibility of perpetual motion.

WORK AND ENERGY

The physicist and the layman often have quite different conceptions of work. The layman usually considers any exertion involving a push or pull to be work; the physicist demands that the push or pull shall cause an object to move. You will doubtless believe you are doing work if you come to the door of your home carrying a heavy package of groceries, find it closed, and wait for somebody to let you in. The physicist denies that you are doing work if you are exerting a force just to keep the groceries from falling. Only if you raise the package or otherwise exert the force through a distance is work being done.

Energy is formally defined as *ability to do work*. In attempting to recognize forms of energy, ask yourself, "What force is acting and through what distance?"

Fig. 5-2.

A pile driver. When the elevated weight falls and strikes an object such as a wooden post (pile), a force is exerted on it and it is driven into the ground (distance).

Potential Energy A pile driver is a device consisting of a huge weight and an engine for raising it (Fig. 5-2). When the elevated weight is allowed to fall it exerts a *force* on a vertical post (pile) placed under it, driving the pile a certain *distance* into the ground. In its elevated position the weight has potential energy; it is capable of doing work. The amount of work which it can do depends on its weight and the distance it may fall:

$$\text{Potential energy} = \text{weight} \times \text{height}$$

The heavier the weight is and the greater its possible distance of fall, the larger is its potential energy.

ILLUSTRATIVE PROBLEM

The 500-lb weight of a pile driver is 20 ft above the ground. Calculate its potential energy.

Solution

Potential energy = weight × height = 500 lb × 20 ft = 10,000 ft lb

A car parked on a hill has potential energy. The farther up the hill it is located and the greater its weight, the greater is its potential energy.

The truck which is farther up the hill has the greater potential energy. (Weights are assumed to be equal.)

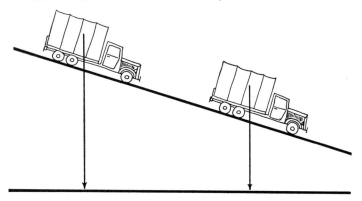

Fig. 5-3.

Kinetic Energy Kinetic energy is the energy which an object has because of its motion. Objects which are in motion may strike other objects, exerting forces on them and moving them. Moving objects have the ability to do work; hence they must possess energy. Water flowing in a river or over a waterfall, a vehicle in motion, and even tiny submicroscopic rapidly moving air molecules all have kinetic energy.

The two factors which determine the amount of kinetic energy a moving body has are mass and velocity. A heavily laden truck can exert larger forces on objects in its path than a lighter automobile traveling at the same velocity; similarly, an automobile which is traveling at high velocity can do more work on objects than one which is moving more slowly. Kinetic energy is calculated by means of the equation

$$K.E. = \tfrac{1}{2}mv^2 \qquad\qquad (5\text{-}a)$$

As the equation shows, the kinetic energy of a moving body is proportional to the square of its velocity. Anyone who compares the feeling of catching a "slow ball" with the feeling of catching a baseball moving only a little faster will realize what this proportion means in experience.

ILLUSTRATIVE PROBLEM

A 100-lb *mass* moves with a velocity of 12 ft/sec. Calculate its kinetic energy.

Solution

$$K.E. = \tfrac{1}{2}mv^2 = \tfrac{1}{2} \cdot 100 \text{ lb} \cdot 12^2 \, \frac{ft^2}{sec^2}$$

$$= \tfrac{1}{2} \cdot 100 \text{ lb} \cdot 144 \, \frac{ft^2}{sec^2}$$

$$= 7200 \text{ foot poundals}$$

Tables 5-1 and 5-2 give the units for potential energy and kinetic energy which are consistent with given units of weight and height, or of mass and velocity, respectively.

Table 5-1   POTENTIAL ENERGY: P.E. $= w \times h$

Potential Energy Will Be Expressed in	If Units of Weight Are	And Units of Height Are
ABSOLUTE UNITS		
foot poundals	poundals	feet
dyne centimeters (ergs)	dynes	centimeters
newton meters (joules)	newtons	meters
GRAVITATIONAL UNITS		
foot pounds	pounds	feet
gram centimeters	grams	centimeters
kilogram meters	kilograms	meters

Table 5-2   KINETIC ENERGY: K.E. $= \frac{1}{2}mv^2$

Kinetic Energy Will Be Expressed in	If Units of Mass Are	And Units of Velocity Are
foot poundals	pounds	feet/sec
dyne centimeters (ergs)	grams	centimeters/sec
newton meters (joules)	kilograms	meters/sec
foot pounds	$\dfrac{\text{pounds weight}}{g \; (\text{ft/sec}^2)}$	feet/sec
gram centimeters	$\dfrac{\text{grams weight}}{g \; (\text{cm/sec}^2)}$	centimeters/sec
kilogram meters	$\dfrac{\text{kilograms weight}}{g \; (\text{m/sec}^2)}$	meters/sec

The Pendulum   The pendulum clock has been a familiar article of furniture in New England homesteads for generations. The pendulum of the physics laboratory lacks the charm and grandeur of one of these old masterpieces—it is often merely a weight suspended from a string —but it serves to illustrate the concepts of potential and kinetic energy just discussed.

In order to set a pendulum in motion it must be pulled aside from its vertical position (Fig. 5-4). This sidewise pull also lifts it; work is

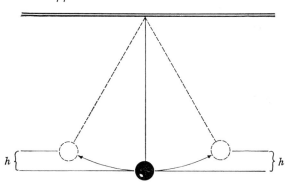

If a pendulum bob is pulled aside to a height h and then released, it cannot reach a height greater than h on the opposite side.

Fig. 5-4.

done on the bob. The amount of work is the product of the weight of the bob and the vertical distance it is elevated. This product is also the potential energy of the bob.

Releasing the elevated bob subjects it to the accelerating force of gravity. Its velocity increases as long as it continues to fall. At the lowest point of the swing it is moving rapidly; inertia keeps it moving and it rises with decreasing velocity as gravity opposes its motion on the upswing. Finally it comes to rest again on the far side and then the cycle is repeated.

At the ends of the swing the bob has no kinetic energy because it is momentarily at rest; its velocity is zero. At the bottom of the swing the bob has its maximum kinetic energy because there its velocity is greatest.

The potential energy is greatest at the extreme ends of the swing where the bob reaches its greatest height. The potential energy decreases as the bob falls and becomes zero at the low point of the swing where the height of the bob is zero.

The potential energy of the bob is at a maximum, then, when its kinetic energy is zero, and vice versa. As the bob falls and loses potential energy, there is a corresponding increase in the amount of its kinetic energy. The potential energy at the top of the swing is equal to the kinetic energy at the bottom, and at any intermediate position the sum of the two kinds of energy is equal to either the maximum potential or maximum kinetic energy.

ILLUSTRATIVE PROBLEM

Find the maximum kinetic energy and the maximum potential energy of a pendulum bob weighing 3 lb which is raised to a height of 4 ft.

Solution

Max. P.E. $= wh = 3 \text{ lb} \cdot 4 \text{ ft} = 12 \text{ ft lb}$
Max. K.E. $= \frac{1}{2}mv^2$; $v^2 = 2gd = 64 \text{ ft/sec}^2 \cdot 4 \text{ ft} = 256 \text{ ft}^2/\text{sec}^2$,
$\qquad = \frac{1}{2} \cdot 3 \text{ lb} \cdot 256 \text{ ft}^2/\text{sec}^2 = 384 \text{ lb} \cdot \text{ft}^2/\text{sec}^2 = 384 \text{ ft poundals}$
(Since 1 lb $= 32$ poundals, these two maximums are equal.)

In all of the preceding discussion the effects of friction and air resistance have been assumed to be negligible.

Other Forms of Energy   Kinetic and potential energy, which have been discussed above, are frequently referred to collectively as "mechanical energy." Let us now turn to other common forms of energy and discuss briefly, in terms of the definition of energy, why they are so classified.

Heat is readily recognized as a form of energy. We know that the combustion of a gasoline-air mixture (a chemical reaction) is a heat-producing process. If the combustion takes place very rapidly within a confined space such as the cylinder of a gasoline engine (Fig. 5-5), it is called an explosion. This explosion sets countless millions of tiny,

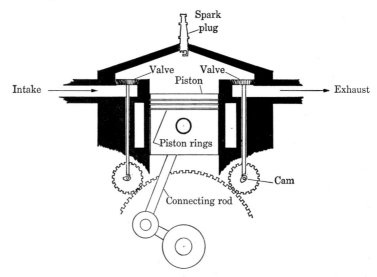

The combustion of gasoline in the cylinder of a car results in millions and millions of tiny gas molecules being hurled at high speeds against the piston and cylinder walls. The piston, which is movable, is forced down.

Fig. 5-5.

high-speed gas molecules in motion; these are hurled against a piston, causing it to move. By means of the motion of the tiny particles (heat) a force has acted through a distance; work has been done. It is proper, therefore, to refer to heat as a form of energy.

The common dry-cell (Fig. 5-6) produces a flow of electrons (an electric current) in a piece of wire, for example in the filament of a flashlight bulb, as a result of a chemical reaction. Even though electrons, which are constituents of the metallic atoms of the filament, are very tiny, they do have mass and work must be done to make them move. The chemical reaction which has supplied the force to cause their movement has been a source of "chemical energy."

When an electric current flows through a wire lying between the poles of a magnet, the wire is subject to a force which makes it move (Fig. 5-7). Hence it is appropriate to speak of "electrical energy."

Fig. 5-6.

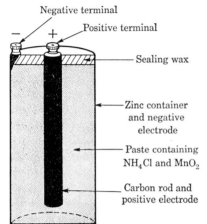

Negative terminal

Positive terminal

Sealing wax

Zinc container
and negative
electrode

Paste containing
NH₄Cl and MnO₂

Carbon rod and
positive electrode

*Cross section of a dry cell or flashlight bat-
tery. The conversion of chemical energy into
electric energy is brought about by changes
in the components of the cell. When the
pole marked + is connected by means of a
wire with the pole marked −, electrons
flow from − to + and are capable of doing
work.*

A rapidly vibrating tuning fork, violin string, or human vocal cord
sets in motion air particles (which have mass). These particles in turn
transmit their motion to others and eventually impinge on human ear-
drums (Fig. 5-8), making these membranes move. Thus sound has
exerted force and caused objects to move. Hence sound qualifies as a
form of energy.

In 1903 Nichols and Hull carried out an experiment in which vanes
suspended in a vacuum moved when they were struck by light waves.
The experiment demonstrated that light could exert a force upon
objects and move them. Light, then, is also a form of energy.

*In a magnetic field a wire or metallic bar is subjected
to a force when an electric current passes through it.
Work is done on it as a result of the passage of the electric current.*

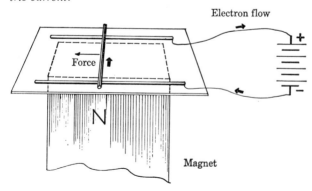

Electron flow

Force

N

Magnet

Fig. 5-7.

Fig. 5-8.

Sound energy sets the eardrum vibrating and eventually reaches the inner ear as the kinetic energy of the fluid therein.

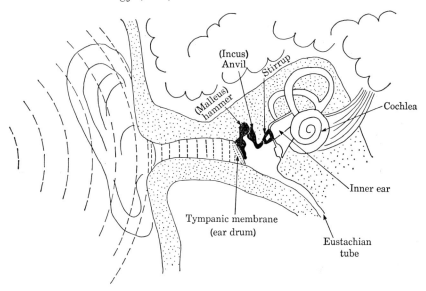

(Incus)
Anvil

Stirrup

(Malleus) hammer

Cochlea

Inner ear

Tympanic membrane
(ear drum)

Eustachian
tube

Power vs. Energy   *The Seven Follies of Science,* a delightful little volume written many years ago by Phin,* tells of a nineteenth-century inventor who thought he had at long last devised a machine which would turn out more work than the equivalent energy supplied to it. He knew that carbon disulfide (CS_2) was a highly volatile (and incidentally very foul-smelling) liquid. This liquid changed into a vapor when it was heated. When the liquid carbon disulfide was injected into the boiler of a steam engine, many millions of tiny, rapidly moving gas molecules of CS_2 were introduced along with the steam already there. The gas pressure in the boiler increased; the engine took a new lease on life and its speed was miraculously increased. However, the ultimate energy source was the hot water (or steam) of the boiler; no new energy had been created. The inventor's exuberance turned to despair when he discovered he had only increased the rate of doing work—or the *power.*

Power depends upon both the amount of work done and the time interval. An engine which is capable of doing 550 foot pounds of work in 1 second is a 1-horsepower engine.

* John Phin, *The Seven Follies of Science,* D. Van Nostrand Co., 1912, p. 66.

ILLUSTRATIVE PROBLEM

The 500-lb weight of a pile driver is lifted a vertical distance of 20 ft in 5 sec. What is the horsepower of the engine?

Solution

$$500 \text{ lb} \cdot 20 \text{ ft}/5 \text{ sec} = 10{,}000 \text{ ft lb}/5 \text{ sec} = 2000 \text{ ft lb/sec}$$
$$550 \text{ ft lb/sec} = 1 \text{ horsepower}$$

$$2000 \text{ ft lb/sec} = \frac{2000}{550} \text{ horsepower} = 3.64 \text{ horsepower}$$

Let us now return to a consideration of the relation between different forms of energy.

THE MECHANICAL EQUIVALENT OF HEAT

Once different forms of energy were recognized, the question arose of the equivalency between them. The mechanical equivalent of heat is such an equivalency; it is the amount of work which must be done if a given quantity of heat is to be produced.

About 1840 a German physician, Julius Robert von Mayer (1814-1878), predicted a value of the mechanical equivalent of heat. His prediction was based only on theoretical considerations (see Chapter 6) but its accuracy was confirmed about a year later when the British physicist James Prescott Joule (1818-1889) carried out his famous laboratory measurement of the mechanical equivalent of heat (described later in this chapter).

Mayer had predicted theoretically and Joule had proved experimentally that 778 * foot pounds of work must be expended in order to produce 1 Btu (British thermal unit) of heat. The Btu is defined on page 80.

TEMPERATURE

The English philosopher John Locke (1632-1704), a contemporary of Isaac Newton, suggested an experiment which demonstrates how unreliable the physical senses are in judging temperature. In this experiment a person plunges his hand into a basin of ice water and then into water at room temperature. He reports that the latter is "warm."

---

* The original value proposed was actually smaller; this is a corrected modern value.

A second person thrusts his hand into a basin of hot water and then into a basin at room temperature. He reports that the latter is "cold." Each man makes a different judgment concerning the temperature of the same bucket of water. Apparently some device is needed for distinguishing temperatures which will be more reliable than the human sensations of hot and cold.

Even before the time of John Locke the need for such temperature-recording devices had been recognized. Galileo's "thermoscope" (Fig. 5-9), invented near the close of the sixteenth century, was probably

Fig. 5-9.

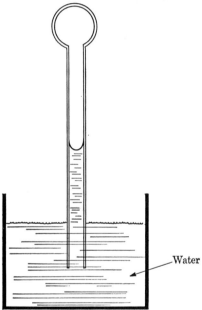

Galileo's thermoscope. One of the earliest temperature-measuring devices. Unfortunately the water level of this instrument responded to both temperature and pressure changes.

Water

one of the earliest temperature-recording devices. It was actually a combination of barometer and thermometer. When the bulb was warmed, the air inside expanded and pushed the liquid down the tube, thus recording an increase in temperature. However, since changes of air pressure also effected changes in the level of the liquid, the thermoscope was hardly a reliable instrument for measuring temperature.

In the years which followed, Isaac Newton, Robert Hooke, Otto von Guericke, and Robert Boyle experimented with a variety of forms of thermometers. Apparently there was among scientific investigators an increasing recognition of the importance of being able to reproduce particular temperature conditions with accuracy.

Early in the eighteenth century the German physicist Fahrenheit (1686-1736) devised a thermometer consisting of a glass tube of small bore (capillary) which contained a column of mercury as the working liquid. He selected as the 32-degree mark the freezing point of water and as the 212-degree mark its boiling point. This scale of 180 degrees between the freezing and boiling points was a bit less convenient than the scale selected somewhat later by Celsius, a professor at the University of Uppsala in Sweden. Celsius chose the freezing point of water as the 100-degree mark, and its boiling point as zero. The modern centigrade scale reverses these, putting the freezing point at zero degrees and the boiling point at 100 degrees (Fig. 5-10).

Common temperature scales. The Fahrenheit scale is familiar in the United States because of its everyday use. The centigrade and Kelvin scales are almost universally used in scientific work. Zero degrees Kelvin (absolute zero) is −273°C.

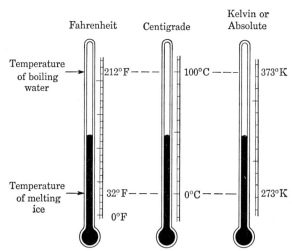

Fig. 5-10.

The absolute or Kelvin scale employs a degree of the same size as the centigrade scale. On this temperature scale the freezing point of water is 273° and the boiling point 373° (at 1 atmosphere of pressure). "Absolute zero" is thus 273 centigrade degrees below the freezing point of water.

Fixed Points of a Thermometer   If a thermometer is placed in a beaker containing both ice and water (Fig. 5-11), its mercury column shortens as its temperature falls to that of the surroundings. Soon the mercury column stops falling and its length becomes constant. The position of the top of the mercury column represents the temperature called the freezing point of water. This temperature is designated

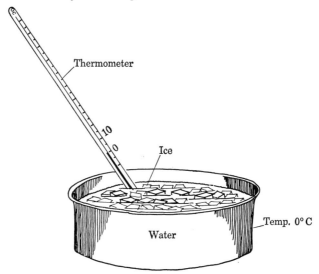

The freezing temperature of water provides a fixed point on a thermometer, zero degrees centigrade. It may be established by immersing a thermometer in ice and water.

Thermometer

Ice

Temp. 0° C

Water

Fig. 5-11.

0° on a centigrade thermometer, or 32° on a Fahrenheit thermometer.

If the thermometer is placed in a boiler (Fig. 5-12) where it is bathed in steam (under a barometric pressure of 1 atmosphere), the mercury column will lengthen and eventually reach a fixed position. This point, called the boiling point of water, is designated 212° on a Fahrenheit thermometer or 100° on a centigrade thermometer.

Two points have thus been established on each thermometric scale; they are called "fixed points." The linear distance between these fixed points is divided into 100 equal divisions on the centigrade scale and 180 on the Fahrenheit scale. Thus a single division (degree) on the centigrade scale is equal to 180/100 or 1.8 Fahrenheit degrees.

The relation used to convert a centigrade temperature into its corresponding value on the Fahrenheit scale is $F = \frac{9}{5}C + 32$, where

Fig. 5-12.

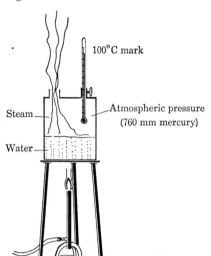

The boiling temperature of water may be used to determine a fixed point on a thermometer scale. If the barometric pressure is 760 mm of mercury, the temperature in freely escaping steam will be 100°C.

F and C represent the Fahrenheit and centigrade temperatures. Note that F will be 32° if C is assigned a value of 0° (the freezing temperature of water).

ILLUSTRATIVE PROBLEM

What Fahrenheit temperature corresponds to 20° centigrade?

Solution

$$F = \tfrac{9}{5}C + 32$$
$$F = \tfrac{9}{5} \cdot 20 + 32 = 68°$$

In order to change centigrade to absolute temperatures (degrees Kelvin) simply add 273 to the centigrade temperature. Thus 25°C = 298°K and −50°C = 223°K.

QUANTITY OF HEAT

Earlier in the chapter the Btu—British thermal unit—was mentioned but not defined. We come now to that definition. A Btu is the quantity of heat needed to change the temperature of 1 pound of water 1 Fahrenheit degree. It is a unit of heat quantity just as the cubic foot is a unit of volume. In order to calculate the number of Btu transferred to or from water we need only multiply the weight of the water in pounds by the temperature change in Fahrenheit degrees.

Ten Btu are needed to raise the temperature of 2 pounds of water 5 Fahrenheit degrees.

The _calorie_ is another much smaller unit of heat quantity; it is the quantity of heat needed to change the temperature of 1 gram of water 1 centigrade degree. The calorie is more commonly used in scientific work today than the Btu (Fig. 5-13).

The relation between a calorie of heat and a British thermal unit.

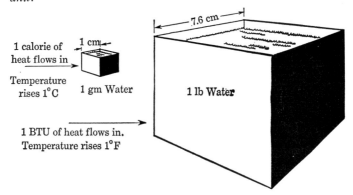

Fig. 5-13.

There is still a third unit of heat also called the Calorie. The dietician uses it in measuring the energy values derived from foods; this calorie is 1000 times as large as the calorie just described and is called the kilogram-calorie, or the _large_ calorie. It is usually written with a capital letter (Calorie) in order to distinguish it from the smaller calorie.

One (small) calorie of heat raises the temperature of 1 gram of water 1 centigrade degree. Ten calories of heat are required to change the temperature of 10 grams of water 1 centigrade degree. One hundred calories are needed to raise the temperature of 10 grams of water 10 centigrade degrees. One calorie is needed, then, for each gram of water for each centigrade degree of temperature rise.

Persons who have lived near the ocean or other large bodies of water know that the heat-absorbing capacity of water is unusually high. They know that in general, larger quantities of heat are required to change the temperature of water than are required for equal temperature changes in the same masses of other materials—for example aluminum or lead. Nearly five times as much heat is needed to effect a 1-degree temperature rise in a gram of water as is needed for the same temperature increase in a gram of aluminum. Stated another way, aluminum requires 22/100 as much heat per gram of material per centigrade degree of temperature change as does water. This fraction of the amount of heat required per gram of material per degree, as compared with water, is called the *specific heat*. Aluminum has a specific heat of 0.22.

The quantity of heat required to change the temperature of a certain amount of water by a certain number of degrees is calculated by multiplying the mass of the water by the number of degrees temperature change, as illustrated above. For *any other material* such as aluminum, lead, or copper, this product must also be multiplied by the specific heat of the material. The general expression for calculating the quantity of heat required is

(Mass of substance) · (temperature change) · (specific heat)

This product will be calories when mass is expressed in grams and temperature change in centigrade degrees; it will be British thermal units when mass is expressed in pounds and temperature change in Fahrenheit degrees. The same value of the third factor—specific heat—is used to calculate calories as Btu. When dealing with temperature changes in water, it can be omitted, since the specific heat of water is 1.

ILLUSTRATIVE PROBLEM

Calculate the number of calories of heat absorbed by 10 gm of lead if its temperature is raised from 20°C to 40°C. The specific heat of lead is 0.03.

Solution

$$10 \text{ gm} \cdot (40°C - 20°C) \cdot 0.03 = \text{heat absorbed}$$
$$10 \text{ gm} \cdot 20°C \cdot 0.03 = 6 \text{ calories}$$

Temperature is often described as a measure of *intensity* of heat. The calorie is a measure of quantity of heat. The latter depends on the quantity of matter under consideration, while the former does not. In cooling a given number of degrees, 100 grams of water will give up more heat than will 10 grams—in fact 10 times as much, as measured in calories—even if they are both at the same temperature initially.

MEASURING HEAT TRANSFER:
THE METHOD OF MIXTURES

Measurement of heat quantity is often carried out in a shiny metal cup called a calorimeter. The calorimeter contains a quantity of water whose mass and temperature are known. A hot object, such as a metal cylinder, of known mass and temperature is quickly transferred from a bath and immersed in the water of the calorimeter. The mixture is stirred and the temperature increase of the water noted.

Heat flows when two objects of different temperatures are in thermal contact; it flows from the object whose temperature is higher to that which is lower until both temperatures are the same. The basic assumption of the method of mixtures is the equality of the amounts of heat transferred: all of the heat lost by the warmer object in cooling is gained by the colder object as it is warmed to the final common temperature. The following equality expresses this basic assumption:

$$\begin{matrix} \text{Quantity of heat lost} \\ \text{by hot object (or objects)} \end{matrix} = \begin{matrix} \text{quantity of heat absorbed} \\ \text{by cold object (or objects)} \end{matrix}$$

The quantity of heat transferred (liberated or absorbed) depends on the three factors discussed earlier—the mass of the material, its specific heat, and the temperature change. The above equation may then be written

$$\begin{pmatrix} \text{Mass of} \\ \text{substance,} \\ \text{metal} \\ \text{cylinder} \end{pmatrix} \cdot \begin{pmatrix} \text{temperature} \\ \text{change} \end{pmatrix} \cdot \begin{pmatrix} \text{specific} \\ \text{heat} \end{pmatrix} = \begin{pmatrix} \text{mass of} \\ \text{substance,} \\ \text{water} \end{pmatrix} \cdot \begin{pmatrix} \text{temperature} \\ \text{change} \end{pmatrix}$$

ILLUSTRATIVE PROBLEM

Calculate the specific heat of a metal if 180 gm at 100°C cool to 24°C when plunged into 250 gm of water initially at 20°C.

Solution

Since 24°C is the final common temperature, the change in the temperature of the water is 24°C − 20°C = 4C°

By substituting the given values in the equation above:

$$(180 \text{ gm}) \cdot (76C°) \cdot (\text{S.H.}) = (250 \text{ gm}) \cdot (4C°)$$

$$\text{S.H.} = \frac{250 \cdot 4}{180 \cdot 76} = \frac{25}{342} = 0.0731$$

The heat absorbed by the calorimeter cup and stirrer has been neglected in the above problem. This quantity of heat should be taken into account in laboratory practice. It is calculated for each object

Fig. 5-14.

The method of mixtures. A block of metal of known mass is heated in freely escaping steam until its temperature is 100°C throughout. It is then quickly immersed in a known mass of water contained in a calorimeter, where the temperature increase is determined.

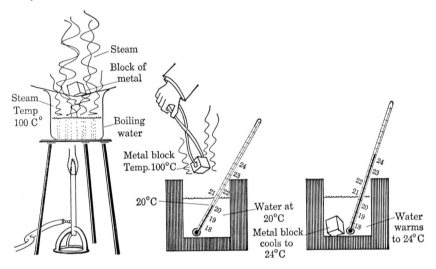

by multiplying the three factors—mass, specific heat, and temperature change—as described above. The total heat absorbed or liberated is simply the sum of the individual amounts.

JOULE'S EXPERIMENTAL EVALUATION OF THE MECHANICAL EQUIVALENT OF HEAT

Mention has already been made of the Joule experiment designed to show the quantitative relation between the amount of work expended and the quantity of heat produced. This experiment should be understandable now that we are familiar with the calorimetric method of measuring heat.

The apparatus used by Joule to determine the value of the mechanical equivalent of heat is shown in Fig. 5-15. A weight is suspended vertically from a pulley. The supporting string passes over the pulley and is wound around a drum which is free to rotate. The falling weight causes rotation of the drum and hence of the attached paddle wheels, which are immersed in water. The frictional effect of the

Fig. 5-15.

Joule's experiment for determining the mechanical equivalent of heat.

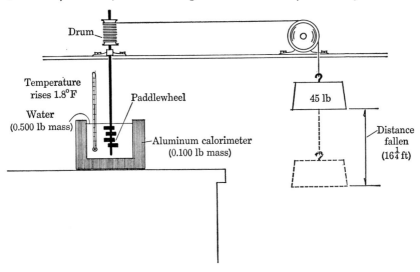

rotating paddle wheels produces heat and causes a rise in the temperature of the water.

The weight has potential energy in its elevated position. As it falls, potential energy is lost and the work expended is equal to this loss (obtained through multiplication of its weight by its distance of fall). The quantity of heat produced by the falling weight is determined as described earlier, by multiplying the mass of the water in the calorimeter by its temperature rise. In a more exact experiment, account would be taken of the heat absorbed by the calorimeter cup.

Joule spent years in efforts to perfect this experiment and to obtain an exact value of the mechanical equivalent of heat. He made use of the British thermal unit in his calculations.

ILLUSTRATIVE PROBLEM

A 45.0-lb weight falls 16.25 ft and causes a temperature rise of 1.80F° in an aluminum calorimeter containing 0.500 lb of water. The mass of the calorimeter is 0.100 lb, and its specific heat is 0.220. Calculate the mechanical equivalent of heat in ft lb/Btu. (See Fig. 5-15.)

Solution

Work done = 16.25 ft · 45.0 lb = 731.25 ft lb
Heat absorbed by water = (0.500 lb) · (1.80F°) = 0.900 Btu
Heat absorbed by calorimeter = (0.10 lb) · (1.80F°) · (0.220) = 0.0396 Btu
Total heat absorbed = work done

$$0.9396 \text{ Btu} = 731.25 \text{ ft lb}$$

$$1 \text{ Btu} = \frac{731.25}{0.9396} \text{ ft lb} = 778 \text{ ft lb}$$

In the metric system 4.186 joules of work are equivalent to a calorie of heat.

CONSERVATION OF ENERGY

James Prescott Joule, whose name has already figured so prominently in our story of energy, was a pupil of the Manchester (England) schoolmaster John Dalton, famous as a founder of the modern atomic theory of matter (Chapter 7). The flame of scientific interest appears to have been kindled early in his pupil, for we know that Joule experimented with electric motors when he was a very young man.

In these experiments, Joule calculated the power of different electric motors by measuring the rates at which they were able to lift weights. He operated the motors by means of electric batteries. At first he regarded a battery as an inexhaustible source of energy,[*] but was not long in correcting this error. He soon recognized that the energy which could be derived from a given battery was limited and that it might appear in different forms.

If a strip of zinc metal was immersed in a sulfuric acid solution, bubbles (hydrogen) rose from the metal surface and the liquid became warm; a considerable amount of heat was liberated as a result of the chemical action. If a similar piece of zinc was immersed in sulfuric acid and was connected by a wire to a copper metal strip also in the sulfuric acid, then less heat resulted from the dissolving of the zinc because some of the chemical energy was used up in pushing electrons through the wire. If the battery was used to run an electric motor, still more energy was required for this and still less heat was available to warm the solution.

[*] Alexander Wood, *Joule and the Study of Energy*, G. Bell & Sons, 1925, p. 46.

Joule seems to have grasped the idea of conservation of energy, namely, that energy may be neither created nor destroyed but may be changed from one form to another. A combination of chemical substances such as zinc and sulfuric acid may be considered to have a certain quantity of available energy. The operation of the electric motor uses up much of this energy; little is left to be converted into heat. Joule thought that heat, electrical energy, and mechanical energy were all related; the appearance of a certain quantity of one was accompanied by the disappearance of an equivalent amount of another.

This concept of the equivalence of different forms of energy was not acceptable to his contemporaries; Joule was a man ahead of his time. His paper published in 1842 entitled "On the Calorific Effects of Magneto Electricity and the Mechanical Value of Heat" seems to have attracted very little attention. Again in 1847 Joule ventured to present his ideas at a scientific meeting. The program was crowded and running behind schedule. The chairman requested that Joule summarize his paper briefly rather than give it in its entirety.* At the close of his brief summary the chairman did not even invite discussion, since he regarded the matter as being of trifling importance. This paper too would have passed unnoticed except for William Thomson (Lord Kelvin), who rose and called to the attention of the gathering its far-reaching implications. Needless to say, Kelvin and Joule became life-long friends.

During the same year (1847) the German physiologist Hermann von Helmholtz (1821-1894), better known for his discoveries in the field of sound than mechanics, published a paper which contained perhaps the first explicit general statement of the principle of energy conservation. This stated that the energy existing in the universe was constant in quantity; its form might be altered but not its amount. When one form of energy was created, an equivalent quantity of another form disappeared.

The principle of conservation of energy remained an important pillar of science into the twentieth century. As we shall see in the next section, it was in turn succeeded by another still more inclusive principle. This new principle in no way invalidates the equivalency of different forms of energy but merely extends its scope to include matter as a form of energy.

* Wood, *Joule*, p. 51.

The law of the conservation of *energy* denied the possibility of creating or destroying energy; the law of the conservation of *matter* stated that there was also a fixed amount of matter in the universe. Man could do nothing that would alter this amount. Atoms might be cajoled into hitching together or into becoming detached, but they could not, by any process of science or magic, be obliterated. Such at least was the prevailing belief until the early years of the twentieth century,

Albert Einstein, 1879-1955.

when Einstein informed the world that Lavoisier had been wrong. Matter should be destructible. If it could be destroyed, a perfectly enormous energy release should result. At that time he stated the now-famous equation, $E = mc^2$ in which E is the new energy produced, m the amount of matter destroyed, and c the velocity of light.

In a sense there was nothing very startling about this equation. The equivalence between work and heat had been worked out by Joule, and the equivalence of other forms of energy was recognized in the law of the conservation of energy. The really exciting aspect of Einstein's new equation was the extension of the concept of energy to include matter. If a method of annihilating matter could be discovered, an enormous new energy source, hitherto untapped, should be available. The enormousness of the energy release becomes apparent when one considers the factor c^2. Its value will be 9×10^{20} cm²/sec² if the velocity of light is expressed in cm/sec. When this huge number is multiplied by even a very small mass change, say 10^{-6} (a millionth) gram, the resulting energy change will be 9×10^{14} or nearly 10^{15} ergs, equivalent to approximately 21 million calories of heat. This is enough to change 500 pounds of water from the freezing point to the boiling point. It is a surprisingly large energy release, considering the tiny amount of matter destroyed.

For many years there was little direct experimental evidence to support the Einstein mass-energy equivalence principle. About 1940 the much-needed corroborating evidence was at hand. Under appropriate conditions (to be discussed in Chapter 14) atoms of uranium-235 could be made to fission (split into parts). The combined mass of the resulting fragments was slightly smaller than that of the original atom; the energy release was of enormous proportions. Here at last was experimental evidence which lent convincing support to the theoretical principle which Einstein had first announced over thirty years earlier, and which suddenly emerged now as a key factor in the development of nuclear energy. The utility of a theoretical principle is frequently not immediately apparent; often a new instrument or new technique is needed before supporting experimental evidence can be found.

Does the mass-energy equivalence principle invalidate the law of the conservation of energy? Insofar as the latter denies the possibility of creating new energy, it does; new energy is created when matter is destroyed. On the other hand it is still true that energy may be converted from one form to another; it is still true that in such a process, energy of one variety is produced only at the expense of another form.

Does the principle of conservation of mass still hold? The new principle of mass-energy equivalence allows for the destruction or creation of matter, which is denied by the law of the conservation of matter. On the other hand the law of the conservation of matter still remains the foundation of quantitative relations in the science of chemistry, as will be shown in Chapter 7.

The mass-energy equivalence principle is really an extension of the two laws of conservation. For a hundred years we have known that 4.186 joules of work are equivalent to 1 calorie of heat. The Einstein principle simply establishes a similar equivalency between matter and energy. It explains that in the process of nuclear fission new energy is created at the expense of matter. Henceforth it is the sum of the energy and the matter in the universe which is conserved.

EXERCISES AND QUESTIONS FOR CHAPTER 5

1. Calculate the number of calories which are equivalent to 1 Btu.

2. A bomb having a weight of 4 tons is dropped from a height of 18,000 ft. What kinetic energy will the bomb have just before it strikes the ground? (Neglect air resistance.)

3. Calculate the kinetic energy of a speed boat having a mass of 900 lb and traveling at the rate of 20 mi/hr. Express the result in foot poundals.

4. A car is parked at the top of a 3000-ft incline which drops 1 ft vertically for every 12 ft along the road. If the car *weighs* 2900 lb, what is its potential energy?

5. A machine lifts an 80-kg weight 120 cm vertically in 3 sec. How much work is done? Calculate the horsepower.

6. Calculate the kinetic energy of a stone weighing 20 gm and having a velocity of 500 cm/sec.

7. A brass cylinder (specific heat = 0.089) whose temperature is 100°C has a mass of 200 gm. It is dropped into an aluminum calorimeter (specific heat = 0.220) having a mass of 100 gm and containing 150 gm of water, both at 20.0°C. Calculate the final temperature.

8. Normal body temperature is 98.6°F. What is the corresponding temperature on the centigrade scale?

9. At what temperature do the readings of a Fahrenheit and a centigrade thermometer coincide?

10. How are work and energy defined by the physicist?

11. Give the meanings of kinetic energy, potential energy, power, and mechanical equivalent of heat.

12. Describe the changes in the potential and kinetic energies of a pendulum bob as it swings back and forth.

13. Draw diagrams of three commonly used temperature scales, showing the boiling and freezing points of water on each.

14. Describe how you might check the correctness of (calibrate) the scale on a laboratory thermometer.

15. Define (a) calorie, (b) Calorie, and (c) specific heat.

16. In calculating quantities of heat in Btu, do you use the same or a different value of the specific heat as in a calculation involving calories? Explain.

17. What factors determine the heat transferred between two substances such as a block of hot aluminum and cold water?

18. Describe the basic assumptions of the so-called "method of mixtures."

19. Describe the Joule experiment for determining the mechanical equivalent of heat.

20. State the law of conservation of energy; the law of conservation of mass. Does the Einstein mass-energy equivalence principle invalidate either or both of these? Explain.

REVIEW

1. If an object is thrown vertically into the air, gravitational action will decrease its velocity by 32 ft/sec for each second it rises. Calculate the maximum height to which an object will rise if it is shot up vertically with an initial velocity of 150 ft/sec.

2. An irregular block of metal has a mass of 160 gm in air. When it is lowered into a graduated cylinder containing 70 cc of water, the level rises to 130 cc. Calculate the specific gravity of the metal.

3. What force must act on an 800-gm mass in order to accelerate it 25 cm/sec^2?

CHAPTER 6

The Frenzy of Molecular Motion

SOME of the principles learned in our brief excursion into the study of mechanics will now be applied in studying the submicroscopic behavior of matter. The idea that material substances are composed of huge numbers of tiny particles did not originate with modern science; it dates back at least to the time of the Greeks in the pre-Christian era. Democritus, about 400 B.C., conceived of matter as being composed of tiny rigid particles moving through empty space. These particles were believed to be indivisible and indestructible and to have properties such as roundness, smoothness, and roughness. However, not all the outstanding philosophers of the pre-Christian

HUMPHRY DAVY, 1778-1829 (Courtesy, N.Y. Public Library)

era accepted this theory. The great Aristotle, for example, rejected it, holding that matter was of a continuous structure.

Only fragments have come down to us of the first-hand records that would give the actual views of the Greeks. Much of our information reaches us by way of the Roman poet Lucretius (99-55 B.C.). His famous poem, *De rerum natura* (Concerning the Nature of Things), is our principal source of knowledge concerning the nature of matter as conceived during his time and earlier.

A Greek saying ran, "Nature abhors a vacuum." The idea seems to have persisted, for we find Galileo some 2000 years later expressing amazement that the abhorrence of nature for a vacuum ceases in a water pipe after a pump has lifted a column of water to a height of about 34 feet (Fig. 6-1). The great argument concerning the nature

Fig. 6-1.

"Nature Abhors a Vacuum." The common pump with its piston and valve, removes air from the pipe. Nature, abhorring the vacuum, causes water to rush in and fill the empty space. Galileo was perplexed by the fact that water fails to rush in after the column reaches a height of about 34 feet. The lift pump will not raise water to a greater height.

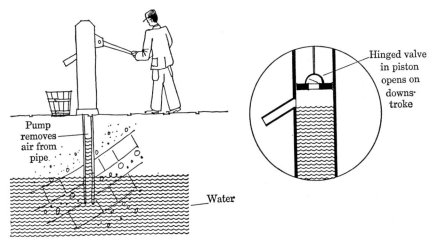

Hinged valve in piston opens on downstroke

Pump removes air from pipe.

Water

of matter seems to have been revived and intensified in Galileo's time. One group, known as the "plenists," agreed with the principle that nature abhors a vacuum. They argued that all space was *filled* with matter and nature saw to it that a vacuum did not form. Descartes (1596-1650), the famous French mathematician and philosopher, was an adherent of this school.

Pierre Gassendi (1592-1655), on the other hand, was a "vacuist"; he believed that matter was composed of particles, and he conceived of these particles as moving through a void. He seems to have had an inkling that the particles making up a gas were far apart relative to their sizes. He also believed that the structural particles were closer together in solids than in liquids, and that in liquids they were in turn closer together than in gases. Here is a hint that knowledge of the properties of gases, in particular, had reached the stage of development where a new theory might blossom forth at any time.

The honor of collecting the information and suggesting the first outline of the kinetic theory belongs to Daniel Bernoulli. He is called the "father of the kinetic theory" because of his famous work, the *Hydrodynamica* (1739), in which he laid the foundations of the kinetic theory of gases. He was one of the first to explain gas pressure as resulting from the force exerted by millions of tiny particles continually bombarding a surface. Certain passages of the *Hydrodynamica* indicate that he also understood the relation of the temperature of a gas to the speeds of its particles.

THE KINETIC THEORY OF GASES

What is the nature of a gas as interpreted by kinetic theory? First of all, gases are composed of tiny submicroscopic particles—molecules—which are moving rapidly in all directions. In order to visualize a gas, try to imagine that the room in which you are sitting swarms with millions of minute ping-pong balls moving very rapidly in all directions. They collide with one another and rebound from the walls of the room. For the most part they move with approximately the same speed; occasionally one may be observed to be moving considerably faster or slower than the average.

Let us see why gas particles are believed to be in a rapid state of motion. If a tank of ammonia gas is opened in one part of a room, its odor is soon detected in all parts of the room. The ammonia molecules have somehow moved in among the air particles of the room. This movement of one kind of gas particles through others is called *diffusion*. Similarly, if a jar containing air is placed over a jar of chlorine (a very heavy gas), the yellow color of the chlorine will gradually diffuse upward into the covering jar, showing that even heavy gas particles such as chlorine will, because of their motion, eventually move up and against the force of gravity into all of the space available to them. These two experiments make plausible the supposition that the movement of gas particles is rapid, and also that a gas is a porous structure with large spaces between the molecules.

If the room filled with tiny ping-pong balls is heated, we may picture the balls as moving more briskly. Again there may be a few slow-moving or fast-moving balls, but the mean speed is greater at the higher temperature. The mean speed of molecular movement is associated with the temperature of a gas.

Now imagine that the gas particles halt their motion momentarily like a moving picture when the projector is stopped. Some particles may be in contact, that is, in collision with one another; others are separated (Fig. 6-2). On the average, the distances between particles

A gas is a collection of tiny particles, or molecules, moving rapidly in all directions. As they move freely through space, some rebound off one another or off the sides of the vessel. The distances between them are large in comparison with their diameters.

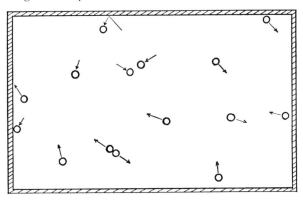

Fig. 6-2.

are large in comparison with their diameters. One reason for believing this to be true is the high compressibility of gases. They do behave as if they were coiled springs if large numbers of gas particles are crowded into a small volume. Robert Boyle spoke of the "spring of the air."

If you were to push down on the handle of an old-fashioned tire pump whose outlet tube was stopped up, the particles of entrapped air which formerly occupied a larger space would be squeezed into a smaller space. If you then let go of the handle, it would fly up at you.

When a gas is compressed, the volume in which the particles may move is diminished; on the average the distances between molecules are smaller.

The speed with which gas molecules rebound from a wall of the room or of the container is the same as the speed with which they hit the wall. We describe this situation by saying that the impacts of molecules are elastic. There is no loss of kinetic energy by gas molecules either at rebound with each other or with the walls of a confining vessel.

Newton's law of universal gravitation, stated in Chapter 4, that "*Every* body in the universe attracts every other with a force which is proportional to the product of the masses, and inversely proportional to the square of the distance between them." It is to be expected, then, that molecules of a gas attract one another. However, since the masses of gas particles are very small and their distances apart comparatively large, the forces of attraction exerted are so minute that they are considered negligible. (This would not be true of gases near their points of liquefaction.)

In summary then, the basic assumptions of the kinetic theory of gases are:

(1) Gases are composed of tiny particles called molecules.

(2) These molecules are in rapid movement in all directions.

(3) The distances between molecules are large relative to the sizes of the molecules.

(4) The average speeds of the molecules are increased when the temperature of the gas is raised.

(5) The impacts of gas molecules are elastic.

(6) The forces of attraction between gas molecules are negligible.

THE SEA OF AIR ABOUT US

We take it pretty much for granted today that there is a sea of air, or atmosphere, everywhere about us. But very little was known about the atmosphere or about the constituents of the air until about the seventeenth century. Only then did facts emerge which assisted in solving a problem that was puzzling many of the great brains of the day—the curious limits, already mentioned, to nature's abhorrence of a vacuum. If we try to evacuate a 40-foot vertical water pipe, which is standing in water, by means of an ordinary lift pump, the water behaves at first as the Greeks said it should, rushing in to avert the formation of the abhorred vacuum. But once the water level has risen in the pipe to a height of some 34 feet, no amount of pumping, however vigorous, will suffice to lure more water in to fill the evacuated space.

Galileo pondered over this problem. One of his co-workers, Torricelli (1608-1647), wondered to what extent nature would abhor a vacuum in a glass tube filled with the heavy liquid, mercury. In 1643 he carried out his famous experiment of inverting a mercury-filled glass tube, about a yard long, in a bowl partly filled with mercury (Fig. 6-3). This device, which was eventually called a barometer,

Fig. 6-3.

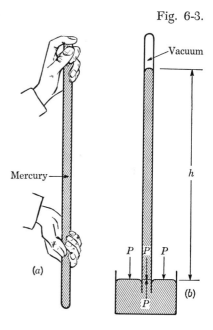

A Torricellian barometer. The height h of the mercury column varies around an average of about 76 cm or 30 in. at sea level. Is there a relationship between this height and the height that water will rise in a pipe exhausted by a pump? What is it?

showed that mercury was supported not 34 feet but rather about 30 inches above its level in the reservoir, and also that the height of the mercury column in the tube fluctuated from time to time.

The famous French scientist Pascal (1623-1662) reasoned that if air pressure was responsible for the changes in the height of the mercury column in the barometer tube, it should be possible to reduce this height by merely climbing up to a greater altitude above the bottom of the sea of air where a shorter column of air would be pressing on the mercury in the bowl. One of the simplest ways to test this was to climb to the top of a church steeple with a barometer. Apparently the experiment was not conclusive, for Pascal prevailed upon his brother-in-law, Périer, to carry the instrument up the mountain known as the Puy de Dôme. The falling of the mercury level in the barometer tube as the ascent was made up the mountainside dramatically supported the contention of those who believed that we walk about at the bottom of a vast sea of air.

At about this same period in France, Jean Rey heated tin in an open dish (Fig. 6-4) and found that an increase in weight resulted.

Fig. 6-4.

Jean Rey knew 300 years ago that tin metal gained weight when it was heated in the presence of air. This fact proved a stumbling block to the phlogiston theory, which demanded that when a substance was heated, the departure of the combustible principle phlogiston should result in a weight decrease. Today we attribute the weight increase to the oxygen which combines with the tin.

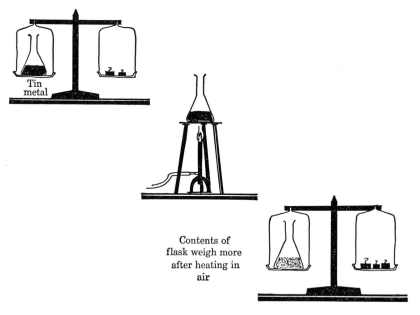

Tin metal

Contents of flask weigh more after heating in air

He speculated concerning the cause, and wondered if it might be due to the presence of some substance in the air. His speculation later proved to be a correct one but nobody paid any attention to it at the time. Not enough was known concerning the nature of the air to lend support to his guess. It was a century or more before the functional element, oxygen, was recognized as a constituent of the air.

BOYLE'S LAW

Robert Boyle (1627-1691) has often been called "the father of chemistry." He was certainly the outstanding chemist of his day, but he was also interested in many other types of natural phenomena. He wrote on the "Spring of the Air" and explained the "spring" by assuming that the particles of air behaved like minute watch springs.* The law which bears his name deals with the spring of gases. The events which led to the discovery of Boyle's law came about roughly as follows.

Torricelli had invented the mercury barometer when Boyle was a lad in his teens. For years there had been a controversy as to what held up the column of mercury. About 1660 Boyle published his *New*

Fig. 6-5.

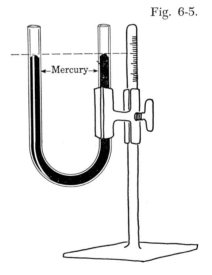

"Liquids seek their own level" in an open U tube: that is, in every one of many connected open vessels in which a liquid is standing, the height of the column is the same.

Experiments Touching the Spring of the Air. A certain Franciscus Linus took issue with him concerning the manner in which the mer-

* Louis T. More, *The Life and Works of the Honorable Robert Boyle*, Oxford University Press, 1944, p. 242.

cury was held up in the barometer tube above its level in the reservoir. It was a well-known fact that in an open U tube a liquid such as water or mercury would seek the same level in each tube (Fig. 6-5). What was holding mercury above its level in the barometer tube? According to Linus an invisible cord called a *funiculus* was responsible (Fig. 6-6). In order to disprove what he believed to be a crackpot idea, Boyle devised his J-tube experiment.

Fig. 6-6.

Franciscus Linus and Robert Boyle disagreed concerning the manner in which the mercury column in a barometer tube was held up above its level in the bowl.

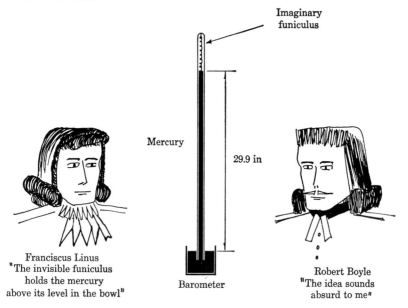

Imaginary funiculus

Mercury

29.9 in

Franciscus Linus
"The invisible funiculus holds the mercury above its level in the bowl"

Barometer

Robert Boyle
"The idea sounds absurd to me"

In the Boyle experiment the short arm of the J is sealed and the long arm open, as shown in Fig. 6-7. If the mercury column in a Torricellian barometer tube has a vertical height of 760 millimeters above its level in the reservoir, the pressure of the air supporting it is said to be 1 atmosphere; if air pressure is reduced so that the column is only half as high, the pressure will be half an atmosphere. Before mercury is placed in the J tube, the air pressure everywhere inside the tube is the same as atmospheric pressure. At the instant that sufficient mercury is added to just close off the short (sealed) end of the tube, the pressure is still substantially equal to atmospheric pressure. As soon as more mercury is added, the heavy liquid tends to pile up higher in the open tube and its weight squeezes the air, confined in the sealed end, into a smaller space; the gas pressure in this closed tube is increased. The amount of increase is determined by the difference of

Boyle's J-tube experiment. The barometer is used to measure the air pressure in the open J tube. The amount by which the air pressure in the closed tube exceeds atmospheric pressure is measured by the difference in mercury level in the open and closed tubes.

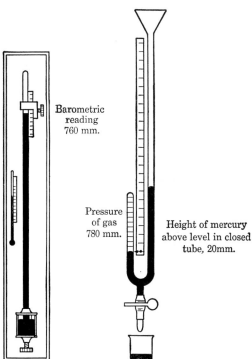

Barometric
reading
760 mm.

Pressure
of gas
780 mm.

Height of mercury
above level in closed
tube, 20mm.

Fig. 6-7.

level of the mercury in the two tubes. Suppose that atmospheric pressure is 760 millimeters of mercury and that the mercury in the open tube is 20 millimeters higher than in the sealed tube. The pressure of the gas in the sealed tube will be 780 millimeters.

In carrying out the experiment, Boyle had recorded data showing the volumes of the enclosed gas at different pressures. He had put the notebook aside without having observed the mathematical relation which now bears his name—that the product of the pressure and the corresponding volume was always almost exactly the same value for a given amount of air trapped in the tube. Some friends observed this later when looking over the recorded data, but they insisted that Boyle deserved credit for the discovery of the principle.*

Here is a scientific principle which was discovered because of a very fanciful misinterpretation of the manner in which the mercury column was supported in a barometer tube. Boyle's experiment was

Fig. 6-8.

Boyle's law: If the volume of a given mass of gas is reduced, the pressure is proportionally increased. In any actual experiment special precautions must be taken to maintain the same temperature in the comparison. The temperature of a gas rises when the gas is compressed and is lowered when the gas expands.

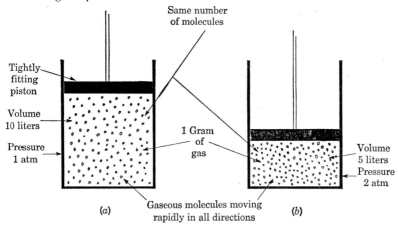

designed, not to prove a new principle, but to disprove what he regarded as a false conclusion. One of the by-products of the experiment was a set of data from which friends were able to discover a generalization. In this discovery we have a glimpse of the inductive method. A generalization emerged from a group of apparently unrelated data concerning the pressures and volumes of gases. The sequence of events hardly corresponds to that described in the traditional interpretation of "the scientific method."

* James B. Conant, *Robert Boyle's Experiments in Pneumatics*, Harvard University Press, 1950, p. 62.

$\left(P \sim \frac{1}{V} \right) \left(PV = k \right) \left(P_1 V_1 = P_2 V_2 \right)$

Stated mathematically, Boyle's law merely says that $PV = k$; in words, the product of the pressure of a gas and its volume is constant. This is true as long as the temperature and mass of the gas under consideration do not change. As an illustration, suppose that 1 gram of a gas is confined in a cylinder fitted with a piston as shown in Fig. 6-8a. The volume occupied by the gas is 10 liters and its pressure is 1 atmosphere. Substituting these values in the formula $PV = k$, we find that 1 (atm) · 10 (liters) = k, or that for these particular conditions k has a value of 10 liter atmospheres. If the piston is moved down so that the new volume is 5 liters, as in Fig. 6-8b, the pressure must increase to 2 atmospheres, since the product, 10, is constant. If the volume is shrunk to 2 liters, the pressure must increase to 5 atmospheres. As the amount of space available to the molecules—the volume —is altered, the product of P and V will always be 10 for 1 gram of gas at the particular temperature (presumed to remain constant).

Table 6-1   SAMPLE DATA, BOYLE'S LAW

Pressures in Atmospheres	Volume in Liters	PV Product
1	10	10
2	5	10
4	2.5	10
5	2	10

HEAT: MATTER OR MOTION?

The Greeks included fire among their four elements—earth, air, fire, and water. With the revival of the particle structure concept of matter some 2000 years later (seventeenth century), it is understandable that heat might again have been regarded as a material substance. Jean Rey suspected that the increases in weight which occurred when tin was heated in air might be due to something in the air. Robert Boyle believed the weight increase was caused by particles of heat from the fire attaching themselves to the tin. A century later the famous Scottish chemist Joseph Black (1728-1799) considered heat to be a "subtle elastic fluid" called caloric.

However, the natural philosophers were not all agreed concerning the nature of heat. There was a growing conviction that heat was not a material, but vibration of the particles composing a substance. An

American-born scientist made a discovery which lent strong support to the vibration theory of heat.

Count Rumford: Cannon-Boring Experiments In the history of science there is scarcely a figure more colorful and contradictory than Benjamin Thompson, a Massachusetts boy who later became a Count in the Holy Roman Empire. He was born in 1753 in North Woburn, Massachusetts. His willingness to walk from his home to Cambridge (about eight miles) to observe demonstrations in natural philosophy at Harvard is evidence of his early interest in scientific matters. As a boy he was seriously burned while making fireworks for some of the celebrations attending the repeal of the Stamp Act. It seems very likely that he witnessed the Boston Massacre and the Battle of Bunker Hill. During the Revolutionary War he was several times brought before local committees because he was suspected of supporting the British cause. There is little doubt that he actually passed military intelligence reports to General Gage, the British commander in Boston, though no such charges were proved against him at that time.*

When the British evacuated Boston in 1776, Thompson went to England. Very shortly thereafter he was appointed to an important position under Lord Germain, who was head of the British Colonial Office in London. When Germain fell into disfavor several years later, Thompson realized he would soon be out of a job and he returned to America to lead a regiment of soldiers against his fellow countrymen.

Returning again to England a short time later, he found no wars in progress and so turned to the continent in quest of adventure. Eventually his path led to Munich, Bavaria, and here he became Count Rumford under Karl Theodor, Elector of Bavaria.

As superintendent of the arsenal in Munich Thompson marveled at the enormous amount of heat evolved in the operation of cannon-boring. Just as long as the horse supplying the motive power for the boring operation continued to walk around to keep the cannon rotating, the heat came streaming forth in apparently inexhaustible supply. The count could not understand how heat, if a material substance, could continue to issue forth without effecting at least some change in the mass or the specific heat of either cannon or shavings. He was

* Allen French, *General Gage's Informers,* University of Michigan Press, 1932, pp. 119-146.

finally led to conclude that heat must be a motion of particles rather than the supposed material substance called caloric. The cannon-boring experiments were thus a decisive factor in establishing heat as a mode of motion.

The Royal Institution: Humphry Davy   In Munich, Count Rumford had accomplished a great deal for the rulers of Bavaria. The king's hunting ground had been neglected for years; Rumford converted it

The Royal Institution, London, a society devoted to the encouragement of scientific study. Many outstanding British scientists including Thomas Young, Humphry Davy, and Michael Faraday have been associated with the Royal Institution.

into a beautiful English garden. He cleaned the beggars from the streets of the city, clothed, fed, and housed them and taught them trades. His reforming zeal eventually caused embarrassment to the Elector, and Rumford was sent to London as ambassador. Back in London he found that his credentials were not acceptable at the Court of St. James, but being a British subject, he nevertheless stayed on in London and in 1800 established the famous Royal Institution for the promotion of science and scientific research.

In 1801 a lad by the name of Humphry Davy came to London to be interviewed for a position at the Royal Institution. Davy had just finished serving an apprenticeship as an apothecary. His personal appearance on the occasion of the interview was unkempt; Rumford was not at all impressed on first glance at his prospective employee, and he required Davy to give a private lecture. This task the young man carried out most capably and convincingly; and so it was that the future discoverer of the elements sodium, potassium, and iodine obtained his position at the Royal Institution. It is quite possible that Davy's experiment of rubbing two pieces of ice together and thus melting them, published two years earlier under the title "An Essay on Heat, Light, and the Combinations of Light," had attracted Rumford's attention. Both of these men were influential in convincing the world that heat was a mode of motion of the particles making up a substance.

KINETIC THEORY PREDICTION
OF THE MECHANICAL EQUIVALENT
OF HEAT: MAYER

Mayer's theoretical prediction of the value of the mechanical equivalent of heat was made some forty years after the founding of the Royal Institution. With the knowledge of only a few basic principles of kinetic theory, and of the quantity of heat needed to raise the temperature of a cubic foot of air 1 Fahrenheit degree, Mayer was able to make a surprisingly accurate prediction. This theoretical calculation preceded by about a year the famous experiment of Joule described in Chapter 5.

In order to understand his line of reasoning, let us consider a cylinder fitted with a piston (Fig. 6-9) which encloses 1 cubic foot of air at 32°F. The piston is bombarded on the outside by air molecules tending to push it down and by the molecules in the interior tending

gas law $PV = KT$ $\left.\dfrac{V_1}{V_2} = \dfrac{T_1}{T_2}\right\}$ *charles law*

to push it up. The following calculation will neglect the weight of the piston and assume equilibrium of internal and external pressures when 1 cubic foot of air at a given temperature is in the cylinder.

A calculation of the mechanical equivalent of heat, based on the kinetic theory of gases. For every Fahrenheit degree of temperature rise, a gas expands 1/492 of its volume at 32°F. A rise of 492 F° will cause 1 cu ft of gas at 32°F to expand to 2 cu ft if the pressure remains the same. We measure in Btu the amount of heat absorbed in the work of moving the piston against the pressure of 15 lb/sq in. for a distance of 1 ft.

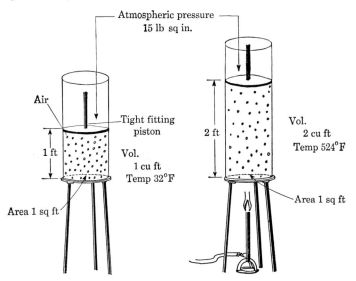

Fig. 6-9.

When the gas inside the cylinder is heated, the speed of movement of the gas particles is increased and these particles strike the piston from below with increased force. Since the speed of movement of air particles on the outside is the same as before (assuming atmospheric pressure to be constant) the upward force becomes larger than the downward force and the piston moves up. When it has moved up a certain distance, the larger volume available for the movement of the enclosed molecules compensates for their increased speeds, the internal and external pressures become equalized, and the piston comes to rest. An expansion in the volume of the gas has taken place.

Late in the eighteenth century, Jacques Charles, a physicist in the French Bureau of Standards, was able to show that any gas at 0°C would expand 1/273 of its volume for each centigrade degree of tem-

$$\frac{V_1}{V_2} = \frac{T_1}{T_2}$$

perature rise (Charles's law). Since there are 100 degrees on the centigrade scale between the freezing point and boiling point of water, and 180 degrees on the Fahrenheit scale, a Fahrenheit degree is 100/180 or 5/9 as large as a centigrade degree. Hence a gas would expand $1/273 \times 5/9$, or 1/492 of its volume at 32°F when its temperature was increased 1 Fahrenheit degree.

When the temperature of the cubic foot of air in Fig. 6-9 was raised 492 F° above an original temperature of 32°F, its volume increase was $492 \cdot 1/492$ times its volume, or one cubic foot; the original cubic foot of air doubled in volume. In order to permit the volume of the gas to increase, the piston had to move out against the bombardment of particles of the atmosphere, which were exerting a force of approximately 15 pounds on each square inch of piston surface. The cross-sectional area of the piston was 1 square foot, so the total force exerted on it by the atmosphere was $15 \text{ lb/in}^2 \cdot 144 \text{ in}^2 = 2160 \text{ lb}$. A piston 1 square foot in cross-sectional area had to move a linear distance of 1 foot in the cylinder for the volume increase to be 1 cubic foot. When the piston moved 1 foot against a force of 2160 pounds, the work done was 2160 foot pounds.

In doing this amount of work, 9.725 Btu of heat energy flowed into the interior of the cylinder from an outside heat source. However, we would not be justified in assuming that 9.725 Btu were equivalent to 2160 foot pounds because part of the heat absorbed was used up in making the gas particles move faster—that is, in bringing about the temperature increase. It will be remembered that the temperature of the gas increased 492 F°. The next problem was to determine how much of the heat was used up in increasing the speeds of the molecules.

In order to determine this quantity, a cubic foot of air at 32°F was again heated 492 F°, but this time the piston was kept fixed so that it could not move against the pressure of the atmosphere. Under these new conditions only 6.950 Btu were required to obtain the same temperature rise. Mayer assumed, then, that in heating a cubic foot of air 492 F°, 6.950 Btu were used in increasing molecular speeds whether or not the *pressure* of the gas inside the vessel remained constant, and hence 2.775 (i.e., $9.725 - 6.950$) Btu were actually used in doing the 2160 foot pounds of work. When 2160 foot pounds were divided by 2.775 Btu, it was found that 778 foot pounds of work were equivalent to a single Btu of heat: 778 foot pounds of work is called the mechanical equivalent of 1 Btu of heat.

In Chapter 5 this equivalence was also given as 4.186 joules = 1 calorie. The joule and the foot pound are work units of different size, just as the foot and the centimeter are linear units of different size. The Btu is equal to 252 calories.

Mayer's remarkably accurate prediction of the value of the mechanical equivalent of heat illustrates very well the value of a theory in guiding the course of development of a scientific principle. Research is, to be sure, always a venturing into the unknown, and no theory can lead unerringly to new discovery. However, the more fruitful the deductions from the theory are, the more assurance we have that the theory itself is basically correct and the greater the confidence is with which we use it in solving problems. The fact that this calculation of the mechanical equivalent of heat based on kinetic theory corresponded so closely with the experimental value later reported by Joule tended to lend support to the essential correctness of the kinetic theory.

THE SPEEDS OF GAS MOLECULES

Just before the middle of the nineteenth century, James Prescott Joule became interested in determining the speeds which gas molecules would need to have in order to exert their observed pressures. The results of his calculations astounded him. It appeared that hydrogen molecules at standard temperature and pressure (0°C and 760 mm Hg) should be moving about 1 mi/sec. A velocity of 1 mi/sec is the equivalent of 3600 mi/hr, a very considerable speed even in an era of jet planes.

The first reaction to Joule's suggestion concerning the magnitude of molecular speeds was skepticism: the speed sounded fantastic. Everybody knew that if a bottle of ammonia was opened, its characteristic odor could not be detected almost instantaneously in all parts of the room. A certain amount of time had to elapse. What should have been taken into consideration, however, was that the ammonia molecules would not be traveling through evacuated space but would be colliding with millions of oxygen and nitrogen molecules en route.

Joule's calculation of molecular speeds adds further detail to the concept of a gas. Individual gas molecules are pictured as moving relatively short distances between impacts, the average distance of movement between impacts being known as the *mean free path*. If a gas molecule travels only about a millionth of a centimeter before striking another molecule, it is understandable why gas diffusion is slow in spite of the enormous speeds of the molecules.

MODERN KINETIC THEORY AND
THE IDEAL GAS EQUATION

In 1857 the great German mathematical physicist Clausius (1822-1888) published the first comprehensive kinetic theory of gases, which embodied essentially the assumptions given in summary form earlier in the chapter. On the basis of these he was able to deduce an ideal gas equation

$$PV = \tfrac{1}{3}mnu^2 \qquad\qquad (6\text{-a})$$

where P = pressure, V = volume
$\quad m$ = mass of a single gas molecule
$\quad n$ = number of molecules
$\quad u$ = molecular speed

Gas molecules have differing speeds. At a given temperature (T) *the distribution of speeds is as shown. A majority of the molecules have speeds clustering about a most probable value. Very few speeds are either greatly in excess of or less than this value. At a higher temperature* (T_2) *the most probable value of the speed is greater than at* T_1.

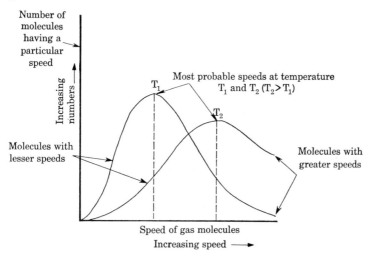

Fig. 6-10.

In deriving this equation Clausius assumed that all molecules had the same speed. Somewhat later, Maxwell and Boltzmann applied statistical methods in the representation of the speeds of molecules and showed that at a particular temperature the distribution of the speeds was quite similar in form to the familiar normal curve. Most gas molecules have speeds which cluster about a most probable value, as shown in Fig. 6-10. A very few molecules have much smaller speeds than the most probable value, and a very few have speeds a great deal larger. Hence, when the molecular speed at a certain temperature is mentioned, the reference is to the mean of all the values. As the temperature is raised, the peak of the normal curve shifts to the right; in other words, on the average more of the molecules will have higher speeds at a higher temperature.

THE IDEAL GAS LAW

From Equation 6-a the following ideal gas equation may be derived:

$$PV = NRT \qquad\qquad \text{(6-b)}$$

where N is the number of molecular weights of the gas* ($N = 1$ for 32 gm of oxygen gas, $N = 2$ for 64 gm of oxygen, etc.), T is the absolute or Kelvin temperature, and R is a constant known as the gas constant, whose value is determined by the units of pressure and volume chosen and equals 0.082 when pressure is expressed in atmospheres and volume is expressed in liters.

This ideal gas equation summarizes a great deal of information concerning the behavior of gases. However the basic assumptions of the kinetic theory of gases must be kept in mind when applying the equation in a given situation. For example, earlier in this chapter it was pointed out that the assumption of negligible forces of attraction between gas molecules would not be valid for gases near their points of liquefaction. The equation would not then accurately predict the behavior of ammonia, a gas which is easily liquefied. Furthermore, since the kinetic theory assumes the distances between gas molecules to be large compared with their diameters, the ideal gas equation does not accurately predict the behavior of highly compressed gases.

To show how Boyle's law may be derived from this equation we consider a given weight of a gas (call $N = 1$) at a temperature of

* The unit here is the mole, explained in Chapter 7, page 137.

$0°$C (or $273°$K) and assign R a value of 0.082. Note that the absolute temperature (degrees Kelvin) must be used in this equation. We then have

$$PV = NRT$$
$$PV = 1.0 \cdot 0.082 \cdot 273 = 22.4$$

In our earlier discussion of Boyle's law we indicated that $PV = k$ provided the weight of gas and temperature are constant. For the particular weight of gas and temperature cited we may rewrite the equation $PV = 22.4$.

ILLUSTRATIVE PROBLEM

50 liters of gas initially at 0.75 atm pressure are compressed until the pressure is 2.5 atm. Calculate the new volume. Assume that temperature and weight of gas are constant.

Solution

$$P_1V_1 = P_2V_2$$
$$2.5V = 0.75 \cdot 50$$
$$V = 15 \text{ liters}$$

We have stated that the ideal gas law does not accurately describe the behavior of gases which are near their points of liquefaction. Let us now be more specific with reference to this point and Boyle's law. There are large forces of attraction between gas molecules whose conditions of temperature and pressure are such as to easily allow of their being changed to a liquid. Under such circumstances a further pressure increase is accompanied by a more than proportionate reduction in volume. The product PV does not remain constant as demanded by Boyle's law. Hence we say the ideal gas law is not applicable.

Similarly the ideal gas law assumes that the distances between gas molecules are large compared with their diameters. If gases are highly compressed and gas molecules come very close together, further pressure increase is not accompanied by the expected decrease in volume. Again, the product PV does not remain constant but increases.

Boyle's law is then applicable to gases which are not easily liquefied, such as nitrogen, oxygen, and hydrogen, and at pressures not too different from atmospheric pressure.

One more illustration will be given to show how a particular law, Charles's law in this case, may be derived from the ideal gas equation. It states that the volume of a given weight of gas at constant pressure is directly proportional to its absolute temperature. We again assign in the ideal gas equation $PV = NRT$, $N = 1$, $R = 0.082$, and a constant pressure of 1 atmosphere $(P = 1)$.

$$PV = NRT$$
$$1 \cdot V = 1.0 \cdot 0.082 \cdot T = 0.082T$$

$$\frac{V}{T} = 0.082$$

This equation requires that the quotient V/T remain constant under the conditions stated. Thus an increase in the absolute temperature T must be accompanied by a corresponding volume increase. If the absolute temperature is doubled, so is the volume.

ILLUSTRATIVE PROBLEM

Ten liters of an ideal gas at 0°C will occupy what volume if heated to 100°C?

Solution

$$\frac{V_1}{T_1} = \frac{V_2}{T_2}$$

T must be expressed in degrees Kelvin.

$$\frac{10 \text{ liters}}{273°K} = \frac{V_2}{373°K}$$

$$V_2 = \frac{3730}{273} \text{ liters} = 13.7 \text{ liters}$$

It is surprising how much information concerning the behavior of gases is summarized in a simple mathematical expression such as the ideal gas equation. Still other relationships will be discovered by an alert mind.

EXERCISES AND QUESTIONS FOR CHAPTER 6

1. What pressure in millibars* is equivalent to 770 mm of mercury?

2. 10 liters of a gas at 740 mm (of mercury) pressure will occupy what volume at 770 mm pressure? (Assume weight of gas and temperature are constant.)

* See Units Conversion Table in the Appendix.

3. 20 liters of a gas at 10°C should be heated to what centigrade temperature if its volume is to increase to 30 liters, pressure remaining constant?

4. The mercury level in the open arm of a J tube is 35 cm higher than in the shorter, closed arm. If the barometer reading is 76.0 cm of mercury, calculate the pressure of the gas in the enclosed arm.

5. From the ideal gas equation show that $P/T = k$ if V and the weight of gas are constant. If a gas initially at 273°K and 760 mm pressure is heated to 373°K, what is the final pressure?

6. Describe the nature of a gas as conceived by the kinetic theory.

7. State the basic assumptions of the kinetic theory of gases.

8. Describe how to construct a mercury barometer. Does the diameter of the barometer tube affect the height of the mercury column?

9. A barometer tube has a cross-sectional area of 1 sq in. What is the weight of the mercury above the level in the reservoir at 1 atm?

10. Describe how to carry out Boyle's J-tube experiment. What measurements must be made in order to verify Boyle's law by means of this experiment? Describe.

11. Describe the reasoning used in Mayer's prediction of the value of the mechanical equivalent of heat. What kinds of data did he need?

12. What is the approximate speed of gas molecules near room temperature?

13. Show that Boyle's and Charles's laws may be deduced from the ideal gas equation.

14. Boyle's law is an ideal gas law. It does not apply to all gases under all circumstances. Explain.

REVIEW

1. Two grams (mass) of hydrogen gas contain 6.02×10^{23} molecules. Calculate the kinetic energy of a single hydrogen molecule which is moving at 1 mi/sec.

2. Calculate the value of gravitational acceleration in inches/sec².

CHAPTER 7

Atomic Building Blocks

A GAS has been described as a whirling, frenzied swarm of submicroscopic particles, which we have likened to minute ping-pong balls. These particles will now be examined more closely. Since no supermicroscope yet exists through which atoms may be observed directly, our knowledge of them must of necessity be based upon the experimentally observed behavior of millions and millions of them under a great variety of circumstances.

In most substances atoms occur combined in characteristic clusters called *molecules*. (In some substances atoms occur singly; in these a distinction between an atom and a molecule is unnecessary. The inert gas helium is an example.) In ordinary oxygen gas, for example, the atoms are thought to occur in clusters of two. Each cluster of two atoms constitutes a molecule. Water molecules consist of clusters of three atoms—two atoms of hydrogen and one of oxygen (H_2O). The discussion which follows deals with atoms as conceived by the nineteenth-century English schoolmaster John Dalton, the teacher of James Prescott Joule. He thought that all atoms of a particular variety, for example hydrogen, had the same weight. Modern refinements of this theory will be discussed in Chapter 11.

ELEMENTS, COMPOUNDS, AND MIXTURES

Every material substance—solid, liquid, or gas—is composed of tiny particles called atoms. A substance which is composed of only a single species of atom is an element. Elements cannot be reduced to simpler

Fig. 7-1.

Helium atoms never combine with one another or with other atoms; they always remain unattached. Helium is an element.

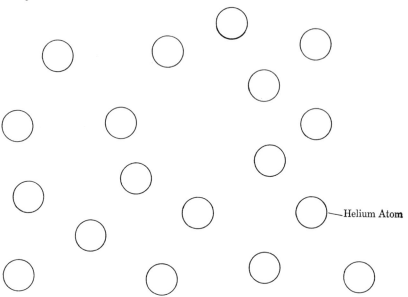

—Helium **Atom**

In oxygen gas, the atoms are normally combined in clusters of two. Each cluster is called an oxygen molecule.

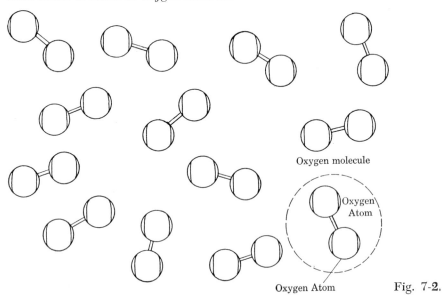

Oxygen molecule

Oxygen Atom

Oxygen Atom

Fig. 7-2.

chemical substances by means of chemical reactions. At present about 100 different elements have been identified. The beautiful crystalline diamond is composed of atoms of carbon. The liquid metal, quicksilver, is composed of atoms of mercury. Each of these is an element. Helium gas is an element: it is composed of particles each of which is a single atom of helium (Fig. 7-1). The pairs of atoms constituting

Fig. 7-3.

Carbon dioxide gas molecules have three atoms each, one of carbon and two of oxygen. Carbon dioxide is a compound.

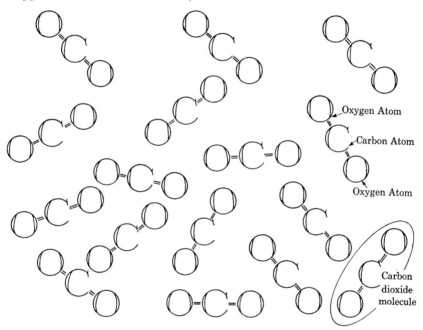

oxygen gas molecules are schematized in Fig. 7-2. Since there is still only a single atomic species present, oxygen is also an element.

Molecules may consist of like atoms, as in oxygen, or of unlike atoms, as in carbon dioxide. If a substance is made up of more than one kind of atom, then it is not an element and must be either a compound or a mixture. One of the criteria of a compound is that each of the millions and millions of molecules composing it is similarly constituted with respect to the number and kind of atoms. Every molecule in carbon dioxide gas is composed of a central carbon atom with an oxygen atom on either side (Fig. 7-3): carbon dioxide gas is thus called a compound. Water is also a compound: each of its molecules consists of two atoms of hydrogen and one atom of oxygen.

A sample of gas which consists of molecules having *different* numbers or kinds of atoms is called a mixture. Nitrogen and oxygen molecules in the same enclosing vessel (Fig. 7-4) constitute a mixture.

Nitrogen and oxygen molecules in the same vessel constitute a mixture.

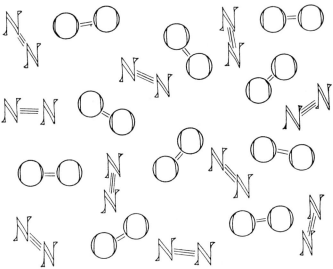

O=O Represents an Oxygen molecule
N≡N Represents a Nitrogen molecule

Fig. 7-4.

Air is made up of molecules of nitrogen, oxygen, argon, and carbon dioxide; it is a mixture. Three of its constituents—nitrogen, oxygen, and argon—are elements, while the fourth, carbon dioxide, is a compound.

Under appropriate conditions, atoms of carbon and oxygen may combine, not in the relation of one of carbon to two of oxygen, as in carbon dioxide, but rather one to one. This chemical compound is called carbon monoxide (CO). If the molecules within a vessel are of two varieties, some containing one atom each of carbon and oxygen and some containing one of carbon and two of oxygen (Fig. 7-5), a mixture is said to exist.

In summary: in an element, all atoms are the same; in a compound,

Fig. 7-5.

Carbon monoxide and carbon dioxide molecules in the same vessel constitute a mixture. The molecules of the two compounds contain the same kinds of atoms but different numbers of each in a given molecule.

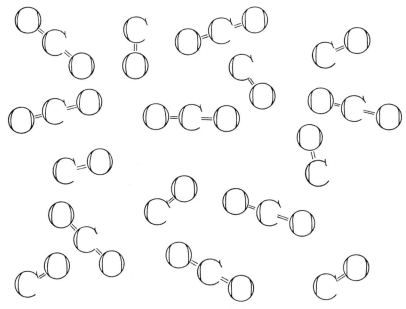

O=C=O   Represents a carbon dioxide molecule
C=O   Represents a carbon monoxide molecule

all molecules* are the same; and in a mixture, molecules differ in either the kind or the number of atoms constituting them.

The Concept of an Element: An Idealization   In an earlier chapter it was mentioned that the generalizations of science are often idealizations. Strictly speaking, the notion of an element is an idealization if by "element" we mean an isolated group of particles composed of a *single* atomic species. As a practical matter this is virtually impossible of attainment. There will inevitably be at least small amounts of other kinds of atoms—that is, impurities—present.

By way of illustration, consider one of the methods of preparing oxygen gas. A white solid compound called potassium chlorate ($KClO_3$) and a black powder, manganese dioxide (MnO_2), are mixed and put in a test tube. A delivery tube is attached as shown in Fig.

* Some compounds are composed of structural units other than molecules.

7-6. Contained in the test tube above the chemical substances and in the delivery tube is some air. When the test tube is heated with a Bunsen burner, the air in the tube expands and is forced out of the delivery tube and up through the heavier surrounding water. As the heating continues, the potassium chlorate ($KClO_3$) in the test tube decomposes, forming oxygen gas, which pushes more air bubbles out into the delivery tube and up through the water. After the bubbling has continued long enough to sweep out all the air, a bottle filled with water is inverted over the end of the delivery tube. The oxygen gas now rises to the top of the bottle, displacing the water downward, and very soon the vessel is completely filled with oxygen. A wooden

Fig. 7-6.

Oxygen gas may be prepared by heating potassium chlorate ($KClO_3$) in the presence of manganese dioxide (MnO_2). It is collected by the downward displacement of water.

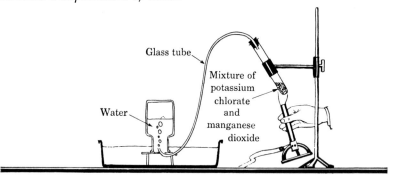

splint with a glowing spark on the end bursts into flame when thrust into the bottle. This is the common test for oxygen.

As a practical matter, do we have a single atomic species in the bottle? Very probably not. In the first place, the water doubtless contains some dissolved air, and as the oxygen passes through the water a small amount of this air will very likely be entrained (carried along). If the oxygen is collected over water, some of the more energetic of the water (H_2O) molecules escape from the surface into the space above, so that water vapor molecules will also be present in the oxygen. Thus, when oxygen is prepared in the chemistry laboratory by this method, although there may be an overwhelming majority of oxygen molecules in the enclosing volume, there will undoubtedly be other kinds of atoms and molecules present in at least small amounts. Even if an attempt is made to remove the last traces of water, nitrogen, or carbon dioxide molecules by causing them to react with other chemical substances, it is unlikely that it will ever be possible to take out every last atom that is not oxygen. Similarly, the notion of a compound in the sense of a single molecular species is also an idealization. Even distilled water will inevitably contain some small quantities of dissolved materials; when distilled water is placed in a glass vessel, there will be a very slight dissolving of some of the sodium compounds of the glass. These limitations must be recognized when an element is described as consisting of a single variety of atom, or a compound as consisting of a single variety of molecule. As a practical matter the concept of a single atomic or molecular species is as much of an idealization as the assumption of a frictionless plane or of a vacuum.

CHEMISTRY THROUGH THE CENTURIES

The structural differences among elements, compounds, and mixtures described above are based on a concept of the atom not too different from that brought forward by John Dalton in the early years of the nineteenth century—that is, quite a recent concept in the long history of mankind. What preceded it? Let us mention now a few of man's earliest observations concerning chemical phenomena and materials, and trace briefly his quest for a basic pattern of order among the myriads of different materials found on the earth.

The Early Beginnings of Chemistry   Man was acquainted with materials now regarded as elements thousands of years before he made any distinction between elements and compounds or mixtures, just as he used gadgets and machines long before he understood the principles explaining their operation.

Gold was probably the earliest known metal, and copper objects have been identified from most of the ancient civilizations of the world. Both these metals occur at many sites on the earth's surface in the uncombined state. Another such "native" element, sulfur, is mentioned in the Bible as "brimstone." At some early date the art of converting ores into useful metals—metallurgy—was developed, no doubt from chance beginnings. We can imagine the amazement of primitive man when a reddish earth (iron ore), accidentally mixed with charcoal (carbon) and subjected to prolonged heating, yielded a crude metal which could be shaped into useful iron objects. As the art of the smith advanced, bronze (an alloy) and iron became the favored metals, still thousands of years before Christ.

Baking and brewing, both chemical arts, have their origins in the very distant past. Even though the *science* of chemistry is only a few centuries old, many of the operations performed by today's chemist— for example, distillation, crystallization, and sublimation—were known long before the Christian era.

As early as the sixth century B.C. man groped for unifying principles and searched for simplifying relations in a bewildering world of apparently unrelated phenomena. Thales (640-546 B.C.), one of the first of the Greeks whose names are associated with science, considered water to be the basic material from which all others were derived. He observed that when water evaporated it left behind a small amount of solid residue, and concluded that water had been converted into the solid. According to modern kinetic theory this phenomenon is explained by evaporation: the molecules of water, like those of a gas, are moving rapidly in all directions and those near the surface attain sufficient velocity to escape; when all the water molecules have escaped, the small amounts of soluble salts of the elements calcium and magnesium which were dissolved in the water remain as a solid.

The Greek philosopher Empedocles early in the fifth century B.C. developed a theory of four elements—earth, water, air, and fire. These were not thought of as elements in anything even remotely resembling the present sense; they represented the three physical states of matter— solid, liquid, and gas, plus a fourth—glowing gas, "fire"—taken as the basic qualities out of which all substances were composed.

The name of Democritus (approximately 460-370 B.C.), another famous Greek philosopher, is associated with the origin of the concept of atoms. He opposed the view held by many of his contemporaries that matter was continuous in its structure, maintaining that it was composed of discrete particles or very tiny marble-like atoms. His highly developed theory assumed that these atoms were rapidly moving through empty space and reminds us that the kinetic theory of matter was anticipated many centuries before Daniel Bernoulli (1738).

Alchemy very likely had its origins in Alexandria, Egypt, shortly after the beginning of the Christian era, and it flourished for nearly two millennia. At one time it was fashionable for the monarchs of Europe to have their court alchemists. Since it had been known for thousands of years that a reddish earth could be converted into iron, it is not surprising to find men reasoning that it should also be possible to change the commoner metals into precious gold. Hundreds of human beings spent their lives in search of the illusory "philosopher's stone," the mythical substance which was reputed to convert baser metals into gold.

At about the time that Christopher Columbus made his celebrated trip to the New World, there was born in Switzerland a child who was to become a physician and to exert a great influence on the future development of the science of chemistry. Paracelsus (1493-1541), as he was called, attempted to steer man away from the vain pursuit of the mythical philosopher's stone to the search for medicines which would alleviate human suffering. His efforts gave rise to a new movement in chemistry, elevating its status to a higher plane than that of alchemy. The medical chemists—"iatrochemists"—in their search for the elixir of life brought forth much new factual information about the properties of substances and provided a considerable amount of grist for the mill from which the great generalizations of science were to evolve.

Seventeenth-Century Experimentation in Chemistry   Though Paracelsus initiated a new trend in chemistry, alchemy was hardly banished in a single stroke. Jan Baptista van Helmont (1577-1644) of Brussels was destined to make important contributions to the understanding of chemistry, even though he clung to the belief that baser metals might be transmuted into gold. He regarded water and air as the basic elements, since they could not be converted into one another nor could they be reduced into simpler elements;* in this respect he did not progress significantly beyond Thales who had lived 2000 years earlier. In the experimental work of Van Helmont, however, we see the unfolding of a new trend in science, that of added attention to quantitative relations. This was the time of Francis Bacon ("father of scientific method"), of Jean Rey's experiment of heating tin metal and speculating on its increase in weight; time was ripe for discoveries of a quantitative nature. Van Helmont's famous willow tree experiment shows concern for the questions "How much?" and "From whence?"

* J. R. Partington, *A Short History of Chemistry,* Macmillan, 1939, p. 51.

He planted a tree weighing 5 pounds in a vessel containing 200 pounds of dried earth. During a five year period he supplied only water to the growing tree. It continued to increase in size, and at the end of this period weighed nearly 170 pounds. The earth in which it was planted was dried and weighed; its weight was found to be almost exactly the same as its original weight (within a few ounces). The weight increase could not, then, have come from the soil. What was more natural than to suppose it was due to the water? We now realize that his conclusions were wrong, but find in his work one of the early attempts to gain knowledge through quantitative measurement, crude though it was.

Van Helmont knew that a strip of silver metal when dissolved in nitric acid (HNO_3) was concealed in the liquid much as sugar or salt is when dissolved in water (see Fig. 7-7). If water was evaporated

Van Helmont understood that a metal might undergo a series of reactions and then be reclaimed in its entirety. Atoms are neither created nor destroyed as a result of chemical action.

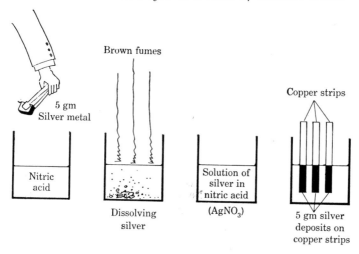

Brown fumes

5 gm
Silver metal

Copper strips

Nitric
acid

Dissolving
silver

Solution of
silver in
nitric acid
($AgNO_3$)

5 gm silver
deposits on
copper strips

Fig. 7-7.

from the solution of the silver in nitric acid, a white substance resembling salt was left in the evaporating dish. Van Helmont believed that this white salt contained all of the silver which had been dissolved in the acid. This was confirmed by the fact that every particle of the original silver could be regained from a water solution of the white salt by simply immersing strips of copper metal in it. When this was done, solid silver separated from the liquid and was deposited on the surface of the copper. Thus early in the seventeenth century it was clear that metals were not destroyed in chemical reactions; they could undergo transformations, but no matter would be destroyed or created in the process. Although not explicitly stated, this could be regarded as an anticipation of the principle of the conservation of matter which states that in a chemical reaction matter may not be either created or destroyed.

Emergence of the Concept of an Element As Van Helmont approached middle age, another famous chemist, Robert Boyle, whom we met in Chapter 6, was born in Ireland. The most famous of Boyle's written works is entitled *The Sceptical Chymist*. This dealt a death blow to the four elements of the Greeks, and stated clearly the concept of an element as we now understand it: an element was simply a substance which could not be resolved into a simpler form by means of chemical reactions. If a material defied all efforts to further resolve it into simpler substances it was to be considered an element. Thus Boyle is to be remembered not only for the gas law which bears his name, but also for his clarification of one of the most important concepts of chemistry, that of a chemical element. He did not, however, evolve any experimental method of ascertaining which substances were elements, nor was a single gaseous element identified during his lifetime.

An English physician, John Mayow (1640-1679), who devoted much of his leisure to scientific pursuits, was one of the earliest to recognize that air was a mixture and not an element. He realized that it contained one constituent which would support life and combustion and another which would not. The study of gaseous substances and in particular their relation to the process of combustion proved to be an essential key in establishing the concept of an element on an experimental basis.

Perhaps the most important discovery resulting from the study of gaseous substances was that of the element oxygen. During the latter part of the seventeenth century the *phlogiston theory* proposed by Becher and Stahl in Germany gained wide acceptance in interpreting the nature of combustion. "Phlogiston" was the substance which combustible material was believed to contain. When a material burned, phlogiston departed. The phlogiston theory did give a plausible explanation of burning. The flame soon went out if a combustible material was burned in a limited supply of air. The phlogiston theory explained that air was needed to absorb the phlogiston which left the combustible substance during the burning process; when the air became saturated with phlogiston, the fire went out. The air had to be dephlogisticated before it would again support combustion. So far, so good! Other facts were more difficult to explain.

When wood was burned, the ash weighed *less* than the original material. On the other hand if certain metals, such as tin, were heated in air, the resulting calx (tin oxide, in modern terminology) weighed *more* than the original tin. It was a bit difficult to understand why a loss of phlogiston would result in a weight decrease in one case and an increase in another. To the proponents of the phlogiston theory this was but a minor obstacle: the explanation was given that phlogiston might have either positive or negative weight.

In the early 1770's we find both the Englishman Priestley (1733-1804) and the French scientist Lavoisier (1743-1794) struggling with this and other troublesome questions concerning the nature of combustion and calcination (conversion of metals into their oxides). Lavoisier had proved that many substances such as sulfur, phosphorus, and metals increased in weight when heated in air, the phlogiston theory notwithstanding. He suspected that this weight increase was derived from the air, but it took him several years to prove it. One of the important clues came from Priestley's discovery of "dephlogisticated air" (oxygen) by heating red mercuric oxide. Lavoisier was quick to realize that there might be a connection between the newly discovered element and the processes of calcination and combustion. He soon carried out the now famous experiment of heating mercury in contact with a confined volume of air (Fig. 7-8) and found that the mercury increased in weight while $\frac{1}{5}$ of the air disappeared. Oxygen was removed from air as it combined with mercury to form the heavier mercuric oxide.

Lavoisier had now put together the pieces of this complex puzzle of combustion and calcination; the element oxygen, a constituent of air, combined with a combustible material as it burned, or with a metal as it calcined.° One should not however conclude that Lavoisier's views were at once universally accepted. Even with all the facts available to him, Priestley remained a phlogistonist to his dying day.

° For a detailed account see James B. Conant, *The Overthrow of the Phlogiston Theory,* Harvard University Press, 1950.

Although he had established himself as one of the immortals of science, during the French Revolution Lavoisier, along with many of his countrymen, fell victim to the guillotine. His judges declared,

Lavoisier's demonstration that calcination depends on a constituent of the air.

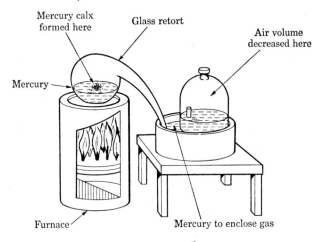

Mercury calx formed here

Glass retort

Air volume decreased here

Mercury

Fig. 7-8.   Furnace   Mercury to enclose gas

"France has no need of scientists." The famous mathematician Lagrange commented that it took but a moment to cut off Lavoisier's head, though perhaps a hundred years would be needed to produce another like it.

THE LAW OF CONSTANT PROPORTIONS

Just before the turn of the nineteenth century a French chemist, Joseph Proust (1754-1826), who had made an extensive study of the composition of metallic compounds, announced his law of constant proportions. According to this law, the elements contained in a compound were always found in the same proportions by weight. In water the oxygen always weighed eight times as much as the hydrogen; the ratio of these weights never changed irrespective of the amount of water under consideration. The constituent elements of a given compound were never found in different ratios. If carbon and oxygen were found combined in different ratios by weight it meant that there must be two distinct compounds, as for example carbon monoxide and carbon dioxide.

It was not long before Proust's idea of constant proportions was challenged by another French chemist, Berthollet (1748-1822), who pointed out that when a metal such as copper was heated in air, it might react with either a very small or a very large amount of oxygen from the air. In fact a series of experiments convinced Berthollet that the amount of oxygen combining with a metal such as copper could be varied almost continuously up to a certain maximum amount.* It was absurd, then, to suggest that copper and oxygen combined in a definite ratio by weight. Proust argued that not all of the copper atoms might have enough oxygen atoms with which to combine, but if the two elements did unite to form a given compound, then the same numbers of atoms of each would always be involved. The argument was eventually resolved in favor of Proust. It is now thought that one of the important characteristics which distinguishes a compound from a mixture is the constancy of composition of the former.

The controversy between Proust and Berthollet regarding the nature of chemical composition illustrates very well how even famous scientists may interpret essentially the same set of data quite differently. This suggests further that the methods of science are far more complex than the mere extracting of generalizations from masses of apparently unrelated facts. This controversy was resolved shortly before Dalton published his famous atomic theory.

DALTON'S ATOMIC THEORY

The concept of atoms, which originated 2000 or more years ago in the time of the Greeks, remained dormant until the seventeenth century. At that time the French philosopher and mathematician Pierre Gassendi (1592-1655) did much to revive interest in the particle structure of matter. During this century and the next the words corpuscle and particle became increasingly prominent in scientific writing.

John Dalton (1766-1844) published his atomic theory in the early years of the nineteenth century. This theory conceived all substances to be composed of tiny particles called atoms. Furthermore all similar atoms—for example, all hydrogen atoms—were believed to have the same weight. The weight of a hydrogen atom was different from that of the atom of any other element, as for example oxygen. The idea

* J. R. Partington, A Short History of Chemistry, Macmillan, 1939, p. 156.

that all hydrogen atoms had the same weight was later modified to conform to more modern experimental evidence regarding the structure of the atom, but it may be clearer for the present to think of a given element as composed of atoms all of which have the same weight.

Dalton's theory also indicated that atoms might combine with one another to form compounds. It will be seen that there is a very natural relation between the atomic concept and the law of constant proportions as stated by Proust. If the atoms composing water molecules are always present in the same numbers (two hydrogen to one oxygen atom), and the weights of each of the constituent atoms are always the same, then it should follow that water will always contain the same weight ratio of hydrogen to oxygen: one-ninth of the weight of all water is due to its hydrogen atoms, the other eight-ninths to its oxygen atoms; or stated another way, a sample of water always contains eight times as much oxygen, by weight, as hydrogen.

SYMBOLS AND FORMULAS

Dalton used the symbols shown in Fig. 7-9 to represent the various atoms known in his day. More recently the symbol for representing

Dalton's symbols for chemical elements.

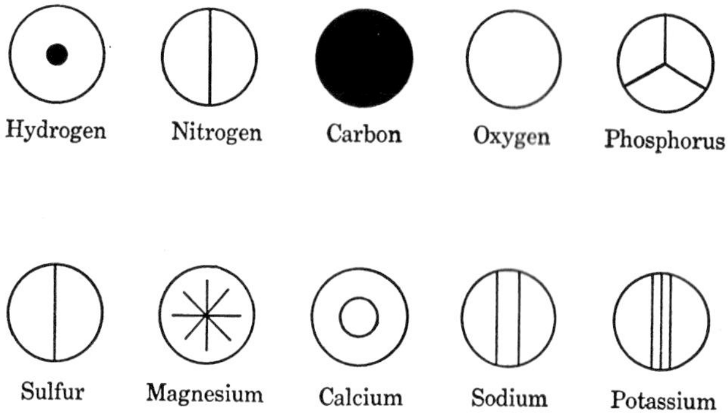

Hydrogen   Nitrogen   Carbon   Oxygen   Phosphorus

Fig. 7-9.

Sulfur   Magnesium   Calcium   Sodium   Potassium

a single atom of an element has become a capital letter (as O for oxygen) or a capital letter followed by a small letter (as Pb for lead). Associated with the symbol for each element is a number called the atomic weight. This number indicates the weight of the atom relative to the weight of an oxygen atom, which has been assigned an arbitrary value of 16. If sulfur has an atomic weight of 32, a single atom will weigh twice as much as one of oxygen. The elements and their symbols listed in Table 7-1 are those of most frequent occurrence. A more complete list of the elements, with their symbols, atomic weights, and atomic numbers, is given in the Appendix.

Table 7-1   SOME IMPORTANT ELEMENTS

Ag	Silver	Fe	Iron	N	Nitrogen
Al	Aluminum	H	Hydrogen	Na	Sodium
C	Carbon	Hg	Mercury	O	Oxygen
Ca	Calcium	I	Iodine	P	Phosphorus
Cl	Chlorine	K	Potassium	S	Sulfur
Cu	Copper	Mg	Magnesium	Si	Silicon
				Zn	Zinc

Table 7-2 lists some of the compounds referred to in this chapter. Atoms combine to form compounds, which are represented in chemical shorthand by means of formulas. Often the unit which the formula represents is the molecule, although this is not true in all cases. Carbon dioxide as a gas is composed of molecules consisting of 1 atom of carbon and 2 of oxygen; its formula is CO_2. Similarly, the symbol for oxygen is O, but its formula is O_2, since each oxygen molecule consists of 2 oxygen atoms.

Table 7-2   SOME COMMON COMPOUNDS

NH_3	Ammonia	MnO_2	Manganese dioxide
NH_4Cl	Ammonium chloride	HNO_3	Nitric acid
$BaCl_2$	Barium chloride	$KClO_3$	Potassium chlorate
$CaCl_2$	Calcium chloride	KNO_3	Potassium nitrate
$Ca(NO_3)_2$	Calcium nitrate	$AgNO_3$	Silver nitrate
CaO	Calcium oxide	$NaCl$	Sodium chloride
CO_2	Carbon dioxide	SO_2	Sulfur dioxide
CO	Carbon monoxide	H_2SO_4	Sulfuric acid
$Cu(NO_3)_2$	Copper nitrate	$ZnCO_3$	Zinc carbonate
		ZnS	Zinc sulfide

THE CHEMICAL EQUATION

The practical side of the science of chemistry is concerned with getting atoms to combine in different ways. In some cases it will be a matter of causing atoms of different elements to combine to form compounds. An example is the union of carbon and oxygen to form carbon dioxide:

$$C + O_2 \rightarrow CO_2 \tag{7-a}$$

Equation 7-a shows that the element carbon (represented by the symbol C) unites with the element oxygen (represented by the formula O_2) to form the compound carbon dioxide (represented by the formula CO_2). The carbon may be a piece of charcoal. The source of the oxygen molecules may be air, of which about 20% is oxygen. As a result of heating the charcoal in the presence of air, the atoms are activated in such a way that they attach to one another, a single carbon atom slipping in between the two atoms of an oxygen molecule to give the cluster of three atoms which is called the carbon dioxide molecule. Fig. 7-10 is a diagrammatic representation of the change.

The formation of carbon dioxide by the burning charcoal.

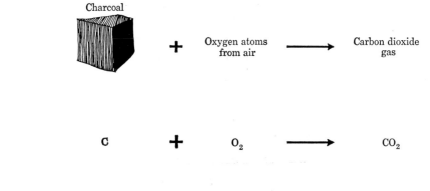

Charcoal

\+   Oxygen atoms from air   ⟶   Carbon dioxide gas

C   + O_2 ⟶ CO_2

Fig. 7-10.

In other cases an equation may indicate that one element is displacing another, as in the reaction

$$Pb + Cu(NO_3)_2 \rightarrow Cu + Pb(NO_3)_2 \tag{7-b}$$

This reaction indicates that metallic lead (an element) is combining with (a water solution of) copper nitrate $Cu(NO_3)_2$ (a compound). The reaction takes place when strips of lead are immersed in a solution of copper nitrate (Fig. 7-11). (Nitrates are salts of nitric acid; nearly

all are soluble in water.) There is nothing in the equation to suggest
that the copper nitrate is dissolved in water, but the chemist soon
learns to recognize when a solution is implied. A reddish deposit of
copper metal forms on the lead strips, and the blue color of the solu-

Fig. 7-11.

*When a strip of lead metal is immersed in a copper nitrate solution, a coat-
ing of copper plates out on the lead. Lead nitrate is found dissolved in the
liquid. A single replacement reaction has taken place.*

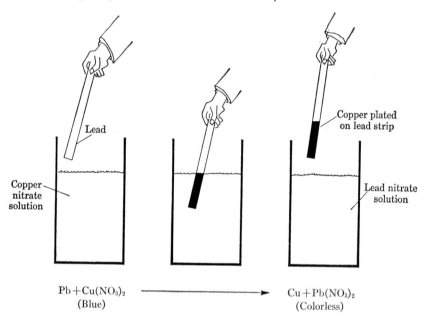

$$Pb + Cu(NO_3)_2 \longrightarrow Cu + Pb(NO_3)_2$$
(Blue)   (Colorless)

tion gradually disappears. If the clear, colorless solution which eventually results is evaporated, a white salt, lead nitrate, $Pb(NO_3)_2$ is
formed. Note that all of the atoms found on the left-hand side of the
arrow in Equation 7-b are also present on the right side. The net effect
of the reaction is to substitute free copper atoms for free lead atoms.
It is a single displacement reaction.

Sometimes a chemical reaction is used to separate a compound into
its constituent elements, as in the equation

$$2NaCl \rightarrow 2Na + Cl_2 \tag{7-c}$$

Equation 7-c indicates the chemical reaction taking place if salt is
melted in an appropriate container and an electric current is passed

Fig. 7-12.   (Courtesy, International Salt Co.)

Avery Island Salt Mine in Louisiana. The ceiling is about 100 ft high. The machinery in the background is a self-propelled platform rig used for drilling holes in the salt, for loading the holes, and for scaling the sidewalls and ceiling.

through the molten material. The electric current separates sodium atoms from chlorine atoms. Thus two elements, sodium metal and chlorine gas, are produced from a compound containing them. No atoms have been created, none destroyed. The atoms which were present in the salt crystal were simply sorted out into two like groups.

Sodium chloride (NaCl) is a very abundant and hence inexpensive material, salt. It occurs in huge underground deposits as shown in Fig. 7-12 and may serve as a raw material from which to make chlorine gas for chlorinating water supplies and swimming pools or for use as a bleaching agent.

There are numerous other types of reactions, but those cited will suffice to illustrate the point that a chemical equation is a shorthand representation of the alteration in the manner of combination of atoms brought about by means of a chemical reaction. Our ability to cause atoms to combine in ways other than those in which we find them in nature makes possible the production of a great variety of different chemical substances which are needed in everyday life.

The essential condition for all equations, including chemical equations, is the existence of some sort of an equality. In each of the above equations there are equal numbers of each kind of atom on either side of the arrow. In its relation to the atoms on either side, the arrow is equivalent to an equality sign.

ATOMIC WEIGHTS

Dalton held that each kind of atom had a very definite weight which distinguished it from all other atoms. If two atoms had different weights they were simply atoms of different elements.

For our purpose it will suffice to say that the atomic weight of an element is a number indicating the weight of its atom relative to the weight of an oxygen atom. Whenever comparisons of weights are to be made, a standard must be agreed upon, as discussed in Chapter 1. In chemistry the standard chosen is an atom of oxygen, whose weight is arbitrarily assigned a value of 16.* If another atom has an atomic weight of 8, it will be half as heavy as an atom of oxygen. One with an atomic weight of 80 will be five times as heavy as an oxygen atom. The atomic weight unit is thus defined as 1/16 the weight of the oxygen atom.

The choice of 16 as the atomic weight of oxygen is largely a matter of convenience. Lavoisier used an arbitrary value of 100 for oxygen, so all of his atomic weights were larger than ours, and mathematical computations were correspondingly more time-consuming. On the other hand, if the value 1 were selected as the atomic weight of oxygen, then the lightest of all elements, hydrogen, would have a weight of 1/16, and all elements lighter than oxygen would have fractional values less than 1. Again it is more convenient not to work with fractions. The choice of 16 as the atomic weight of the standard, oxygen, makes the values of other atomic weights as small as possible without the necessity of using fractional values.

It is impossible to isolate and weigh single atoms. The Italian scientist Avogadro stated a particle-counting principle which has made it

---

* The standard used by the chemist is slightly different from that used by the physicist.

possible to compare the weights of single atoms by weighing two groups of atoms each of which has the same number of molecules. He stated that "equal volumes of gases under the same conditions of temperature and pressure contain the same number of particles (molecules)." For example, a cubic foot of oxygen gas would contain the same number of molecules as a cubic foot of hydrogen if they were both measured at the same temperature and pressure (Fig. 7-13). If

Equal volumes of gases under the same conditions of temperature and pressure contain the same number of molecules. A liter of oxygen weighs 16 times as much as a liter of hydrogen. Hence single oxygen molecules are 16 times as heavy as single hydrogen molecules. Since each oxygen molecule consists of two oxygen atoms and each hydrogen molecule consists of two hydrogen atoms, individual oxygen atoms are likewise 16 times as heavy as individual hydrogen atoms.

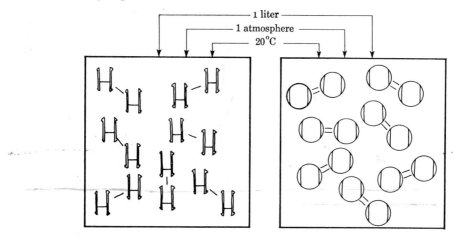

H_2 = 1 molecule of hydrogen

Fig. 7-13.

O_2 = 1 molecule of oxygen

the two gases were weighed, the oxygen would be 16 times as heavy as the hydrogen. There would be many billions of molecules in each cubic foot volume, but as long as there was the same number of molecules in each, it might be logically concluded that a single oxygen molecule weighed 16 times as much as a single hydrogen molecule. Carrying this reasoning one step farther, since molecules of oxygen and hydrogen are known to contain 2 atoms each, it might also be concluded that a single oxygen atom weighed 16 times as much as a single hydrogen atom.

The foregoing is far from a complete story about atomic weights, and merely illustrates a method which has been used for determining them. Ultimately they stem from a multitude of meticulously done quantitative experiments. One of the pioneers in the field of atomic weight determinations was the Swedish chemist Berzelius (1779-1848). Like Lavoisier, he used oxygen, taken as 100, for his standard. One of his reasons for choosing oxygen as a standard was that it combined with so many other elements. By determining the combining ratios of many pairs of elements he was able to establish other "atomic weights." His tables of atomic weights, published in the early decades of the nineteenth century, were remarkably good considering the apparatus which was available to him.

Formula Weights Just as there is associated with every chemical element an atomic weight, there is also corresponding to every formula a numerical value known as its formula weight. Often this quantity is called the molecular weight of the compound which the formula represents. (However, a formula does not necessarily imply that the aggregates making up the compound are molecules, and hence it is perhaps better to speak of the formula weight, even though in many cases such as CO_2, SO_2, and CH_4, the term molecular weight would be equally appropriate.) The quantity N, which appeared in the ideal gas equation of Chapter 6, referred to the number of molecular weights (or moles of the gas under consideration).

The formula weight of a compound is the sum of the atomic weights of the constituent atoms.

ILLUSTRATIVE PROBLEM

Calculate the formula weight of $Cu_3(AsO_4)_2$. See the Appendix for a table of atomic weights.

Solution

The subscript 3 after the Cu indicates three atoms of copper. The subscript 2 following the parenthesis has the effect of doubling everything within it. Therefore, in this formula there are

$$3 \text{ atoms of Cu} = 3 \times 63.5 = 190.5$$
$$2 \text{ atoms of As} = 2 \times 74.9 = 149.8$$
$$8 \text{ atoms of O} = 8 \times 16 = 128.0$$
$$\text{Formula weight} = 468.3$$

We saw in Chapter 6 that substitution in the ideal gas equation $PV = NRT$, of $T = 273°K$, $R = 0.082$, and $N = 1$ (1 mole) gave $PV = 22.4$. The value of R used presumed that pressures would be expressed in atmospheres (see Chapter 6) and volumes in liters. If a pressure, $P = 1$ atmosphere is specified, then $V = 22.4$ liters. The molecular weight of a *gas* is defined as the weight (in grams) occupied by 22.4 liters at Standard Temperature and Pressure (S.T.P.): 0°C (or 273°K) and 760 mm Hg (1 atmosphere). Knowledge of this definition permits the calculation of the weight of any other volume of gas.

ILLUSTRATIVE PROBLEM

Calculate the weight of 10 liters of ethane (C_2H_6) gas at S.T.P.

Solution

A mole (molecular weight) of ethane is 30 gm.

2 atoms of carbon	$= 2 \times 12 = 24$
6 atoms of hydrogen	$= 6 \times 1 = 6$
Molecular weight or formula weight	$= 30$

$$\frac{30 \text{ gm}}{22.4 \text{ l}} = \frac{x \text{ gm}}{10 \text{ l}}$$

$$x = 13.4 \text{ gm}$$

VALENCE AND FORMULA WRITING

Oxygen combines with many other elements. Why is the correct formula for water H_2O, whereas that of calcium oxide is CaO? Why is it necessary to show two atoms of hydrogen attached to a single atom of oxygen, whereas with calcium, single atoms of each element are attached? Similarly, how does it happen that HCl and $CaCl_2$ are both correct formulas?

The answer will become clearer after electronic structures are considered, but it is apparent that the ability of calcium atoms to combine with other atoms is different from the ability of hydrogen atoms. The combining capacity of an atom is called its valence. Hydrogen is assigned a valence of $+1$. Any other element, such as chlorine, which will combine with hydrogen, atom for atom, is said to have a valence of -1. If a table of valences is available (see Appendix), the writing of correct formulas involves only the equalization of the positive and negative charges of the constituent parts. HCl is a correct formula since the $+1$ of hydrogen balances the -1 of chlorine. Since the valence of Ca is $+2$ and of oxygen -2, the correct formula for calcium oxide is CaO. The plus valence of the calcium and the minus of the oxygen are equal.

In writing formulas, subscript numbers are introduced to balance the positive and the negative charges. For example, $CaCl_2$ is the correct formula for calcium chloride, since a single calcium atom has a valence of $+2$, and a single chlorine atom has a valence of -1. What is the correct formula for aluminum chloride if aluminum has a valence of $+3$? For stannic chloride, if stannic tin has a valence of $+4$? Why is Al_2O_3 the correct formula for aluminum oxide (aluminum, $+3$; oxygen, -2)? Cf. Formula Writing Sheets on p. 795.

Note that the use of a valence table alone may lead to the writing of formulas of compounds which are not known to exist. Despite such limitations, the procedure just outlined is the simplest rule-of-thumb method that will give a clear understanding of how to write correct formulas.

Valence has been described, then, as the charge, plus or minus, on a single atom of an element. Occasionally a group of atoms may preserve its identity in a series of reactions. Groups of atoms which go through a reaction as a unit are called radicals. For example, a nitrogen atom and three oxygen atoms may as a group carry a charge of -1; this group is called a nitrate radical and is written NO_3^-. This radical does not occur alone; it is always found in combination with an element of positive valence. KNO_3 is potassium nitrate; $Ca(NO_3)_2$ is calcium nitrate; $Al(NO_3)_3$ is aluminum nitrate.

Another group of atoms is known as the sulfate radical, written $SO_4^=$. The two minus signs following it indicate its valence. Like the nitrate, it does not exist except in combination with elements of positive valence, as for example Na_2SO_4, $CaSO_4$, or $Al_2(SO_4)_3$. Other radicals with negative valence include the carbonate $(CO_3^=)$, and the phosphate $(PO_4^{\equiv})$.

Radicals with positive valences are somewhat less common. A single nitrogen combined with four hydrogen atoms has a charge of $+1$. This group is called an ammonium radical. It exists only in combination with negatively charged atoms or radicals. Ammonium chloride is NH_4Cl and ammonium sulfate $(NH_4)_2SO_4$.

Certain elements have more than one valence. For example, iron has valences of $+2$ and $+3$. There are two chlorides of iron, $FeCl_2$ (ferrous chloride) and $FeCl_3$ (ferric chloride). Note that the -ic compound indicates a higher valence of the positive element than the -ous.

FROM CHEMICAL REACTION TO BALANCED EQUATION

Essential to any equation is the existence of an equality. A chemical equation is said to be balanced when all of the atoms which are present in the reacting materials are found in the products, even though they are differently combined.

The following reaction indicates that sulfuric acid, H_2SO_4, reacts with metallic aluminum, producing aluminum sulfate $Al_2(SO_4)_3$ and hydrogen gas, H_2.

$$2 Al + 3H_2SO_4 \rightarrow Al_2(SO_4)_3 + 3H_2 \uparrow \qquad (7\text{-}d)$$

(The arrow at the end, pointing upward, indicates that hydrogen gas separates from the reaction mixture. When a substance will precipitate —i.e., form as a solid within a liquid and separate from the solution— a downward pointing arrow indicates this.) Equation 7-d as it stands is not a true equation because there is not yet an equality of atoms on the two sides of the arrow. An atom of aluminum has been conjured up out of nothing, for there are two atoms of Al represented on the right-hand side of the equation and only one on the left.

There is always a temptation to ask, "Why not drop the subscript after the Al in $Al_2(SO_4)_3$?" In working out the correct formulas for each of the reactants and products, we use appropriate subscripts as described above under valence. After we have written a formula correctly, the subscripts must not be altered in balancing. Balancing is accomplished by introducing coefficients before the appropriate formulas. This point can hardly be overemphasized. In reactions considered so far, these coefficients have been determined by trial and error, the aim being to bring about an equality between the number of atoms on the two sides of the arrow.

In Equation 7-d, there are three sulfur atoms on the left and one on the right. By introducing a coefficient of 3 before H_2SO_4

$$Al + 3H_2SO_4 \rightarrow Al_2(SO_4)_3 + H_2$$

we bring about a balance between S atoms (3 on either side) and between O atoms (12 on either side). (Note that a coefficient in front of a formula affects each element within it: $3H_2SO_4$ means 6 hydrogens, 3 sulfurs, and 12 oxygens.) But the reaction is still not balanced. Introducing a 2 before Al balances the aluminum

$$2Al + 3H_2SO_4 \rightarrow Al_2(SO_4)_3 + H_2$$

and introducing a 3 before H_2 balances the hydrogen. The numbers of atoms of all elements are now the same on one side of the arrow as on the other, and so the reaction is balanced. The balanced equation is

$$2Al + 3H_2SO_4 \rightarrow Al_2(SO_4)_3 + 3H_2$$

LEFT MEMBER	RIGHT MEMBER
2 atoms of aluminum	2 atoms of aluminum
6 atoms of hydrogen	6 atoms of hydrogen
3 atoms of sulfur	3 atoms of sulfur
12 atoms of oxygen	12 atoms of oxygen

WEIGHT RELATIONS IN CHEMICAL REACTIONS

One of the most amazing things about the preceding information concerning chemical formulas, formula weights, and equations, is the power it gives us to predict the quantities of chemical substances which will react. Hydrogen burns in air (unites with the oxygen of the air); water is formed. The reaction may be represented

$$2H_2 + O_2 \rightarrow 2H_2O$$

Is the reaction balanced? No. It appears that as a result of the reaction, two atoms of oxygen have been reduced to one. The law of conservation of matter denies this possibility. But if coefficients of 2 are introduced before hydrogen and water, then the equation is balanced.

$$2H_2 + O_2 \rightarrow 2H_2O$$

In this balanced equation, hydrogen has a weight of 4 (two formula weights), oxygen of 32 (one formula weight), and water of 36 (two formula weights). The weight of the oxygen is eight times as great as the weight of the hydrogen, or in other words, the ratio by weight in which hydrogen and oxygen combine is 4:32. This ratio never changes. Once the equation has been worked out and there is assurance that this is the only reaction taking place, the formula weights predict correctly the reaction ratios. The weight of water formed in this reaction will always be 9 times the weight of the hydrogen used.

ILLUSTRATIVE PROBLEM

How much water is produced by burning 5 gm of hydrogen?

Solution

Let $x =$ the number of grams of water produced.
Since the weight of water is 9 times that of the hydrogen used,

$$\frac{H_2O}{H_2} = \frac{x}{5 \text{ gm}} = \frac{9}{1}, \text{ and } x = 45 \text{ gm}$$

45 gm of water would be produced by burning 5 gm of hydrogen.

Consider the following reaction. Is it balanced?

$$2 \text{ Mg} + O_2 \rightarrow 2\text{MgO}$$

No. There are 2 oxygens on the left and 1 on the right. Introducing a 2 before MgO balances oxygen; a 2 before Mg balances magnesium.

$$2\text{Mg} + O_2 \rightarrow 2\text{MgO}$$

The formula weights may be calculated as follows

$$
\begin{aligned}
2\text{Mg} &= 2 \times 24 = 48 \\
O_2 &= 2 \times 16 = 32 \\
2\text{MgO} &= 2(24 + 16) = 80
\end{aligned}
$$

The weight relation of the quantities is

$$2\text{Mg} + O_2 \rightarrow 2\text{MgO}$$
$$\phantom{2\text{Mg}}48 32 80$$

It is now possible to answer such questions as "What weight of magnesium will be needed to react completely with 10 grams of oxygen?" Magnesium and oxygen always react in the ratio of 48:32, i.e., of 3:2. Stated another way, the weight of magnesium reacting will always be $1\frac{1}{2}$ times as large as the weight of oxygen with which it unites: 15 grams of magnesium will react with 10 grams of oxygen.

The fraction 48/32 is obtained from the formula weights of the two chemical substances under consideration. Even though there will often be more than two participants in any chemical reaction, in calculating weight problems we must focus on two at a time. Other necessary reactants are assumed to be present in appropriate quantities: other

products than the one under consideration may be formed. The two
quantities under consideration may both be reactants, or both may be
products.

ILLUSTRATIVE PROBLEM

What weight of zinc sulfate is produced by the reaction of 10 gm
of zinc with an appropriate quantity of sulfuric acid?

Solution

The balanced equation for the reaction is

$$Zn + H_2SO_4 \rightarrow ZnSO_4 + H_2$$
$$65 \quad\quad 98 \quad\quad\quad 161 \quad\quad 2$$

The formula weights are given below each substance. We see that
the weight of zinc sulfate produced will be 161/65 the weight of
the zinc used. Consequently, if $x =$ the number of grams of zinc
sulfate produced by the reaction of 10 gm of zinc,

$$\frac{ZnSO_4}{Zn} = \frac{161}{65} = \frac{x}{10 \text{ gm}}, \quad x = \frac{1610 \text{ gm}}{65} = 24.8 \text{ gm}$$

24.8 gm of zinc sulfate would result if 10 gm of zinc metal were
placed in enough H_2SO_4 to react completely with it. The proportion
relates only to the quantities of Zn and $ZnSO_4$. H_2SO_4 and H_2 appear
in the equation but are disregarded in this particular problem.

An entirely different problem might have been stated concerning
this same equation:

ILLUSTRATIVE PROBLEM

How many grams of zinc must react with sulfuric acid in order to
produce 5 gm of hydrogen?

Solution

$$Zn + H_2SO_4 \rightarrow ZnSO_4 + H_2 \uparrow$$
$$65 \quad\quad 98 \quad\quad\quad 161 \quad\quad 2$$

$$\frac{Zn}{H_2} = \frac{65}{2} = \frac{x}{5 \text{ gm}}$$

$$2x = 325 \text{ gm}$$
$$x = 162.5 \text{ gm}$$

162.5 gm of zinc reacting with a sufficient amount of sulfuric acid
(which is perfectly definite and predictable by means of the equation) produces 5 gm of hydrogen gas. Note that there is no mention
of the amount of zinc sulfate formed along with the hydrogen. The

quantity of it formed from the given amount of zinc is definite and predictable even though of no consequence in this problem.

The quantitative basis of chemistry is found in the above principles. The chemist uses them to calculate how much of a particular reactant must be used in order to produce a desired quantity of a certain product. Economical operation of chemical industry depends upon such considerations.

THE METALLURGY OF ZINC

As an illustration of how chemical reactions are brought about on an industrial scale, consider the metallurgy of zinc.

Two commonly occurring ores of zinc are the sulfide (ZnS) and the carbonate (ZnCO$_3$). These never occur in an ore deposit as pure compounds, but are always mixed with impurities such as silica (sand). Accordingly, an early stage of refining is concentration, frequently accomplished by a flotation process which takes advantage of the fact that ore and impurities have different densities. Concentration, which leaves the ore richer in the desired metallic compound, involves physical changes only; there is no alteration of the chemical structure of the constituents.

After concentration, sulfide ores are roasted, i.e., heated in the presence of an abundance of air. This results in the substitution of an oxygen atom from the air for a sulfur atom of the zinc sulfide. Zinc oxide is formed according to the following equation

$$2ZnS + 3O_2 \rightarrow 2ZnO + 2SO_2 \uparrow$$

(Once again, the vertical arrow following the SO$_2$ indicates that sulfur dioxide is a gas.)

What has this step in the process accomplished? Why is it any better to have zinc oxide than zinc sulfide? The answer is that the inexpensive industrial chemical substance coke or coal (largely the element carbon) is quite effective in removing the oxygen, whereas no equally inexpensive method is available for removing the sulfur. Reduction of a metallic oxide by carbon is a method widely used in separating other metal atoms from the oxygen with which they are combined in the oxide. (In some oxides the metal and oxygen atoms are so tightly bound that such a process will not work.)

Zinc carbonate ores are easily converted to the oxide by heating and driving out carbon dioxide gas according to the equation

$$ZnCO_3 \rightarrow ZnO + CO_2 \uparrow$$

Starting with either ore, the first step is to form the oxide. The oxide and coke or coal are then mixed, heated, and formed into briquettes which are fed into a reduction furnace. The carbon removes oxygen from the oxide, the metal zinc is formed, and carbon monoxide gas escapes.

$$ZnO + C \rightarrow Zn + CO \uparrow$$

The heat evolved in the above reaction is sufficient to cause the zinc

Fig. 7-14.

Zinc Reduction Furnaces. Coked briquettes containing zinc are fed into the furnace. The heat resulting from the reaction of zinc oxide and carbon is sufficient to vaporize the zinc. The vertical retort furnace shown is equipped with a very efficient condenser capable of removing 96% of the zinc from the effluent products.   (Courtesy, New Jersey Zinc Co.)

metal to vaporize. Fig. 7-14 shows a modern vertical retort zinc reduction furnace capable of condensing over 96% of the zinc vapor.

After suitable reheating, zinc may be used in alloys such as brass,

Fig. 7-15. (Courtesy, New Jersey Zinc Co.)

Galvanizing Sheet Iron. The carefully cleaned sheet iron is passed through molten zinc. The thin film which adheres to the surface of the iron prevents rusting.

bronzes, and German silver. A very considerable fraction of the industrial output of zinc is used to protect the surface of sheet iron in the process known as "galvanizing." In this process (Fig. 7-15) sheets of iron are carefully cleaned and then dipped in the molten zinc, which adheres to the surface in a thin coat. This is one of the most effective methods of protecting an iron surface. Another common use of zinc metal is for the casings of dry-cell batteries. In these it serves as the negative terminal as well as the container for the other materials.

In preparing the metal zinc, then, the metallurgist starts with an ore of which only a small proportion may be the metal. Many chemical constituents are likely to be present in the ore; it is really a mixture. Concentration of the ore is often a process of physical separation of impurities, not a chemical reaction. The chemical stages of the metallurgical process take place during the roasting of the ore concentrate and during the reaction of zinc oxide with coke. At the start, zinc atoms are mixed with a variety of other atoms; when the process is finished, the product consists almost wholly of zinc atoms. Thus separating atoms has been brought about on an industrial scale.

EXERCISES AND QUESTIONS FOR CHAPTER 7

1. Calculate the formula weights of the following compounds:

   NaCl   NaOH $Al_2(SO_4)_3$ C_2H_5OH
   $NaHCO_3$ $CaCO_3$ $Ca_3(PO_4)_2$ HNO_3

2. Balance the following equations:

   a. $H_2 + O_2 \rightarrow H_2O$ $2H_2 + O_2 \rightarrow 2H_2O$
   b. $N_2 + 3H_2 \rightarrow 2NH_3$
   c. $CaCO_3 + 2HCl \rightarrow CaCl_2 + H_2O + CO_2$
   d. $2Al + 3H_2SO_4 \rightarrow Al_2(SO_4)_3 + 3H_2$
   e. $MgCl_2 + 2AgNO_3 \rightarrow 2AgCl + Mg(NO_3)_2$
   f. $BaCl_2 + K_2CrO_4 \rightarrow BaCrO_4 + 2KCl$
   g. $2Na_3AsO_4 + 3Ca(NO_3)_2 \rightarrow Ca_3(AsO_4)_2 + 6NaNO_3$
   h. $2NaBr + 2H_2SO_4 \rightarrow Na_2SO_4 + Br_2 + SO_2 + 2H_2O$

3. Write correct formulas for each of the following substances and balance the equation: $2 AgNO_3 + CaCl_2 \rightarrow 2AgCl + Ca(NO_3)_2$
   a. Silver nitrate + calcium chloride → silver chloride + calcium nitrate
                                                    (precipitate)
   b. Barium chloride + aluminum sulfate →
                                          barium sulfate + aluminum chloride
                                                    (precipitate)
   c. Ammonium iodide + calcium hydroxide →
                                          calcium iodide + ammonia + water
                                                    (gas)

4. a. Calculate the weight of carbon dioxide gas (CO_2) produced when 25 lb of limestone ($CaCO_3$) reacts with hydrochloric acid (HCl) according to the equation of Exercise 2c above.
   b. Calculate the weight of barium chromate ($BaCrO_4$) precipitate formed when 10 gm of barium chloride ($BaCl_2$) reacts with potassium chromate (K_2CrO_4) as indicated by the equation of Exercise 2f above.

5. Calculate the percentage by weight of:
   a. carbon in $NaHCO_3$
   b. nitrogen in HNO_3

c. water in $BaCl_2 \cdot 2H_2O$ (The dot indicates that water is chemically combined with $BaCl_2$)

6. The concept of an element as a single atomic species is an idealization. Explain.

7. Did the Greeks of 2000 years ago have any knowledge concerning chemistry? Explain.

8. What great contribution did Paracelsus make to the development of chemistry?

9. Who first defined an element as we now understand it? State this definition.

10. One of the first great theories of chemistry was the phlogiston theory. It interpreted certain aspects of combustion adequately but failed in others. Explain.

11. What does a chemical symbol represent? What does a formula represent?

12. Every equation represents some sort of equality. What is the nature of the equality represented by a chemical equation?

13. What is meant by the atomic weight of an element?

14. Explain how valences are used in writing the formulas of chemical compounds. Illustrate.

15. Briefly describe the metallurgical process for preparing zinc.

REVIEW

1. Calculate the force (parallel to the road) needed to push a 3000-lb automobile up an inclined road which rises 5 ft vertically for every 100 ft along the road. (Neglect friction.)

2. Calculate the time required for a mail pouch to fall 500 ft, the distance from an airplane to the ground. (Neglect air resistance.)

CHAPTER 8

Rainbows from Atoms and Molecules

A RAINBOW spans the sky when rays of sunlight are dispersed by raindrops. The same effect may be observed in the spray of a garden hose in the bright sunlight. Both are reminders that white light is a complex of many colors, the colors of the rainbow. Though rainbows had been observed since the dawn of mankind, the scientific study of color began early in the seventeenth century when Galileo invented or developed the telescope. When objects were observed through one of these early telescopes, the images were blurred by color fringes, a consequence of the complex nature of white light. Two generations later, at Trinity College, Cambridge, the undergraduate Isaac Newton became interested in the properties of lenses and particularly in the annoying color fringes. It was Newton's interest in correcting this defect of lenses which led him to his study of color.[*] One sunny day he poked a hole in a curtain, thus allowing a narrow beam of sunlight to enter a darkened room (Fig. 8-1). He placed a glass prism so that the beam met one of its surfaces obliquely, as shown in Fig. 8-2. To his amazement the spot of sunlight which fell on the wall was oblong in shape rather than circular like the hole in the curtain, as might have been expected. Furthermore the light on the wall, instead of being white, was a rainbow of color, a "continuous

[*] Abraham Wolf, *History of Science and Technology in the Sixteenth and Seventeenth Centuries*, Macmillan, 1950, p. 264.

148

spectrum"—violet at one end and a continuous blending into the other colors to red at the other end. This experiment seemed to Newton to indicate that light was not homogeneous; certain components were bent (refracted) more than others in passing through the prism. If the

Galileo demonstrating his telescope in Venice, as pictured by a modern artist. With it he discovered four moons of the planet Jupiter. (From the painting by W. F. Soare, Courtesy, Bausch & Lomb Optical Co.)

beam of sunlight was taken as a line of reference, the beam of red light was deviated through a smaller angle than that of the violet light. He clinched this argument concerning the complex nature of white light by showing that after the colors had been so separated, they could be brought back together again to produce white light like the original beam.

THE SPECTROMETER

If a triangular glass prism like Newton's is mounted as shown in Fig. 8-3 with a collimator tube on one side and telescope tube on the other, the device is called a spectrometer. An adjustable slit at one end of the *collimator* admits a very narrow vertical beam of light. A lens

A modern artist depicts Isaac Newton using a prism to disperse the components of white light. (Courtesy Bausch & Lomb Optical Co.) The sausage-shaped spectrum is a succession of overlapping images of the round hole in the curtain.

Fig. 8-1

A beam of white light is dispersed by a glass prism into a rainbow of color, or continuous spectrum.

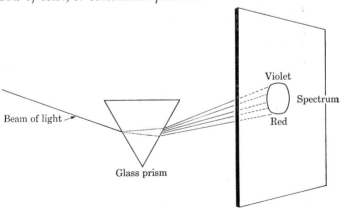

Beam of light

Violet

Spectrum

Red

Glass prism

Fig. 8-2

system within the tube renders the beam parallel as it passes toward the prism. The prism serves to spread out the components of the white light, bending the red least and the violet most. The telescope tube has a lens system to give the observer a magnified image of the slit for every different component present. (When spectra are observed through a spectrometer, the room should be darkened and the prism covered so that the light reaching the prism can come only through the slit of the collimator tube.)

Fig. 8-3.

Construction of a prism spectroscope or spectrometer. The collimator is a device for making divergent rays parallel. Its tube excludes all light from the source except a beam admitted through the slit in a diaphragm at one end. At the other end of the collimator tube a lens renders the rays of this beam parallel. The rays proceed through the prism and are dispersed into color bands that are magnified for an observer by the two lenses of the telescope.

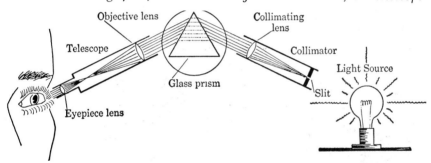

The spectrometer is essentially a light analyzer. The light which reaches the eye after passing through the instrument depends on the physical state of the material which is emitting the light and on its temperature. If a metal ball is placed in front of the slit and heated up, the observer sees nothing until the ball is red hot. Then a red color appears at one side of the field of vision. As the temperature of the ball is raised, orange appears, then yellow, green, blue, and finally when it is white hot, the rainbow is complete; the observer sees a continuous spectrum. Glowing *solids* give this type of spectrum. An incandescent light bulb will give a continuous spectrum since the source is the glowing filament which is made of tungsten metal. Unfortunately a continuous spectrum will not serve to identify the solid material that is emitting the light rays.

However, if a high-voltage electric current is passed through a glass tube containing a *gas* such as sodium vapor or neon (at low pressure) and the glowing gas is used as a light source, the observer sees in the spectrometer a pattern of vertical colored lines. This is called a *line spectrum* and will serve in the hands of a spectroscopist to identify the

Fig. 8-4.

A university model spectrometer. The long narrow camera attachment at the left is used to photograph spectra. When the telescope tube is removed and replaced by the camera we have a spectrograph. *The black cover with side tube attached (shown at the right) fits over the table supporting the prism (center of spectroscope). When the end of the side tube is illuminated, a graduated scale is superimposed upon the spectrum. This scale makes convenient the location of spectral lines. (Courtesy American Optical Co.)*

material that is emitting the light rays. Much of the usefulness of the spectrometer depends upon the identification of elements by means of these characteristic patterns of lines.

PROPERTIES OF WAVES

Many of the phenomena associated with light are best explained by assuming that it moves in the form of waves. The human eye cannot of course directly observe that light has a wave form. On the other hand water waves can be observed and are familiar to all.

Consider, for a moment, water waves such as are set up when a ball is dropped into a placid pool. The waves form a series of expanding concentric rings. Fig. 1-7 shows a typical water wave. Though

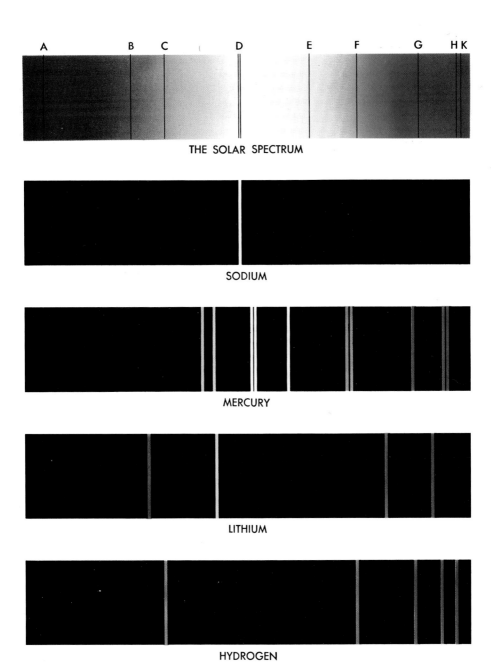

Fig. 8-5. Emission and Absorption Line Spectra. The solar spectrum (top) shows the Fraunhofer (absorption) lines which enable us to identify elements on the sun. The remaining line (emission) spectra are characteristic bright-line spectra in the visible region. The patterns of lines shown would permit the identification of the excited gaseous atoms emitting them.

water waves are in some respects unlike light waves, they do make clear the meaning of a *wave length*. Wave length has been defined as the linear distance between the crests (or for that matter, between any corresponding parts) of two successive waves. Light waves also are characterized by wave length, and when we say that red waves are the longest of the visible light waves, orange and yellow are shorter, and so on down to violet, which are the shortest (Fig. 8-6), what is

Fig. 8-6.

In the visible spectrum, waves of red light are longer than those of yellow light, which in turn are longer than those of blue. The wave lengths are measured in angstrom units. (Å), i.e., in hundred-millionths of a centimeter. The visible spectrum, between the infrared and the ultraviolet, is composed of light ranging from 4000 to 7800 Å in wave length.

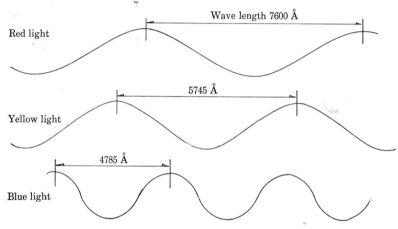

Wave length 7600 Å

Red light

5745 Å

Yellow light

4785 Å

Blue light

"long" or "short" is the wave length. Differences in the color of light are associated with rays of different wave length.

The number of waves which pass a reference point R in 1 second is a measure of the *frequency* of the wave. Since red rays of light have a longer wave length than violet rays and all light travels at the same rate, fewer waves of red light pass a given point in a second, and red light has a lower frequency than violet; if waves of red light and of violet light are traveling side by side, a larger number of violet waves than red waves pass a given point in a given time interval.

In the study of sound, frequency determines the pitch of a musical tone. International standard pitch is "A 440," i.e., the musical tone "A" sends out 440 waves per second. It should be noted in passing that

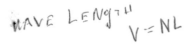

WAVE LENGTH $V = NL$

sound waves are of a type known as longitudinal waves, quite different from light waves, which are transverse (see below).

The horizontal line in Fig. 8-7 shows the surface of the pool of water

Fig. 8-7.

The propagation of a wave on water. In a transverse wave, the direction of vibration is at right angles to the direction of propagation. Electromagnetic waves, including light, are transverse, in contrast to the longitudinal waves of sound. A water wave is not a purely transverse wave, since there is a slight back-and-forth movement of water particles.

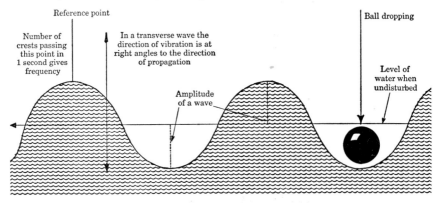

Reference point

Number of crests passing this point in 1 second gives frequency

In a transverse wave the direction of vibration is at right angles to the direction of propagation

Amplitude of a wave

Ball dropping

Level of water when undisturbed

before the ball is dropped in. The waves formed when the ball hits the water are superimposed in the same figure.

The length of a wave and its frequency are related by the equation

$(NL = VT)$ $V = \dfrac{1}{N}$

$N = \dfrac{1}{V}$

$V = NL$

T = time for 1 wave to pass

$T = \dfrac{L}{V}$ *or* $L = VT$

V represents the velocity at which the wave travels (186,000 mi/sec or 3×10^{10} cm/sec for light, 1090 ft/sec at 0°C for sound), N is the number of waves passing a point in 1 second (that is, the frequency) and L is the wave length. Note that the linear unit used to express wave length must be the same as that used in expressing the velocity. For example, if the velocity of light is expressed in *meters* per second, the wave length must be expressed in *meters*. Since frequencies and velocities are usually expressed in units per second, it will rarely be necessary to be sure that the time units are the same.

ILLUSTRATIVE PROBLEM

Find the length of a wave of violet light if the frequency is 7.5×10^{14} waves per sec.

Light Waves In Water Bend Away From The Perpendicular Toward

Solution

$$V = NL$$

$$3 \times 10^{10} \left(\frac{cm}{sec}\right) = 7.5 \times 10^{14} \left(\frac{1}{sec}\right) \cdot L \ (cm)$$

$$\frac{3 \times 10^{10}}{7.5 \times 10^{14}} = \frac{1}{2.5} \times 10^{-4} = 0.4 \times 10^{-4} = 4 \times 10^{-5} = L$$

$$L = 4 \times 10^{-5} \ cm$$

Wave lengths of spectral lines are usually expressed in linear units known as angstrom units. 1 Å (angstrom unit) = 10^{-8} cm. Let us see how many angstrom units there are in 4.5 × 10^{-5} cm.

$$L = 4 \times 10^{-5} \ cm = 4 \cdot 10^3 \times 10^{-5} \cdot 10^{-3}$$
$$L = 4000 \times 10^{-8} \ cm = 4000 \ \overset{\circ}{A}$$

Light waves are said to be transverse. In Latin, *trans* means *across:* in light waves the vibrations are across the direction of propagation of the wave, as shown in Fig. 8-7.

One may ask, "What is set in motion as a light wave moves through space?" A hundred or more years ago the answer would probably have been "the luminiferous ether" (not to be confused with the liquid ether that is used as an anesthetic). It had been known for many years that if the air were pumped out of a bell jar in which a ringing bell was suspended, the sound would gradually diminish as air was removed; so air was necessary for the transmission of sound waves. But the vibrating bell hammer would still be *visible,* so light waves were able to travel in space which would not transmit sound. Since it was believed that a medium must be present to allow for the propagation of any wave, it was suggested that the hypothetical medium called ether was responsible for the transmission of light waves.

Late in the nineteenth century Michelson and Morley at the University of Chicago devised an experiment by which they hoped to detect the drift of the ether past the earth. They were unable to detect such an effect and there is still no convincing experimental method of detecting the presence of the ether if it exists. Transverse waves seem to require a rigid material for their transmission; on the other hand there should be no problem in detecting the presence of a material having the rigidity of steel. The ether question must at present be relegated to the category of unsolved problems.

Subsequent evidence has shown that in certain phenomena, for example, the photoelectric effect,* light has particle properties as well as wave properties. Light must then be considered to have a dual nature; in some cases it seems to be acting as if composed of waves, in others as if made up of particles.

ELECTROMAGNETIC WAVES

The waves which are called light waves are only one variety of a more general class known as electromagnetic waves. All of these waves travel with a velocity of 186,000 mi/sec, may be reflected or refracted, and in general behave quite similarly. On the other hand there are certain differences. X rays, for example, will penetrate many materials which light will not. Ultraviolet rays cause sunburn in a human being too long exposed to them.

The differences between the various types of electromagnetic waves are essentially differences in the lengths of the waves, which vary all the way from a small fraction of an angstrom unit to many miles. The waves of visible light have lengths from about 4000 Å at the violet end

The electromagnetic spectrum consists of the types of radiation whose waves are transverse and have a velocity of 186,000 mi/sec (the so-called "speed of light"). X-rays, ultraviolet, visible light, infrared, and radio waves are included in this classification.

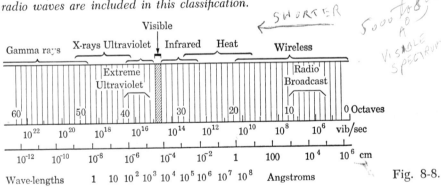

Fig. 8-8.

of the visible spectrum to about 7800 Å at the red end; this region of the spectrum, between 4000 and 7800 Å, is called the visible spectrum, since the human eye is able to detect these waves. Beyond the red end of the spectrum is a group of longer waves known as infrared and

* E. Hausmann and E. P. Slack, *Physics*, 3d ed., Van Nostrand, 1956, p. 757 ff.; Ira Freeman, *Modern Introductory Physics*, McGraw-Hill, 1949, p. 389.

ranging to about 80,000 Å, or about 0.008 millimeter in length. Beyond infrared waves are radio waves, which extend to several miles in length.

On the other side of the visible spectrum, next to violet rays, is the ultraviolet region. Here the rays are shorter than the rays of the visible spectrum, and have a range of about 150 to 4000 Å in length. X rays, which are so useful in medical and dental diagnosis, are a group of waves shorter than the ultraviolet; gamma rays, which are emitted by radioactive substances, are in turn shorter than X rays although the distinction between the two has been unimportant since high-voltage X-ray machines have been available. The shortest of all electromagnetic waves and the most penetrating were supposed for a long time to be cosmic rays, but more recent work indicates that the effects of these rays may be explained on the basis of high-speed particles.

The spectroscope described above, with its glass prism and lenses, enables us to observe spectra produced by a white-light-emitting material and is hence useful only in the visible region of the spectrum —that is, it is limited to observation of waves approximately 4000 to 7800 Å in length. For observation, spectral lines (see below) in the ultraviolet region are usually photographed. The spectroscopist finds this region particularly valuable in identifying chemical elements, for example, the metals composing alloys, by means of their characteristic lines, and he soon learns to recognize particular patterns of lines as belonging to certain elements. X-ray spectra are also recorded photographically.

LINE SPECTRA

In 1752 Thomas Melvill reported to the Medical Society of Edinburgh that when he looked through a prism at the light coming through a hole in a piece of pasteboard (the light source being an alcohol flame in which there was alum or potash) he saw a variety of colored rays, with the yellow most prominent.* (One of the constituents must have been sodium.) This is doubtless one of the earliest reports of a characteristic bright-line or *emission spectrum;* not for a hundred years was there worked out a general method of analysis based on characteristic line spectra.

* Henry Crew, *The Rise of Modern Physics*, Williams & Wilkins, Baltimore, 1935, p. 331.

Shortly after the turn of the nineteenth century the London physician Wollaston (1766-1828) admitted a beam of sunlight through a narrow slit into a darkened room and arranged a prism in the path of the beam so that he could look into the prism. Against the rainbow background he observed a series of seven dark lines. He supposed that these narrow dark lines separated the spectrum into regions of different color. He was doubtless one of the first to observe a *dark line* or *absorption spectrum*.

About a decade later a Bavarian optician, Fraunhofer (1787-1826), used a similar experimental arrangement, but examined the solar spectrum with a telescope tube rather than with the naked eye. He was able to count several hundred dark lines instead of Wollaston's seven. The dark lines of the solar spectrum, observed against a rainbow background, are still called *Fraunhofer lines*. Fraunhofer was also probably the first investigator to produce a spectrum by passing light through a glass plate upon which were ruled very fine lines, that is, a *diffraction grating*. However, when he discovered the large number of absorption (dark) lines in the solar spectrum, Fraunhofer apparently had no inkling that there might be a connection between these lines and the gaseous chemical elements surrounding the luminous inner sphere of the sun.

A solution of lithium chloride, when soaked in asbestos and placed on a wire gauze above a colorless Bunsen flame, imparts the same crimson color as a similarly observed solution of strontium chloride. It is difficult to tell whether lithium or strontium is the element present by observing the color of the flame. In 1826 the wealthy Englishman William Talbot (1800-1877) observed that if the light from a flame colored by first one and then the other of these substances was passed into a spectrometer, the number and position of the colored lines were distinctive for each substance: each chemical substance gave its own pattern of vertical colored lines against a dark background. This made it possible for the experimenter to distinguish between the two elements. Talbot was of course making use of the spectroscopic method as a tool of qualitative analysis; he was distinguishing between two chemical elements by means of their line spectra. In his hands the spectrometer provided an isolated test rather than a method which was recognized as widely applicable in the identification of a great variety of elements.

In 1849 Foucault took two carbon rods through which a high-voltage electric current passed, and "struck an arc" by touching them and then separating them. A dazzling white light resulted. This brilliant light source gave a continuous spectrum when viewed in a spectrometer. Due to the presence of minute amounts of sodium compounds in the carbon rods, a faint yellow line (actually two lines very close together) stood out against the continuous background. If a beam of bright sunlight was focused on the arc, a dark line, called an absorption line, replaced the faint yellow line. This absorption line became more pronounced when the beam of sunlight was passed through a tube of glowing sodium vapor (sodium vapor lamp). Evidently sodium vapor could act both as a source in producing a line spectrum and as an *absorber*, removing from white light the wave lengths which it produced as an emission source.

Kirchhoff (1824-1887), a German physicist, used a luminous white light source instead of the beam of sunlight, and he discovered that what was true of sodium also applied to many other elements. A substance which when made to glow gave a bright-line (emission) spectrum would when cool absorb from white light passing through it the same components as it had emitted; a dark line would appear at the very point where the bright line had appeared before.

The two great German scientists Bunsen and Kirchhoff were the first to recognize the generality of the spectroscopic method. Various elements under particular conditions of excitation emitted light which, when examined in a spectrometer, made possible the identification of the emitting element. No element except sodium gave the yellow line —the so-called D lines—in exactly the same position in the spectral field. Other elements in the atomic condition gave spectra with lines of different number, color, and location in the spectral field, but the pattern for a given element was always the same. The wave lengths of each of the lines emitted was determinable with great accuracy.

In summary, line spectra are of two kinds, *emission* (bright-line) spectra and *absorption* (dark-line) spectra. An emission spectrum is produced by a gaseous substance when excited to a light-emitting condition. An absorption spectrum is produced when a gaseous substance absorbs those wave lengths from white light which it would emit in a light-emitting condition. A particular gaseous substance gives the same characteristic line pattern whether the spectrum is an emission or an absorption spectrum.

Line spectra are produced by gaseous substances in the *atomic* (rather than the molecular) condition. The spectra produced by gases in the molecular condition, i.e., in which atoms are linked into molecules, have broad bands of color (or dark bands against a rainbow background) instead of fine lines, and are called *band spectra*. Nitrogen gas, when excited to light emission, gives this type of spectrum.

DISCOVERY OF INERT GASES

The invention of a new tool in science such as the spectrometer has frequently opened up opportunities for a whole series of new discoveries. Shortly after the discovery of the spectroscopic method Bunsen made use of it in identifying the chemical elements rubidium and cesium. Somewhat more spectacular was the prediction of an element on the sun in 1868 by Lockyer. There was an absorption line in the yellow region of the solar spectrum for which there was no known emission line. No substance was known on the earth which, when excited to a light-emitting condition, gave a bright yellow line in the exact same position of this absorption line given by the element on the sun. The unknown element on the sun was called helium, from the Greek word for sun, *helios*. Not until 1895 did Ramsay find that the mineral clevite yielded a gas whose bright-line spectrum contained a yellow line in exactly this position. Thus the existence of helium was predicted more than twenty-five years before it was known on the earth.

The spectrometer proved to be of immeasurable value in identifying the other inert gases in the atmosphere. Inert gases do not form compounds, and they undergo no ordinary chemical reactions at all; they would thus be exceedingly difficult to identify without the spectrometer. In Chapter 1 it was mentioned that the inert gas argon was discovered as a result of the observed discrepancy between the density of the "nitrogen" obtained from air and that from ammonium compounds. When a high-voltage electric current was passed through a Geissler tube (see Fig. 11-5) containing the nitrogen obtained from the ammonium compounds, the tube glowed, and in the spectrometer produced color bands like those described above as being characteristic of molecules. When the "nitrogen" from air was similarly excited in a Geissler tube, a series of bright lines was superimposed on this band spectrum. If the nitrogen in the tube were removed by making it combine with a metal such as magnesium, there was always a small gaseous residue which could not be coaxed into combination with any other element. When this gaseous residue was placed in a Geissler tube and excited with high voltage, the spectroscope showed a line spectrum totally different from the band spectrum of nitrogen. The new gas emitting the line spectrum was called argon.

INDUSTRIAL APPLICATIONS OF SPECTROSCOPY

All chemists, as a part of their professional training, take courses in qualitative and quantitative analysis. The names suggest the province of each branch of chemical science. In qualitative analysis one determines which elements are present in a sample; in quantitative analysis, how much of each constituent. Obviously a quantitative analysis presupposes a qualitative analysis.

Without spectroscopy, the problem in the qualitative analysis of an unknown alloy would be, first, to find a reagent or reagents which would dissolve the sample completely. The solution would then be subjected to a "systematic analysis," a series of reactions which would either affirm or deny the presence of the different metals. This procedure is often long and involved. How different is the situation now that the modern spectrograph is available! An arc is struck between electrodes tipped with the unknown alloy. This arc serves as a light source for the spectrograph. The spectral lines are photographed. The plate is developed and the spectroscopist may examine it at his leisure. If necessary, a complete analysis may be carried out in twenty to thirty minutes, and it will be possible to state quite conclusively that there is, for example, no vanadium in the particular alloy.

Fig. 8-9 shows a photograph (spectrogram) of several spectra. It will be noted that the pattern of lines is distinct for each element. The experienced spectroscopist recognizes the patterns and can thus quickly identify the common elements.

Quantitative spectrographic analyses may be obtained by means of special devices (densitometers) which record the intensity of exposure of the different lines. The greater the quantity of material present in the light source, the more intense are the spectral lines produced.

About seventy elements (atoms) may be identified by the spectroscopic method. Since molecules of substances such as dyes and vitamins would in many cases be broken up by the high temperatures of the electric arc, emission spectroscopy is not generally useful in detecting substances in the molecular condition. The characteristic lines of a gas, e.g., nitrogen, are often in a region of the spectrum not readily

Metallic elements vaporized in an electric arc emit light which is dispersed by a spectrograph into a series of spectral lines. The experienced spectroscopist learns to recognize in a developed spectrogram the pattern of lines characteristic of each element present in the sample.

Fig. 8-9.

accessible. The color bands are not sufficiently distinctive to identify such gases. Emission spectroscopy finds its greatest use in the analysis of metals.

ABSORPTION METHODS

Even substances that would decompose if we tried to bring them to a glow in an arc can be identified with the aid of spectra. They are first dissolved in a solvent—water, alcohol, benzene, etc. Then the solution is poured into a transparent vessel and set in the path of a beam of light. The amount of absorption of light at various wave lengths can be observed and measured with a form of spectroscope. The instrument used to measure the fraction of light absorbed during transmission through a given thickness of solution is called a spectrophotometer (Fig. 8-10). Because certain structural groups of complex organic substances will absorb light in particular regions of the spectrum, this method is useful in elucidating their characteristic structures. In one form of spectrophotometer a very narrow wave-length portion of the spectrum is examined at a time, and the absorption of light at different wave lengths is determined by means of a photoelectric cell. As new instruments are developed, the scientist is step-

Fig. 8-10.

The spectrophotometer is an instrument which measures the percentage of the incident light which is transmitted by solutions placed in the light beam. Since different chemical substances in solution absorb light at particular wave lengths, this instrument may aid in the qualitative identification of substances. Since the amount of absorption at a particular wave length and given thickness of solution is often a linear function of concentration, the instrument may also be used as a quantitative analytical device.

(Courtesy, Beckman Instruments, Inc.)

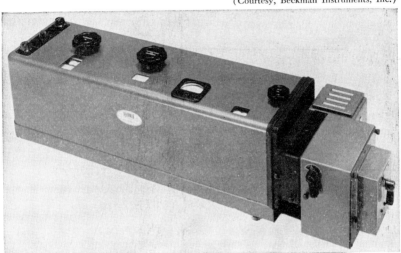

ping up tremendously the speed of both qualitative and quantitative analyses of unknown materials.

EXERCISES AND QUESTIONS FOR CHAPTER 8

1. The wave length of a spectral line is 5880 Å. Calculate its frequency.

2. Calculate the wave length of a spectral line whose frequency is 10^{16} waves/sec. In what region of the electromagnetic spectrum will this line be found?

3. Consult a newspaper and find the frequency of a local radio station. Calculate the length of the wave it sends out. (A kilocycle is the same as 1000 waves/sec.)

4. Describe Isaac Newton's experiment which established that white light was a complex of many colors.

5. Draw a diagram representing a prism spectrometer. Label the most important parts and describe the function of each.

6. Describe what is meant by each of the following characteristics of a wave (a) wave length, (b) frequency.

7. Draw a diagram showing the different regions of the electromagnetic spectrum.

8. What type of light source is used to produce the following: (a) line spectrum, (b) band spectrum, (c) continuous spectrum.

9. How are absorption spectra produced? Illustrate.

10. Describe some of the advantages of the spectroscopic method of analysis. Why is this method usually superior to systematic qualitative analytical procedure?

Review

1. Calculate the velocity of a freely falling body after 8 sec if it starts from rest.

2. The boiling point of liquid benzene is 80°C. Calculate the corresponding Fahrenheit temperature; the corresponding absolute temperature.

3. If 12 liters of oxygen gas at 20°C are heated to 150°C calculate the new volume. (Assume that pressure is constant and that no gas molecules enter or leave the space during the change.)

CHAPTER 9

Atoms with Family Resemblances: The Periodic Table

SHORTLY after the beginning of the nineteenth century several elements were discovered in quick succession, including sodium (Na), potassium (K), barium (Ba), strontium (Sr), calcium (Ca), and magnesium (Mg). The early years of the nineteenth century also marked a period of growing interest in atomic weights. These proved to be very important in a developing concept of how the elements were to be classified into groups sharing similar properties, i.e., into chemical families.

ATOMIC WEIGHTS, EARLY KEY TO THE CLASSIFICATION OF ELEMENTS

In a paper read at the beginning of the nineteenth century to that select body of scientists known as the Royal Society of London, John Dalton included a list of atomic weights. Since the difference between an atom and a molecule was not understood at that time the collection is a very strange one indeed when judged by modern standards. His atomic theory nevertheless represented a forward step in characterizing the properties of atoms and describing the manner in which they combined.

In 1815 the first of a series of anonymous papers, later credited to an Englishman by the name of Prout, stated that the atomic weights of all elements were multiples of that of hydrogen. Prout was in effect suggesting that all atoms were clusters of different numbers of hydrogen atoms. Many leading scientists of the day were much impressed with this idea, and Dumas, the outstanding French chemist, was inspired by it to develop, several years later, his vapor-density method of determining, as he thought, "atomic weights." This method was based essentially on the counting principle of Avogadro (see Chapter 7), but it soon led Dumas into perplexing questions. His results for the atomic weights of phosphorus and sulfur differed so much from the atomic weights obtained by analysis of phosphorus and sulfur compounds that he dared not publish them at first. Moreover, some atomic weights proved to have fractional instead of integral values, and this fact was difficult to reconcile with the idea that all atoms were composed of hydrogen atoms of unit weight.

It was not long before more exact atomic-weight determinations sounded the death knell of Prout's hypothesis, a glowing example of a principle which looked rather promising as long as comparatively few data were available. There have been other instances of scientists embarrassed because they based generalizations on too few data.

The atomic weight values which were known in the late 1820's still left much to be desired in the way of accuracy, and the relation between an atomic weight and a molecular weight was not clarified until many years later (about 1860). Nevertheless, as we shall see in the next section, the discovery of a numerical relationship between the values of the atomic weights of certain elements gave us one of the early hints that elements might be classified into families.

THE ALKALI METALS: DÖBEREINER'S TRIADS

Humphry Davy, the lad who had come down to London to the Royal Institution founded by Count Rumford, discovered the elements sodium and potassium. They were both metals whose freshly cut surfaces had a metallic sheen which was quickly covered with a dull coating of the oxide when left exposed to air. The metals were so light that they floated on water, sizzling vigorously around over its surface, setting free hydrogen gas from the water and making the water feel soapy to the touch. Though the densities of the two metals were somewhat different, and though potassium was much more active in its behavior toward water, there was an unmistakable similarity in the properties and general behavior of these two metallic elements. They belonged to the chemical family known as the alkali metals.

Somewhat later a third element, lithium, was shown to be very similar in its properties to sodium and potassium. In 1829 Döbereiner pointed out the interesting fact that the atomic weights of the three elements were in arithmetic progression (the middle one was the average of the other two):

THE ALKALI METALS

$$\begin{array}{l} \text{Li} = 6.9 \\ \text{Na} = 23.0 \\ \text{K} = 39.1 \end{array} \qquad \frac{6.9 + 39.1}{2} = 23.$$

The group of three elements was called a "triad." Several other triads were found, e.g.:

ALKALINE EARTH METALS	THE HALOGENS
Ca = 40.0	Cl = 35.5
Sr = 88.0	Br = 80.0
Ba = 137.0	I = 127.0

The triads helped to focus attention on the fact that certain groups of elements had similar properties.

THE LAW OF OCTAVES

During the year 1860 an international congress of chemists was convened at Karlsruhe, Germany. A controversy concerning the relation of atoms and molecules had raged for decades. Chaos still reigned.

Scientists from all over the world attended the Karlsruhe congress. They discussed, among other things, the perplexing questions of whether chemical substances were composed of atoms and whether matters were simplified at all if the existence of molecules was also postulated.

Avogadro had anticipated the correct answers to these questions, but he died unrecognized and unknown several years before the congress met. At the congress his fellow countryman Cannizzaro, after pleading to no avail for the recognition of Avogadro's principle, distributed a pamphlet describing the principle.* The meeting adjourned without settling the point at issue, but subsequently the German chemist Lothar Meyer read the pamphlet and recognized its great importance. He discussed Avogadro's principle in his *Modern Theories of Chemistry*, published in 1864, and henceforth there was a medium through which chemists might become acquainted with it. The list of atomic weights made up as suggested by Cannizzaro was to become quite crucial in further developments concerning classification of the elements and in the evolution of the periodic table.

In the same year that Meyer's textbook *Modern Theories of Chemistry* appeared, an English chemist, Newlands, published a paper in which he discussed his so-called "law of octaves." He showed that if the 14 elements starting with lithium and ending with chlorine were arranged in horizontal rows of seven in the order of increasing atomic weights, as shown in Table 9-1, every eighth element showed certain

Table 9-1   "OCTAVES" AMONG THE ELEMENTS

Li	Be	B	C	N	O	F
Na	Mg	Al	Si	P	S	Cl

resemblances to the one above it. Lithium and sodium had similar properties, as did beryllium and magnesium, boron and aluminum, etc. Since in a musical scale the notes repeat after the seventh (do, re, mi, fa, sol, la, ti, do), the parallel with the chemical elements suggested the octave relation. Perhaps most important of all, he noted that this octave relationship was evident only when the order of arrangement of the elements was based on Cannizzaro's new atomic weights.†

Unfortunately, if the principle was extended much beyond the 14 elements mentioned, it broke down. On one occasion when Newlands was presenting his views at a scientific meeting, one of his colleagues asked him if he had ever tried arranging the elements alphabetically. Actually Newlands was anticipating a great principle, but his evidence was fragmentary and he succeeded only in evoking derisive remarks from his fellow scientists.

* Partington, *op. cit.*, p. 256.
† Partington, *op. cit.*, p. 346.

THE PERIODIC TABLE OF MENDELEEV

The Russian chemist Mendeleev (1834-1907) published information concerning his famous periodic table in 1869. Lothar Meyer in Germany independently worked out a similar arrangement at about the same time. More than once in the history of science as soon as a suf-

Dmitri I. Mendeleev, 1834-1907.

ficient body of information was available, several investigators working independently have arrived almost simultaneously at essentially the same conclusions.

More than sixty chemical elements had been discovered at the time of Mendeleev's announcement. Like Newlands, he started his table with two horizontal groups of seven elements each, arranging them in the order of increasing atomic weight. In the third horizontal group (period), which started with the element potassium (K), the pattern of similarity was no longer consistent. The first two members of the period, K and Ca, each resembled the element 8 places behind it, as expected. But selenium (Se), the next element in the sulfur family, was 17 places ahead of sulfur (S)* bromine (Br) was 17 places ahead of chlorine (Cl), rubidium (Rb) 17 ahead of K, strontium (Sr) 17 ahead of Ca, and iodine (I) 17 ahead of Br. Mendeleev was then successful in extending the family relationship idea far beyond the stage where only the law of octaves applied.

Mendeleev's Periodic Law   Mendeleev was almost uncanny in his prediction of the properties of several elements which were at that

* The inert gases had not yet been discovered.

time unknown. He must have had a very detailed knowledge of the properties of the chemical elements, for he even made graphs by plotting the values of some property such as density or atomic volume against atomic weights. As the atomic weights of the elements increased, their atomic volumes (volume occupied by a gram-atomic weight of an element) fluctuated, as shown by the graph in Fig. 9-1.

Graph showing how the atomic volumes of the elements vary with changes in atomic weight. Note the periodic (wavelike) character of the variations.

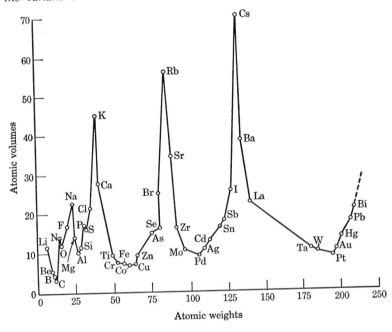

Fig. 9-1.

Furthermore, elements which were in the same family in his periodic table were found in the same relative position in each part of a wave. If one member of a family was at the peak of a wave, the same would be true of the others; if one was on the upward sloping portion, all other members of the family would be somewhat similarly situated. In the graph each of the alkali metals (Li, Na, K, Rb, and Cs) is at a peak; each of the alkaline earths (Ca, Ba, and Sr) is on the descending portion of a curve; each of the halogens (F, Cl, Br, and I) is on the ascending portion of a wave.

In making his arrangement of the elements, Mendeleev shrewdly left blank spaces in the table where the properties of an element did not fit in with those of the family with which it fell. Several spaces were thus left unoccupied. He also predicted many of the properties of undiscovered elements. When these were later discovered, the correspondence between his predictions and the experimentally determined values was remarkably good. The success of these predictions was undoubtedly of considerable importance in calling attention to his work.

THE MODERN PERIODIC TABLE

Early in the twentieth century, when experimental data concerning properties of the elements were already far more abundant, it was discovered that an arrangement of the elements based on atomic numbers (see Chapter 11) eliminated some of the difficulties involved with that based on atomic weights. For example iodine, whose atomic weight was 126.9, preceded tellurium, whose atomic weight was 127.6, and when thus arranged iodine did not appear in the same family with fluorine, chlorine, and bromine, all of which it closely resembled; nor was tellurium in the same family as oxygen, sulfur, and selenium, with which it was closely related. It was evident enough that the order of these elements based on their atomic weights should be reversed, and this hinted that in placing elements with their correct families, there might be a property of the atom more fundamental than the atomic weight. The order of arrangement based on atomic numbers placed tellurium and iodine in their proper families (Table 9-2).

The "zero" vertical column in the modern periodic table consists of the inert gases; this column was not added until some thirty years after the date of Mendeleev's table.

In the modern periodic table, hydrogen and helium are alone in the first horizontal row. Since hydrogen has a valence of $+1$, it is placed in vertical column I, although there is scarcely any further resemblance to the alkali metals which follow it. Helium (He) is the lightest of the so-called "inert gases." The next horizontal group (period) consists of eight elements, beginning with lithium (Li) and ending with neon (Ne). This short period of elements is the same as the first row in Newlands' law of octaves, except for neon, which was not discovered until a later date. The same is true of the next period of eight elements starting with sodium and ending with argon. Each of the

Table 9-2. The Periodic Table of the Elements.

Group	I-A	II-A	III-B	IV-B	V-B	VI-B	VII-B	VIII	VIII	VIII	I-B	II-B	III-A	IV-A	V-A	VI-A	VII-A	O
First Period	1 H 1.008																1 H 1.008	2 He 4.003
Second Period	3 Li 6.940	4 Be 9.013											5 B 10.82	6 C 12.011	7 N 14.008	8 O 16.0000	9 F 19.00	10 Ne 20.183
Third Period	11 Na 22.99	12 Mg 24.32											13 Al 26.98	14 Si 28.06	15 P 30.98	16 S 32.066	17 Cl 35.457	18 Ar 39.944
Fourth Period	19 K 39.100	20 Ca 40.08	21 Sc 44.96	22 Ti 47.90	23 V 50.95	24 Cr 52.01	25 Mn 54.94	26 Fe 55.85	27 Co 58.94	28 Ni 58.71	29 Cu 63.54	30 Zn 65.38	31 Ga 69.72	32 Ge 72.60	33 As 74.91	34 Se 78.96	35 Br 79.916	36 Kr 83.80
Fifth Period	37 Rb 85.48	38 Sr 87.63	39 Y 88.92	40 Zr 91.22	41 Nb 92.91	42 Mo 95.95	43 Tc [99]	44 Ru 101.1	45 Rh 102.91	46 Pd 106.7	47 Ag 107.880	48 Cd 112.41	49 In 114.82	50 Sn 118.70	51 Sb 121.76	52 Te 127.61	53 I 126.91	54 Xe 131.3
Sixth Period	55 Cs 132.91	56 Ba 137.36	57–71 Lanthanum Series	72 Hf 178.5	73 Ta 180.95	74 W 183.92	75 Re 186.22	76 Os 190.2	77 Ir 192.2	78 Pt 195.08	79 Au 197.0	80 Hg 200.61	81 Tl 204.39	82 Pb 207.21	83 Bi 209.00	84 Po [210]	85 At [210]	86 Rn 222
Seventh Period	87 Fr [223]	88 Ra 226.05	89– Actinium Series															

Lanthanum Series	57 La 138.92	58 Ce 140.13	59 Pr 140.92	60 Nd 144.27	61 Pm [145]	62 Sm 150.35	63 Eu 152.0	64 Gd 157.26	65 Tb 158.93	66 Dy 162.51	67 Ho 164.94	68 Er 167.27	69 Tm 168.9	70 Yb 173.04	71 Lu 174.99
Actinium Series	89 Ac [227]	90 Th 232.05	91 Pa 231	92 U 238.07	93 Np [237]	94 Pu [242]	95 Am [243]	96 Cm [245]	97 Bk [249]	98 Cf [249]	99 Es [254]	100 Fm [254]	101 Md [256]		

the mass of the most stable known isotope.

elements in it resembles the element immediately above in the preceding period. The horizontal group starting with potassium (K) consists of a group of seven elements, followed by three—iron, cobalt, and nickel—which are called transition elements. The family relation in the transition elements is among the three members of the group rather than 8 or 18 elements removed. These three come in between the two parts of this *long period* of 18 elements which starts with potassium and ends with the inert gas krypton (Kr).

Starting with rubidium (Rb), there is another period of 18 elements, which ends with the inert gas xenon (Xe). A fifth and longer period of 32 elements starts with cesium (Cs) and ends with radon (Rn).

In summary, then, 2 elements stand alone at the beginning of the periodic table, followed by two groups of 8 elements each, two of 18 each, and one of 32 (this does not account for all of the known elements). Note the *numbers* of elements in a period (8, 18, and 32); these will be significant later when electronic structures are discussed (Chapter 13).

WHAT ARE ATOMS COMPOSED OF?

While in the nineteenth century evidence accumulated to establish the atom as being both distinct from the molecule and an indestructible unit which could not be further subdivided, another series of observations was leading inexorably to the conclusion that atoms were actually composed of still more minute particles. The very fact that atoms of certain different elements closely resembled each other strongly hinted that these had some basic underlying structural similarity. Evidence concerning the subatomic structure of matter hardly started to form a coherent picture before the early years of the twentieth century. The rest of this chapter offers only a brief outline of the structure of the atom as it is understood today; the supporting evidence will be considered in subsequent chapters.

The atom of any element is pictured as resembling the solar system. Just as the sun is the central body of the solar system, so the nucleus is the core of the atom. Just as the planets revolve about the sun, planetary electrons are thought of as revolving about the nucleus. The nucleus of an atom is composed of at least two types of particles —neutrons and protons. Collectively these nuclear particles are known as nucleons. Protons have positive electrical charges; neutrons are electrically neutral. Each has about the same mass as a hydrogen atom; in fact the nucleus of an ordinary hydrogen atom is a single proton without neutrons.

The planetary electrons, each a unit of negative electrical charge, are far lighter particles than either protons or neutrons. An electron has about 1/1840 the mass of the proton (or of the neutron): in other words, about 1840 electrons would have the mass of a single proton. An atom of the heaviest of the naturally occurring elements, uranium (U^{238}), is composed of 92 electrons, 92 protons, and 146 neutrons. It should be apparent that if 1840 electrons are needed to equal the mass of a *single* proton, the total mass of the 92 electrons will constitute only a very tiny fraction of the mass of the atom.

The electrons, with their negative charges, revolve about the nucleus, which is always positively charged. Opposite electrical charges attract one another. Accordingly the moving electron will orbit about the nucleus in a path which is a circle (or an ellipse). The electrons farthest from the nucleus (called the valence electrons) may on occasion be more powerfully attracted by the nucleus of another atom. An electron-hungry atom may take away electrons from another atom which does not have a firm hold upon them. Electrons play an important role in the forces binding atoms together.

Protons and neutrons in the nucleus are bound together with forces far more potent than the forces that attract electrons to the nucleus. Much more energy is needed to crack apart an atomic nucleus than to separate electrons from atoms. Electrons are usually separated from atoms in every chemical reaction, and even by exciting the atoms in an electric arc or by high-voltage sparks. But cracking a nucleus involves "atom smashing." It is understandable that the electrons, because of their lighter mass and less firm binding, are much more mobile units in the structure of the atom than protons or neutrons.

Different atoms, then, contain different numbers of these fundamental particles—electrons, protons, and neutrons. The nucleus of the hydrogen atom is a single proton; circulating about this nucleus is a single electron. The oxygen atom has a nucleus of 8 protons and 8 neutrons, and 8 electrons revolve about its nucleus.

The atomic number of an element is the number of protons in the nucleus of a single atom. The atomic number of hydrogen is 1, that of oxygen is 8. The sum of the numbers of protons and neutrons in a single atom is the atomic weight. The atomic weight of hydrogen is 1, that of oxygen is 16. Further explanation is necessary to account for the structure of the nuclei of those atoms whose atomic weights are not integral.

OTHER NUCLEAR PARTICLES

Other subatomic particles have been discovered which are probably not present in atoms as such but are often produced as a result of nuclear reactions. One of these, the positron, was predicted about 1930 by the English theoretical physicist Dirac. He pointed out that there should be a particle whose mass was the same as that of the electron, but whose charge was opposite (i.e., positive). The existence of this particle was demonstrated in 1932, during the course of an investigation of cosmic rays by Anderson, a Nobel prize winning American physicist. (Dirac was likewise so honored.) Positrons had only a very transitory existence, which made them difficult to observe.

In 1935, Yukawa, a Japanese physicist, predicted the existence of particles intermediate in mass between the electron and the proton. Once again Anderson was the discoverer of these particles, called mesons, whose masses were approximately 200 times that of the electron. Later experiments proved the existence of pi (π) mesons of mass 276 times that of the electron, and mu (μ) mesons of mass 210 times that of the electron. Pi mesons are unstable and change readily into mu mesons. Positive, negative, and neutral mesons are known. Pi mesons appear to be the particles involved in holding together the atomic nucleus, and are often referred to as "cosmic glue." Mesons are produced as the result of cosmic ray interactions, and they are also produced in some of the higher-energy particle accelerators such as the 184-inch Berkeley cyclotron and the Brookhaven cosmotron. Fig. 9-2 shows the π^+ and π^- mesons resulting when a neutron collides with a hydrogen nucleus.

The neutrino was postulated by Pauli in order to interpret some otherwise unexplainable aspects of certain radioactive changes to be discussed in Chapter 12. This neutral particle of negligible mass, which has eluded the scientist so long, has now been observed experimentally.

The antiproton, another subatomic particle whose existence has

Fig. 9-2.

Cloud-chamber photograph of a neutron-proton collision produced by the Brookhaven Cosmotron. The long thin streaks originating at top center, and spreading out as they continue down, are tracks due mainly to protons and mesons. The three intersecting tracks, at center right, result when a neutron strikes a hydrogen nucleus (proton). The proton shoots downward toward the center and the two mesons downward and to the left respectively. (Courtesy of Brookhaven National Laboratory)

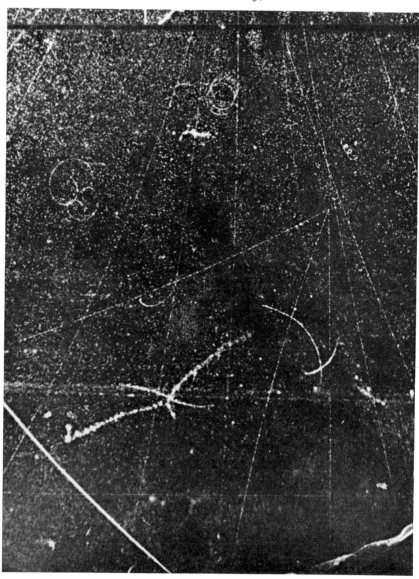

been predicted for some time, has the same mass as the proton but differs in having a negative charge. It too has been observed experimentally.

The emphasis in subsequent sections of this volume will be principally upon protons, neutrons, electrons, and their relation to the properties of matter. The other particles—positrons, mesons and neutrinos—have been described because their names occur frequently in the literature and their relation to protons, neutrons, and electrons should be understood.

EXERCISES AND QUESTIONS FOR CHAPTER 9

1. Calculate the number of molecules of oxygen in 1 cc of the gas at S.T.P. (standard temperature and pressure, 760 mm Hg and 0°C) if 22.4 liters of oxygen at S.T.P. contain 6.02×10^{23} molecules.

2. Calculate the fraction of the mass of a uranium (U^{238}) atom which is due to its electrons, assuming that 1840 electron masses are equal to a single proton. Also assume that protons and neutrons have equal masses.

3. In Table 9-2, pick out two other groups of elements whose atomic weights form triads as described by Döbereiner.

4. What is meant by a family of elements? Illustrate.

5. Early versions of the periodic table based the arrangement of the elements on the order of their atomic weights. The order of the elements in the modern periodic table is based on their atomic numbers. Why is the latter arrangement considered a better one?

6. State Mendeleev's periodic law. How does the statement of the modern periodic law differ from it?

7. Name the three fundamental particles of which all atoms (except hydrogen) are composed.

REVIEW

1. A gas occupies a volume of 10 liters at 2.5 atm pressure. Calculate the new volume if the pressure is reduced to 0.75 atm. Assume constant temperature, and that no molecules of the gas leave or enter during the change.

2. $Pb(NO_3)_2 + K_2CrO_4 \rightarrow PbCrO_4 \downarrow + KNO_3$. Calculate the weight of lead chromate ($PbCrO_4$) precipitated if 50 gm of potassium chromate (in solution) is added to a sufficient amount of lead nitrate solution.

3. Calculate the potential energy of the 500-lb weight of a pile driver if it is raised 25 ft above the ground.

CHAPTER 10

Chemistry and Electric Currents

STATIC ELECTRICITY

An EBONITE (hard-rubber) rod which has been rubbed with a piece of fur will attract and pick up bits of paper or straw. It is said to be charged electrically. The charge is called *static* or *electrostatic* in contrast to a flowing charge, or current. Since it will exert forces on the light objects mentioned, an electric field exists in the region about it. This phenomenon was recognized by Thales of Miletus (600 B.C.), a famous Greek scientist. Benjamin Franklin suggested that the kind of static charge resulting from rubbing a hard-rubber

Fig. 10-1.

Ben Franklin is pictured performing his famous kite experiment. The object on the ground between the experimenters is a Leyden jar—a form of capacitor, or device for storing charges of static electricity. (Courtesy, Museum of Science and Industry, Chicago.)

rod (Fig. 10-2) with fur be called "negative," and that from rubbing
a glass rod with silk, "positive." These conventions are still in use
today.

Fig. 10-2.

*An ebonite (hard-rubber) rod may be electrified by rubbing with wool or
fur.*

Ebonite
  rod   Fur

Both objects are neutral   Rubbed   Fur is positively   Rod is
                  together   charged   negatively charged

                                                       Bits of paper
                                                    are attracted

Two glass rods which are positively charged will repel each other
or push apart. A hard-rubber rod (negative charge) and a glass rod
(positive charge) will attract each other and be drawn together. We
may generalize these observations by stating that objects with like
electric charges (either positive or negative) repel, those with unlike
charges attract.

Fig. 10-1 shows Franklin performing his famous kite experiment.
When the electric charge from the thundercloud was conducted to
two silk threads attached to the kite string, they became similarly
charged. Since like charges repel, the stiffening and separation of the
silken threads served to indicate the presence of a static electric charge
on them.

Before being rubbed, the ebonite rod shows no evidence of being
electrically charged. It contains substantially equal numbers of positive and negative charges and hence is electrically neutral. When the
rod is rubbed with fur, electrons (negative charges) are transferred
from the fur to the ebonite, leaving the latter with many more negative
charges than positive. When the negative charges outnumber the positive, the rod is said to be negatively charged. The fur, which was also
neutral originally, has lost many electrons and hence bears a net positive charge.

In the early 1780's a considerable body of knowledge concerning electrostatic phenomena was available. In Bologna, Italy, a Dr. Galvani (1737-1798) was working with an electrostatic "influence machine" (a device which produced electric sparks) in his laboratory. Upon one occasion a metal scalpel came close to the machine at just about the time the blade touched one of the nerves in a frog's leg which was hung up close by. The frog's leg twitched. The follow-up of this simple observation culminated in the discovery of the electric battery.

ANIMAL ELECTRICITY

The incident excited Galvani's curiosity. He wondered if the same effect could be produced by lightning, so he hung the frog's leg by brass hooks from an outdoor iron railing. Although twitching did seem occasionally to accompany flashes of lightning, the same result could be realized by touching the frog's leg to the iron rail, and it soon became clear that neither the lightning nor the influence machine was a necessary condition for the twitching. After many such experiments Galvani erroneously concluded that the twitching was due to "animal electricity"; his conclusion was wrong, but his work served to dramatize a new source of energy, and the term "galvanic cell," which has persisted through the years, reminds us of the importance of his contribution to science. Often the statement of an erroneous principle has stimulated others to think about the implications of a problem and has led to great advances: Galvani's fellow countryman Alessandro Volta (1745-1827) challenged the idea of animal electricity. According to Volta the important aspect of repeating this effect was that two dissimilar metals, such as copper and iron, should come in contact. The contraction of the frog's leg was due to the conduction of the impulse; it was not the source of the impulse.

THE VOLTAIC PILE

Volta, the originator of the battery, found that the electrical effect of a single pair of metals in contact was multiplied if several pairs of metal strips such as silver and zinc, separated by strips of leather or pasteboard soaked in a solution of table salt, were arranged in a "pile"

Fig. 10-3.

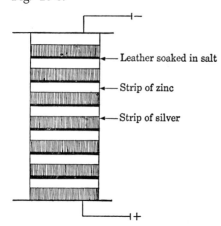

Leather soaked in salt

Strip of zinc

Strip of silver

The voltaic pile, a forerunner of the modern electric cell or battery. The invention by Alessandro Volta opened the Age of Electricity in the year 1800. It was promptly applied to chemical and biological research.

(Fig. 10-3). Anyone who completed the electrical circuit by touching the bottom silver strip and the top zinc strip could receive a substantial electric shock.

Shortly after Volta's discovery, the pile was used to separate water into its constituent elements, hydrogen and oxygen. Wires were attached to the pile and the electric current was led into the water by

Shortly after its invention, the voltaic pile was used by Nicholson and Carlisle for decomposing water into its constituent elements, hydrogen and oxygen. Decomposition of a substance by means of an electric current is known as electrolysis.

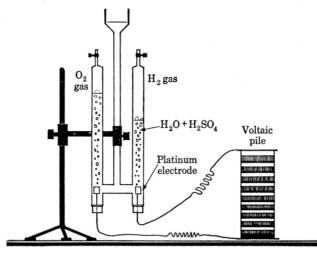

O_2 gas

H_2 gas

$H_2O + H_2SO_4$

Voltaic pile

Platinum electrode

Fig. 10-4.

metal pieces known as electrodes (Fig. 10-4). A small amount of material such as sulfuric acid had to be added to the water in order to make it an electrical conductor. This process of bringing about a chemical change by means of an electric current was known as *electrolysis*. Within a few years of its discovery several new chemical elements had been discovered by means of it—among others, barium (Ba), strontium (Sr), calcium (Ca), and magnesium (Mg). Humphry Davy made use of the electrolysis of fused (melted) solids in his discovery of the two elements, sodium (Na) and potassium (K).

A SIMPLE ELECTRICAL CIRCUIT

An electric current is a flow of electrons, the negatively charged constituents of atoms discussed in Chapter 9. Electrons, it will be recalled, have very tiny masses compared with the other constituents of atoms. They are more mobile than protons and neutrons. It will come as no surprise that if any of the fundamental structural units of metallic atoms can be set in motion, electrons can be.

If wires are attached connecting a dry cell to a light bulb and completing a path for the electrons, the glowing of the bulb serves as a detector of the electron flow. The electrons are present in the wires; the cell merely provides the motive force to set them in motion.

A voltaic pile or its modern counterparts, the dry cell and storage battery, are often described as electron pumps, being likened to water pumps. The latter must always have an energy source to operate. The energy source for the windmill-driven pump is the wind; for the engine-driven pump it is gasoline, kerosene, or possibly steam. In the cell the energy source is the combination of chemical substances of which it is composed. A chemical reaction at one of the electrodes of the battery produces an abundant supply of electrons, and they are pushed out into the external circuit, the wire and light bulb (Fig. 10-5). The reaction at the other electrode produces a deficiency of electrons. Electrons flow from the electrode where they are abundant, through the external circuit, and into the cell again at the electrode where they are removed.

The greater the horsepower of a water pump, the more gallons per second will be pumped through a given pipe. The greater the *voltage* of a cell, the more electrons per second will pass through a wire of given resistance. If the interior of a water pipe is rough, friction will be large and correspondingly there will be a large loss of pressure per linear foot of flow. In like manner different varieties of electric wire offer different amounts of opposition, called resistance, to the flow of electrons. The "voltage drop" accompanying current flow along a conductor is proportional to the resistance of the wire. Nichrome wire, for example, has about sixty times as much resistance as copper wire of the same length and diameter, and hence there

Fig. 10-5.

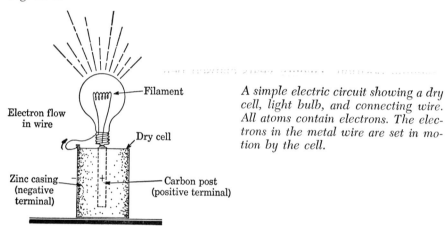

Filament

Electron flow
in wire

Dry cell

Zinc casing
(negative
terminal)

Carbon post
(positive terminal)

A simple electric circuit showing a dry cell, light bulb, and connecting wire. All atoms contain electrons. The electrons in the metal wire are set in motion by the cell.

will be about sixty times as much voltage drop in nichrome wire as in copper wire carrying an equal current.

An electrical circuit, then, requires a source of energy to set up a flow of electrons and a complete (closed) path to conduct them. The battery—the pumping device—has two electrodes, one at which a chemical reaction is pushing electrons into the external circuit (called the negative terminal), the other a reaction which removes electrons from the external circuit (the positive terminal).* The electric current is the electron flow which results from the difference in electrical pressure maintained between the electrodes.

* There are two ways of describing the direction of flow of electric currents. Electric currents were known before the discovery of electrons, and for many years it was assumed that currents (positive charges) left a battery at the positive terminal, went through the external circuit, and back into the cell at the negative terminal. Later, when the nature of the electron and its behavior were better understood, it was found that the *flow of electrons* was in just the opposite direction. By that time many texts had been written, and that is why we still find some authors describing the current as leaving the cell at the positive terminal, while others describe the electron flow as issuing from the negative terminal.

Georg Simon Ohm   The relationships between voltage, resistance, and current were worked out by Georg Simon Ohm (1784-1854) and stated in Ohm's law. Ohm was the son of a Bavarian locksmith. In his earlier years he was a teacher in elementary schools and later in the secondary schools. It was his ambition to become a university professor, and one way in which he was likely to attain this goal was to carry out an important research investigation.* For years he spent much of his spare time studying the factors which affected the ability of metal wires to conduct an electric current.

When the results of his research were published, a storm of criticism broke loose. Not only did he fail to receive the recognition needed for the prized university appointment; he even lost his secondary-school teaching position. Twenty years elapsed before the importance of his earlier work began to be recognized by his fellow scientists, and late in life he was actually appointed to a professorship in physics at the University of Munich. The principle which he enunciated is one of the most important in the study of electric currents.

OHM'S LAW

The great contribution Ohm made to the study of electricity, like many of the other principles of science, may be most concisely expressed by a mathematical equation

$$E = IR,$$

where E stands for electromotive force, I for electric current, and R for resistance. E is expressed in volts, I in amperes, and R in ohms: E (volts) $= I$ (amperes) $\cdot R$ (ohms). As electrons pass along a conductor, a loss of electrical pressure, called the potential drop, takes place; the total of all the potential (voltage) drops in the circuit is equal to the electromotive force. Since there is always a small voltage drop due to the flow of current through the internal resistance of the cell itself, the voltage between the terminals will always be a bit less than the electromotive force of the battery. Electromotive force, E, is measured with great accuracy by an instrument called the potentiometer. The potential drop across any *part* of a circuit is most conveniently measured by shunting a *voltmeter* across it. The volt-

---

* Lloyd W. Taylor, *Physics the Pioneer Science,* Houghton Mifflin, 1941, p. 664.

meter is in effect a galvanometer having a high resistance in series
with the movable coil.

In order to determine the voltage drop due to an electric light bulb,
the terminals of the voltmeter would be connected to those of the
socket as shown in Fig. 10-6. The instrument so connected provides

Fig. 10-6.

*The voltage drop across a resistance may be measured by connecting a volt-
meter in parallel with it. Since light bulb A has a lower resistance than light
bulb B, the current after passing through A is still capable of more work than
after passing through B. It retains a higher potential (available voltage).*

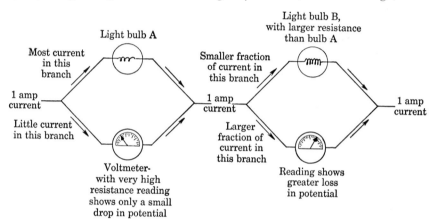

an alternative path for the current, which may go either through the
light bulb or through the voltmeter: the larger the resistance of the
bulb, the greater the fraction of the current diverted through the voltmeter, and hence the larger the voltage drop registered by the instrument.

I, the electric current, is a measure of the number of electrons
passing a given point in the circuit during 1 second. The greater the
number of electrons that pass in a given time, the larger the current.
The ammeter is the instrument used to measure electric currents. It
is in effect a galvanometer having in parallel with its coil a low-resistance strip of metal called a shunt. The ammeter impedes the flow
of current to a negligible extent. It is connected directly in the line in
which the current flow is to be measured (i.e., in series rather than
in parallel). Fig. 10-7 shows how an ammeter is connected in the
circuit to measure the current flowing through the light bulb.

An ammeter is connected in an electric circuit in series with the resistance through which the current flow is to be measured.

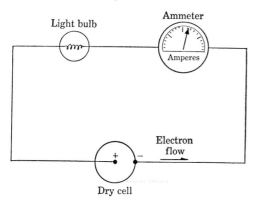

Fig. 10-7.

R, the resistance which a conducting wire offers to electron flow, depends on the material of the wire, its length, and its diameter. Iron wire has greater resistance than silver or copper wire of the same length and diameter. Wires of large diameter have lesser resistances per linear foot than do smaller wires.

ILLUSTRATIVE PROBLEM 1

Calculate the current flowing if a 1.5-volt dry cell is connected in the circuit of Fig 10-8A. The total resistance is 10 ohms.

Solution

$$E = IR$$
$$1.5 \text{ (volts)} = I \text{ (amperes)} \cdot 10 \text{ (ohms)}$$
$$1.5 = 10I$$
$$I = 0.15 \text{ ampere}$$

0.15 ampere will flow through the circuit.

ILLUSTRATIVE PROBLEM 2

Calculate the current flowing (Fig. 10-8B) if the 100-ohm resistance is attached to a 1.5-volt dry cell.

Solution

$$E = IR$$
$$1.5 = 100I$$
$$I = 0.015 \text{ ampere}$$

The current is one-tenth as large as in the previous problem. Fewer electrons are pushed through the circuit by the same voltage if the resistance is greater.

Fig. 10-8.

More current is driven through a 10-ohm resistance than a 100-ohm resistance by a given voltage. A 6-volt battery combination will push more current through a 100-ohm resistance than will a 1.5-volt cell.

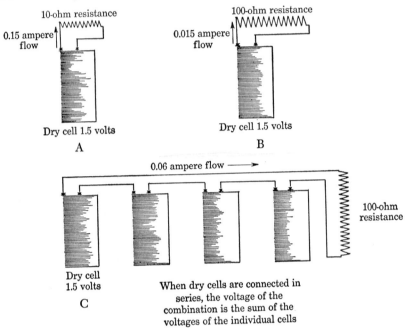

Dry cell 1.5 volts
A

Dry cell 1.5 volts
B

C
Dry cell 1.5 volts

When dry cells are connected in series, the voltage of the combination is the sum of the voltages of the individual cells

ILLUSTRATIVE PROBLEM 3

Calculate the current flowing if four dry cells are connected in series (voltages are additive: 4×1.5 volts $= 6.0$ volts) in a circuit whose resistance is 100 ohms (Fig 10-8C).

Solution

$$E = IR$$
$$6.0 = 100I$$
$$I = 0.06 \text{ ampere}$$

A fourfold increase in the voltage has resulted in a fourfold increase in the current passing through the same resistance. Increased potential difference has resulted in setting more electrons in motion through the same resistance as was used in the second illustration.

THE STORAGE BATTERY

The storage battery (Fig. 10-9), a familiar part of the equipment of the modern motorcar, is one of several types of cells which are improvements on the voltaic pile. Instead of alternate pairs of different metals, the storage battery has two sets of electrodes, one composed of lead (Pb), the other lead impregnated with lead dioxide (PbO_2). The electrolyte in the voltaic pile was a salt solution soaked up in

A modern storage battery. Alternate lead and lead dioxide grids may be observed in the cut-away section. (Courtesy, Willard Storage Battery Co.)

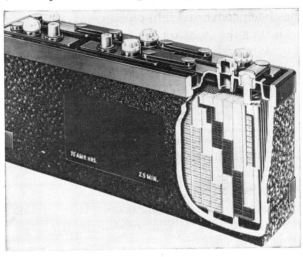

Fig. 10-9.

strips of leather or cardboard; the electrolyte used in the modern storage battery is dilute sulfuric acid.

The electrical energy produced by a storage battery is derived from chemical action: the reaction responsible for pushing electrons is

$$Pb + PbO_2 + 2H_2SO_4 \rightarrow 2PbSO_4 \downarrow + 2H_2O$$

If a coil of wire or other suitable resistance is connected across the terminals of the battery, a path for electrons is completed. Electrons leave the cell at the negative terminal (lead plates), pass through the external circuit, and return to the cell at the lead dioxide plates. The usefulness of the battery depends upon the fact that an electric motor, a horn, or headlight may be operated if arranged appropriately in this external circuit. Thus the energy of the chemical materials of the battery may be converted into mechanical energy (by the electric motor), into sound (by the horn), or into light (by the headlight).

Once again it should be emphasized that the law of conservation of energy holds for each of these energy conversions. Energy cannot be conjured up from nothing; one form must be used up if a new form is to be produced. The potential energy of a stone resting on the top of a mountain is greater than its potential energy after it has rolled half-way down the mountainside: some of its potential energy has been converted into kinetic energy. Similarly, the chemical energy level of sulfuric acid, lead, and lead dioxide in the reaction above is higher than that of lead sulfate and water: some of the energy of the former has been converted into electric energy.

Just as the stone on the mountain top tends to roll down the mountainside, and heat to flow from a region of higher to one of lower temperature, so electrons tend to flow from a region where they are abundant to one where they are scarce. The chemical reaction of the battery creates an abundant supply of electrons at the negative terminal and a scarcity of electrons at the positive terminal. The resulting difference in electrical levels causes a movement of electrons from the negative terminal of the cell, through the external circuit, to the positive terminal.

The lead sulfate, a white solid substance, collects on each electrode as the chemical reaction takes place, gradually covering its surface and thus reducing the amount of lead metal left exposed to the action of sulfuric acid. The other product of this chemical reaction, water, tends to dilute the sulfuric acid as the cell discharges and thus to decrease the specific gravity of the acid. Recharging a battery reverses the chemical reaction, dissolving the lead sulfate from the plates and increasing the specific gravity of the electrolyte. The condition of battery charge is usually determined by measuring the electrolyte's specific gravity with a hydrometer.

HEATING EFFECTS OF AN ELECTRIC CURRENT

If a piece of copper wire is connected across the terminals of a new dry cell, the wire grows hot. This is a brutal way to treat a battery, but it demonstrates the effect of a flow of electrons along the wire. No. 18 bell wire has a resistance of about 6.5 ohms for every 1000 feet. The resistance of a small piece of this wire, say 1 foot long, will be negligibly small; and hence the current flowing, even with a small voltage, will be very large. Attaching a low-resistance wire across the terminals of a cell is called "short-circuiting" the cell (Fig. 10-10) and will ruin the cell in a short time.

The magnitude of the heating effect produced by an electric current passing through a wire is given by the equation

$$H = 0.24I^2Rt,$$

where H represents the quantity of heat, in calories, when the current flowing is I amperes, the resistance of the wire R ohms, and the time of

Fig. 10-10.

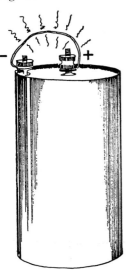

Shortcircuiting a cell. This is a shameful way to treat it. The provision made by the manufacturer for clearing away the chemical products cannot keep up with the reactions accompanying so large an electron flow, and the battery is permanently injured.

flow t seconds. As this equation shows, doubling the amperage will have a greater effect on the heat produced than doubling the resistance or the time.

If a nichrome wire is connected to a 110-volt source of electric current by copper lead-in wires, as in an electric toaster, the nichrome will be heated red hot while the copper will not (Fig. 10-11). Since there is only one path for the current, the number of amperes flowing in the copper wire must be the same as in the nichrome wire. Any difference in heating effects must be due to difference in resistance. Nichrome wire has a resistance approximately sixty times that of copper wire of the same size and length, so that the heating effect in the nichrome will be about sixty times as great.

If two uninsulated wires in a 110-volt house circuit come in contact, there is a sputtering and shower of sparks; a short circuit is said to have occurred. A short circuit is a low-resistance path for the current; it allows an enormous current to flow and results in a considerable heating of the wires. To guard against these dangerous effects a fuse

The current which makes the coil of wire in a toaster turn red hot does not noticeably heat the copper wire. Heating effects of similar currents are directly proportional to resistances.

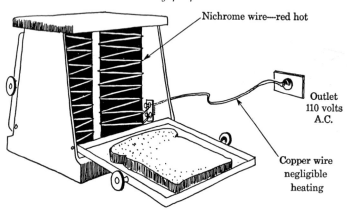

Fig. 10-11.

is placed in the house circuit: the fuse contains a piece of easily melted wire. If a large amperage flows through it the wire in the fuse heats and melts and the circuit is broken. Breaking the house circuit obviates the danger of overheated wires, and hence of fire within the partitions of the house.

MAGNETISM

In very ancient times loadstone, an oxide of iron, was known to attract other iron objects. Thales, the famous Greek wise man, was acquainted with its attractive force in the sixth century B.C. He suggested that it must have a soul because of its attractive power for iron objects.

There were many stories in ancient times concerning the power of the magnet. One story caused sailors to insist that the ships on which they sailed should be built without iron nails; too close an approach to one of the supposed "magnetic islands," it was rumored, had pulled more than one ship apart at sea.

Sir William Gilbert demonstrates the effects of static electricity at the court of Queen Elizabeth. Painting by A. A. Hunt. (Courtesy, American Institute of Electrical Engineers)

Very early in history, experimenters were struck by the curious behavior of a short slender piece of the loadstone suspended from a string and free to rotate in a horizontal plane. The loadstone pointer always oriented itself so that one end pointed to the north. It was the forerunner of our modern compass, which makes use of a magnetized needle, appropriately pivoted and encased (Fig. 10-12).

The magnetic compass is simply a bar magnet suspended in such a way as to turn freely. The step from (a) to (c) was taken by the Chinese a thousand years ago or more.

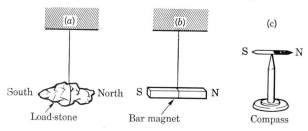

Fig. 10-12.

The first comprehensive study of magnetism was made by an Englishman, William Gilbert (1540-1603), who was court physician to Queen Elizabeth. In 1600 he published his famous work *De Magnete*.

Fig. 10-13.

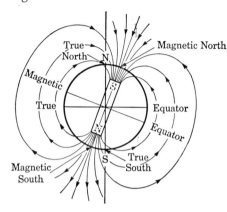

Sir William Gilbert believed the earth's magnetic field to be like that of a bar magnet imbedded in a sphere.

In this he noted that the earth behaved as if it were a huge magnet (Fig. 10-13). He also observed that opposite magnetic poles attracted each other. Fig. 10-14, which is taken from his famous book, shows how a bar of iron or steel may be magnetized by pounding.

Magnetic Fields   A field is simply a region in which forces act on a body. We speak of bodies on the earth as being in a gravitational field because forces of gravity are acting on them all. A magnetized iron or steel bar attracts or repels other nearby objects of like materials and hence a field of magnetic force is said to exist in the region around a magnet. To demonstrate the presence of a magnetic field, let us lay a bar magnet flat on a table, cover it with a sheet of paper, and scatter iron filings over the paper. The filings will arrange themselves in the pattern shown in Fig. 10-15. The string-like chains of iron filings are often referred to as "lines of force." A tiny compass needle which is carefully placed on these lines of force will align itself parallel to them. The direction of a compass needle in a magnetic field will, then, indicate the direction of the lines of force in that region.

Magnetic Poles   The lines of force surrounding a bar magnet appear to crowd in together at the ends of the magnet. These regions where the magnetic property seems to be concentrated are called magnetic poles. If the bar magnet is suspended from a string so as to be balanced in a horizontal plane, one pole will point in the direction of magnetic north and will be a north-seeking or a north pole. The opposite end will be a south pole.

Producing a magnet by pounding, from De Magnete, *1600, by William Gilbert. Gilbert announced that iron bars showed polarity even though they had never been excited by a loadstone or another iron magnet.*

DE MAGNETE, LIB. III.

CAP. XII.

Quomodo verticitas exiſtit in ferro quouis excoǎo
magnete non excito.

Aǎenùs naturales & ingenitas cauſas, & acquiſitas
per lapidem potentias declarauimus: Nunc verò
& in excoǎo ferro lapide non excito, magnetica-
rum virtutum cauſæ rimandæ ſunt. Admirabiles
nobis magnes & ferrum promunt & oſtendunt ſub-
tilitates. Demonſtratum eſt anteà ſæpiùs, ferrum lapide non excitum in ſeptentiones ferri & meridiem ; ſed & habe-
re verticitatem, id eſt proprias & ſingulares polares diſtinǎiones,
quemadmodùm magnes, aut ferrum magnete attritum. Iſtud qui-
dem nobis mirum & incredibile primùm videbatur: Ferri metallum
ex vena in fornace excoquitur, effluit ex fornace, & in magnâ maſ-
ſam indureſcit, maſſa illa diuiditur in magnis officinis, & in bacilla
ferrea extenditur, ex quibus fabri rurſus plurima componunt inſtru-
menta. & ferramenta neceſſaria. Ita variè elaboratur & in plurimas
ſimilitudines eadem maſſa tranſſormatur. Quid eſt igitur illud quod

conſeruat

Fig. 10-14.

Fig. 10-15.

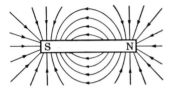

Lines of force about a bar magnet, from a photograph.

If the north poles of two different magnets are brought near together, they will push apart or repel. Two south poles will likewise repel. On the other hand two unlike poles will attract. These so-called laws of magnetism may be summed up by saying that like magnetic poles repel and unlike poles attract. The patterns of the lines of force between two like poles and two unlike poles is shown in Fig. 10-16.

Lines of force between magnetic poles: (A) unlike poles, (B) like poles.

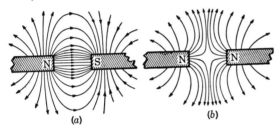

(a)   (b)   Fig. 10-16.

Magnetic Effects of an Electric Current   The discovery of magnetic effects due to electric currents was not made until more than 200 years after *De Magnete* was published, for the voltaic cell and current electricity were not available until near the close of the eighteenth century. In 1819, Hans Christian Oersted of Denmark discovered that there was a magnetic field about a wire in which an electric current was flowing.

If a straight piece of copper wire is placed directly over a compass so that the direction of the wire is parallel to that of the needle, and the ends of the wire are then attached to a battery, the compass needle will rotate so as to be at right angles to the wire, when the electric current is flowing (Fig. 10-17). Apparently the lines of force of the magnetic field about the wire lie in a plane perpendicular to it, since the compass needle takes up a position parallel to lines of force.

Oersted's experiment illustrating that a wire which is conducting an electric current is surrounded by a magnetic field. A compass needle which is placed beneath a horizontal wire and parallel to it turns at right angles when an electric current passes through the wire. Since a magnet (e.g., a compass needle) aligns itself with magnetic lines of force, these must be in a plane perpendicular to the wire.

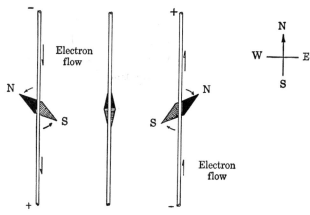

Fig. 10-17.

Furthermore, if a straight wire passes vertically through a horizontal piece of cardboard as shown in Fig. 10-18, iron filings sprinkled on the cardboard will arrange themselves in concentric circles when an electric current flows through the wire. The magnetic field about

Iron filings line up in concentric circles around a wire carrying an electric current.

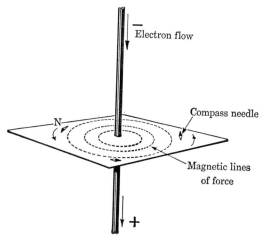

Fig. 10-18.

A compass needle aligns itself tangent to the concentric magnetic lines of force surrounding a wire carrying an electric current.

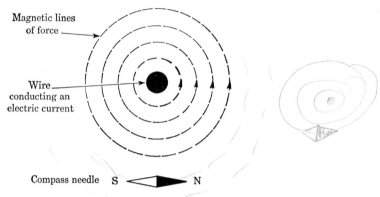

Magnetic lines of force

Wire conducting an electric current

Compass needle S ◄━━━ N

Fig. 10-19.

the wire consists of a series of concentric lines of force in a plane perpendicular to the wire (Fig. 10-19). If a compass is placed on the cardboard next to the wire, the needle will orient itself tangent to the circular lines of force.

A compass needle, then, may be used to detect an electric current in a copper wire; if a current is flowing in the wire, the compass needle

Fig. 10-20.

A coil of wire through which an electric current is passing, behaves like a magnet. Note the north pole at one end and the south pole at the other. Such a coil is called a solenoid.

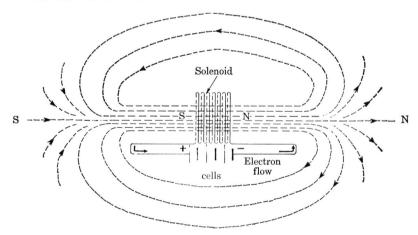

Solenoid

S ━━► ◄━ S | N ━━ ━━ ━━ N

+   −

cells   Electron flow

will turn from a position parallel to the wire through a 90-degree angle. We have also seen how an electric current may be detected by means of the heating effect in the wire.

The instrument used for detecting and measuring minute electric currents is called a galvanometer. To construct a galvanometer, wind a coil of wire on a cylindrical insulating form, as shown in Fig. 10-20. The coil behaves like a magnet, with a north pole at one end and a south pole at the other, when an electric current is flowing through it. In one form of galvanometer this coil is very small and is suspended between the poles of a permanent magnet in such a manner that it may rotate clockwise or counterclockwise (Fig. 10-21). If the direc-

Fig. 10-21.

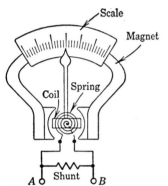

A galvanometer. The movable coil becomes a magnet when a current flows. The coil turns against the resistance of a spring toward the right or left, depending on the direction of current flow. The distance turned is proportional to the amount of current.

tion of the current in the coil is such as to induce a north pole on the top of the coil, then according to the law that like poles repel, the needle which is rigidly attached to the coil will be deflected in a direction away from the north pole of the permanent magnet.

INDUCED CURRENTS: MICHAEL FARADAY

Before considering Faraday's laws of electrolysis, let us introduce this great nineteenth-century investigator of electricity and magnetism. Faraday was born near London, of humble parentage. At an early age he was apprenticed to a London bookbinder. As he was binding books he came upon a few that dealt with scientific subjects. These so aroused his interest that he found a way to attend lectures given by Humphry Davy at the Royal Institution in London. After one of the lectures he sent Davy a copy of the notes he had made.

Davy was so much impressed that he appointed Faraday to be an assistant. Eventually Faraday became director of the famous institution which had been founded by Count Rumford.

Faraday and the American scientist Joseph Henry, who taught at Albany Academy in Albany, New York, discovered almost simultaneously the phenomenon predicted by Faraday, that a magnet moving in the vicinity of a coil of wire would generate in it an electric current. This electric current is known as an induced current.

Joseph Henry was later a professor at Princeton and eventually secretary of the Smithsonian Institution in Washington, D.C. Faraday is usually given credit for the discovery of induced currents, since he published his work before Henry. The commercial electric generators which produce the enormous amounts of electric power in use today are based on his principle of induction.

ELECTRIC CURRENTS THROUGH ELECTROLYTIC SOLUTIONS

About forty years after the discovery of the voltaic pile, Faraday announced his finding that when an electric current passes through a solution which is a good conductor (an electrolyte), the amount of

According to Faraday the amount of chemical action taking place during electrolysis is proportional to the number of coulombs of charge flowing through a solution.

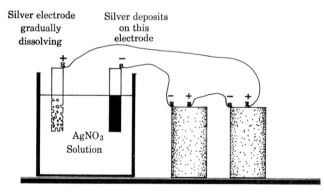

Silver electrode gradually dissolving

Silver deposits on this electrode

$AgNO_3$ Solution

Fig. 10-22.

the resulting chemical action is proportional to the number of amperes of current flowing multiplied by the time of flow in seconds. Let us now see what the resulting chemical action is and how it is measured.

If two strips of silver (Ag) metal, called electrodes, are immersed in a solution of silver nitrate ($AgNO_3$) and connected to a source of direct current such as a pair of dry cells (Fig. 10-22), a chemical reaction takes place. The electrode which is attached to the positive terminal of the battery gradually dissolves. This piece of metal loses weight as atoms are torn off and go into solution. The other strip, which is attached to the negative terminal of the battery, increases in weight as silver atoms from the solution are deposited upon it. The amount of silver nitrate in the solution remains constant, since as much is added by the silver dissolving from one electrode as is removed by deposition on the other electrode. Faraday's law relates the amount of chemical action at either electrode to the quantity of electric charge causing it.

Three cups, each containing electrodes and electrolytes are arranged as shown in Fig. 10-23. The first cup contains two strips (electrodes)

Fig. 10-23.

A faraday (96,500 coulombs) of charge is equal to the charge on 6.02 × 10²³ electrons. It is sufficient to deposit during electrolysis 107.88 gm (the atomic weight) of silver, 31.8 gm (half an atomic weight) of copper (II) or 18.6 gm (a third of an atomic weight) of Iron (III).

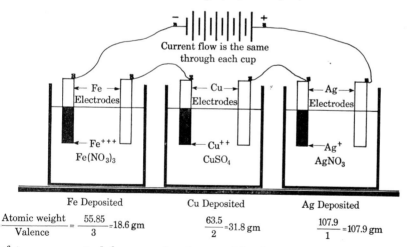

Current flow is the same
through each cup

Fe Electrodes
Cu Electrodes
Ag Electrodes

Fe^{+++}
$Fe(NO_3)_3$

Cu^{++}
$CuSO_4$

Ag^+
$AgNO_3$

Fe Deposited	Cu Deposited	Ag Deposited
$\dfrac{\text{Atomic weight}}{\text{Valence}} = \dfrac{55.85}{3} = 18.6\,gm$	$\dfrac{63.5}{2} = 31.8\,gm$	$\dfrac{107.9}{1} = 107.9\,gm$

of iron separated from each other and both immersed in a solution of ferric nitrate, $Fe(NO_3)_3$; the second, copper electrodes in a cupric sulfate ($CuSO_4$) solution; the third, silver electrodes in a silver nitrate $AgNO_3$) solution. The electric current from the battery is led into each solution through one electrode and out through the other in such a manner (series connection) that the same quantity of current (amperes) flows through each solution. In each cup the metal electrode nearer to the negative battery terminal gains weight. The quantity of current which causes 107.88 grams of silver to deposit on the silver electrode from the silver nitrate solution will cause 63.54/2 grams of copper to deposit and 55.85/3 grams of iron to accumulate on the iron electrode. The atomic weights of these three metals are: Ag, 107.88, Cu, 63.54 and Fe, 55.85. Hence the quantity of electric current required for the deposition of one atomic weight of silver will deposit half an atomic weight of copper and a third of an atomic weight of iron (III), an interesting fact when it is known that silver has a valence of +1, copper +2, and iron (III) +3. The quantity of an element obtained through division of its atomic weight by its valence is called the equivalent weight. This is defined as the weight of the element which will combine chemically with 8 grams of oxygen or its equivalent. Faraday noted in his laws of electrolysis that the weights of different elements deposited from their solutions by a given amount of current were proportional to their equivalent weights.

If the number of amperes of current flowing in a circuit is multiplied by the time of flow (in seconds) the resulting quantity of charge is expressed in *coulombs*.

$$1 \text{ coulomb} = 1 \text{ ampere flowing 1 second}$$
$$= 0.1 \text{ ampere flowing 10 seconds}$$

A "faraday" is 96,500 coulombs of charge and will cause 1 gram equivalent weight of an element to deposit from a solution of one of its salts.

ILLUSTRATIVE PROBLEM

Calculate the weight of cadmium metal deposited on a negative electrode (cathode) from a solution of $CdSO_4$ if a current of 0.1 amp flows for 15 min. Cadmium has an atomic weight of 112.4 and a valence of +2.

Solution

0.1 amp · 15 · 60 sec = 90 coulombs of charge deposit cadmium metal.
96,500 coulombs deposit 1 gm equivalent weight of cadmium.

$$90 \text{ coulombs deposit } \frac{90}{96,500} \text{ gm eq. w.}$$

$$\frac{90}{96,500} \text{ gm eq. w.} = \frac{9}{9650} \cdot \frac{112.4}{2} \text{ gm} = 0.0524 \text{ gm}$$

Since there are the same *number* of atoms in a gram atom of any element, and a gram atom is the weight in grams which is numerically equal to the atomic weight of the element, there are the same number of silver atoms in 107.88 grams of silver as there are copper atoms in 63.54 grams of copper, or as there are iron atoms in 55.85 grams of iron. Hence the amount of electric charge needed to deposit 1 gram atom of silver will deposit only one-half a gram atom of copper, or half as many atoms of copper as silver, and only one-third as many atoms of iron as of silver. This is very suggestive of the fact that an electric current is composed of units of electric charge of a certain size. Silver atoms need only one unit charge per atom in order to deposit; copper atoms require two units each, and hence for the same available quantity of charge only half as many atoms can deposit; iron atoms need three units of charge for each atom that deposits.

Faraday's laws of electrolysis provided one of the early hints that electricity might be expected to consist of particles each of which had the same quantity of charge.

ELECTRIC AND MAGNETIC PHENOMENA COMPARED

Theoretically any substance may be given an electric charge; as a practical matter, only the nonconductors, such as hard rubber, glass, and sulfur, are able to retain a charge for any considerable length of time. Likewise only a few metals—the most important is iron—and a few alloys can be magnetized.

Magnets have regions, called poles, where the magnetic effect appears to be concentrated. A bar magnet usually has a north pole at one end, a south at the other. Electrically charged objects, on the other hand, have an excess of either positive or negative charge so that the entire body appears to have a single kind of charge.

There is an interesting parallel in the laws which formulate the force of attraction or repulsion between two magnetic poles and the force between two electrically charged bodies. For electrostatic charges the relation is

$$F = \frac{q_1 \cdot q_2}{K \cdot d^2} \tag{10-a}$$

The corresponding relation for magnet poles is

$$F = \frac{m_1 \cdot m_2}{\mu \cdot d^2}$$ (10-b)

Each of these is of the same form as Newton's law of universal gravitation, which was considered in Chapter 4:

$$F = G\frac{m_1 m_2}{d^2}$$ (10-c)

In Equation 10-a, q_1 and q_2 are quantities of electrostatic charge. In Equation 10-b, m_1 and m_2 are magnetic pole strengths. K, μ, and G are constants. In Equation 10-c, m_1 and m_2 are masses. In each case, F is directly proportional to the product of two quantities and inversely proportional to the square of the distance between them.

There is an electrostatic field between two parallel plates of metal which are attached to a battery as shown in Fig. 10-24. The battery

Electrically charged objects located between the metal plates are attracted to the plate of opposite charge. Since forces are exerted on the objects, an electric field is said to exist between the plates.

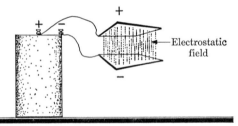

Electrostatic field

Fig. 10-24.

removes electrons from one plate, charging it positively, and adds them to the other, giving it a negative charge. An electrically charged body, when brought into the field between the plates, will be attracted to the plate of opposite charge.

If a coil of insulated copper wire is wound about a nail as shown in Fig. 10-25 and the ends of the coil attached to a battery, the device is called an electromagnet. It will pick up tacks or iron filings just like any permanent magnet. It will repel one end of a compass needle brought near and will attract the opposite end of the needle, indicating that the polarities at the ends are opposite just as in a permanent magnet. If a piece of cardboard is placed horizontally above the coil and iron filings are sprinkled on it, they will arrange themselves in a pattern very similar to that obtained with a bar magnet. If the north pole of one electromagnet is brought near the south pole of another and both are covered with a cardboard and iron filings, we may see that the lines of force extend between the poles just as with permanent magnets. It should be evident, then, that a coil of wire through which

Fig. 10-25.

An electromagnet may be constructed by winding wire around a nail or spike and connecting the end of the wire to a cell. The behavior of an electromagnet is very similar to that of a permanent bar magnet.

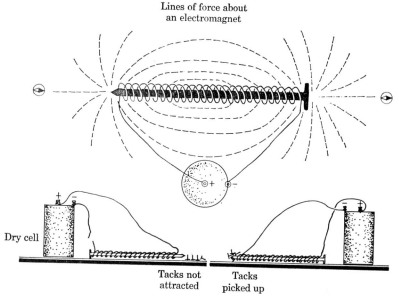

Lines of force about
an electromagnet

Dry cell

Tacks not
attracted

Tacks
picked up

an electric current is passing behaves in all essential respects like a magnet.

Obviously there is a close relationship between electric and magnetic charges. At the same time it must be recognized that these are two distinct phenomena.

EXERCISES AND QUESTIONS FOR CHAPTER 10

1. In a flashlight, two 1.5-volt batteries are connected in series. Find the current flowing through the filament of the light bulb if its resistance (assumed to be the entire resistance of the circuit) is 9 ohms.

2. What resistance must be inserted in an external circuit if a 6-volt storage battery is to cause a current flow of 0.4 ampere?

3. A silver spoon is to be replated. It is made the cathode (negative electrode) in an electrolytic solution of silver salt in which also projects a silver anode (positive electrode). Calculate the weight of silver deposited on the spoon by a current of 0.05 ampere flowing for 30 min.

4. Calculate the resistance of a piece of No. 18 (copper) bell wire 6 in. long if the resistance of this wire is 6.5 ohms per 1000 ft. Calculate the amperes flowing if the wire is connected across the terminals of a 1.5-volt battery. (Neglect the internal resistance of the battery.)

5. Name the essential features of an electric cell (or battery).

6. What is an electric current?

7. Describe some of the analogies between electric current flow in wires and water flow in pipes.

8. Explain the meaning of each of the symbols in Ohm's law, $E = IR$.

9. Describe how to properly connect a voltmeter in an electric circuit. An ammeter.

10. Describe the construction of a lead storage battery. Which electrodes are positive? Which negative?

11. What is the energy source in a cell (or battery)?

12. What factors affect the amount of heat produced when an electric current flows along a wire?

13. Explain the purpose of a fuse in an electrical circuit.

14. How may magnetic fields be detected?

15. Describe the construction of a simple form of galvanometer.

16. How may the amount of chemical decomposition brought about by the action of an electric current be predicted by means of Faraday's laws of electrolysis?

17. Compare the similarities and differences in the behavior of objects bearing electrostatic charges with those bearing magnetic charges.

Review

1. How long after a stone is dropped from the top of a building 1100 ft tall will it strike the pavement in the street below? (Assume free fall.)

2. Nine liters of a gas at S.T.P. weigh 17.6 gm. Calculate the molecular weight of the gas. Is it heavier or lighter than air? How many times? A liter of air weighs 1.293 gm.

3. In order to melt a gram of ice at 0°C without any change in temperature, 80 calories of heat are required. Calculate the final temperature attained if a 30-gm cube of ice at 0°C is placed in a calorimeter containing 200 gm of water at 30°C. (Assume no heat loss to surroundings or to the calorimeter.)

CHAPTER 11

Evidences Concerning Atomic Structure: Discharge Tubes

ATOMS are so tiny they are invisible even in the most powerful microscopes. But the smallest atom, that of hydrogen, is a giant compared with the electrons which are set in motion in a metallic wire by means of a battery. Reference was made in Chapter 9 to the electron and other subatomic particles. We now consider in greater detail some of the experimental evidence which leads us to conclude that they exist.

Fig. 11-1.

Otto von Guericke used his newly discovered vacuum pump to evacuate the Magdeburg hemispheres. The force exerted on them by air pressure was so great that two teams of horses were unable to separate them. (From a modern painting. Courtesy, Fisher Scientific Co.)

The discharge tube and its numerous modifications have proved to be among the most important experimental tools for supplying this evidence. A discharge tube is often a highly evacuated glass tube through which metal electrodes are sealed. In the neon sign, perhaps the best known adaptation of a discharge tube, the passage of a high-voltage current through the low-pressure neon gives a characteristic reddish-orange glow.

Since the invention of the discharge tube was dependent upon obtaining a suitable vacuum it will be of interest to discuss briefly the development of this art.

VACUUM PUMPS

In Torricelli's barometer the space above the mercury column within the glass tube was found to be evacuated. Some investigator conceived of the idea of enlarging the end of the barometer tube so that an evacuated space was available for enclosing far larger objects. This was one of the earliest methods of doing experiments "in vacuo."

Eventually another ingenious person reasoned that it should be possible to obtain a vacuum in a more convenient way. The first extraction vacuum pump was probably invented by Otto von Guericke (1602-1686), at one time mayor of the city of Magdeburg, Germany. With his pump he was able to perform his memorable experiment of evacuating the famous Magdeburg hemispheres (Fig. 11-1). The hemispheres when set together formed a large hollow brass ball. They were machined so as to fit together very tightly. In a famous demonstration, the air was pumped out of the ball formed by the joined hemispheres and a team of horses was attached to each hemisphere, trying to pull them apart in a sort of tug of war. The force of air pressure on the evacuated hemispheres was so great that the horses were unable to pull them apart until air was admitted by opening the valve. The two hemispheres then fell apart of their own weight. This illustrated convincingly the magnitude of the pressure effects of the sea of air about us.

The famous Irish scientist Robert Boyle improved the vacuum pump and used it a great deal in his experimental work. About two centuries passed, however, before the German scientist Geissler invented a much more efficient pump in which a column of mercury replaced the leaky pistons of earlier models.* A diagrammatic representation of Geissler's vacuum pump is shown in Fig. 11-2. Evacuation was accomplished by the opening and closing of stopcocks and the raising and lowering of the leveling bulb in proper sequence.

Fig. 11-2.

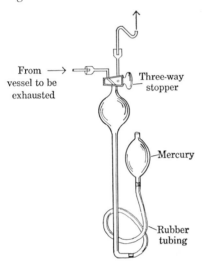

From ⟶
vessel to be
exhausted

Three-way
stopper

Mercury

Rubber
tubing

Geissler's vacuum pump replaced the leaky pistons of earlier models by a mercury column which could be moved up or down by a leveling bulb. The method was slow but gave a much higher vacuum than had hitherto been attainable.

(What sequence of operations would be necessary to evacuate a vesse by means of this device?)

With the new pump it was possible to remove so great a proportior of the air particles from a glass vessel that electrical effects whicl occur only in a highly rarified gas could be observed.

ELECTRICAL CONDUCTIVITY IN FLUIDS

If the electrodes of the conductivity apparatus shown in Fig. 11-are immersed in a dish of water and attached to a source of electric current, the light bulb does not glow. Very little electric current flow through the circuit because the water which fills the space between the electrodes is a poor conductor. If, on the other hand, a solution of hydrochloric acid (HCl) is placed in the dish, the light bulb glow brilliantly. The acid solution is an *electrolyte*, a good conductor of electricity.

* Lloyd W. Taylor, *Physics, The Pioneer Science,* Houghton Mifflin, 1941, p. 769.

An electrolyte is a solution which is a good conductor of an electric current.

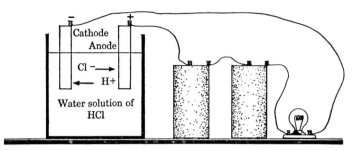

Fig. 11-3.

If the medium between the electrodes is air at atmospheric pressure, rather than a liquid or a solution, there will be only a momentary surge of current as an electric field is built up. The flow soon stops, for air is a poor electrical conductor. If an induction coil is substituted for the battery and a very much higher voltage applied (see Fig. 11-4)

An induction coil changes the low voltage of a dry cell to high voltage capable of exciting a Geissler tube or X-ray tube.

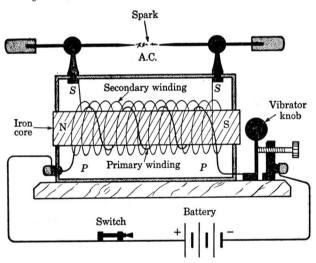

Fig. 11-4.

sparks will jump across the air space between the electrodes. This shows that under appropriate conditions air conducts an electric current.

If the air pressure in a glass tube such as that shown in Fig. 11-5 is reduced to about 0.01 millimeter of mercury, and if a high voltage is applied to electrodes sealed into the tube, then a glow is observed in the tube. This type of tube is called a Geissler tube in honor of Heinrich Geissler, the German glass blower who so skillfully fashioned it. The German physicist Plücker observed that the glow shifted when

A Geissler tube. Metal pieces called electrodes which are sealed through the ends of the tube conduct electric current in and out of the tube. The tube is highly evacuated and a trace of gas such as helium, hydrogen or neon is introduced before it is finally sealed. When a high-voltage current is passed through it, light is emitted.

Electrode

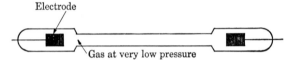

Gas at very low pressure   Fig. 11-5.

a magnet was brought near the tube. If the poles of the magnet were reversed, so was the direction of the deflection. Hittorf, a student of Plücker and perhaps best known to chemists for his discoveries concerning the electrical conductivity of solutions, observed that objects placed in front of the negative electrode (cathode) cast shadows on the far end of the tube.

THE CROOKES EXPERIMENT

The English physicist Sir William Crookes (1832-1919) became much interested in the properties of the "fourth state of matter," the title accorded to the matter issuing from the cathode of a low-pressure tube under the influence of a high voltage. With his famous Crookes tube (Fig. 11-6) he too observed that a metal object such as a cross, placed in the path of the "cathode ray," cast a shadow in the luminescence produced at the far end of the tube. It was a sharply defined shadow which showed that whatever was passing the edge of the interposed piece of metal was traveling in a straight line. Crookes also had a tube constructed with a pinwheel on a horizontal track, as shown in Fig. 11-7. When the high voltage from an induction coil was turned on, the pinwheel moved away from the negative terminal as though pushed. If the direction of the current was reversed and what had been the anode was made the cathode, the pinwheel went

A Crookes tube. Streams of electrons from the cathode, called cathode rays, reach a luminescent material coating the interior of the end of the tube and cause it to light up. Where electrons are stopped by intervening objects a shadow is cast.

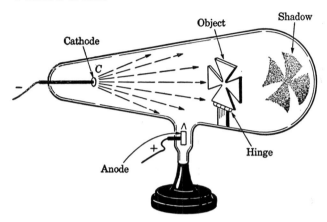

Fig. 11-6.

in the opposite direction. It appeared that material particles must be leaving the cathode, since motion was imparted to an object like a pinwheel.

Near the close of the nineteenth century, Perrin (1870-1926), like Crookes a Nobel prize winner, carried out an experiment which indicated that cathode rays were negatively charged. This experiment was regarded by many as inconclusive, but a short time later J. J. Thomson

Cathode rays cause a pinwheel to move away from the cathode. They must consist of particles since motion is imparted to an object (the pinwheel).

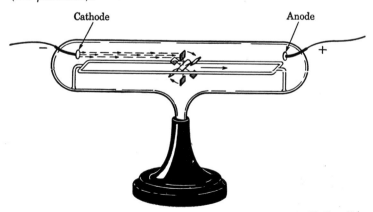

Fig. 11-7.

was able to show that cathode rays were deflected toward the positive pole in an electric field, and it was also known that they were deflected in a magnetic field (Fig. 11-8). As the twentieth century approached, it was a fairly well established fact that under the influence of a high

The American scientist Rowland discovered that particles bearing electric charges and traveling at high velocities gen- erated a magnetic effect, much the same as that produced by electrons flowing along a conducting wire. Cathode rays (high-speed electrons) are deflected when their paths are perpendicular to the lines of force of a magnetic field.

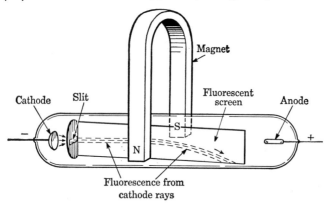

Fig. 11-8.

voltage, negatively charged particles were emitted from the negative terminal of a Crookes tube in which the gas pressure was very low.

THOMSON'S MEASUREMENT OF E/M

Sir J. J. Thomson (1856-1940), physicist at Cambridge University and at one time professor at the Royal Institution in London, will long be remembered as one of the intellectual giants in the field of atomic physics. One of his classic achievements was the evaluation of e/m, the ratio of charge to mass for the electron. Recall that up to this time the atom had been regarded as the fundamental structural unit of all material substances and hence was presumably indivisible. To be sure, a whole series of experiments had hinted at the possible complexity of the atom, but nobody had yet been able to make a comparison between the masses of atoms and subatomic particles.

Thomson used a Crookes tube modified as shown in Fig. 11-9. The right-hand end of the tube is coated with a material which luminesces

(emits visible light) when an electron beam strikes it. Two diaphragms, each with a tiny hole, are placed near the cathode so that
only a narrow beam of electrons travels through the tube. The beam
travels in a straight line and strikes the luminescent coating at A,
producing a spot of light at this point.

Fig. 11-9.

*Apparatus used by Thomson in evaluating the ratio e/m for the electron.
D, D, diaphragms with pinholes—P+, P−, plates that can be charged electrically—A, point at which the undeviated electron beam strikes when the
solenoids carry no current—B, point struck by a ray bent in the magnetic
field produced by current through the solenoids. The effect of electrostatic
charges on the plates is to bend the electron beam upward, counteracting the
effect of the magnetic field.*

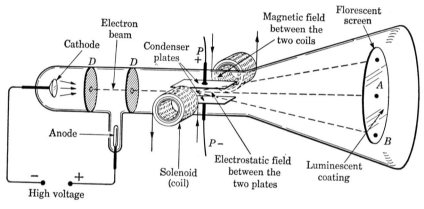

If an electric current is now made to flow through the coils of wire
on either side of the tube, magnetic lines of force extend across the
tube between the coils; the electron beam meets these lines of force
at right angles and the beam is bent downward, striking the luminescent material at a point such as B instead of at A. The path of the
beam, instead of being a straight line, now becomes a circular arc
whose radius of curvature r may be determined geometrically.

The amount of force exerted on the electron beam by the magnetic
field is the product *Hev*, where *H* represents the magnetic field
strength, *e* the quantity of charge on the electron, and *v* the velocity
of the electron. The value of *H* is determined by the size of the coils
and the amount of current flowing through them; the values of *e* and
v are not yet known.

The magnetic force behaves as a centripetal force would, bending the electron beam into a circular path. Centripetal force is calculated by the expression mv^2/r, where m stands for the mass of the electron, v for its velocity, and r for the radius of curvature of the beam. When the electron beam is held stationary at B, the force exerted by the magnetic field is equal to the centripetal force:

$$Hev = \frac{mv^2}{r} \qquad \text{(11-a)}$$

Dividing both sides of this equation by Hmv gives

$$\frac{e}{m} = \frac{v}{Hr} \qquad \text{(11-b)}$$

H and r can both be determined, as stated above; in order to evaluate v we must use the electric field in the Crookes tube as well as the magnetic field.

When the horizontal metal plates inside the tube are attached to a battery, there is an electric field between them. With the electron beam still bent to point B by the magnetic field, current is passed into the plates so as to make the upper one positive and the lower one negative. The force exerted on the beam by the electrostatic field is now opposite to that of the magnetic field. The electrostatic field strength X is determined by the size and the spacing of the metal plates and the voltage applied between them. This electrostatic field strength can be adjusted until the electron beam returns to a straight line, as recognized by the light spot returning from point B to point A. The forces exerted by each of the fields must now be equal:

Force exerted by electrostatic field = force exerted by magnetic field   (11-c)

The force exerted by the electrostatic field is the product of the field strength X and the charge on the electron e. Substituting this value in Equation 11-c gives

$$Xe = Hev \quad \text{or} \quad X = Hv \quad \text{or} \quad v = \frac{X}{H} \qquad \text{(11-d)}$$

Thus the value of v is also determined, and the value of e/m can now be calculated by means of Equation 11-b. A modern value for electrons is

$$\frac{e}{m} = 1.76 \times 10^8 \text{ coulombs/gm}$$

Note that this is a ratio and gives no direct information about either the charge or mass of the electron; it merely shows how the two compare.

From Faraday's laws it was known that 96,500 coulombs of electric charge were needed to deposit at a cathode, by electrolysis, 1 gram of hydrogen gas from a solution containing positively charged hydrogen atoms (hydrogen ions). Ions are atoms which have either gained or lost electrons. The value of e/m obtained for the electron was nearly 2000 times as great as its value for a hydrogen ion, which was derived from the lightest element known at that time. If it could be assumed that the quantities of charge on the hydrogen ion and the electron were equal, this would mean that the mass of the latter was close to 1/2000 the mass of the hydrogen ion.

Several experiments were designed to obtain the value of e, the charge on the electron, by suspending charged droplets of water between electrified plates, that is, in an electric field. While the results indicated that the approximate value of the charge on the electron was about 10^{-19} coulombs, there was considerable variation in the values obtained. Nevertheless, the notion that atoms contained particles having masses of about 1/2000 that of hydrogen atoms was well established by the turn of the twentieth century. Let us now turn to the experiment which gave a precise measure of the quantity of charge on the electron and hence a value for its mass.

THE MILLIKAN OIL DROP EXPERIMENT

In 1911 Robert Andrews Millikan (1868-1953), a professor of physics at the University of Chicago and later at California Institute of Technology, performed the famous oil drop experiment by which the value of e, the charge on the electron, was evaluated. For this work he was awarded a Nobel prize in 1923.

The apparatus used in performing this experiment is shown in Fig. 11-10. Two metallic plates suspended horizontally are attached to a high-voltage battery. In the top plate is a small hole through which an oil drop is admitted to the space between the plates. Since the oil drop is very tiny, the course of its movement can be followed only by means of a short-focus telescope. There is a source of bright illumination at one side of the apparatus. X rays (or radiations from a radioactive material) are introduced at the other side. This ionizing radiation can be used to alter the amount of charge on the oil drop.

Oil drops are sprayed above the opening in the upper plate and a few fall through the opening. The motion of a single drop is observed. Gravity tends to accelerate the falling drop; frictional effects with rarefied gas tend to retard it. Experiments indicate that for a tiny

Fig. 11-10.

The Millikan oil-drop experiment established the unit which we call the electronic charge. Once the numerical value was known, it was possible to evaluate the electronic mass, 1/1840 that of the hydrogen atom. A convenient way of remembering the relation of these masses is to compare the mass of the electron to the pound and that of the hydrogen atom to the ton. The mass of the electron is very tiny compared with the mass of the smallest of all atoms, hydrogen.

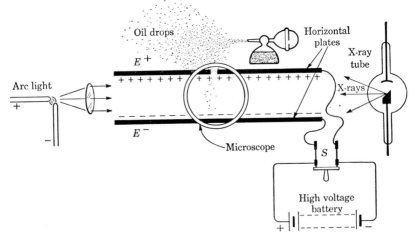

drop, terminal velocity is quickly reached and thereafter the drop falls with uniform velocity. Sir George G. Stokes showed a method, applicable here, of calculating the radii of small particles falling through a viscous medium at constant velocity. The velocity is determined by noting the time required to fall a measured distance. This value is always the same for the fall of a given drop. If the density of the oil is known and the volume of the drop calculated, the mass of the oil drop is readily ascertained. So far, the voltage source has not been connected to the plates and there has been no electric field (see p. 204).

Each time the oil drop approaches the bottom of the scale seen through the telescope, the high-voltage source is connected to the horizontal plates in such a manner that the oil drop is driven upward again. Thus a given oil drop may be made to rise and fall many times. The downward velocity remains the same time after time. The upward velocity is found to vary, becoming greater as the negative charge on the oil drop increases. Why?

By measuring the variations in the upward velocity, the quantities of charge on the oil drop may be calculated. The striking feature of the values of these is that they are all multiples of a simplest number. If, for example, a series of values such as those in Table 11-1 were

Table 11-1 DISCOVERING A UNIT VALUE FROM
A SERIES OF VALUES

6	18	30	12
36	24	42	18
54	12	60	72

obtained, it might be concluded that the smallest charge ever to be found—the unit charge—was 6, and that in the case of the drop containing a charge of 54 there would be 9 such units. Actually, the modern value of the smallest quantity of charge observed is 1.60 $\times 10^{-19}$ coulombs, the value of e, the quantity of charge on the electron.

If this value of e is substituted in

$$\frac{e}{m} = 1.76 \times 10^8 \text{ coulombs/gm}$$

the mass of the electron may be calculated, and is found to be 1/1840 as great as the mass of a hydrogen atom. Electrons are very tiny compared with even the lightest of all atoms. If this ratio were 1/2000, it could be stated that the electron compares with a hydrogen atom in the same way that a pound compares with a (short) ton.

CANAL RAYS

In 1886 the German physicist Goldstein devised a new type of discharge tube with a perforated cathode like that shown in Fig. 11-11. With it he was able to demonstrate the existence of "canal rays," that is, rays which emerged from the perforations or canals in the cathode. Later it was shown that these rays could be deflected by electric and magnetic fields in a direction which indicated that they were positively charged. Canal rays were then called "positive rays."

When a high voltage is applied between the electrodes of the tube, electrons leave the cathode at high velocities. They plow through the molecules of the low-pressure gas, removing some of the electrons of these molecules and thus leaving them with net positive charges as

The discharge tube used for producing canal rays or positive rays. The modern mass spectrograph is simply a modified canal-ray tube which separates by electric and magnetic fields, the components of a beam of positive rays.

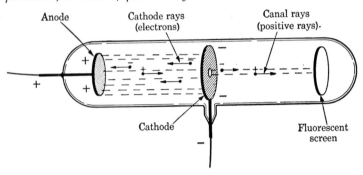

Anode   Cathode rays   Canal rays
          (electrons)   (positive rays).

          Cathode   Fluorescent
                           screen

Fig. 11-11.

positive ions. The positive ions are attracted to the cathode (opposite charges) and the force of attraction accelerates them to high speeds. Many of them shoot through the perforations in the cathode and come out on the other side in pencils of positive rays. The values of e/m for these positive rays depend on the gas in the tube. The largest of all these values is obtained when the residual gas in the tube is hydrogen because the mass of a hydrogen ion gives the smallest possible denominator in the fraction e/m. Thus a singly charged hydrogen atom may be regarded as the smallest positively charged unit found in an atom (i.e., a proton).

THE MASS SPECTROGRAPH

About 1910, as knowledge concerning radioactive atoms (to be discussed in Chapter 12) was accumulating rapidly, it became apparent that there might be atoms which were alike in their chemical properties but had different atomic masses. A great English chemist and pioneer in the field of radioactivity, Frederick Soddy, suggested the name *isotopes* for these chemically similar atoms of different atomic masses. The identification of isotopes was made by means of the *mass spectrograph* and came about in the following way.

Early in the twentieth century, Thomson carried out a series of experiments by which he determined the value of e/m for different positive rays. The apparatus used was that shown in Fig. 11-12. The electric field between the metal plates and the magnetic field between

Fig. 11-12.

Thomson's mass spectrograph. Atoms with different values of e/m were brought to a focus on different parabolic curves. With this device, Thomson proved that neon was composed of atoms of two different masses, 20 and 22. Soddy called these atoms, with different masses but identical chemical properties, isotopes.

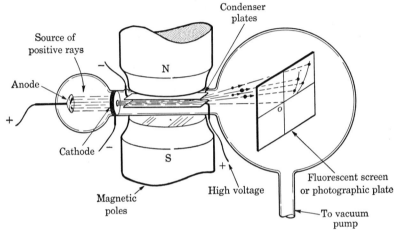

the coils are arranged so that the force exerted on a beam of positive rays by the one would be at right angles to that caused by the other. The combination of the two forces would bend the positive rays into a parabolic curve.

In each experiment a trace of the gas to be investigated was introduced into the highly evacuated tube. If the gas was hydrogen, the beam of positive rays consisted of hydrogen ions, or protons. A photographic plate placed at the end of the tube was exposed to these positive ions. The developed photographic plate showed a characteristic parabolic curve. Different atoms formed these parabolic curves at different locations on the plate: the difference in the location on the plate corresponded to the difference in the masses of the atoms of the gas investigated.

About 1910 Thomson introduced neon gas into a tube and found a prominent parabolic curve corresponding to an atomic mass of 20 and

Fig. 11-13.

Aston's mass spectrograph. Aston's design greatly improved precision of measurement of atomic masses and ability to detect different isotopes and to measure their relative abundances.

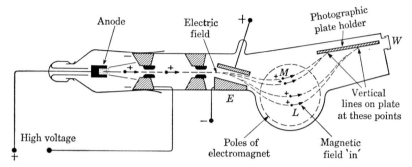

a fainter curve corresponding to an atomic mass of 22, rather than a single curve corresponding to the expected value of 20.2 which was the known atomic mass of neon. It appeared that there might be two different varieties of neon atoms present, those of mass 20 predominating, with lesser numbers of mass 22.

Some years later, Thomson's student, Aston, redesigned the apparatus so that all particles having the same value of e/m would, by deflection in electric and magnetic fields, be brought to a focus, not on the same parabola as in Thomson's apparatus but on the same vertical line. A diagrammatic representation of Aston's apparatus is shown in Fig. 11-13. This *mass spectrograph* provided the scientist

The mass spectrogram of hydrogen. The mass spectrogram is so called because it resembles a spectrogram of light. Just as the spectroscope separates the components of a beam of light and presents them as a series of bands along a scale of increasing wave length, so the mass spectrograph separates the components of a stream of particles and presents them as a series of bands along a scale of increasing unit mass. Any such presentation may be called a spectrum.

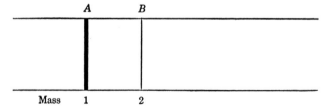

Fig. 11-14.

with a precision instrument for identifying the isotopes which were predicted by Soddy.

Fig. 11-14 shows a mass spectrogram of the element hydrogen. The very intense line at A indicates that nearly all hydrogen atoms have a mass of 1; the faint line at B shows that a few atoms of mass 2 are also present. Hydrogen atoms of mass 2 are called deuterium atoms, or heavy hydrogen. Hydrogen and deuterium are isotopes. They undergo the same chemical reactions although their masses are different.

X RAYS

In 1895 the German physicist Wilhelm Konrad Roentgen was carrying out an investigation using Crookes tubes. He found that some sort of radiation was issuing from the tube which affected a photographic plate even when the plate was wrapped in black paper.

A fluorescent screen placed near the Crookes tube glowed just as long as the high voltage was applied between the electrodes of the tube. If a solid object was placed between the tube and a photographic plate, the exposure of the plate was in inverse relation to the density of the object. An object of very high density such as lead would screen the rays from the photographic plate better than a less dense metal such as aluminum. When the rays passed through gases they became better conductors of an electric current—i.e., they were ionizers of gases.

These penetrating rays were called X rays and proved to be electromagnetic waves of much shorter wave lengths (and hence much higher frequencies) than visible light rays. In many respects they behaved like visible light, but they penetrated objects that were opaque to light rays.

An X-ray tube is simply a Crookes tube modified by placing a piece of a heavy metal such as tungsten (called the target) in the path of the high-speed electrons issuing from the cathode (see Fig. 11-15). Whenever streams of electrons moving at very high speeds impinge on solids, X rays are produced. In general, the higher the voltage applied to the terminals of a tube, the higher the velocities of the electrons striking the target and the more penetrating the X rays which are emitted.

As more penetrating X rays have been needed, it has been necessary to apply higher voltages to these tubes. It is not uncommon to accelerate electrons by voltages as high as a million or more volts in modern X-ray machines. A device called a betatron, by whirling electrons in a doughnut-shaped evacuated tube and then allowing them to fall on a target, makes electrons travel at higher speeds than can

Fig. 11-15.

An X-ray tube is a modified Crookes tube in which the electron beam is focused on a metal target. The higher the voltage, the greater the speed with which the electrons crash into the target atoms and the greater the penetrating power of the X rays.

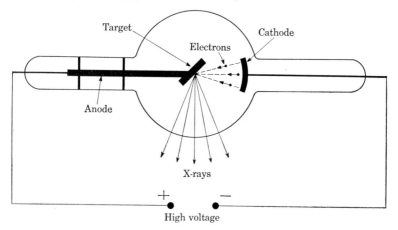

be attained by high-voltage acceleration alone. Thus a betatron is in effect a super-X-ray machine.

X rays are used in dental and surgical work for identifying structural features of teeth or bones, in treatment of cancer, and in detecting flaws in metal castings.

X-RAY SPECTRA: ATOMIC NUMBERS

The periodic law of Mendeleev was based on atomic weights; and, as was pointed out in Chapter 9, when this law was strictly adhered to, certain pairs of elements such as tellurium and iodine fell in the wrong families of the periodic table. It was apparent that their order had to be reversed in spite of the fact that their weights would be out of sequence.

We saw in Chapter 8 that a luminous vapor such as sodium or mercury vapor emits visible light waves which are dispersed by a prism into a series of characteristic lines. If it is understood that visible light and X rays are both forms of electromagnetic radiation having different wave lengths, it will be no surprise to learn that it is also possible to obtain characteristic X-ray spectra.

An X-ray picture of a human hand and wrist bones. Denser parts of the bone allow less exposure of the photographic plate beneath. (Courtesy, Stamford Research Laboratories, American Cyanamid Co.)

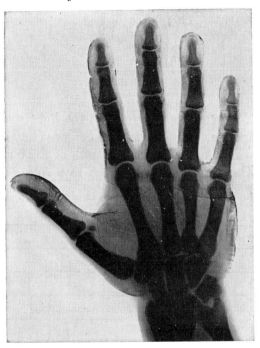

Fig. 11-16.

In 1913 a brilliant young British physicist, Henry G. Moseley, was experimenting with X-ray spectra. In order to observe these spectral lines Moseley used an X-ray tube with an interchangeable target: when one picture had been made, the metallic target was replaced by a target made of a different metal. For a diffraction grating, instead of a finely lined glass plate, he used a crystal of some material such as table salt. A photographic plate was used for recording the positions of the lines.

A diagram of the X-ray spectrograph is shown in Fig 11-17. The

Fig. 11-17.

An X-ray spectrograph employs a source of electromagnetic waves (the X-ray tube), a crystal for dispersing the beam into different wave lengths and a photographic plate for recording the presence of the waves.

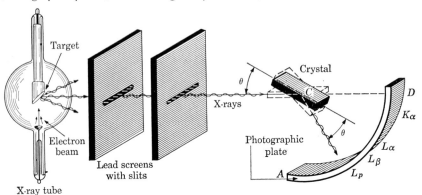

X-ray tube corresponds to the light source used in producing optical spectra. The X rays produced are characteristic of the target materials which are placed in the path of the electron beam in the X-ray tube. The spreading out of the rays into a spectrum is accomplished by

The order of the elements as determined by characteristic X-ray spectrum lines.

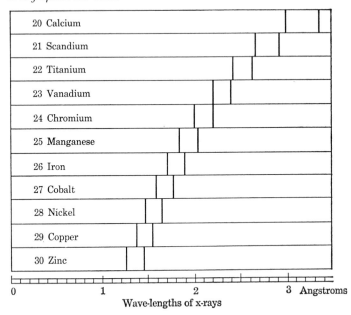

Wave-lengths of x-rays   Fig. 11-18.

means of the crystal of salt, which is rotated on its axis so that the diffracted X-ray beam sweeps over the photographic plate. The spectrum so recorded is simple in structure when compared with many other optical spectra. When the photographic plate is developed, two sets of characteristic lines are obtained. Fig. 11-18 shows a set of characteristic lines for each of several metallic elements.

Moseley arranged the elements in the order dictated by the shifting of the characteristic X-ray lines. He also discovered that by plotting the order number so obtained against the square root of the frequency of one of the characteristic lines, a straight line was obtained.

Plot of the square root of the frequency of a characteristic line in the X-ray spectrum of various elements vs. the atomic number of the element.

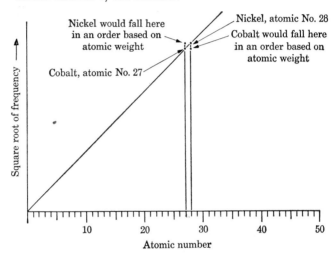

Nickel would fall here in an order based on atomic weight

Nickel, atomic No. 28

Cobalt would fall here in an order based on atomic weight

Cobalt, atomic No. 27

Square root of frequency

10   20   30   40   50

Fig. 11-19.

Atomic number

If nickel and cobalt were placed in order of increasing atomic *weight* (Ni = 58.69, Co = 58.94), neither of them fell on the straight line just mentioned. However, when they were placed according to the order established by their X-ray spectra, their order was reversed and they fell on the line. The periodic law (Chapter 9) was revised to state that the properties of the elements are periodic functions of their order numbers. These order numbers were called *atomic numbers.* Later, experimental evidence was obtained by Chadwick which linked the atomic number with the number of positive charges (protons) on the nucleus of the atom.

In summary, the discharge tube was the means for establishing many of the properties of the electron, a constituent of all atoms. The Crookes tube was then modified to demonstrate the existence of positive rays, and from this modified Crookes tube evolved the mass spectrograph. This in turn enabled scientists to distinguish isotopes—atoms which were chemically alike but which had different masses. The introduction of a heavy metal target in the path of an electron beam in a Crookes tube produced X rays, and by means of the X-ray spectra, atomic numbers were determined.

EXERCISES AND QUESTIONS FOR CHAPTER 11

1. Describe some of the characteristics of cathode rays.

2. What does e/m represent? Why is it important in atomic physics?

3. Describe Thomson's experiment for evaluating e/m.

4. Describe how the Millikan oil drop experiment is carried out. What important result is obtained from it?

5. How are positive rays or canal rays produced?

6. What use does the scientist make of the mass spectrograph?

7. Describe the construction of an X-ray tube. How are X rays produced?

8. Both X rays and visible light rays are forms of electromagnetic waves. Compare their behavior.

9. Describe the construction of an X-ray spectrograph. How may characteristic X-ray spectra be used to determine the atomic numbers of the elements?

REVIEW

1. Centripetal force is calculated by means of the relation $F = mv^2/r$. Calculate the centripetal force required to keep a 2-lb mass revolving in a circle of 2-ft radius at a velocity of 20 ft/sec. In selecting the appropriate units of force refer to Table 3-1 and keep in mind that $F = ma = mv^2/r$. Make the calculation for a 2-lb weight, keeping other conditions the same.

2. Calculate the wave length of a musical tone whose frequency is 512 vibrations per second. The speed of sound at 0°C is 1090 ft/sec.

CHAPTER 12

Exploding Atoms: Radioactivity

Sнокtly after Roentgen made his world-shaking discovery of X rays, it was reported that their origin was in the portion of the X-ray tube where the luminescent glow was observed. The French physicist Henri Becquerel (1852-1908) was curious to know if luminescent materials such as uranium ores, some of which were known to phosphoresce (glow after exposure to light), would produce effects similar to X rays. He exposed various uranium ores to the action of light and was delighted to discover that after exposure, some sort of penetrating radiation from the ores could be detected on a photographic plate. The radiation was so penetrating that it could still be detected on the plate after passing through a thick layer of black paper. Quite by chance on one occasion, he left some ore which had not been exposed to sunlight on a photographic plate wrapped in heavy paper; when this plate was developed, he found that penetrating radiation had affected the plate just as it had when the ore had first been exposed to light. He thus discovered that the exposure of the minerals to light was not a necessary condition for the production of the penetrating radiation; the rays were continuously emitted by these materials. This new radiation soon assumed the name of "Becquerel rays." If Becquerel rays were not identical with X rays, they were certainly very close relatives.

MADAME CURIE'S DISCOVERY OF POLONIUM

Marja Sklodowska Curie (1867-1934), who, as Madame Marie Curie, is popularly associated with the early history of radioactivity, was born in Poland a few years after the close of the Civil War in the United States. At the time of the discovery of Becquerel rays she was a student in Paris working with radioactive materials. She knew that they could be detected by their ability to discharge an electroscope.

An electroscope is an instrument used to detect electric charge. It consists, basically, of a metal strip or leaf which is fixed and a second leaf which is hinged to it, both enclosed in a case as shown in Fig. 12-1. The fixed leaf is connected to a metal knob outside the case. If

Radiations from radioactive materials produce ions (electrically charged atoms) in the air through which they pass. If these ions are formed in the vicinity of a charged electroscope, it discharges.

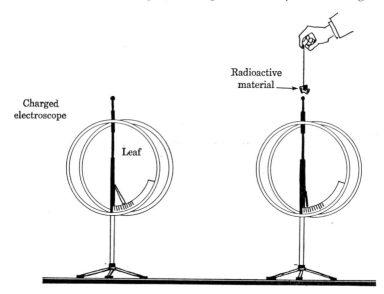

Radioactive
material

Charged
electroscope

Leaf

Fig. 12-1.

the knob becomes negatively charged, the negative charge spreads through the leaves, and since like charges repel, the movable leaf swings out. A positive charge on the knob has the same result. The greater the amount of charge, the higher the leaf rises; when there is no electric charge on the knob, either positive or negative, both leaves re neutral and the movable leaf falls. Becquerel rays cause air mole- ules to become electrically charged or ionized, some positively, some negatively. Ions whose charges are opposite to that of the electroscope re attracted, and upon reaching the knob allow some of the electric charge on the leaves to be dissipated: the movable leaf falls as shown n the illustration. Thus it is possible to detect radioactive substances by their ability to discharge an electroscope.

Madame Curie used a type of electroscope which enabled her to compare quantitatively the amounts of radioactivity in different sam- ples. She found that in general, the higher the percentage of uranium in the ore sample, the greater the amount of radiation emitted and the more rapidly the leaf of the electroscope fell. The uranium ore pitchblende was found to be more radioactive than would be expected from its uranium content alone. This strongly hinted that there might be present in pitchblende an element whose activity exceeded that of uranium.

Madame Curie now undertook to separate out the suspected new element. A familiar step in chemical analysis is the separation of one chemical species from another, whether element or compound. To a solution, in which both species are dissolved, a reagent is added which will form a precipitate (insoluble solid) with one but not with the other. For instance, both silver nitrate and magnesium nitrate are soluble in water. A solution of the two is clear and colorless. It looks like water. If hydrochloric acid (likewise clear) is added, an insoluble solid separates which gives the liquid a milky appearance. This solid, or precipitate, is silver chloride. Adding enough acid will result in a virtually complete separation of silver from the solution. If the mix- ture is filtered, the silver chloride will be retained by the filter paper and the magnesium will pass through as the filtrate (the clear liquid issuing from the filter funnel). Thus a separation of silver from mag- nesium has been effected.

Madame Curie dissolved uranium ore and added a reagent which would precipitate (form a solid with) certain impurities. After filtra- tion of this solution, she compared the activity of the filtrate and the precipitate by means of the electroscope. She was thus able to trace the location of an element which was many times as radioactive as uranium and eventually, in 1898, to isolate a new chemical element. She called it polonium in honor of her native Poland.

THE DISCOVERY OF RADIUM

Shortly after the discovery of polonium, Madame Curie discovered that a material of still greater radioactivity could be separated from a solution of a uranium ore. It was precipitated from this solution along with the element barium, an impurity frequently associated with uranium.

The separation of the new, more active element from the accompanying barium proved to be a long and tedious process. It was accomplished by an operation known as fractional crystallization. A solution containing barium and the new element was allowed to partially evaporate: as the solution became saturated, crystals of a barium compound formed. After the solution containing these crystals was filtered, it was possible to determine by means of the electroscope whether the crystals or the liquid contained the stronger radioactivity. By repeated recrystallization over a considerable period and removal of essentially all of the barium, a tiny amount of radium chloride was finally crystallized and isolated from the solution.

Once again the spectroscope proved to be a most valuable tool. The spectrum of the crystalline barium compound which first separated from the solution contained several spectral lines not found in a sample of pure barium. As the process of concentrating the new element progressed, the intensities of these new spectral lines became more prominent. It became evident that they were characteristic lines of a new radioactive element, later called radium.

RADIATION FROM RADIOACTIVE SUBSTANCES

Little has been said concerning the nature of the radiation given off by the radioactive materials whose discovery has just been recounted. As far as external appearances are concerned, radioactive materials do not look different from other substances, but they emit rays which will affect a photographic plate and discharge an electroscope.

One of the great names associated with the development of knowledge concerning radioactivity is that of Sir Ernest Rutherford (1871-1937). He was born in New Zealand and after graduating from college there, traveled halfway around the world to study at the famous Cavendish Laboratory in Cambridge, England.

During the last few years of the nineteenth century, Rutherford made one of the earlier discoveries of his distinguished career by showing that there were at least two components in the radiation emitted by radioactive materials. The less penetrating variety he called the alpha ray; the more penetrating one, the beta ray. Shortly thereafter a third component, the gamma ray, was discovered; it was shown to be a close relative of the X ray, though of slightly shorter wave length than the X rays then in common use.

After Rutherford's discovery, developments came in rapid succession. A pencil of rays issuing from a radioactive source as shown in Fig. 12-2 was shown to be separated into three distinct components

Fig. 12-2.

Alpha and beta rays, which consist of electrically charged particles, are deflected toward opposite poles in an electric field. Gamma rays have no charge and hence are unaffected. Since alpha and beta particles are electrically charged and travel at high velocities, they will behave like an electric current flowing in a wire, that is, produce a magnetic effect. They will be bent when they pass perpendicular to the lines of force in a magnetic field. Gamma rays are not deflected in a magnetic field.

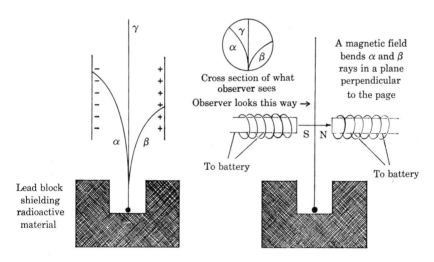

by means of a magnetic or electric field. The part of the radiation which was bent toward the negative pole in an electric field must have carried a positive charge. It was composed of alpha particles, the less penetrating of the radiations demonstrated by Rutherford. The value of e/m (ratio of charge to mass) of the particles was half the value of

e/m for protons. Later, alpha particles were found to have four times the mass of the proton and double the quantity of charge:

$$\left(\begin{array}{c}\text{Value of } e/m \\ \text{for proton}\end{array}\right) = \frac{e_p}{m_p} \qquad \left(\begin{array}{c}\text{Value of } e/m \text{ for} \\ \text{alpha particle}\end{array}\right) = \frac{2e_p}{4m_p} = \frac{e_p}{2m_p}$$

Alpha particles were eventually shown to be helium atoms without the usual two electrons—that is, helium ions.

The component of the pencil of rays which deflected toward the positive terminal in an electric field was found to have the same value of e/m as electrons had. The more highly penetrating beta particles, then, proved to be electrons.

The positively charged alpha particle had a mass over 7000 times that of the beta particle, but it had the least penetrating power of any of the three types of radiation (Fig. 12-3). Alpha particles were

Fig. 12-3.

The relative pentrating powers of alpha, beta, and gamma radiation. Alpha rays are the least penetrating, being stopped by paper, clothing, and the like. Beta particles are more penetrating, requiring on the average about ⅛ inch of aluminum to stop them. Gamma rays are difficult to stop completely, even with considerable thicknesses of material such as lead or concrete.

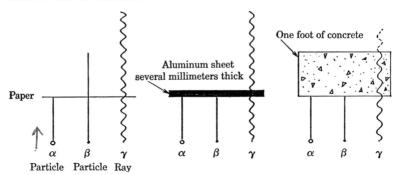

stopped by a thick piece of paper which was readily penetrated by beta particles and gamma rays. A piece of aluminum metal several millimeters thick stopped beta particles but readily transmitted gamma rays. Gamma rays had to pass through a thickness of a foot or more of concrete to reduce their intensity to harmless levels.

Whereas alpha particles had poor penetrating ability, they were excellent ionizers of any gases through which they passed—that is, they were very effective in tearing electrons away from gas atoms and

α = helium nucleus

β = electron

thus changing gas atoms into ions. They were ejected from the nuclei of radioactive atoms at velocities as high as one-tenth the velocity of light. Beta particles were hurled from the nuclei of radioactive atoms at far greater velocities than alpha particles, sometimes reaching 90% of the velocity of light, but were far less effective as ionizers. Gamma rays, the most penetrating of the three radiations, proved to be the poorest ionizers; they were thus the least effective in causing the collapse of the leaf in a charged electroscope. Here is a convenient way of remembering the relative ionizing and penetrating powers of the three types of radiation:

	Alpha Particles	Beta Particles	Gamma Rays
Comparative penetrating ability	1	100	10,000
Comparative ionizing ability	10,000	100	1

DETECTION OF RADIOACTIVITY— THE GEIGER COUNTER

The Geiger counter is fast becoming the traditional detection device of the uranium hunter. All is not gold that glitters. Correspondingly, all is not uranium that makes a Geiger counter chatter. A typical instrument is shown in Fig. 12-4. It consists essentially of a Geiger tube attached by means of an electric cord to an electronic recording device.

The Geiger tube itself, shown in Fig. 12-5 is often a glass envelope containing a hollow metal cylindrical tube which is connected to the negative terminal of a high-voltage source or battery. A wire which runs longitudinally along the axis of the metal tube is attached to the positive terminal of the battery. A potential difference of 900 or more volts is applied between the metal tube and the wire. Even though the glass envelope is highly evacuated, there are always sufficient residual molecules in it to furnish millions and millions of gas ions should an alpha, beta, or gamma ray penetrate the interior of the tube.

A positively charged radioactive particle which plows through the atoms of low-pressure gas in the tube ionizes them by tearing loose electrons. The positively charged nucleus of an atom and the electron constitute a so-called ion pair. These positive nuclei and electrons are attracted to the electrodes of opposite charge, are accelerated by this force, gain in kinetic energy, and create still more ions. An

γ = affect photo. plates most

enormous avalanche of ions results almost instantaneously, and a pulse of current surges across between the electrodes. This minute surge is recorded by an electronic current registering device, heard as a click, or seen as the flash of a light bulb or the movement of a needle on a portable survey meter. The Geiger tube is often attached to a scaler which counts the pulses if a quantitative comparison of the strengths of radioactive sources is desired.

A Geiger counter survey meter. This portable instrument has a Geiger tube for detecting radiation and electronic circuits to indicate the rate at which radiation is being received. (Courtesy, Tracerlab Inc.)

Fig. 12-4.

The Geiger counter may be used to count all three types of radiation—alpha, beta, and gamma rays. Which particles are actually detected depends to a large extent on the "window" thickness that admits the radiation to the tube. This must be very thin if alpha particles are to enter. A window admitting alpha particles would permit the entry of the more penetrating betas and gammas. A thicker window would exclude alphas but still admit betas and gammas. A window of sufficient thickness to stop betas would count gamma rays only.

Even if all known radioactive substances are removed from the vicinity of an operating Geiger tube, it still chatters occasionally or otherwise indicates that radiation is reaching it. In spite of everything we can do there are always small amounts of radioactive materials present in tiny quantities in the walls of the room and the surroundings. Cosmic rays* coming from outer space may also contribute to what is known as the "background count."

> *A Geiger tube consists of a thin central wire (anode) coaxial with a metal cylinder (cathode). Radiation passing through the low-pressure gas in the tube of a survey meter produces ionization, which reduces the potential difference between the electrodes. This actuates an electronic meter which is usually calibrated to read milliroentgens per hour.*

Metal cylinder
(cathode)

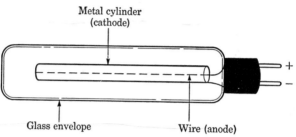

Fig. 12-5.   Glass envelope   Wire (anode)

In counting a radioactive sample, then, counts which are due to the background must be deducted from the number of counts obtained from the sample. Thus if a radioactive source is giving 1000 counts per minute and the background count is 50 counts per minute, then 950 counts per minute are due to the sample.

The Scintillation Counter   One of the earliest methods used to detect radiation depended on the tiny flashes of light (scintillations) produced when alpha particles struck a zinc sulfide screen. Gamma rays were also found to cause scintillations when they struck a crystal of sodium iodide (thallium activated). The enormous advances in electronics which took place during and after World War II have made possible in recent years the invention of a device known as a photomultiplier tube which converts the flashes of light into measureable electric currents. These minute pulses of current are amplified, fed into a scaler, and counted in a manner similar to that described above in connection with the Geiger counter.

* See Otto Oldenburg, *Introduction to Atomic Physics*, 2nd ed., Chapter 20.

This new type of detector, known as the scintillation counter tube, has gradually been replacing the Geiger tube as a means of counting gamma rays because of its higher efficiency. At present the cost of a scintillation counter tube is considerably higher than that of a Geiger tube.

RADIOACTIVE DECAY

Radioactivity is the result of an unstable energy condition of the atom. Particles are ejected and waves are emitted from the nucleus of a radioactive atom as the atom moves toward greater energy stability. Just as a stone on the hillside tends to roll down the hill, decreasing its potential energy as it goes, so the radioactive atom also assumes lower energy states as it decays.

The atom of uranium, in approaching energy stability, hurls an alpha particle from its nucleus. A transmutation is thus brought about. The resulting nucleus is that of another atomic species, called uranium X_1. This element is still radioactive and is a beta emitter; after emission of a beta particle, uranium X_1 is converted into the element uranium X_2. A whole series of other transformations takes place before a given atom of uranium has finally been converted to a stable atom of lead. This is the end of the road as far as radioactive decay processes are concerned. When an atom of lead has resulted from a whole series of these "disintegrations," the original atom of uranium has finally reached energy stability. The series of transformations is known as the uranium disintegration series (see Appendix). *URANIUM — LEAD*

Attempts to change the rate of radioactivity decay by altering external conditions—temperature, pressure, and other factors—have been unsuccessful; the radioactive process continues as inevitably as time and tide. This suggests that the nucleus is involved in radioactive change, for it is well known that changes in temperature and pressure will alter the speeds of chemical reactions in which extranuclear electrons are thought to be involved. Furthermore, the fact that the rate of decay is independent of the state of chemical combination seems to support this point of view. It seems to make no difference, as far as rate of decay is concerned, whether a radioactive material is in the form of an element like uranium, or in the form of a compound like uranium hexafluoride.

only way to change amount of radiation is to
vary the amount of radioactive material

rate of decay

Half-life Period   The period of time required for one-half of the atoms of a given radioactive species to decay is known as its half-life period. After four and a half billion years, one-half of a given number of radioactive uranium atoms will have decayed. Day to day variations in the activity of a uranium sample are thus hardly observable. Polonium, on the other hand, has a half-life period of about four and a half months. After this period of time has elapsed its activity will be reduced to half of its original value.

I^{131}, which is much used by the medical profession (see Chapter 14) in the diagnosis and treatment of thyroid disorders, has a half-life of about eight days; after eight days, one-half of the radioactive atoms will have disintegrated. During the next eight days, one-half of those remaining will have disintegrated. After 24 days, only one-eighth of the original radioactive atoms will be active, that is, still able to undergo decay. The half-life period tells us, then, whether the rate of decay is rapid or slow, an important consideration if people are being treated with radioactive substances.

Table 12-1   HALF-LIVES OF SOME COMMON
RADIOACTIVE ATOMS

Element	Radioactive Species	Half-life Period
Carbon	C^{14}	5600 years
Cobalt	Co^{60}	5.3 years
Iodine	I^{131}	8.0 days
Phosphorus	P^{32}	14.3 days

EVIDENCE THAT ATOMS HAVE NUCLEI

As radioactive materials came into more general use in the early years of the twentieth century it was recognized that there might be a possibility of using the high-speed particles ejected by them in probing the secrets of atomic structure. In the first decade of the twentieth century, Geiger and Marsden, colleagues of Sir Ernest Rutherford, tried bombarding very thin sheets of gold with high-speed alpha particles.

When the alpha particles emitted by an element such as radium were collimated by being passed through a circular opening and

Half life is part of compound interest law

directed upon a screen coated with a substance such as zinc sulfide, a circular luminescent spot similar to the opening was observed on the screen (Fig. 12-6). If a gold foil was interposed between the source and the screen, the sharp ring of light changed to a larger, more diffuse luminescent spot. Furthermore, if the zinc sulfide screen was moved

A beam of alpha particles from a radium source giving a small, sharp image on a luminescent screen becomes larger and more diffuse when a thin gold foil is interposed between the source and the screen. Many alpha particles are scattered through small angles in passing through the foil.

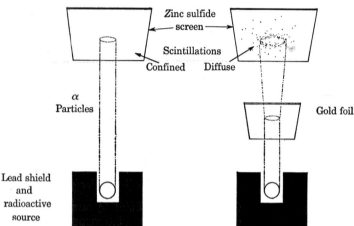

Fig. 12-6.

out of the direct path of the rays and around beside the gold foil as shown in Fig. 12-7, there were a few scintillations on the screen which indicated that some of the alpha particles were being scattered to one side by the gold foil. Some alpha particles even returned in the direction from which they had come—in other words, were turned through an angle of 180 degrees.

Rutherford suggested that the alpha-particle scattering could best be accounted for by assuming that the atom contained a central core having nearly all the mass of the atom, a diameter not greater than 10^{-12} centimeters, and a positive charge. Most of the alpha particles passed through the thin gold foil unaffected, as if the structure of the atom were very porous. However, when an alpha particle closely approached a similarly (positively) charged nucleus it was deflected (repelled). Once in a great while an alpha particle would approach

α particle may be changed by a magnetic or electric field, or hitting another particle

Fig. 12-7.

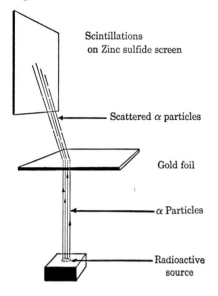

Scintillations
on Zinc sulfide screen

Scattered α particles

Gold foil

α Particles

Radioactive
source

A small proportion of the alpha particles in the beam are scattered through wide angles as shown by the scintillations on the screen when it is completely out of the path of the main beam. From his scattering experiments, Rutherford concluded that an atom was a highly porous structure with most of its mass concentrated in a central positive core called the nucleus. The scattering equation which he deduced from these experiments made it possible to compute for the first time the nuclear charge, Z. This was eventually shown to be the number of protons in the nucleus.

the core of an atom head on, and its direction would be reversed. This positively charged central core is now called the nucleus of the atom.

THE FIRST CONTROLLED NUCLEAR REACTION

In 1919 another milestone in the field of nuclear physics was passed when Rutherford reported a series of experiments using alpha particles as atomic projectiles. It had been well established that alpha particles had definite ranges, that is, traveled a certain distance before losing their kinetic energy. When an alpha particle source was nearer to a zinc sulfide screen than this distance, numerous scintillations were observed on it; beyond this distance the number of scintillations decreased rapidly and soon ceased.

In 1919 Rutherford reported on experiments dealing with the ranges of observed scintillations when high-speed alpha particles traveled through different gases before reaching a luminescent screen. When alpha particles passed through oxygen gas or carbon dioxide, the ranges worked out as expected. However, when they passed through dry air, scintillations were observed at unexpectedly large ranges. Additional experiments proved that nitrogen gas in the air was responsible for this unusual result.

α particle travel further in nitrogen gas than in other gas

Magnetic deflections of the particles responsible for these long-range scintillations indicated that they were protons. Rutherford gave the explanation that high-speed alpha particles had struck nitrogen atoms and cracked off protons.

The distance from an alpha particle source to a zinc sulfide screen is adjusted until scintillations are barely observed. This distance is called the range of the alpha particles.

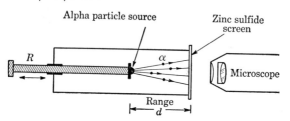

Fig. 12-8.

The reaction taking place was the first nuclear reaction which man had been able to control. Radioactive disintegration, which had been known many years, involved nuclear change, but there was nothing that could be done either to start, stop, or alter the speed of the process. Rutherford's nuclear reaction was controllable in the sense that one could choose the target atoms to be bombarded. In the symbolism of nuclear reactions it was written as follows

$$_2\text{He}^4 + {_7}\text{N}^{14} \rightarrow {_8}\text{O}^{17} + {_1}\text{H}^1$$

alpha particle   oxygen isotope   proton

The subscript numbers represent the atomic numbers of the elements. Occasionally these are omitted when nuclear reactions are written, since the appropriate atomic number is implied by the symbol. The superscript numbers indicate the masses of the atoms. Alpha particles, which are hurled with very high speeds from the nuclei of radioactive atoms, are the bombarding "artillery." The nuclei of nitrogen atoms are the targets. An alpha particle which strikes one of them will fuse momentarily producing an unstable nucleus, which in turn cracks, giving a proton and an oxygen atom. Most oxygen atoms have an atomic mass of 16; the oxygen atom produced in this reaction has a mass of 17. The nucleus of oxygen 17 has one more neutron than that of oxygen 16. They are isotopes.

The above is classified as an (α, p) reaction, which means that the alpha particles are the bombarding projectiles and that protons are produced as a result of the reaction. The target atoms are not designated, but if their identity is known in addition to the type of reaction, the other product atom may be determined since the sum of the atomic numbers will remain unchanged in the reaction.

ILLUSTRATIVE PROBLEM

Assuming that an (α, p) reaction is possible with $_{13}Al^{27}$ target atoms, determine the atomic number and atomic mass of the other product.

Solution

$$_2He^4 + _{13}Al^{27} \rightarrow ? + _1H^1$$

The sum of the atomic numbers (subscripts) on the left is 15. If a proton is formed (atomic number 1), the product atom must have an atomic number 14. The element must therefore be silicon. Since the sum of the atomic masses on the left is 31, the silicon atom must have a mass of 30. It must be an isotope of silicon. The completed nuclear equation is

$$_2He^4 + _{13}Al^{27} \rightarrow _{14}Si^{30} + _1H^1$$

Transmutation has taken place in the above reaction. The alchemists' dream has, in a sense, actually been realized. While it is now possible to convert one kind of atom into another, relatively few of the target atoms are transmuted in any given reaction, and the problem of separating from the target atoms the minute quantities of new atoms produced is indeed a formidable one. The day when gram quantities of gold can be economically produced from baser metals still seems far distant, despite the fact that it is now possible to convert one element into another.

We should carefully distinguish a chemical reaction from a nuclear reaction. The equation for the chemical reaction of hydrogen and chlorine follows.

$$H_2 + Cl_2 \rightarrow 2HCl$$

A hydrogen molecule (H_2) consists of two hydrogen atoms; a chlorine molecule, of two chlorine atoms. When the two have reacted, the *same atoms* are present but hydrogen atoms are now attached to chlorine atoms, and hydrogen chloride molecules have been formed in the reaction. Chemical changes involve only the valence electrons (see

Chapter 13); the nucleus and lower electron levels are left unchanged. How different is the nuclear (α, n) reaction with beryllium target atoms:

$$_2He^4 + _4Be^9 \rightarrow _6C^{12} + _0n^1$$
alpha   neutrons
particles

High-speed alpha particles from a radioactive substance strike a piece of beryllium metal. Carbon atoms are formed on the metal, but in such small quantities as to defy detection except by the most sensitive of analytical methods. One kind of atom (Be) has been converted into another variety (C); a transmutation of elements has been accomplished rather than just a regrouping of the atoms as in the chemical reaction of hydrogen and chlorine.

THE NUCLEAR CHARGE OF THE ATOM

As evidence accumulated that atoms were composed of electrons and protons, there was increasing interest in the question, "How many of these particles are there in a single atom of a particular element?" A partial answer to this question was obtained from the alpha-ray scattering experiments of Geiger and Marsden. Their mathematical equation which predicted the extent of scattering contained a factor Z, the nuclear charge of the scattering element. The value of Z appeared to be roughly half the atomic weight: since the atomic weight of carbon was 12, the number of positive charges on its nucleus would be 6. Soon after, a series of experiments on the scattering of X rays was carried out by Barkla; he concluded that the number of electrons associated with an atom was also roughly half the atomic weight: carbon would have about 6 electrons associated with it. Unfortunately both of these relations held for only a few of the lighter elements in the periodic table. Since an uncombined atom had equal numbers of positive and negative charges, these two sets of results amounted to essentially the same thing.

In 1913 the Dutch physicist Van den Broek suggested that the number of positive charges on the nucleus of an atom was equal to the order number of the element in the periodic table, or its atomic number. It was not until after World War I that this fact was definitely established by Chadwick's more precise method of measuring alpha-ray scattering.

ATOM SMASHERS

After Rutherford's classic controlled nuclear reaction performed in 1919, interest in further nuclear experiments was stimulated. Soon it was apparent that high-velocity protons might be more effective as atomic artillery than alpha particles. In 1932 Cockcroft and Walton

The Van de Graaff generator. The accelerating voltage in this atom smasher can be precisely controlled, and hence the energies of bombarding particles can be exactly known.

Fig. 12-9.

at Cambridge University first succeeded in bringing about a nuclear reaction with protons accelerated in one of the earliest of the particle accelerators or "atom smashers."

Because the masses of particles like protons and electrons are so very tiny, even at high velocities they will have very small kinetic energies. For this reason the energies of particles used in atom smashing are usually expressed in terms of very small energy units called electron volts, or more often in millions of electron volts (mev). An electron volt is the energy possessed by an electron after acceleration through a potential difference of one volt. The Cockcroft-Walton "voltage multiplier" mentioned above was capable of accelerating protons to 2 or 3 mev. The modern bevatron is a particle accelerator capable of imparting to bombarding particles energies of the order of billions of electron volts (bev).

An electron volt is equal to 1.6×10^{-12} ergs and one mev is 1.6×10^{-6} ergs. Alpha particles from radioactive materials often have energies as high as from 5 to 10 mev. They are sufficiently energetic to drive protons out of lighter atomic nuclei. However, in the bombardment of heavier target elements in which the positive charge on the nucleus is greater, the proton is much more effective than the alpha particle. Both alpha particles and protons have positive charges which repel the nuclei of target atoms (also positively charged) as they approach. One of the reasons for the effectiveness of the neutron as a bombarding particle is that it carries no charge.

There are numerous types of particle accelerators, such as the Van de Graaff machine, the cyclotron, the linear accelerator, and the synchrocyclotron. These are all very expensive devices, and their purpose is simply to accelerate atomic particles to high velocities in order to bring about nuclear reactions. By means of these nuclear reactions,

Fig. 12-10.

The cyclotron is a particle accelerator which whirls positive ions guided in circular paths by a magnetic field. The ions are accelerated as they pass between two dees which are rendered alternately positive and negative by a high-frequency oscillator. As ions travel faster, they spiral out and eventually go out through a "window" when they reach the periphery.

man is greatly extending his knowledge concerning the structure of matter.

THE NEUTRON

High-speed alpha particles ejected from the nuclei of radioactive atoms also made possible the discovery of neutral particles in the nuclei of atoms. In 1930 Bothe and Becker in Germany discovered that radiation even more penetrating than gamma rays resulted when alpha rays struck certain metals, e.g., beryllium. For a while it was thought to be nothing more than high-energy gamma rays. Somewhat later, Madame Curie's daughter, Irène Curie Joliot, discovered that protons of high velocity were ejected if this radiation fell on certain materials such as paraffin. In 1932 Chadwick suggested that this experimental evidence could best be interpreted by assuming that the protons had been removed from the paraffin by particles of essentially the same mass but with no electric charge. Chadwick called the new particles neutrons.

Neutrons are believed to be present in the nuclei of all atoms, except of course H^1, whose nucleus is a proton. Neutrons make ideal atomic artillery because of the absence of electric charge. They are not affected by the repulsive forces encountered by alpha particles and protons in approaching target atoms. The great importance of the neutron in nuclear science will be further emphasized in Chapter 14.

ARTIFICIAL RADIOACTIVITY

In 1934 the Curie-Joliots discovered that positive particles much lighter than protons were emitted if aluminum was bombarded with alpha particles. These lighter positive particles had the same mass as the electron and were called positrons, or positive electrons. They had the same quantity of charge as the proton but masses which were 1/1840 as large.

One of the most important features of the Curie-Joliot experiment was the discovery that emission of positrons continued even after the bombarding alpha particle source was removed. After its removal, positron emission decreased with time in a manner which suggested radioactive decay. Thus artificially radioactive materials had been produced in this reaction: it was probably the first instance of their creation by man. Previous to this, man had been limited to the use of naturally occurring radioactive materials, but now he could fashion radioactive atoms at will, selecting the one whose half-life and other properties best suited his needs.

The discovery of artificial radioactivity held many interesting possibilities for the nuclear scientist. If it was possible to induce radioactivity in atoms, he might slip a few of them into chemical substances and then follow the course of their reactions by means of a Geiger counter. This so-called "tracer technique" has proved to be a most important research tool.

Eleven elements in the periodic table are naturally radioactive, but since each of these has several isotopes, there are forty known nuclides of these elements. Today radioactive isotopes of all elements have been produced artificially, some in considerable quantities. For example, I^{131}, which is in common use today in diagnostic and therapeutic thyroid work, may be prepared in a nuclear reactor or atomic pile (see Chapter 14).

It has been shown in this chapter that high-speed particles ejected at high velocities from the nuclei of radioactive atoms have enabled scientists to establish that the atom has a positively charged nucleus comprising most of its mass, to determine the number of positive charges on the nucleus of the atom, and to discover the neutron. Rutherford's experiment in 1919, involving the first controlled nuclear reaction, initiated the study of nuclear reactions and eventually the production of a wide variety of radioactive isotopes.

Exercises and Questions for Chapter 12

1. The half-life period of I^{131} is 8 days. Out of an original 10^8 atoms of I^{131}, how many will still be radioactive at the end of 40 days?

2. Calculate the kinetic energy of an alpha particle in mev if it has a velocity of 10^9 cm/sec. 6.02×10^{23} atoms of helium have a mass of 4 gm. (Neglect the difference in mass between the helium atom and the alpha particle.)

3. Describe the method used by Madame Curie to compare the activities of two radioactive samples.

4. What is meant by fractional crystallization? Explain how two substances may be separated by means of this process.

5. Compare the properties of alpha, beta, and gamma rays with respect to: (a) charge, (b) mass, (c) ionizing power, (d) penetrating power.

6. What instruments are used to detect the presence of radioactive substances? Describe briefly the method of operation of each detector.

7. What is meant by the half-life of a radioisotope? Illustrate.

8. Describe the experiments of Geiger and Marsden which proved that an atom had a positively charged nucleus containing most of its mass.

9. Describe how the first controlled nuclear reaction was carried out. How was it proved that protons were produced in this reaction?

10. Write an equation for the (d, n) reaction in which the target atoms are $_{29}Cu^{63}$. (d = deuterium = $_1H^2$.)

11. Compare the characteristics of an ordinary chemical reaction and a nuclear reaction.

12. Why are the energies of nuclear particles usually expressed in electronvolts or multiples thereof?

13. Describe the experiments which led to the discovery of the neutron.

14. Describe the discovery of artificial radioactivity by the Curie-Joliots.

15. How are radioactive isotopes usually produced for commercial use?

REVIEW

1. A 750-lb load of limestone is 85% calcium carbonate. Calculate the weight of quicklime (CaO) obtained by heating it if the following reaction takes place.

$$CaCO_3 \rightarrow CaO + CO_2 \uparrow$$

Assume that the reaction goes to completion.

2. Devise a temperature conversion formula to change Fahrenheit temperature to a scale on which the freezing point of water is $0°$ and the boiling point $40°$. Represent a given temperature on this scale by X, just as you would represent a Fahrenheit temperature by F.

fission (split)

fusion (adding)

3. According to Graham's law, the rates of effusion (escape from a vessel through a small opening) of gases are inversely proportional to the square roots of their densities. Compare the rates of effusion of hydrogen and carbon dioxide gases. (Assume that the temperatures and pressures of the gases are the same.)

CHAPTER 13

The Ties That Bind: The Electronic Structure of Atoms

Newton discovered in the 1660's that white light was a complex of many colors. Nearly two centuries later, Bunsen and Kirchhoff demonstrated that there was a connection between the light emitted by a luminous gaseous substance and the chemical elements composing it. Michael Faraday, in studying the properties of magnets, found that a magnet could rotate the plane of vibrations of polarized light (a beam of light whose vibrations all lie in a single plane). Faraday's work was followed up by the brilliant British physicist and mathematician, James Clerk Maxwell, who became interested in Faraday's discovery of magnetic "lines of force." Maxwell had exceptional ability in interpreting scientific phenomena with mathematical equations and was able to work out equations describing the properties not only of magnetic fields but also of electric fields. These equations, while somewhat complex, brought about a broader understanding of what were eventually called "electromagnetic waves." He predicted that these waves traveled with the speed of light and that light itself was electromagnetic in character. Both of these predictions were subsequently verified. The German scientist Heinrich

Hertz (1857-1894) was the first to actually demonstrate the existence of these waves in 1888.

PROPAGATION OF ELECTROMAGNETIC WAVES

In order to understand the work of Hertz, let us review, for a moment, the method of getting sparks to jump between two metal knobs in air. A spark gap consists of two metal knobs separated by a space which must be crossed by charged particles if an electric circuit is to be completed. When a sufficiently high voltage is applied to the knobs, a spark will jump between them. Hertz simply attached an induction coil (see Fig. 11-4) to a spark gap and found that when the spark oscillated (jumped back and forth) between the knobs, invisible waves spread out into space. Since these waves were invisible, some sort of device for detecting them was necessary. For this purpose a second spark gap was placed near the first but not attached to it: the circuit of the second gap could be adjusted or "tuned" so that when sparks jumped the first spark gap, sparks would also jump the second.

These waves are today called radio waves—electromagnetic waves with wave lengths considerably longer than those of visible light. Hertz demonstrated that they had many of the properties of the electromagnetic waves predicted by Maxwell. They behaved in virtually all respects like waves of visible light even though their wave lengths were far greater. The rapid oscillation of electric charge was sending these electromagnetic waves off into space. Near the end of the nineteenth century it had become apparent that electrons were tiny electric charges. In view of Hertz's discovery, what would be more natural than to associate the wave lengths of light, sent out by atoms, with vibrating electrons, constituents of these atoms?

THE SPECTRUM OF HYDROGEN

Three years before Hertz demonstrated experimentally the existence of electromagnetic waves, a Swiss scientist, Balmer, made a study of a group of lines in the visible spectrum of the element hydrogen. These lines (see Fig. 13-1) were spaced relatively far apart at the long-wave length (red) end of the spectral field; at shorter wave lengths they came closer and closer together, and at the point where they ended (the series limit) a very large number of not easily distinguishable lines crowded in together. The series limit was actually in the ultraviolet region of the spectrum. Balmer devised an equation by which the wave lengths of the spectral lines of the element hydrogen

The relation between electronic transitions and spectral lines (Balmer series). This group of lines, which is located in the visible and near ultraviolet region, results from electrons dropping back to the second energy level.

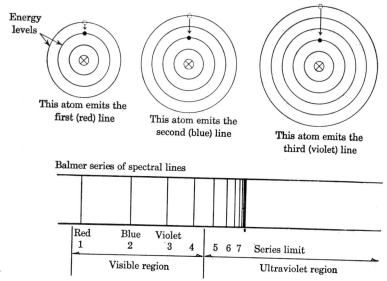

Balmer series of spectral lines

Fig. 13-1.

could be calculated quite exactly. According to the modified form of Balmer's equation which we shall use

$$\frac{1}{L} = K\left(\frac{1}{n_1{}^2} - \frac{1}{n_2{}^2}\right)$$ (13-a)

L represents the wave length of a spectral line; K is a constant; n_1 is an integer whose value is 2 (for the Balmer series only). n_2 is another integer whose lowest possible value is 3, but which may have larger values of 4, 5, 6, etc. The smallest value of n_2 (3) gives the longest wave length and hence corresponds to the line at the red end of the spectrum:

$$\frac{1}{L} = K\left(\frac{1}{4} - \frac{1}{9}\right) = K\frac{5}{36}, \text{ so } L = \frac{1}{K} \cdot \frac{36}{5} = \frac{7.2}{K}$$

The value 4 for n_2 gives the second line,

$$\frac{1}{L} = K\left(\frac{1}{4} - \frac{1}{16}\right) = K\frac{3}{16}, \quad \text{so} \quad L = \frac{1}{K} \cdot \frac{16}{3} = \frac{5.3}{K}$$

By assigning the succeeding values of n_2—5, 6 etc.—the wave lengths of the other visible spectral lines of hydrogen may be calculated. Substitution of successively larger values of n_2 gives smaller and smaller values of L, which approach a limit, as n_2 becomes infinitely large, of

$$\frac{1}{L} = K\left(\frac{1}{4} - 0\right), \quad L = \frac{4}{K}$$

Lyman, a physicist at Harvard University, discovered a similar series of lines in the ultraviolet region of the hydrogen spectrum. Like the Balmer series lines, these lines were relatively far apart at the long-wave length end and were crowded in close together at shorter wave lengths. The wave length of each line could be calculated by means of the same equation, but for this series $n_1 = 1$ and $n_2 = 2, 3, 4$;

for $n_2 = 2$,

$$\frac{1}{L} = K\left(1 - \frac{1}{4}\right) \quad \text{and} \quad L = \frac{1.33}{K};$$

for $n_2 = 3$,

$$\frac{1}{L} = K\left(1 - \frac{1}{9}\right) \quad \text{and} \quad L = \frac{1.13}{K};$$

for $n_2 = 4$,

$$\frac{1}{L} = K\left(1 - \frac{1}{16}\right) \quad \text{and} \quad L = \frac{1.07}{K}, \text{ etc., with } L = \frac{1.00}{K} \text{ as the series limit.}$$

Corresponding series of spectral lines in the infrared region known as the Paschen, Brackett, and Pfund series, were also discovered. For each of these the same equation applied, but for the Paschen series $n_1 = 3$ and $n_2 = 4, 5, 6$; for the Brackett series $n_1 = 4$ and $n_2 = 5, 6, 7$; and for the Pfund series $n_1 = 5$ and $n_2 = 6, 7, 8$. In each of these series, as in those described above, the smallest value of n_2 gives the spectral line of longest wave length.

Let us now see what significance was attached to these seemingly arbitrary numbers in Bohr's theory of the structure of the atom.

THE BOHR THEORY OF THE ATOM

The great Danish physicist Niels Bohr proposed a theory of the atom in 1913 which was remarkably successful in predicting properties of hydrogen and hydrogen-like atoms (atoms with only one orbital electron, such as ionized helium). According to this theory, the negatively charged electron of the hydrogen atom revolved about the positively charged nucleus only in certain definite orbits.* The theory also assumed one of the principles of Max Planck's quantum theory —namely, that a radiating (or absorbing) atom could lose (or gain) energy only in units of definite size. These units of energy were called *quanta*. As long as an electron was revolving in a particular orbit or at a particular energy level, there would be no emission or absorption of energy by the atom.

Remember that an atom must be energized, or excited to a light-emitting condition, in order to give a spectrum. According to Bohr's theory, the absorption of energy by the atom resulted in the electron's being driven farther away from the nucleus (Fig. 13-2). Since an at-

Energy supplied to atoms in the process of excitation drives electrons into a shell farther removed from the nucleus. Work is done as these negatively charged particles move against the attractive force of the positive nuclei.

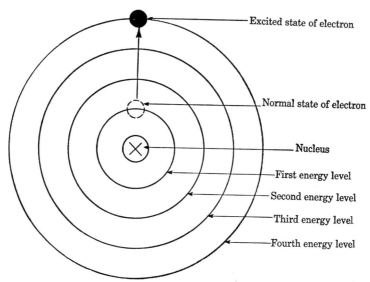

Fig. 13-2.

tractive force exists between the positive nucleus and the negative electron, work had to be done on the atom to remove an electron from an inner orbit (close to the nucleus) to an outer orbit. When the electron

* Subsequent developments in wave mechanics have altered somewhat the concept of electrons revolving in definite orbits about the nucleus.

was located at a greater-than-normal distance from the nucleus, the atom was said to be in an "excited state." Electrons in outer orbits or in higher energy levels tended to drop to orbits nearer the nucleus; as the electron dropped back to an inner orbit, energy was given off by the atom and a spectral line was emitted.

Since in any sample of hydrogen gas there were countless millions of atoms, and since different electrons were making transitions between all possible energy levels, many lines in different regions of the spectrum were observed. Just as Millikan's oil drop experiment revealed that all electric charges were multiples of a unit electronic charge, so Planck's quantum theory reasoned that all quantities of radiated energy E were multiples of a quantity h (known as Planck's constant). According to Planck's equation, the amount of energy in a single quantum was obtained by multiplying h by the frequency of the radiation N:

$$E = hN$$

Since frequency varies inversely as wave length—that is, N is large for short wave lengths and small for long wave lengths—the quanta in the ultraviolet region were larger than those in the visible region.

The Bohr theory dovetailed beautifully with Equation 13-a above, for calculating the wave lengths of lines in the hydrogen spectrum. In the Bohr theory, n_2 and n_1 of this equation become respectively the number of the orbit from which the electron started (in the excited state of the atom) and the number of the orbit to which it dropped. In any large number of hydrogen atoms under excitation, there would always be some electrons in the second, third, fourth, fifth, etc., orbits. In the Balmer series, where $n_1 = 2$, all spectral lines were interpreted as the result of electrons dropping from some outer orbit to the second orbit or second energy level, as shown in Fig. 13-1; the greater the jump, the larger the amount of energy E radiated in a single quantum. Since the energy of a quantum is proportional to the frequency, the greater the jump, the shorter the wave length L. Similarly, the spectral lines of the Lyman series, where $n_1 = 1$, were interpreted as the result of electrons dropping from some outer orbit to the first orbit or first energy level.

Thus the Bohr theory very satisfactorily accounted for the series of lines in a hydrogen (or hydrogen-like) spectrum on the basis of electronic transitions between energy levels. Even though attempts to extend this theory to more complex atoms were unsuccessful, the concept of electronic (and nuclear) energy levels has proved to be very useful and has added to our understanding of the behavior of atoms.

THE ARRANGEMENT OF ELECTRONS IN ENERGY LEVELS

According to the Bohr theory, in a neutral atom the number of electrons is equal to the number of protons on the nucleus, and the electrons circulate about the nucleus much as the planets revolve about the sun. The electrons can be energized and driven outward to higher energy levels; with sufficiently drastic excitation, one or more of them can be driven out completely from the sphere of attraction of the positive nucleus. This process of detaching an electron from a neutral atom is called ionization: when the atom loses an electron, it becomes a positively charged ion. The amount of energy (in electron volts) required to bring about the removal of a single electron is measured by the ionization potential of the atom.

If the values of the ionization potentials are plotted against atomic numbers, as in Fig. 13-3, it will be noted that they vary periodically as

Variation of ionization potential with atomic number.

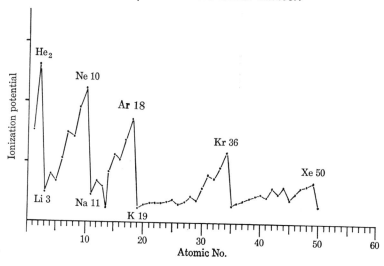

Fig. 13-3.

suggested in the discussion of the periodic law in Chapter 9. The values for the inert gases are much larger than those for any of the other elements: this means that an electron is removed from an atom of an inert gas only by the expenditure of much more work than is required for atoms of other nearby elements in the periodic table. The inert gases are the most stab'e and unreactive of all the elements. The alkali metals —Li, Na, K, Rb, and Cs—have very low ionization potentials, ind;cating that an electron is easily removed from one of these atoms. The group of elements known as the halogens—F, Cl, Br and I—have relatively high ionization potentials and hence the removal of an electron from one of these atoms will be a difficult process; the halogens will borrow electrons rather than lend them when combining with other elements.

The first element in the periodic table, hydrogen, has one electron revolving about its nucleus. The element helium is the second in the period table; its atomic number is 2, and there will be two electrons revolving about its nucleus. The next element, lithium, of atomic number 3, loses its first electron very readily, but to remove a second electron from this atom is about as difficult as it is to remove an electron from the atom of an inert gas. The shell of electrons nearest the nucleus is therefore believed to contain two electrons, just as in the element helium. Hence, in writing the electron structure of lithium we assign two electrons to the first shell, and one to the second. Actually all atoms in the normal (unexcited) state, except hydrogen, have two electrons in the first shell.

The element of atomic number 10 is neon. It is ionized with great difficulty; like helium, it is an inert gas. If the first shell contains two electrons, there will be eight electrons left over for the second shell. An *outer* shell of eight electrons is characteristic of all the inert gases except helium. Hence, an outer shell of eight electrons is referred to as an *inert gas structure.*

Element number 9, fluorine, has two electrons in the first shell and seven in the second. It has a relatively large ionization potential—that is, it will lose an electron only with great difficulty. When it accepts an additional electron from another atom, then its outer shell assumes an inert gas configuration of eight electrons, which is very stable.

The maximum number of electrons possible in the shell of number n is $2n^2$. In the first shell ($n = 1$) there can be no more than 2 electrons, since $2 \cdot 1^2 = 2$. Similarly in the second shell ($n = 2$) there can be no more than $2 \cdot 2^2$ or eight electrons, and in the third shell ($n = 3$) no more than $2 \cdot 3^2$ or 18. It should be emphasized that these represent the *largest* numbers of electrons ever found in the particular shell: there will often be a smaller number, and there are never more than 8 in the outer shell. Furthermore, electrons may be present in an outer shell before the shell inside it has its maximum number. For example, the element potassium has an atomic number 19. This means there will be 19 electrons revolving about the nucleus. Two will be in the first shell and 8 in the second, leaving 9 more; 8 of the remaining 9 go in the third shell and the extra one goes into the outer shell, called the *valence shell*.

Since a shell containing eight electrons is a stable arrangement, eight is often the number of electrons, even when it is not the maximum possible number, in the shell beneath the outer shell of valence electrons.

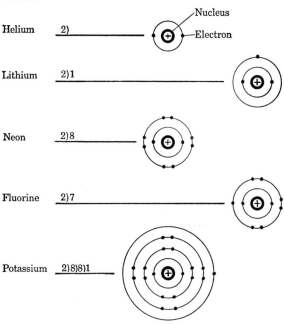

The electronic structures of several common elements.

Fig. 13-4.

By keeping this in mind, it is simple to write the electronic structures of the first twenty elements. Fig. 13-4 shows the electronic structures of five common elements.

ELECTRONIC STRUCTURES OF METALS AND NONMETALS

All the elements in the first vertical column on the left-hand side of the periodic table have atoms with 1 electron in the outer shell. Those in vertical column 2 have 2 electrons in the outer shell, and those in column 3 have 3. In undergoing chemical reaction, all of these elements tend to lose electrons and form positive ions: if an electrically neutral atom loses one or more electrons (negative charges), the positive charges in the atom will then outnumber the negative, and the net charge will be positive. In general, atoms of metals tend to form positive ions.

Nonmetallic atoms, on the other hand, have electronic structures which are generally 1, 2, or 3 electrons short of a stable outer shell of 8. In entering into chemical reaction, these tend to be electron borrowers. If neutral nonmetallic atoms add extra electrons, negative charges will predominate over positive, so nonmetallic atoms tend to form negative ions.

Metals, then, usually have 1, 2, or 3 (sometimes 4) electrons in the outer shell and tend to form positive ions. Nonmetals will usually have 5, 6, or 7 electrons in the outer shell and tend to form negative ions when reacting with other substances. Inert gases have stable outer shells—2 electrons in the case of helium and 8 in all others.

ELECTROVALENCE AND ELECTRONIC STRUCTURE

In Chapter 7, valence was presented as a number. We can now discuss valence in terms of atomic structure, and develop the meaning of two types—electrovalence and covalence. *ionic bond.*

Metals have been described as having 1, 2, 3, or sometimes 4 electrons in the outer or valence shell. In undergoing chemical reactions the metals characteristically lose these electrons. The number of electrons lost by a single atom of the metal is numerically equal to its valence. The sodium atom, for example, has 1 electron in the outer shell. In uniting with another element it will lose this electron and thus be left with a net charge, or valence, of +1. The written symbol for the resulting sodium ions is Na^+. Metals tend to be electron losers in entering into chemical combination, and the number of electrons lost is equal to the valence. The atom of calcium characteristically loses 2

do not share electrons, but strip them from atoms

electrons when combining with other elements; hence the symbol for the calcium ion is Ca^{++}. Ca^{++} has a valence of +2.

Nonmetals, on the other hand, have 5, 6, or 7 electrons in their valence shells and will fill these up to shells of 8 by borrowing electrons from metallic atoms. The number of electrons so borrowed by a single atom of the element is its valence. For example, fluorine, whose atomic number is 9, has 7 electrons in the valence shell. In order to attain an inert gas structure of 8 electrons, it will need to borrow one from a metallic atom. After borrowing an electron, it will have a net charge, or valence, of −1. The fluoride ion is symbolized F^-.

Oxygen, whose atomic number is 8, has an electron structure of 2 electrons in the first shell and 6 in the second or valence shell. The electronic arrangement for this structure is 2)6. Oxygen thus needs 2 additional electrons to complete its outer shell of 8. If it borrows 2 electrons it will have a net charge of −2. Thus it has a valence of −2, symbolized $O^=$.

An electrovalent compound is formed when ions of metals and ions of nonmetals combine. Chemical combination of the electrovalent type

In the combination of sodium metal with gaseous fluorine, each sodium atom transfers an electron to a fluorine atom. Sodium and fluoride ions result from the transfer.

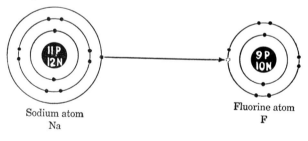

Sodium atom
Na

Fluorine atom
F

Sodium ion
Na+

Fluoride ion
F −

Fig. 13-5.

is, in essence, a competition for electrons. A fluorine atom, for example, needs an extra electron to attain an inert gas structure of 2)8. Sodium has 1 electron in excess of an inert gas configuration. Sodium is an active element, which means that its electron is not very tightly bound. The fluorine atom, which is a potent electron attracter, captures the loosely bound valence electron of sodium; the fluorine atom becomes a negative ion and the sodium atom a positive ion (Fig. 13-5). Both attain inert gas structures by this transfer. The ions are held together, or bonded, in the compound by the electrostatic forces of opposite charges.

A single atom of magnesium readily parts with 2 valence electrons, but a single fluorine will accept only one. Hence, two atoms of fluorine will be needed to combine with a single atom of magnesium to form magnesium fluoride (Fig. 13-6). The formula of this compound is MgF_2. Similarly, a single atom of oxygen needs 2 electrons to complete its valence shell, a single atom of sodium can furnish only 1; hence, 2

Fig. 13-6.

A magnesium atom has two electrons in excess of an inert gas structure; fluorine atoms need an additional electron. Magnesium has a valence of +2, fluorine a valence of −1.

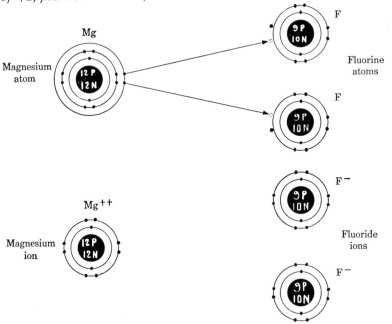

atoms of sodium are needed to combine with 1 atom of oxygen. The formula for sodium oxide is Na_2O. In electrovalent compounds, the valence of an element is determined by the number of electrons lent or borrowed by a single atom of the element.

An ion has been described as an atom which has either gained or lost electrons. An electrovalent compound is a chemical combination of positive and negative ions. An electrovalent compound, when dissolved in water, is a good conductor of electric current—an *electrolyte*. As was shown in Chapter 11, pure water is not an electrolyte, but hydrochloric acid (an electrovalent compound) dissolved in water is an electrolyte. Similarly, the ferric nitrate, copper sulfate, and silver nitrate of Fig. 10-23 are all electrolytes formed by the solution of an electrovalent compound in water.

COVALENCE

In electrovalent compounds the bond is the attraction of negative to positive ions, brought about by the transfer of one or more electrons from one atom to another.

In covalent compounds *an electron pair* is the bonding influence between two atoms. Consider methane, CH_4, "marsh gas," a structurally simple compound which is covalently bonded. Methane is composed of molecules containing a central carbon atom to which are attached four hydrogen atoms. In the valence shell of the carbon atom there are 4 electrons. (In the symbol for this atom, $\cdot \overset{\cdot}{C} \cdot$ the completed undershell of 2 electrons is omitted.) Each of the 4 hydrogen atoms has 1 electron revolving about its nucleus. $H\cdot$ represents a single atom of hydrogen. An electron of the carbon atom and one from a hydrogen are spinning in opposite directions, so that a weak magnetic effect is generated. This magnetic attraction, or bond, attaches the two atoms. The carbon atom holds 4 hydrogen atoms in combination in a molecule of methane and is described as having a covalence of 4. Hydrogen is said to have a covalence of 1.

In covalent compounds, then, there is a sharing of electrons by atoms. With a more symmetrical distribution of electric charge in the covalent compounds, there is an absence of electrical conductivity. If sugar is dissolved in water the solution is not an electrolyte; sugar is a covalent compound. Solutions of covalent compounds in water are called non-electrolytes.

share electrons to fill shells

Another distinction between electrovalent compounds and covalent compounds is the degree to which they lower the freezing point of water, or raise its boiling point. One formula weight of a covalent compound, such as urea, dissolved in 1000 grams of water, will lower its freezing point to −1.86°C and raise its boiling point to 100.52°C. 1.86 C° is called the "normal" freezing point lowering, and 0.52 C° the normal boiling point elevation, per formula weight per 1000 grams of water. A formula weight of an electrovalent compound such as calcium chloride, $CaCl_2$, which has one calcium ion and two chloride ions, will lower the freezing point of 1000 grams of water (or raise its boiling point) by nearly three normal freezing point lowerings (or three normal boiling point elevations), one for each ion; this solution has a freezing point of about −5.58°C and a boiling point of about 101.56°C. Thus in an electrolyte, each ion of the electrovalent compound is nearly as effective in lowering the freezing point (or raising the boiling point) as is a single molecule of a covalent compound (Fig. 13-7).

Fig. 13-7.

The lowerings of the freezing points of solutions of electrolytes are greater than those of nonelectrolytes, and the elevations of the boiling points of solutions of electrolytes are greater than those of nonelectrolytes of the same concentration.

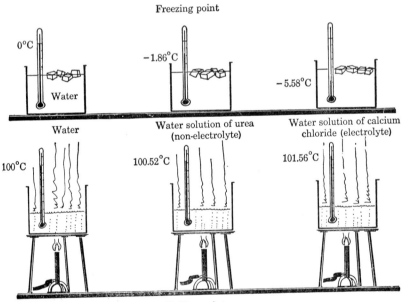

There is no single or simple way of knowing whether a particular compound is electrovalent or covalent, but as a general rule the acids, bases, and salts are ionic or electrovalent. Water solutions of the acid HCl (hydrochloric acid), the base NaOH (sodium hydroxide), and the salt KCl (potassium chloride) are all good conductors of an electric current. However, acetic acid, the principal acid in vinegar, is a much poorer conductor than either HCl or H_2SO_4; it is a "weak acid." The solution contains a few hydrogen and acetate ions and many acetic acid molecules. Ammonium hydroxide is likewise a much poorer conductor of an electric current than sodium hydroxide; it is a "weak base." A solution of a weak electrolyte contains few ions and many molecules.

Cadmium chloride ($CdCl_2$) appears to be a salt just like calcium chloride ($CaCl_2$), but unlike the latter its water solution is a very poor conductor of an electric current. The covalent compounds are most numerous in *organic chemistry*, as the chemistry of the compounds of the element carbon is called.

Let us now turn to the question of the relation of the electron structure of an atom to its reactivity with other atoms.

THE RELATIVE ACTIVITY OF CHEMICAL ELEMENTS

Some elements, like sodium, potassium, and fluorine, react with a great variety of other elements. Others, like silver, gold, and platinum, enter into chemical combination less readily.

Sodium is a very soft metal, so soft in fact that it may be cut with a knife; it has about the consistency of cheese. When freshly cut, its surface is shiny, like that of most other metals. If it is placed in water it floats, skimming around on its surface, reacting violently with the water and liberating hydrogen into the surrounding air. The sodium hydroxide (a base) produced in the water gives the water a soapy feeling and changes the color of litmus paper from red to blue. This property of changing the color of litmus paper is characteristic of the class of substances called bases.

If sodium metal is left exposed to air, its shiny surface rapidly loses its luster as it reacts with oxygen from the air. The substance is so reactive that it is usually stored under kerosene.

Fluorine is a most active nonmetallic element. Because of its great tendency to react with any substance in its vicinity its discovery came later than that of many of the common elements. If fluorine atoms were separated from a fluoride, they would immediately attack the glass or metal vessel in which they were prepared. No sooner were they obtained in a free state than they would combine with another substance. Moissan was finally able to isolate this ill-behaved element in 1886. Fluorine atoms were separated from fluorides by means of an electrolytic process carried out in a copper vessel. The fluorine produced reacted with the copper metal container and in a short time an impervious layer of the fluoride had formed on it. Thenceforth the free element fluorine meeting nothing else in the vicinity with which it could react, could be collected.

Silver and gold are often called the noble metals. Because of their comparative unreactivity they are often found in the native (uncombined) state. Silver, unlike sodium, is quite unreactive in the presence of water, although it dissolves in nitric acid. Gold resists even the solvent action of nitric acid; the much more potent "aqua regia" (a mixture of hydrochloric and nitric acids) is required to dissolve it.

The gaseous element nitrogen is comparatively difficult to combine with other elements. To be sure, it may be coaxed into reaction with some elements like oxygen or hydrogen, but only by such means as electrical discharges or catalysis. The least reactive of all the elements are of course the inert gases. They simply refuse to join with any other atoms in forming compounds.

Table 13-1   ACTIVITY SERIES OF METALS

Potassium
Calcium
Sodium
Magnesium
Aluminum
Zinc
Iron
Tin
Lead

Hydrogen

Copper
Bismuth
Mercury
Silver
Gold

Table 13-1 lists a group of metals in order of decreasing activity; it is called an activity series. At the top are the very active metals such as lithium, potassium, and sodium; at the bottom are the inactive elements such as silver and gold. The atoms of the elements nearest the top of the table are those which most easily lose electrons. These very readily form positive ions, and have a very weak hold on their valence electrons; other atoms easily take them away. On the other hand, atoms of silver and gold near the bottom of the table bind their valence electrons much more tightly. It is very difficult for another element to remove them.

The Activity of Elements and Electric Cells If a strip of zinc metal is suspended in a blue copper sulfate solution, a reddish brown deposit of copper metal forms on the strip and the blue color of the solution gradually disappears. Copper ions from the solution gain electrons, become copper atoms, and as such are deposited. Atoms of zinc dissolve in the solution, as may be demonstrated by testing the solution with appropriate analytical procedures. Atoms of zinc have, then, been changed into zinc ions in this reaction.

The above reaction involves essentially a competition for electrons. The blue solution contains copper in the ionic condition. The valence electrons of copper atoms are much more difficult to remove than those of zinc or aluminum, for example, but once they have been taken away, the resulting ion has a far greater tendency to gain them back than would the ion of an atom higher in the series such as zinc. The valence electrons of zinc behave as if they were attached rather loosely and are fairly easily removed. Once in the ionic condition however, the tendency of the zinc ion to regain the electrons is much weaker than the tendency of copper ions. Thus, when a strip of zinc (atoms) is immersed in a solution containing copper ions, the latter simply take electrons from the former, leaving zinc in the ionic condition and converting copper ions into atoms. In a sense, it is a matter of survival of the strongest: copper ions attract electrons more strongly than zinc atoms do.

If a cell (battery) is formed by dipping strips of zinc and copper metal in zinc and copper sulfate solutions respectively, and the solutions are separated by a porous barrier as shown in Fig. 13-8, the chemical reaction described above takes place, but in this arrangement electrons are transferred from the zinc atoms to the copper ions by means of the wire connecting the two strips rather than by direct transfer in solution. Copper ions in the copper sulfate solution remove electrons from the copper electrode, and atoms of copper deposit upon it. Electrons from the copper wire which constitutes the external circuit move into the copper electrode to replenish the supply. These electrons come from the atoms on the zinc electrode, where zinc atoms become zinc ions, break off from the electrode, and go into solution.

The same reaction takes place in B as in C. In one case electron transfer is direct, in the other via a piece of copper wire.

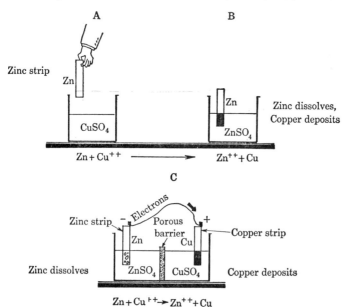

Fig. 13-8.

A supply of electrons is continually being created at the zinc electrode and removed at the copper electrode. The result is that electrons flow out of the cell at the negative terminal (the more active metal, zinc) and in at the positive terminal (the less active metal, copper). Thus the production of electric current by chemical action is readily explained in terms of the relative activities of elements as predicted by their electronic structures.

The activity series of the elements which is based on their behavior as electrodes in electrolytic cells is known as the "electrochemical series." The order of this series differs slightly from Table 13-1, which is based on chemical reactions.

THE STRUCTURE OF THE TWO COMMON ATOMS, CALCIUM AND CHLORINE

By way of summarizing the discussion concerning the structure of the atom, let us consider the structure of the two common elements, calcium and chlorine. The structure of the calcium atom is shown in Fig. 13-9. It has atomic number 20 and atomic mass 40. Since the

Structure of the calcium atom.

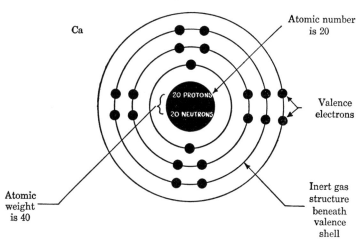

Ca

Atomic number is 20

20 PROTONS
20 NEUTRONS

Valence electrons

Inert gas structure beneath valence shell

Atomic weight is 40

Fig. 13-9.

atomic number is equal to the number of protons in the nucleus, there must be 20 protons. If the uncombined atom is electrically neutral, there must also be 20 electrons revolving about the nucleus. In addition to the 20 protons on the nucleus, there must also be 20 neutrons (obtained by subtracting the atomic number from the atomic mass).

Of the 20 electrons, 2 are in the first shell, 8 in the second, 8 in the third, and 2 in the fourth (the outer or valence shell). Since there are fewer than 4 electrons in the outer shell, the element is a metal; its valence is +2. In chemical combinations, it will tend to be an electron lender. The element is relatively high in the activity series. It will readily react with many substances.

The chlorine atom has atomic number 17 and atomic mass 36.* There are 17 protons and 19 neutrons in the nucleus. In the uncombined atom there will be 17 electrons, 2 in the first shell, 8 in the second, and 7 in

* The atomic weight of chlorine is 35.46. It is composed of isotopes of mass 34 and 36.

the third. The outer shell needs only one additional electron to become a stable shell of 8, an inert gas structure. It will borrow 1 electron in order to complete this shell of 8. Chlorine is, then, a nonmetal with a valence of −1.

An atom of calcium has 2 electrons to lend; a single atom of chlorine can accept only 1. If calcium and chlorine are to combine, 2 chlorine atoms must react with each calcium atom. By losing its 2 valence electrons, the calcium atom attains a net charge of +2; forming a Ca^{++} ion. Each chlorine atom gains a single electron, forming a Cl^- ion. The binding force holding the positive calcium and the negative chloride ions together in the compound $CaCl_2$ results from the attraction of opposite electrostatic charges on the positively and negatively charged ions.

It should be clear, then, that electrons, though contributing very little to the mass of an atom, perform a most important function in binding atoms together in chemical union. Valence, chemical activity, spectra, and the operation of electrolytic cells can all be satisfactorily explained in terms of their electronic behavior.

EXERCISES AND QUESTIONS FOR CHAPTER 13

1. Calculate the energy (in ergs) of a quantum of electromagnetic radiation if its wave length is 10^{-4} angstrom units. Planck's constant $h = 6.62 \times 10^{-27}$ erg sec.

2. Explain how Bohr was able to use Balmer's formula in predicting very exactly the wave lengths of hydrogen's visible spectrum lines.

3. Explain the meaning of each term in Planck's equation $E = hN$.

4. What is meant by an ionization potential? How is it related to the chemical activity of an element?

5. What electronic structures are characteristic of (a) metals, (b) nonmetals, and (c) inert gases?

6. What is the relation between the electrovalence of an atom and its electronic structure? Illustrate.

7. What is meant by a covalent bond? Illustrate.

8. What properties distinguish electrolytes from nonelectrolytes? Illustrate.

9. How is chemical activity related to the electronic structure of atoms? Explain.

REVIEW

1. An arrow is shot upward vertically with an initial velocity of 300 ft/sec. To what height above the ground does it rise?

2. The crank of a windlass is 2 ft long, the drum is 9 in. in diameter. What force applied at right angles to the crank is needed to raise a 300-lb object suspended from a rope attached to the drum?

3. Calculate the kinetic energy of an 80-lb projectile if it is traveling at a velocity of 1500 ft/sec.

4. A 6-volt battery produces a current of 0.25 amp in a certain circuit. Calculate the resistance of the circuit.

CHAPTER 14

Energy from Splitting Atoms

THE key to the release of nuclear energy is the neutron. Production of neutrons in large numbers during the fission of U^{235} atoms has made possible nuclear explosions and the operation of nuclear reactors—and the nuclear reactor is the key to atomic power and large-

Fig. 14-1.

The gaseous diffusion plant at Oak Ridge, Tennessee (Courtesy, United States Atomic Energy Commission, Westcott, Oak Ridge)

scale production of radioisotopes (radioactive isotopes). Thus neutrons play a most important role in applied nuclear science.

Machines for accelerating atomic particles were beginning to reach some degree of efficiency in the early 1930's. Scientists had devised them because they wished to be able to bombard atomic nuclei with high-speed particles other than alpha particles or with particles moving at higher speeds than radioactive atoms could hurl them. Protons and deuterons (heavy hydrogen nuclei) promised to be effective in bombardment if they could be speeded up sufficiently. However, all positive ions have a fundamental drawback as atom smashers: the electric charges which make possible their acceleration also cause them to veer away as they closely approach a nucleus with its repelling positive charge. Neutrons are electrically neutral and are not repelled by the positively charged atomic nuclei. Shortly after they were discovered, it was realized that they had most promising possibilities as bombarding particles.

NEUTRON BOMBARDMENT REACTIONS

Enrico Fermi became interested in the use of neutrons as bombarding particles about 1934. He and his students carried out a wide variety of neutron bombardment reactions. One reaction in particular seemed to hold some exciting possibilities. It was a reaction which made it possible to change an atom of one element into an atom of the next (heavier) element in the periodic table. The following is an illustration of this type of reaction:

$$_{29}Cu^{65} + \ _0n^1 \ \rightarrow \ _{29}Cu^{66} \ + \gamma \text{ rays}$$

copper   neutron   radioactive
atom   copper atom

$$_{29}Cu^{66} \rightarrow \ _{30}Zn^{66} + \ _{-1}e^0$$

A neutron strikes a copper atom and attaches to it, increasing its mass by 1 and thus producing a radioactive isotope of copper and gamma rays. The Cu^{66} atom then undergoes radioactive decay: the neutron splits into a proton and an electron, and the electron is ejected as a beta particle. The nucleus now has 30 protons and is therefore an atom of zinc. Zinc is the element next to copper in the periodic table. Several atoms besides copper were known to undergo a similar reaction. Until 1939, virtually all the known nuclear reactions yielded product atoms whose locations in the periodic table were close to those of the parent atoms. Copper atoms could be converted into zinc; gold atoms could be changed into mercury.

Nuclear Fission   Fermi was curious to know what would happen if the heaviest of the elements then known—uranium, of atomic number 92—was bombarded with neutrons. If uranium behaved as just described when bombarded with neutrons, it seemed logical to suppose that Fermi might be able to prepare a new element of atomic number 93. However, nature sometimes divulges her secrets reluctantly. Element 93 was eventually discovered, but not until scientists had wrestled with many perplexing problems in the fission of uranium atoms.

The results of the neutron-uranium bombardment experiments were difficult to interpret, for scientists were trying to explain them in terms of the nuclear reactions with which they were familiar. Many neutron bombardment reactions had led to products having beta activity, and their decay had resulted in atoms of higher atomic number. Also in the minds of scientists who had a choice to make between conjecturing the formation of radium and conjecturing the formation of barium in such a reaction, radium seemed more likely simply because it stood closer to uranium in the periodic table. Eventually, careful chemical analyses by Hahn and Strassman proved the presence of barium rather than of radium. Gradually it became clear that a new and radically different phenomenon was involved—one in which uranium nuclei were splitting roughly in half. The process represented a distinctly new type of nuclear reaction in the heavier elements, and it was soon called *nuclear fission*.

The Energy Release Accompanying Fission   Theoretical considerations suggested that the process of uranium fission, would be accompanied by an energy release enormously greater than that possible in ordinary chemical reactions. When a U^{235} atom split into two other atoms, the mass of the two resulting atoms was less than that of the U^{235}: this "lost" matter was converted into energy according to Einstein's famous equation, $E = mc^2$.

For many years TNT (trinitrotoluene) had enjoyed the reputation of being the most highly explosive of all substances; a kilogram (2.2 lb) of U^{235}, however, if completely fissioned, would yield an energy release equivalent to 20,000 tons of TNT. This would also be equivalent to 25,000,000 kilowatt hours of electrical energy, enough to keep ten 100-watt electric light bulbs burning continuously for approximately 65 years. Even though, as a practical matter, only a small fraction of the energy theoretically available can actually be realized, a single pound of U^{235} still yields the energy equivalent of hundreds of tons of coal. The discovery of nuclear fission thus marked the beginning of a new era in industrial science.

THE NUCLEAR CHAIN REACTION

While the energy release accompanying the fission of U^{235} atoms was enormous, the question whether the energy resulting from nuclear fission could be useful depended upon whether a self-sustaining process or chain reaction could be established.

Uranium as it emerges from the refining—"natural uranium"—is a mixture of three isotopes—U^{234}, U^{235}, and U^{238}. The proportion of U^{234} atoms is negligibly small. The most fissionable isotope is U^{235}, but U^{235} atoms constitute less than 1 per cent of the atoms in natural uranium. When a neutron strikes a U^{235} nucleus, the latter splits into two fragments, each of which becomes a new atom. The fissioned nucleus also ejects two or three new neutrons. If at least one of these neutrons is able to reach another U^{235} atom, and the neutrons released by this fission are in turn able to reach others, a chain reaction should be possible.

But many other elements also have avid appetites for neutrons. Small amounts of impurities in the uranium may capture so many free neutrons that a chain reaction of U^{235} is impossible. Again, a certain number of neutrons will always escape off into space at the surface of the metal and never reach other U^{235} atoms. Because of this surface effect, a certain minimum amount of uranium, called the *critical mass* is necessary to sustain a chain reaction.

For every atom of U^{235} in a naturally occurring sample of uranium or of a uranium compound there are 140 of U^{238}. Neutrons having just the right velocity are as likely to attach themselves to U^{238} atoms as to fission U^{235}. Very energetic (fast) neutrons can even fission U^{238} atoms, but few of the neutrons emitted during the process of U^{235} fission have sufficiently great energy to do so. A chain reaction based on fast fission of U^{238} is not possible. The capture of neutrons of intermediate energy by U^{238} atoms is known as "resonance capture." Such neutrons are unavailable for the fission of U^{235} atoms.

Fig. 14-2.

A nuclear chain reaction depends on each generation of neutrons reproducing itself. A fissioning atom of U^{235} provides on the average 2.5 neutrons. If the chain reaction is to be maintained, at least one of these must reach another U^{235} atom.

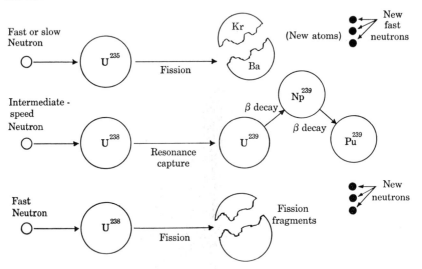

Thus high-speed neutrons and intermediate-speed neutrons do not all aid in maintaining a chain reaction. What about slow neutrons? These will serve effectively. They do not undergo resonance capture by U^{238}, and they will fission U^{235}. If neutrons are slowed down sufficiently their capture by U^{238} is minimized and enough are available for splitting U^{235} atoms to keep a chain reaction going.

Enriching Uranium with Respect to U^{235}   If the U^{235} isotopes are not to be so hopelessly outnumbered by U^{238} isotopes as to make a chain reaction impossible, some of the U^{238}'s must be removed; that is, the uranium must be "enriched" with respect to U^{235}.

The usual procedure for separating two chemical substances is to add a reagent which will react with one substance but not the other, as described in Chapter 12. U^{235} and U^{238} cannot be separated by a process of this type. Being isotopes, they undergo the same chemical reactions.

The method actually used is in fact long, tedious, and expensive, and is based on *gaseous diffusion.* Fig. 14-1 may give some idea of the scale of the operation. It is based on the following principle.

The kinetic energies of gas molecules are proportional to their absolute temperatures:

$$\tfrac{1}{2}m_1v_1^2 = kT_1, \qquad \tfrac{1}{2}m_2v_2^2 = kT_2$$

Hence two gases at the same temperature have velocities whose squares are inversely proportional to their masses:

$$v_1^2 = \frac{kT}{m_1}, \qquad v_2^2 = \frac{kT}{m_2}$$

Thus the molecular speed of a light gas will be greater than that of a heavy gas; a light gas such as hydrogen will diffuse more rapidly than a heavy gas such as carbon dioxide (see Fig. 14-3).

The speeds of diffusion of gas molecules are inversely proportional to the square roots of their densities. Hydrogen, the lightest of all gases, has the greatest speed of diffusion.

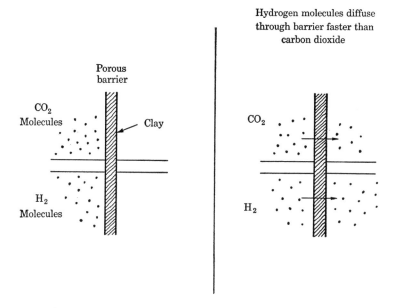

Fig. 14-3.

In the process of enriching uranium with respect to U^{235}, the uranium is first combined with fluorine to give uranium hexafluoride. This gaseous substance is circulated through *diffusion units.* The fluoride of the

U^{235} diffuses through the porous barrier—the wall of a clay tube—at a slightly greater speed than the fluoride of U^{238}, which is slightly heavier (see Fig. 14-4). The actual amount of separation taking place in a single diffusion unit is very small. We recall how Madame Curie had

Fig. 14-4.

The gaseous fluoride of U^{235} (UF_6) diffuses slightly more rapidly than that of U^{238}. Even though the enrichment in a single diffusion unit is very small, if these gases are circulated through a sufficiently large number of units, say 1000 or more, eventually nearly pure U^{235} may be prepared.

Before diffusion

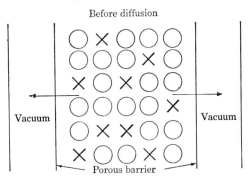

Vacuum   Vacuum

Porous barrier

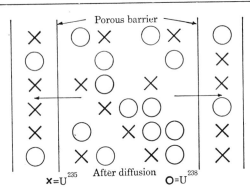

Porous barrier

$x=U^{235}$ After diffusion $O=U^{238}$

to crystallize and recrystallize materials from solution hundreds of times in order to be able to separate a tiny sample of radium from a ton of pitchblende ore. The process involved in separating the isotopes of uranium is similarly repetitious. Even though the amount of separation obtained in a single diffusion unit is exceedingly minute, if the operation is carried out in a sufficiently large number of units the job can be done. A minor miracle was accomplished by putting into operation in a single plant a very large number of diffusion units so that the enriched U^{235} could be obtained in quantities sufficient for military and industrial needs.

THE ATOMIC BOMB

The splitting of U^{235} nuclei is accompanied by the release of 2.5 neutrons per fission, on the average. They are hurled from the exploding nuclei at very high speeds, and are known as "fast neutrons." A fast neutron striking another U^{235} nucleus causes it to fission, and it in turn releases additional fast neutrons. In a small fraction of a second, millions and millions of atoms are fissioning, all releasing neutrons to fission other nearby U^{235} atoms.

As has been mentioned, there is a certain critical size below which a block of uranium is simply incapable of sustaining a chain reaction, since too many of the neutrons released leave the surface of the block. A possible way of setting off an atomic bomb is to fire two subcritical quantities of U^{235} at one another with high velocity (Fig. 14-5). There

One subcritical quantity of uranium is fired at high velocity into another subcritical quantity. When the critical quantity is assembled, a nuclear explosion ensues.

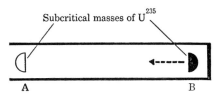

Subcritical masses of U^{235}

A   B

Fire B at A as in a cannon

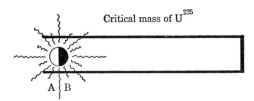

Critical mass of U^{235}

A B

Fig. 14-5.

are always enough stray neutrons to initiate the reaction, which quickly spreads throughout the mass of material.

Fig. 14-6.

A nuclear explosion.

The terrific effects of nuclear explosions are now well known. Searing heat, intense gamma rays, and showers of neutrons extend out to considerable distances from "ground zero," the point directly under the explosion. A tremendous shock wave first pushes objects in its path, then reverses itself, pulling them back. The momentary void at the base of the explosion pulls air and dust up into a central shaft in the familiar mushroom. Neutron activity renders these materials highly radioactive. Sooner or later they fall back to earth, irradiating whatever is in the path of the "fallout."

THE NUCLEAR REACTOR

The device in which fission of uranium is brought about under controlled conditions is known as the nuclear reactor. Both atomic bombs and nuclear reactors are dependent upon neutron fission of U^{235}, but there is an important difference between them. In bombs, neutron multiplication is allowed to proceed very swiftly. In reactors, the neutron levels are carefully controlled so that they will just reproduce themselves. The balance is a delicate one. If too many neutrons are lost through escape or reaction with other materials, the chain reaction ceases; if not enough are used up, the neutron flux will increase; the device will run wild and destroy itself.

There are numerous types of nuclear reactors and we may expect the development of others. Some operate with fast neutrons; others make use of moderators such as graphite or heavy water (deuterium oxide, D_2O) to slow down neutrons. One type uses a water solution of a uranium compound; another makes use of bars of metallic uranium. The bars of uranium may in turn be either natural uranium or the U^{235}-enriched variety. Some reactors produce more fissionable material than they use up and are known as *breeder reactors*.

One of the common forms of reactor is the graphite-moderated thermal reactor, a section of which is illustrated in Fig. 14-7. It consists of bars of uranium metal encased in aluminum cans which are inserted in slots in blocks of pure graphite. Control is effected by means of rods of boron steel, also located in slots in the graphite. Neutrons react readily with boron; it may be regarded as a neutron remover. These boron rods may be pushed into the interior of the pile to reduce the neutron flux or withdrawn to allow it to build up.

If a reactor is to sustain a chain reaction there must be a critical quantity of uranium present. The critical amount of "fuel" needed to sustain a chain reaction will depend upon the type of fuel used. In general, smaller quantities suffice if the uranium fuel is enriched in U^{235}. Larger quantities of natural uranium are needed.

Neutrons resulting from fission of U^{235} atoms in a uranium bar are "fast neutrons." After they have passed through graphite, their energies are reduced so they will not be captured by U^{238} atoms (resonance capture), but are still capable of causing fission of U^{235} atoms in the next uranium bar.

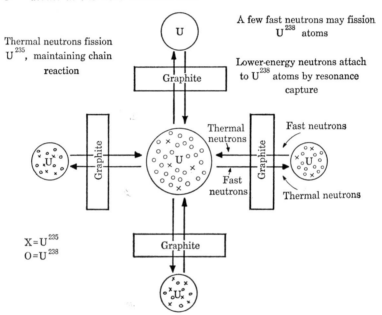

Fig. 14-7.

Let us consider the operation of a reactor using natural uranium, a fuel that contains 140 times as much U^{238} as U^{235}. When a U^{235} atom fissions, the new neutrons produced are fast neutrons. Some of these neutrons are able to fission U^{238} atoms, but not in sufficient quantity to sustain a chain reaction. Neutrons whose speeds have been moderated a bit may attach to U^{238} atoms in resonance capture. When neutrons have been slowed down to "thermal" speeds (roughly equal to those of gas molecules) they will not be captured by U^{238} atoms and will be far more effective in fissioning U^{235} atoms. Thus the neutrons formed by fission of U^{235} within a given bar of uranium may be used up by resonance capture, but those which travel through graphite are slowed

Fig. 14-8.

A graphite-moderated natural-uranium reactor. (Courtesy, Brookhaven National Laboratory, Upton, L.I., N.Y.)

down so they cannot react with U^{238} by resonance capture and are still effective in fissioning U^{235}. The U^{238} atoms which undergo resonance capture ultimately form plutonium atoms, which are also fissionable with slow neutrons and hence valuable as nuclear fuel. The moderator slows down enough of the neutrons below the resonance capture threshold to ensure that not too many neutrons will be used up in producing plutonium and that there will be an ample supply for fission processes.

Neutrons ejected from uranium bars on the edges of the pile travel outward from it and are lost, never to initiate other fissions. Reflectors are used to minimize such losses.

Just as boron in the control rods is an excellent "neutron absorber," impurities in the uranium or graphite may tend to reduce the neutron

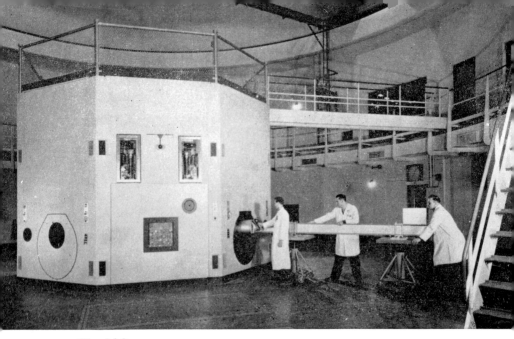

Fig. 14-9.

A research reactor. It uses U^{235} as a fuel and is cooled and moderated by heavy water. The octagon is 20 feet wide and 13½ feet high. Note the compactness attainable when an enriched fuel is used. (Courtesy, Argonne National Laboratory)

flux. The essential problem, then, in the nuclear reactor is to keep U^{235} atoms fissioning by supplying a sufficient number of neutrons without at the same time allowing the neutrons to multiply.

Some of the newer types of reactors use a highly enriched uranium, that is, uranium containing a high percentage of U^{235}, and heavy water as a moderator. While the latter is much more expensive than graphite, some of the units now being designed are considerably more compact. Fig. 14-9 shows a heavy-water-moderated tank-type research reactor now in use.

Uses of the Nuclear Reactor The nuclear reactor is the essential unit in the production of atomic power, of radioisotopes, and of fissionable materials. It is the most important neutron source available today, whether for research neutron bombardment or for production of commercial radioisotopes. Atom smashers like the cyclotron, linear accelerator, and Van de Graaff machine have been and still are valuable research tools in carrying out nuclear reactions that are impossible in an atomic pile. However, in terms of the quantities of radioisotopes (radioactive isotopes) produced, they are like toys compared with the nuclear reactor.

Radioisotopes are produced by introducing the materials to be irradiated into the interior of the reactor, where they are subjected to the action of enormous neutron fluxes and are rendered highly radioactive. For example, if a chunk of cobalt metal is introduced into the pile for a considerable length of time, it becomes a powerful emitter of gamma rays. Small pieces of it may be used by the medical profession to perform nearly any function accomplished with our most powerful X-ray machines. Since its half-life is longer than five years, it can be used for

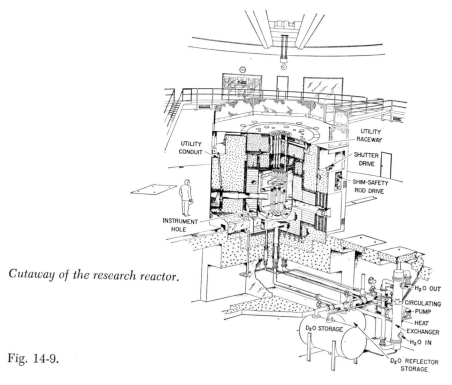

Cutaway of the research reactor.

Fig. 14-9.

a considerable period of time before its activity drops to an ineffectual level.

By proper choice of materials to be irradiated, a wide variety of radioisotopes with different half-lives and different types of rays can be made available. These may be purchased by the research scientist for a multitude of applications in science and industry.

The nuclear reactor is also the basic unit in the production of atomic power. Heat energy produced in a reactor as a result of the fission process may be absorbed by liquid metal (sometimes an alloy of sodium and potassium) which is circulated through pipes in the interior of the reactor. The heated liquid alloy is passed to a heat interchanger where heat is transferred to water, converting it into steam. The steam is in turn used in conventional steam turbines.

As a result of exposure to the high neutron flux in the interior of the reactor, the liquid alloy is rendered highly radioactive. If water itself were circulated through the reactor it would likewise become radioactively "hot" because of bombardment by neutrons. However there is virtually no radioactivity imparted to water when it receives heat from the liquid alloy in the heat interchanger. While the alloy is very radioactive, it is still not emitting neutrons, which are primarily responsible for inducing radioactivity in other substances.

Nuclear energy sources have the advantage of compactness. A few pounds of uranium have the same energy potential as many tons of gasoline, coal, or other more conventional fuels. One of the serious problems, however, in designing an atomic power plant is that of providing adequate shielding from radiation. Thick protecting walls must be erected. The weight of these walls, while not too serious a problem in a ship or a submarine, makes atomic power still impracticable for cars and airplanes.

Uses of Radioisotopes One of the reasons why radioisotopes have become so important in scientific research is that they announce their presence wherever they are by means of the radiations they emit. It is possible to tell their location at any given time by using a radiation detector such as a Geiger or scintillation counter.

In medical practice, the use of I^{131} has proved very valuable in the diagnosis of thyroid dysfunction. The patient swallows a glass of water containing in solution 10 to 50 microcuries (a very tiny quantity) of I^{131}. A day later a scintillation counter tube is placed near the thyroid and the activity counted (Fig. 14-10). The percentage of the iodine taken up by the thyroid gland may be determined by comparing this number of counts with the number obtained from the original sample. A normal thyroid will take up a certain percentage of the I^{131}; an overactive thyroid (hyperthyroid condition) will take up a much higher percentage and an underactive thyroid (hypothyroid condition) a much smaller percentage than the normal.

I^{131} is also used for therapeutic treatment of hyperthyroidism. For this purpose much larger doses (of the order of millicuries rather than microcuries) are administered. The radioiodine which accumulates in the thyroid gland subjects the tissue principally to the action of beta radiation, which impairs the function of the cells and slows down the action of the hyperactive gland.

Fig. 14-10.
Measuring by means of a scintillation counter tube the uptake of I^{131} by the thyroid gland. The scaler records the number of gamma-ray photons detected. The scintillation counter tube is far more efficient than the Geiger counter in detecting gamma rays. (Courtesy, Tracerlab, Inc., Boston)

Radioactive tracers have proved to be of value in locating brain tumors, thus simplifying brain surgery. Such tumors are known to absorb certain dyes. If somewhere in the structure of the dye there are radioactive atoms, these can be detected and hence the tumor located by means of a Geiger tube which scans the surface of the skull.

Radioisotopes may be used to follow the course of the circulation of nutrients from the roots to other parts of a plant. The radioisotopes are placed in the soil about the roots. Later different parts of the plant can be tested with a Geiger tube to show whether the nutrients have moved up the stalk, to the leaves, etc.

Thickness-control gauges employing radioisotopes are in use in a variety of industries. For example, in rug making, if the thickness of the rug becomes too great, radiation will be stopped more effectively so that fewer counts per minute reach the counter, and a correction in the manufacturing process can then be made by a servo mechanism. New uses of radioisotopes are being found almost daily. The possibilities of future developments in this area seem to be limitless.

FISSION OR FUSION?

In general, atoms of elements near the middle of the periodic table have greater stability than those of elements at the very beginning or end. Uranium, the heaviest of the naturally occurring elements, may be fissioned with the release of enormous quantities of energy. The fragments of the original atom must be smaller in mass, and hence nearer the middle of the periodic table. They are then less likely to undergo further fission; they are more stable than uranium. Similarly the lightest of all atoms, hydrogen, under appropriate conditions fuse, yielding heavier atoms, and in the process release enormous quantities of energy. Hence, elements near the middle of the periodic table are the least promising as possible energy sources.

Fusion of the nuclei of light elements, as has just been mentioned, offers a second way of liberating nuclear energy. If hydrogen or its isotopes were heated to a sufficiently high temperature and pressure, they could fuse into the heavier atoms of helium. Temperatures of a million or more degrees are momentarily realized in an atomic bomb explosion. This enormous temperature might suffice to trigger a thermonuclear reaction of hydrogen. Energy releases of this type are of another order of magnitude or so above that of the atomic bomb. Theoretically there is no limit to the energy release attainable in this type of reaction. No doubt a fusion of this kind is at the heart of the so-called hydrogen bomb. The achievement of controlled fusion was reported by British scientists in 1957.

CONCLUSION

We have now traced the development of a few of the important concepts of chemistry and physics. At the dawn of history we found man turning his thoughts to his everyday needs without paying much attention to the question of how the practical gadgets that he devised operated. The Greeks sought to explain many of the natural phenomena they observed, but made relatively little use of experimental methods. One of the important characteristics of science, as it flowered in the sixteenth and seventeenth centuries, was its increased attention to experimentation. Scientific societies, such as the Royal Society in England, also played an important role in the dissemination of ideas and hence in the growth of science. Many scientists and historians regard this seventeenth-century period as the beginning of the era of modern science.

The eighteenth and nineteenth centuries witnessed a wide variety of scientific developments. So much progress was made that an outstanding scientist is reputed to have commented that "all the important scientific discoveries have now been made. Henceforth, all that is left to do is to improve the precision of measurement of the important constants of nature,"—in other words to add a few more significant figures to such quantities as the mechanical equivalent of heat. Nearly all the developments which have been discussed in the last four chapters have taken place since this statement was made.

Enormous advances have been made in our twentieth century. Since World War II many multi-million-dollar industries have been made possible, in part because of scientific research. It is no longer almost exclusively a pursuit in which people may dabble during their spare time; it is, for many men, a profession by which they earn their livelihood. There are now research institutes in all parts of our country and in all the leading countries of the world. The future of scientific research and investigation seems almost limitless.

We have dealt in terms of a few centuries in these final paragraphs; in the next chapters we turn our attention to the study of astronomy, where a million years may play the role of a fleeting second.

Exercises and Questions for Chapter 14

1. Why have particle accelerators such as the cyclotron been important in the development of nuclear science?

2. Why was it expected in 1934 that neutron bombardment of uranium would produce a new element?

3. What is meant by uranium fission? How is it brought about? Which uranium isotope is most readily fissionable?

4. Compare the energy release accompanying the fission of U^{235} with that of equal weights of some common fuels.

5. Explain how a nuclear chain reaction is maintained by nuclear fission.

6. The process of resonance capture of neutrons by U^{238} atoms in a nuclear reactor is both helpful and harmful. Explain.

7. Why is it desirable to enrich with respect to U^{235} the uranium for a reactor?

8. Describe the principle of the gaseous diffusion process for enriching uranium with respect to U^{235}.

9. What is meant by the "critical" quantity of U^{235}?

10. Describe a possible method for setting off an atomic bomb.

11. What is meant by "fallout"?

12. Describe some of the uses of a nuclear reactor.

13. What is the function of the graphite in a graphite-moderated nuclear reactor?

14. Describe how radioactive iodine may be used to diagnose dysfunction of the thyroid gland.

15. How does nuclear fusion differ from nuclear fission?

Review

1. A cube of metal 5.0 cm on a side weighs 338 gm in air. Using Archimedes' principle, calculate (a) its weight when completely immersed in water. and (b) its specific gravity.

2. What force must be applied to a 50-lb mass in order to impart an ac celeration of 15 ft/sec^2?

3. A body which starts from rest falls freely for 12 sec. What is its velocity? How far does it fall?

4. Calculate the molecular weight of a gas 2 liters of which weigh 5.23 gm at 20°C and 740 mm.

5. If a motor runs a pump which lifts 1000 cu ft of water a height of 150 ft each hour, at what horsepower is it operating? (Neglect friction. A cubic foot of water weighs 62.5 lb.)

6. Copper, Cu, and nitric acid, HNO_3, undergo the following reaction

$$Cu + HNO_3 \rightarrow Cu(NO_3)_2 + NO_2 \uparrow + H_2O$$

(a) Balance the equation.
(b) Calculate the weight of cupric nitrate, $Cu(NO_3)_2$, produced from 200 gm of nitric acid when reacting with an appropriate amount of copper metal.

CHAPTER 15

A Journey through Time and Space

Sun, moon, and stars, planets and meteors and comets—these are the age-old objects of the science of astronomy. To them recent centuries have added satellites and asteroids, and in the farther reaches of space "radio stars," clouds of gas and dust, and distant galaxies. For thousands of years the serious study of celestial objects was linked at every point with religion and ritual. The stars were divine for Egypt, Babylon, and Greece and their positions in the sky surely determined human fate. This linkage was severed only some four centuries ago. Modern astronomy is a natural science; the gods banished from it have retreated into a body of lore with a similar name—astrology—which remains among us as an entertaining curiosity.

The Solar Family   The nearest celestial objects are parts of the solar system, and nearest of them all is the planet we live on, the Earth. The Earth is a nearly spherical planet, slightly flattened at its poles and bulging at its equator (Fig. 4-2), about 7900 miles in diameter. It makes one complete spin on its axis (rotation) every 24 hours. This rotation causes the apparent daily east-to-west movement of all celestial objects, including the sun, and subdivides time into day and night. The Earth also makes one complete swing around the sun (revolution) every 365¼ days, thereby subdividing time into years (Fig. 15-1). The

Fig. 15-1.

The Earth's position and motions in space. Every 23 hours and 56 minutes the Earth completes a spin on its axis. In the Northern Hemisphere this axis extends from the Earth's center, through the geographic north pole, and out into space toward the North Star (not shown). The axis makes an angle of 66½ degrees with the plane of the Earth's orbit about the sun; it is tilted 23½ degrees from the vertical to the plane.—The diagram is not drawn to scale. Scale diagrams in astronomy are rarely convenient or possible—distances and disparities of size are far too enormous. The sun's diameter is about 100 times that of the Earth (864,000 vs. 7900 miles). More than 100 of the sun's diameters should separate the sun and the Earth (93,000,000 miles). As the North Star is about 300 light-years away, the Earth's axis points toward it from all orbital positions.—To illustrate counterclockwise motion, the observer should imagine that he is in space somewhere beyond the North Pole looking "down" on the solar system and at a gigantic clock that is face up in the plane of the sun's equator. The counterclockwise direction is the same as that in which the minute hand of a clock moves when it is being turned back. Look toward the clock at all times and consider only the motion on the part nearest you. This is defined as a west-to-east motion and is the common direction of movement in the solar system. Planets revolve about the sun in this direction, the sun and the planets (except Uranus) spin on their axes in this direction, and most of the satellites revolve and rotate similarly. East and west do not refer to fixed locations in space but vary with the position of the observer. South is midway between east and west and outward from the Earth.

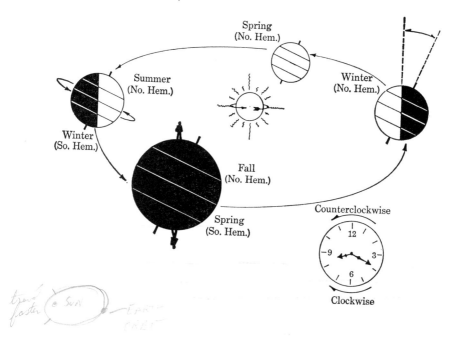

Earth's average distance from the sun is about 93 million miles—the
distance called an *astronomical unit.*
There are eight other major planets in the solar family (Fig. 15-2).
Jupiter, Saturn, Uranus, and Neptune are larger than the Earth;
Mercury, Venus, Mars, and remote Pluto are smaller. Some spin more
rapidly than the Earth and others more slowly. Venus and Mercury
are closer than the Earth to the sun and the rest are more distant; some

Fig. 15-2.

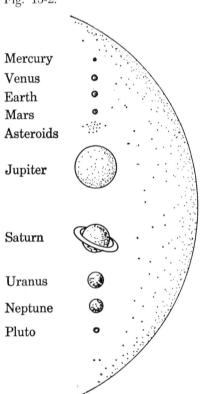

Mercury

Venus

Earth

Mars

Asteroids

Jupiter

Saturn

Uranus

Neptune

Pluto

*Approximate sizes of planets compared
with the sun. The following mnemonic may
be of assistance in remembering the relative distances of the planets from the sun:
Mary's Violet Eyes Make Poor (planetoids)
John Stay Up Nights Permanently.—On a
scale in which 1 yard represents 1 million
miles, the sun would be represented by a
balloon about 30 inches in diameter. Mercury, Venus, the Earth, and Mars would
then be about 36, 67, 93, and 141 yards
away respectively. On this greatly reduced
scale, Mercury and Mars could be represented by peas, and Venus and the Earth
by small marbles. Jupiter, Saturn, Uranus,
Neptune, and Pluto would be located at
distances of approximately ¼, ½, 1, 1½, and
2 miles respectively. Oranges about 3
inches in diameter would represent Jupiter
and Saturn; plums could be used for Uranus and Neptune; Pluto would be the size
of a pea. The moon would be a sand grain
9 inches from the marble representing the
Earth.*

have more than one moon, some have none. All the planets revolve
around the sun in the same west-to-east direction, and their orbital
planes are nearly parallel.
The sun is an enormous, gaseous, intensely hot body which contains
some 332,000 times the mass of the Earth and comprises about 699/700
of the matter in the entire solar system. It is the ultimate source of most
of the energy in the solar system. With its retinue of planets, comets,

planetoids, and meteors, it speeds through space at a rate of about 12 mi/sec toward the bright star Vega. Despite its great size (864,000 miles in diameter) the sun is merely an average star—many stars are larger, many are smaller; some have higher and others have lower temperatures; some are more dense, others less. On the one hand, the sun is so huge that if the Earth could be placed at its center, then the moon in its regular orbit (about 240,000 miles from the Earth) would lie about halfway to the sun's surface. On the other hand, the sun is so tiny that if it could be placed at the center of the giant star Antares, then Mercury, Venus, the Earth, and Mars in their regular orbits would all fit inside Antares, with room to spare!

If the Earth is represented as a grapefruit, then the moon shrinks to the size of a golf ball about 10 feet from it, and the sun can be represented by a sphere some 50 feet in diameter and 1 mile away. The Earth forms only a tiny part of the solar system. Its distance from the sun is such that it is neither too hot nor too cold for vegetation and life.

The Light-Year Seeking a unit of distance adequate for the vast reaches of interstellar space, astronomers have had recourse to the *light-year.* This is the distance that light travels in 1 year while moving, as it does, at the astonishing rate of about 186,000 mi/sec: 186,000 × 60 × 60 × 24 × 365¼, or about 6 trillion miles. If an astronomical unit (93,000,000 miles) were represented by an inch, a light-year would be represented by about a mile. At the unimaginable speed at which light travels, a beam of light sent from the Atlantic to the Pacific across the United States (about 3000 miles) and back again would make about 31 round trips in just 1 second.

The star nearest to the Earth (other than the sun) is approximately 4 light-years away. This star, Alpha Centauri, is the third brightest star in the Earth's sky and is located about 30 degrees from the south celestial pole. It is not visible from the latitude of New York. Despite the huge sizes of the stars, all are located at such tremendous distances from the Earth that they are mere pinpoints of light even in the largest of telescopes, and astronomers have no means of determining whether any of the stars, even the nearest ones, have planetary systems of their own. Distances between individual stars may average about 4 light-years.

The scale of the solar system might be illustrated as follows. If the sun is represented by a golf ball, then the Earth is a small grain of sand about 12 feet from the golf ball, and Pluto, the outermost known planet, is a smaller grain of sand about 1000 feet from the golf ball. The nearest star would be another golf ball several hundred miles away. To illustrate the isolation of the solar system in space, we might represent the sun by a tiny dot such as the period at the end of this sentence; the nearest star on this greatly reduced scale would then be another tiny dot placed at a distance of a few miles. Tiny dots like periods scattered in space a few miles apart—this picture would represent proportionally the sizes of stars and the distances between them. Assuredly, the universe has a plethora of space!

Seeing the Past   A fascinating aspect of celestial distances is the realization that light from celestial objects reaches the Earth after journeys that have taken a very long time. Even the light from the sun requires eight minutes to travel to the Earth. When we look at the sun, we see it as it actually appeared eight minutes before. The light we see when we look at the nearest star left that star more than four years ago and has been traveling at the tremendous speed of 186,000 mi/sec ever since. If a terrific explosion occurred on this star two years ago, astronomers will not find out about it for another two years! Other stars are estimated by astronomers to be tens, hundreds, thousands, millions, and even hundreds of millions of light-years away. Whenever we look at the stars, we are "seeing the past": we may be seeing one star as it appeared a generation ago, another as it appeared twenty centuries ago, another perhaps as it appeared in the remote geologic past.*

Galaxies   The universe is mostly space. In it stars are scattered here and there at enormous distances from one another, but this scattering is not at random. Stars are grouped into gigantic structures called galaxies. Although the vast spaces separating stars and galaxies seem to be better vacuums than man can produce on the Earth, they are not completely empty. According to one estimate, nearly all of the matter in the universe (chiefly hydrogen and helium) exists in the stars. The remaining portion, perhaps 1 to 2 percent, is probably scattered as gas and dust among the stars. Other estimates of the amount of gas and dust in the universe range up to 50 percent.

* The estimated distances in light-years to a number of the brightest stars follow (arranged in order of decreasing brightness as viewed from the earth): Sirius, 9; Vega, 26; Capella, 46; Arcturus, 36; Rigel, 650; Procyon, 11; Altair, 16; Betelgeuse 650; Aldebaran, 68; Spica, 160; Antares, 170; and Deneb, 540.

Fig. 15-3.

NGC 4565 in Coma Berenices. This photograph shows an edgewise view of a spiral galaxy. Our galaxy is thought to have a similar shape. The photograph was taken through a powerful telescope with a time exposure of several hours. Individual stars seen in the photograph are relatively close to the Earth and belong to our galaxy. One must look through the stars in our own galaxy to see other galaxies far beyond. (In some photographs these stars show four spikes, caused by the diffraction of starlight around supports for a mirror located inside the telescope.)—The dark color represents obscuring matter concentrated in the central plane of the galaxy (along its own Milky Way). In our galaxy the solar system appears to be located in the central plane about two-thirds of the distance outward from the center. Our galaxy may have a diameter of 80,000 to 100,000 light-years and a maximum thickness of about one-tenth of this distance. (Photograph from the Mount Wilson and Palomar Observations)

Although galaxies differ in shape, a number of them have a thin, disk-like form, a little like two saucers placed rim to rim with the bottoms outward; some of these lens-shaped galaxies have spiral arms (Figs. 15-3 and 15-4). The Milky Way, that familiar faint band of light in our sky visible to the unaided eye, forms part of the galaxy which contains the solar system and which is commonly called the Milky Way galaxy or "our" galaxy (Fig. 21-11). The universe itself is pictured by astrono-

Fig. 15-4.

M101 in Ursa Major. This photograph shows a spiral galaxy as seen from above. Our galaxy may have a similar pin-wheel shape. The solar system is believed to be located in one of the spiral arms of our galaxy. The shape of the galaxy indicates rotation. If such a galaxy were not spinning, the mutual gravitational attraction of all its stars should cause it to collapse. (Photograph from the Mount Wilson and Palomar Observatories)

mers as millions of galaxies scattered throughout space; each galaxy is thought to contain millions of stars. The solar system forms a very tiny part of only one galaxy. Our sun is merely one of the millions of stars in a galaxy, not distinguished from its distant companions by size, composition, temperature, or other known properties (except, perhaps, its possession of a system of planets). The dimensions of the universe are thus on a scale that far outdistances the range of the imagination.

According to some estimates, the average galaxy may be about 30,000 light-years in diameter, and the average distance separating any two galaxies may approximate 1 million light-years. If these figures are correct, then the ratio of diameter to distance is about 1 to 33. Therefore, galaxies may be represented as silver dollars (1½ inches in diameter) about 4 feet apart. Current measurements suggest that galaxies are distributed in space in clusters of 1000 or so. Our galaxy with an estimated diameter of 100,000 light-years is some three times larger than average. The hypothesis that distances between clusters of galaxies may be increasing rapidly—the expanding universe—is discussed in Chapter 21.

Although the enormous size of the universe fills us with wonder, perhaps even more amazing is the knowledge that, so far as man has been able to determine, the same physical laws which apply to the Earth hold true throughout the universe; matter appears to consist of the same familiar elements, although hydrogen and helium are far more abundant than on the Earth; light seems to be produced and transmitted in a similar manner; celestial bodies apparently obey the laws of motion and gravitation; and the energy-production process in other stars may be similar to that in the sun. Since uniformity seems to be present throughout, we can extrapolate with some confidence to the rest of the universe the knowledge which has been obtained by studying the tiny portion accessible to us at relatively close range.

The Constellations   Groups of some of the brighter stars within our own galaxy which form recognizable patterns for the skywatcher, such as crosses, squares, and circles, are called constellations. Most of the familiar constellations were named long ago by people with vivid imaginations, who traced in the sky the lines and symbols of earthly objects—bears, dippers, heroes (Figs. 15-5 and 15-6). It need hardly be said that the resemblances are not as striking in all instances as they are in some. Yet constellations and bright stars are useful in designating areas in the sky, much as states and cities serve to locate places on the Earth's surface. To become familiar with the outstanding constellations is a pleasant and rewarding task. The joy of a clear, starlit evening will forever be enhanced by this familiarity, once gained. Inexpensive star charts are available which show where the constellations appear in the sky at any hour during the year. These will prove most helpful.

The stars in a given constellation need not be closely associated in space as they are for the eye. Two stars shining side by side may look like intimate neighbors and yet actually be hundreds of light-years apart. When a given celestial object is said to lie in a particular constellation, this means that it will be visible in the general direction of the constellation. The object itself may be situated between the Earth and

Fig. 15-5.

The northern constellations. The stars in a constellation are commonly desig-
nated by small letters of the Greek alphabet in order of brightness: the
brightest star is alpha, the next brightest is beta, etc. Some of the brightest
stars have been given special names.—The map should be held so that the
present month is at the top (representing north). The constellations are shown
as they would appear at 9:00 p.m. standard time. For a time other than 9:00
p.m. the map should be rotated through the proper number of hours, counter-
clockwise for a later time and clockwise for an earlier time. For example, the
Big Dipper will be high in the northern sky at 9:00 p.m. in May or at 9:00
a.m. in November.

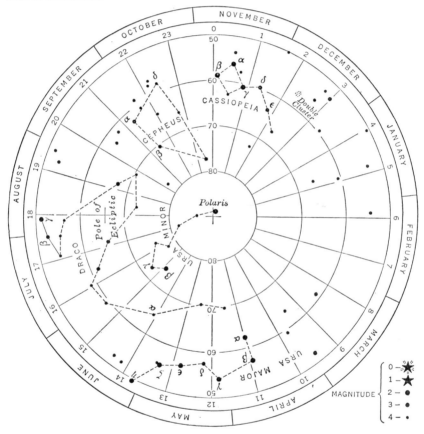

the greater number of the stars in the constellation, or it may be far out
in space beyond them.

The Celestial Sphere   Although some stars are brighter than others,
our eyes have no accurate depth perception and so one star does not

seem closer to the Earth than another. All stars appear to be located at the same distance from us, and together they seem to form a gigantic inverted bowl. Since we can make this same observation from any position on the Earth, the Earth seems to be at the center of a huge hollow

Fig. 15-6.

The region of the square of Pegasus. Messier 31 is the spiral Andromeda galaxy. Note that stars from Pegasus, Andromeda, and Perseus can be combined to form a gigantic dipper.

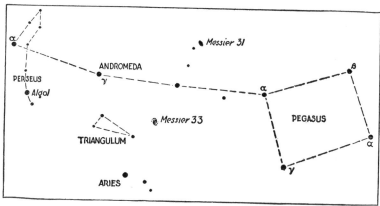

sphere. The stars appear to be attached firmly to the inside of the sphere which seems to turn on a sloping axis daily from east to west. The North Star is very close to the northern end of this axis (the north celestial pole) and follows a small circular orbit in the sky. In the Northern Hemisphere, the altitude of the North Star above the horizon is approximately equal to the latitude of the observer (Fig. 17-2).

The name *celestial sphere* has been given to this imaginary shell. Distances separating celestial objects are measured by the angles they subtend on the celestial sphere. Obviously, one cannot state accurately that a certain star is "100 feet above the horizon," but the altitude of the star can be given in angular degrees. The following angular distances can be used as a scale in estimating other distances: the angular diameters of the sun and moon are about one-half degree; the pointers in the Big Dipper are 5 degrees apart; and the square of the constellation Pegasus is 15 degrees on a side.

EXERCISES AND QUESTIONS FOR CHAPTER 15

1. Obtain a small star chart and learn how to use it. For example, a Bennett-Rice Star Explorer can be obtained from the American Museum-Hayden Planetarium, New York 24, N. Y. for about 50¢. With a little practice you should be able to identify the more prominent constellations and stars in the sky. Familiarity with these constellations combined with a little knowledge of astronomical sizes and distances should make a clear starlit evening one of the most beautiful and intriguing sights in nature.

Lights from cities and houses dim starlight and make observations difficult. Try to find a satisfactory location for your observations. A small flashlight will be more useful in checking your star chart at night if it has a red bulb, if you have coated the glass with red nail-polish, or if you have covered the glass with red cellophane.

2. Calculate a scale model of the solar system similar to that described in Fig. 15-2. (Do not use 1 yard equals 1 million miles as the scale.)

3. Make notes concerning the locations of constellations and bright stars of your choice in the early evening sky now. For example, one star you are tracing may be low in the southern sky, whereas another is at a medium altitude in the northeastern sky. Note also the time and date of your observations. Compare these present positions with those in subsequent months at similar times or now at different times.

4. Describe the size and nature of our galaxy as pictured by astronomers today.

5. With the aid of a star chart, list five winter constellations (prominent in the early evening sky in the winter), five summer constellations, and five nonseasonal constellations.

6. How do you "see the past" when you make observations in astronomy?

7. One evening a friend asks you to point a flashlight beam (a powerful five-cell flashlight makes an excellent pointer in studying stars) parallel to the Earth's axis and to swing it in the sky parallel to the Earth's equator. How can you do this?

CHAPTER 16

Does the Earth Move?

As VIEWED from New York or California, the sun rises each morning above the eastern horizon, moves upward until it is high in the southern sky at noon, and then sinks gradually until it disappears below the western horizon in the evening. This motion is known to all. The fact that the moon, stars, and planets also share this daily east-to-west movement is less well known. Although all these bodies appear actually to move through the heavens (we use words such as sunrise and sunset), we learn early in life that this is only an apparent motion caused by the spinning of the Earth in the opposite, west-to-east direction. Seeing is not believing in this instance. The explanation of celestial motion which is based on the Earth's rotation is comparatively recent; it has been generally accepted for less than 300 years. The opposite explanation, that the Earth was motionless, had been believed more or less without opposition for the preceding two millennia, or indeed as long as there have been men to ask for explanations.

Why should an erroneous concept persist for so many hundreds of years? Were ancient peoples less intelligent than their descendants? For what reasons was this mistaken theory developed? What evidence led to the general adoption of the converse, moving-Earth explanation?

Astronomy developed the way it did because men observed first and tried to explain later. A sharp distinction should be drawn between the actual motions observed and the explanations attempting to account for these motions. The arrangement of material in this chapter parallels the historical development of the interplay between observation and explanation.

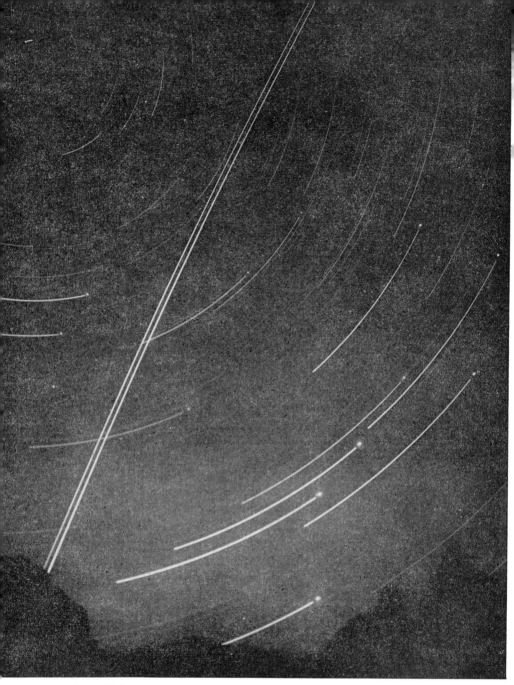

Fig. 16-1.

Star trails in the northern sky. The photograph was made in two parts: (1) A time exposure of about 1½ hours was made through a motionless camera pointed at the northern sky. The daily east-to-west rotation of the heavens produced the concentric star trails shown. (2) A few minutes after Part 1 had been completed, the camera was rotated so that it moved at the same rate and in the same direction as the stars. Thus light from any star was continuously focused on the same spot on the film. A photograph of the constellations resulted. The trails of two meteors are shown. (Photograph, John Stofan, Teaneck, N.J.)

Fig. 16-2.

Star trails in the southwestern sky produced by the constellation Orion and other stars. This photograph was made in the same way as Fig. 16-1. (Photograph, John Stofan, Teaneck, N.J.)

DAILY WESTWARD ROTATION
OF CELESTIAL BODIES

The sun, moon, planets, and stars are familiar examples of celestial bodies which apparently complete circular orbits about the Earth from east to west once each day (Figs. 16-1 and 16-2). The circular paths made by star trails grow larger in diameter toward the equator and

Fig. 16-3.

Solar vs. sidereal day. Orientation: in space looking "down" (i.e., from the "north") upon the plane of the solar system. Sizes and distances are greatly distorted. Imagine that an observer on the Earth at A at noon sees the sun and a reference star lined up exactly. They are due south and high overhead. The observer is at B 23 hours and 56 minutes later because of the Earth's rotation and revolution. The Earth has rotated completely through 360 degrees. The same reference star is again due south and high overhead. However, the sun has not yet reached a due-south position. The Earth must spin the observer from position B to position C to accomplish this. On the average about 4 minutes are required for this additional rotation.—The Earth's orbital velocity varies (p. 329). It moves fastest in January when closest to the sun; so in January the distance from A to B is greater than it is in June (the Earth covers more miles during the sidereal day of 23 hours and 56 minutes). The distance from B to C is hence also greater in January than in June—that is, slightly more than 4 minutes of rotation are needed to bring the sun again to the due-south position. Solar days are thus longest during the winter months and shortest during the summer months. They average 24 hours.

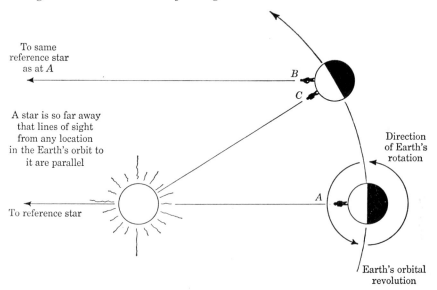

To same
reference star
as at A

B

C

A star is so far away
that lines of sight
from any location
in the Earth's orbit to
it are parallel

Direction
of Earth's
rotation

To reference star

A

Earth's orbital
revolution

smaller in diameter toward the poles. The North Star completes a tiny circular orbit each day.

Careful observation shows that stars complete their daily westward swings through the sky in about 23 hours and 56 minutes—the *sidereal day*. On the other hand, the sun requires about 24 hours to complete its daily journey through the skies—*the solar day*. This difference between the sidereal day and the solar day is caused by the revolution of the Earth around the sun (Fig. 16-3). The effect of this 4-minute difference is a steady eastward shifting of the sun against the background of stars; stated another way, there is a daily westward shifting of the celestial sphere with respect to any given time of night. Since our clocks keep time with the solar day, each evening any given star is observed to rise 4 minutes earlier than it did the previous evening and to set 4 minutes earlier. If a certain star appears above the eastern horizon at 9:00 P.M. on, say, September 1, it will appear at 8:56 P.M. of the evening of September 2, and at about 7:00 P.M. on the evening of October 1 (30 days at 4 minutes per day). Since this daily westward shift of the stars is caused by the Earth's revolution around the sun, the stars will have shifted 360 degrees in a year, and this same star will again appear above the eastern horizon at 9:00 P.M. the following September 1. Constellations which are prominent in the early evening hours during

Fig. 16-4.

Timetable for a winter constellation. This constellation is near enough to the celestial equator to be above the horizon for about twelve hours each day.

DATE	STAR RISES	STAR SETS	COMMENT
November 1	9:00 P.M.	9:00 A.M.	
December 1	7:00 P.M.	7:00 A.M.	
January 1	5:00 P.M.	5:00 A.M.	Visible all night or during the
February 1	3:00 P.M.	3:00 A.M.	convenient early hours of
March 1	1:00 P.M.	1:00 A.M.	the night
April 1	11:00 A.M.	11:00 P.M.	
May 1	9:00 A.M.	9:00 P.M.	
June 1	7:00 A.M.	7:00 P.M.	
July 1	5:00 A.M.	5:00 P.M.	Invisible, or visible at an in-
August 1	3:00 A.M.	3:00 P.M.	convenient hour
September 1	1:00 A.M.	1:00 P.M.	
October 1	11:00 P.M.	11:00 A.M.	
November 1	9:00 P.M.	9:00 A.M.	One year later

Fig. 16-5.

Star maps of the northern sky. Three familiar constellations are shown as observed from New York approximately at the times listed. Other stars are visible in this region of the sky, but are not shown. When observations are made from other areas, different times and locations must be substituted. The sky map shows one half of the sky visible to an observer, or one quarter of the celestial sphere. The North Star is located about 41 degrees above the horizon at the latitude chosen for this illustration.—The star map shows two motions: (1) The daily westward rotation of the celestial sphere, which is counterclockwise as one faces the North Star. The three constellations shown here are too close to the North Star ever to set below the horizon at latitude 41 degrees. (2) The annual westward shifting of the celestial sphere as the Earth revolves about the sun.

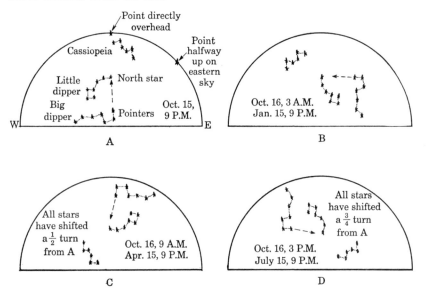

the winter months are known as winter constellations; those prominent in the early evening hours of the summer are known as summer constellations (Fig. 16-4). Figs. 16-5 and 16-6 illustrate both the nightly and the yearly westward movement of the stars.

EASTWARD SHIFT OF THE MOON, SUN, AND PLANETS RELATIVE TO THE FIXED STARS

Stars actually are moving through space, some at rates of tens of miles each second, but they are located at such enormous distances from the

Fig. 16-6.

Daily and annual movements of Orion. Compare these with Fig. 16-5. The rotation of the celestial sphere is clockwise here, since we are facing south, not north. In 2 hours of rotation during any one night, Orion shifts westward 1/12 of the entire path. This equals the westward advance during a 30-day month (at 4 minutes/day).—Six hours are required for an object on the eastern horizon to move to a due-south position. In position A above, Orion has already risen, so only about 4 hours are needed for it to move to position B.

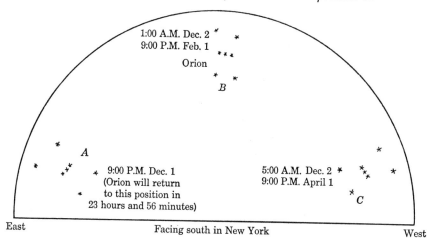

Earth that their movements are usually not discernible except over periods of a few hundred years. The most rapid movement discovered so far is that of a star which shifts an angular distance among its neighbors about equal to the moon's angular diameter (one-half degree) every 175 years. The Big Dipper did not always have its present shape, and since the stars in it are moving in different directions, its shape will continue to change over the centuries (Fig. 16-7). Nevertheless, within

Changes in the shape of a constellation. Telescopic observations of stellar motions show that the present shape (A) of the Big Dipper will change. By coincidence a new dipper should form (B) if present motions (indicated by arrows in A) continue at uniform rates. The reason for the quotation marks sometimes placed around the term "fixed stars" should now be apparent.

Fig. 16-7.   *A*   *B*

any one person's lifetime, the shapes of the Big Dipper and the other constellations do not change. The stars are seen to move each night, rising in the east and sinking in the west, but always they maintain the same positions with respect to each other, and so they are termed "fixed." As will be seen later, this distinguishes them from planets, which look like stars in the sky to the unaided eye but which are not "fixed" against the background of stars. (*Planetes* is the Greek word for "wanderer.")

The moon, sun, and planets all shift their positions eastward relative to the stars. That is, if observations are made on successive evenings, the moon and planets will be seen to keep shifting their positions eastward with respect to the background of fixed stars. The sun likewise shifts its position eastward among the stars, but the movement is more difficult to observe since we cannot see the stars when the sun is in the sky. In addition, the planets occasionally shift westward rather than eastward (Fig. 16-16B). The moon and sun do not do this.

Fig. 16-8.

The moon's eastward shift relative to the background of stars. To simplify the sky map, only one star is shown as a reference point. Each evening at 9:00 P.M. the moon is almost an hour east of its position on the previous evening relative to the reference star. In about 1 month the moon completes an eastward swing among the stars and returns to its starting point. Of course the moon and the reference star participate each evening in the westward rotation of the heavens, but the relative positions of the moon and reference star change slowly and continuously. The same phases do not occur on the same days during any one month from one year to the next (see Fig. 18-2).

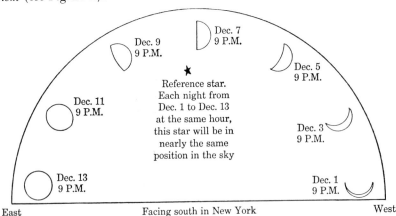

East   Facing south in New York   West

The Moon   Figure 16-8 illustrates the eastward shift of the moon with respect to the stars during a period of about two weeks. Some confusion might result from the statement that the moon rises and sets each night. As a crescent shortly after its new phase, the moon is seen low in the western sky after sunset, and it soon disappears below the western horizon. However, earlier that day the moon appeared above the eastern horizon, and it traveled westward through the daytime sky. It was not readily visible until the sky darkened after sunset.

The Sun and the Stars   Slowly and continuously the sun shifts its position eastward relative to the background of fixed stars and completes its swing in $365\frac{1}{4}$ days. This motion can be observed by noting the stars which appear in the eastern sky shortly before sunrise or in the western sky shortly after sunset. Different stars will be seen in these parts of the sky with the advancing seasons. One full year is needed for the stars to complete the cycle and return to their original position with respect to the sun (Figs. 16-5 and 16-6). This is the basis for the subdivision of time into years. The circle was subdivided into 360 degrees by the ancient sages of Mesopotamia because the eastward shift of the sun approximates 1 angular degree each day.

The ancients were puzzled for some ages before they could explain the disappearance of the stars during the day. Stars are, of course, still present in the sky during the day. A constellation that is high in the sky during a winter evening will be high in the sky during the day in the following summer. But in the same way that the stars become dimmer on successive nights as the moon changes from crescent to full, so also do they become completely invisible in the much brighter glare of the sun's light. Stars can be seen during the day, however, with a telescope, because the light-gathering power of the telescope concentrates light from a star but not from the sky around the star.

Planets   Planets look like stars in the sky. Venus, Jupiter, Mercury, Mars, and even Saturn at certain times are brighter than any of the stars. Uranus is barely visible to the unaided eye. Neptune and Pluto can be seen only through a telescope. The brightness of a planet varies, depending in part upon its constantly changing distance from the Earth. Planets are not visible when their orbital positions place them in line with the sun. For the observer, one distinction between planets and stars is that planets tend to shine with a steady light, especially when high above the horizon, in contrast to the twinkling stars. However, small planets do twinkle vigorously when seen near the horizon. Another distinction is the slow shifting of the planets against the background of fixed stars. The planet Mars, for example, rises and sets with the other celestial bodies, but each night the position of Mars is seen to have changed slightly relative to the fixed stars near it (Fig. 16-9).

Fig. 16-9.

The path of Mars among the stars before and after opposition in 1939. See Fig. 16-16B for explanation. The westward part of the loop (to the right in the diagram) is called retrograde motion.

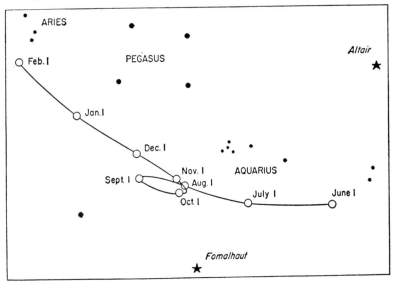

Usually the shift is eastward. Occasionally Mars shifts westward (retrogrades) for several weeks before resuming its eastward motion. The planets take varying lengths of time, depending upon their distances from the sun, to complete their eastward swings.

Most of the features of the heavens that can be studied with the unaided eye were long ago observed and recorded by devotees of that most ancient of sciences—astronomy.

ORIGIN OF ASTRONOMY

Astronomy is one of the oldest of the sciences, partly because answers were desired a long time ago for such simple questions as: What time is it? When will you be back? Before watches and clocks were invented, replies were not easy.

The following scene, with local variations, must have occurred regularly in remote ages. A prehistoric man picks up a stout club and prepares to leave his cave. A woman calls to him, and the man points to a stone resting on the ground in front of the cave. This seems to satisfy

The sun's daily path through the sky during winter, spring, summer, and fall as seen from our northern latitudes. Such changes in the sun's path are caused by the Earth's tilt on its axis, its rotation, and its revolution (Fig. 17-8). The shadow cast by a vertical stick is shortest when the sun is highest in the sky at noon.—During the winter the sun is visible for the shortest period of time and is not high in the sky at noon. It rises late in the southeast and sets at an early hour in the southwest. In the spring or fall, the sun rises in the east and sets in the west. In the summer the sun is visible for the longest time; it rises in the northeast, travels high overhead, and sets at a late hour in the northwest. The difference in altitude of the noon sun between winter and summer is 47 degrees.

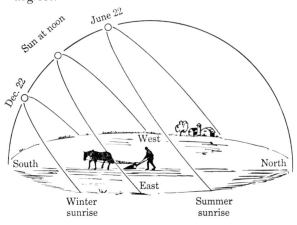

Fig. 16-10.

the woman, and the man leaves. As the day wears along, the sun's shadow moves closer and closer to the stone (Fig. 16-10). When the shadow nears the stone, the woman builds a fire and begins to look expectantly into the distance. Soon her mate appears with a small deer which he has killed for their evening meal. His morning gesture told her that he would return when the sun's shadow reached the vicinity of the stone. Although he could not see the shadow while he was hunting, the man knew when it would reach the stone by the sun's position in the sky. Movements of the sun also supplied a calendar (Figs. 16-11 and 16-12).

Fig. 16-11.

The shadow of a vertical stick at noon is used to subdivide time into years. Noon is the time of day at which the shadow cast by the sun points toward the north in northern latitudes. It is shortest in the summer when the sun attains its highest noon altitude. Marks placed at the end of the shadow at noon thus form a system of subdividing time into years; 6 months are required for the shadow to change from its longest to its shortest position. A vertical stick used to study the motions of the sun is termed a gnomon (Greek: "the one who knows").

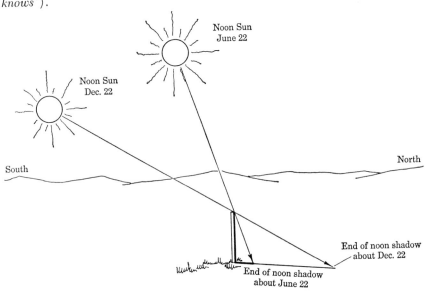

Prehistoric man had a much greater awareness and knowledge of the existence and motions of celestial bodies than do most of today's civilized, educated individuals. The splendor, beauty, and mystery of the heavens doubtless appealed to him; showers of meteors, the sudden appearance of a bright comet, a spectacular eclipse stirred, frightened, and excited him. When men began to live in groups, knowledge of the heavens became necessary to them. Dates had to be arranged for future hunts and campaigns. The phases of the moon provided a ready calendar; it was soon learned that there were nearly 30 days between two successive full moons, and that approximately 12 full moons elapsed before a certain star rose again in the same place at the same time. On this basis the year was subdivided into twelve 30-day months. Shepherds may similarly have subdivided their night watches by the nightly movements of familiar stars or constellations, each watch lasting

Fig. 16-12.

Subdivision of time into years by the shift of the sunset point. This shift was first plotted thousands of years ago to subdivide time into years. In some countries impressive monuments were erected to mark various sunset points.

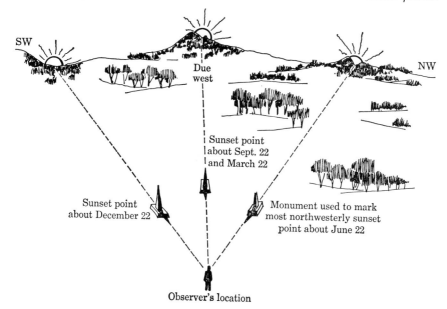

the length of time necessary for certain stars to move through definite angular distances in the sky. The light of the moon was once much more important in the conduct of life than it is today: evening journeys, for example, were best taken at times of full moon. The pole star was an important aid in determining directions. Specific seasonal events came to be associated with the positions of certain stars in the sky: the dates to pick elderberries or to plant corn, the mating seasons for cattle and deer, and the seasons of floods and frosts were all associated with the locations of certain bright stars in the sky that marked the time of the year. From this association of a star position with a seasonal event, it was only a step to ascribe the actual cause of the event to the star: the flooding of the Nile may have been attributed to the rising of Sirius in the east at dawn.

GEOCENTRIC AND HELIOCENTRIC EXPLANATIONS
FOR OBSERVED CELESTIAL MOTIONS

The age-old view that the earth is at the center of the universe can still teach a lesson. Here is an erroneous concept that yet was believed almost without challenge for more than 2000 years. It is one of the examples that abound in the history of science of abandoned theories that once went unchallenged. Doubtless many concepts which seem logical in the light of present knowledge will similarly have to be discarded or radically changed as additional data become available. If the long argument between the *geocentric* and the *heliocentric* theory can teach us this, it is worth following.

In the sixth century B.C. Greeks developed the first scientific explanation of the motions described in the beginning of this chapter. Thales (624-545 B.C.) has been called the founder of Greek astronomy, but he was only one of a number of men who made valuable contributions to the early development of the geocentric theory. The earliest Greek astronomy drew largely upon the lore of Egypt and Mesopotamia. The Greeks, however, being gifted with imagination, logic, and curiosity, attempted to explain the operation of the universe; other peoples

Explanation for the eastward shift of the sun. A similar explanation applies to the moon's eastward shift. Orientation: in space looking "down" on the solar system and the Earth's north pole. Although stars are known to be situated at different distances from the Earth in the heliocentric theory, they seem to be equidistant.

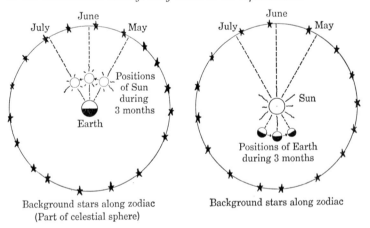

A. Geocentric explanation   B. Heliocentric explanation   Fig. 16-13.

An ancient and erroneous concept of the universe. The classic Greeks imagined the universe to consist of a round, motionless Earth at the center of a huge, hollow sphere. Some believed all stars to be the same distance from the Earth, fastened firmly to the inside of the sphere; some thought, quite fancifully, that the stars were fastened as the heads of great golden nails used to hold the celestial sphere together. As the sphere was thought to spin completely on its axis once each day from east to west (clockwise), the daily movement of the stars was readily explained. The North Star is near one end of the axis.—A long-time exposure with a camera pointed at the North Star produces concentric circular star trails. The circular paths become larger away from the North Star; a camera pointed at about right angles to it records a series of parallel straight lines. A person at the equator can see all of the stars during the course of a year.—From the central position of the Earth outward to the boundary of the celestial sphere, the Greeks located the moon, Mercury, Venus, the sun, Mars, Jupiter, and Saturn in that order. Somehow these celestial bodies inside of the sphere participated in its daily movement from east to west, but they were believed to move more slowly than the stars and to lag behind or shift eastward.—Nighttime occurred when the sun was on the back side of the Earth away from an observer. As the sun shifted slowly eastward against the stellar background during the year, stars were in slightly different positions each night —either higher or lower in the sky at a certain hour; new stars became visible, and formerly visible stars disappeared. Therefore, during the course of a year, all of the stars north of a certain latitude could be seen by an observer in the Northern Hemisphere. Stars near the south pole of the celestial sphere remained invisible to this observer at all times.

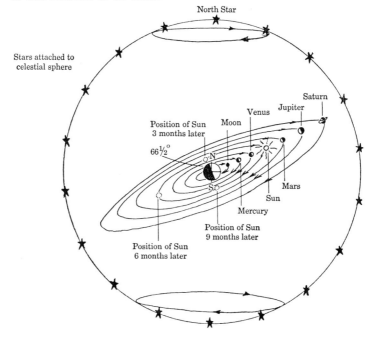

Fig. 16-14.

placed more emphasis upon mapping the positions of celestial objects and assigned responsibility for the guiding mechanism to the separate wills of gods.

The Greeks held a geocentric theory—viz., that the earth was round, motionless, and at the center of the universe. The sun, the moon, and the five bright planets known to them (the "seven stars" for which the days of the week are named), all revolved about the Earth (Figs. 16-13A and 13B). The universe itself was a huge hollow sphere which rotated completely from east to west once each day (Fig. 16-14). Celestial objects within the sphere accompanied it in this daily movement. That is why they were observed rising in the east and sinking in the west. However, special theories were needed to explain why the sun, moon, and planets all lagged behind the stars in this daily westward rotation, shifting eastward relative to the distant background of stars (Figs. 16-13A and 13B). As a matter of observation, the moon lags behind the stars the greatest distance in one day, the sun a lesser distance, and the planets shift eastward at rates which vary.

A few of the early Greeks realized that celestial motions could be explained on the basis of a moving Earth, but their concepts of sizes and distances in the universe had far too small a scope, and the explanation involving a motionless Earth seemed both more understandable and more logical. For example, the sun actually does appear to rise in the east, climb across the sky, and disappear in the west; that this apparent motion could represent the rotation of the Earth in the opposite direction is much less obvious. When the idea was brought forward in ancient times, as indeed it was, many difficulties kept it from being plausible. If the Earth was moving so rapidly, some argued, where were the powerful winds which should exist? Why were men not flung into space? And why did objects thrown into the air always return to the ground at the point where they were projected upward?

An apparently valid scientific test of the theory of the Earth's revolution around the sun was made by Aristotle in the fourth century B.C. (perhaps our old friend Archimedes in the third century B.C. should be credited with this). He reasoned as follows: If the Earth actually revolved about the sun, then near stars should be displaced against the background of more distant stars. A similar displacement of Saturn would occur if the stars were equidistant and part of a celestial sphere located outside of the orbit of Saturn. This displacement is called parallax (Figs. 16-15A and 15B). The brighter stars were assumed to be

Fig. 16-15A.

Parallax illustrated. Hold a pencil motionless a short distance in front of your face. Close one eye, and align the pencil with a convenient point of reference some distance away. Now open the closed eye and close the open eye. Line up the pencil again with a reference point in the distance. The pencil appears to shift against the background of distant objects because the base of the line of sight has been changed.

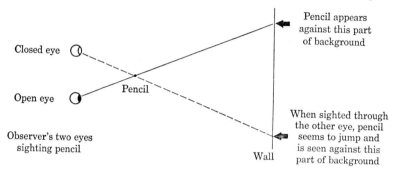

Fig. 16-15B.

Parallactic displacement of a near star against a background of distant stars. (Sizes and distances are not to scale.) Parallax proves that the Earth revolves about the sun, but parallactic displacements are so small that the first one was not measured until 1837-39. Measuring the largest parallactic displacement is approximately equivalent to measuring the diameter of a silver dollar at a distance of a few miles. Parallax likewise provides a trigonometric method for obtaining the distances to the nearer stars (p. 350). A right-angle triangle is formed by the Earth, sun, and near star. The base of the triangle is known (93 million miles) and the angle of parallax can be measured.

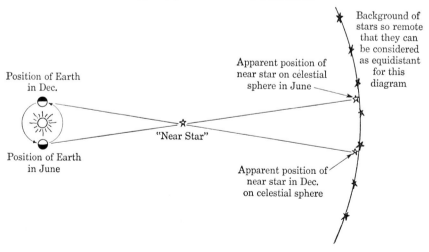

nearer ones (this is not necessarily true). Aristotle searched for evidence of parallactic displacement, found none, and concluded that the Earth was motionless. Aristotle's reasoning was correct: parallax does occur. What he did not realize was that stars are so distant that parallactic displacements caused by the Earth's revolution about the sun were too small for him to measure. The false assumptions about distances in the universe thus invalidated his check and led to an incorrect conclusion—another example of the eternal need for diligence in checking the accuracy of scientific hypotheses and theories.

Accordingly, the Greeks clung to a geocentric view and elaborated

Fig. 16-16A.

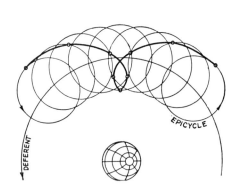

Geocentric explanation for planetary motion. Orientation: in space looking "down" on this part of the solar system. Each 24 hours the planet was supposed to revolve almost completely around the Earth from east to west. However, as the planet lagged slightly behind the stars in the daily westward movement, it shifted slowly eastward among them. This is the motion, shown above, along the deferent.—The planet was thought to revolve about an imaginary point which in turn revolved about the Earth. These simultaneous motions can be likened to a spinning wheel revolving about the Earth. The planet is located on the rim of the rotating wheel whose center follows a circular path about the Earth. Thus it moved through a looped path in space.

special explanations of why the moon, sun, and planets shifted in the sky. Each of these celestial objects was assigned its own transparent "glassy" sphere, like an enormous bubble, rotating at a rate slower than the outermost sphere of the fixed stars.

The special peculiarities of planetary motion were explained by a slight complication (Figs. 16-16A and 16B). A planet followed a circular path (epicycle) about an invisible point set in the sphere which was carrying it around the Earth. A combination of two motions, functioning simultaneously, could be plotted which would yield a general eastward shift against the background of stars on the celestial sphere, and yet allow for an occasional shift westward.

In the second century after Christ, Ptolemy, the last of the great ancient astronomers, summarized, refined, and added to the geocentric theory, which afterward bore his name. He published a book, *The Almagest,* which remained the outstanding astronomical work for nearly 1500 years. By Ptolemy's time the geocentric theory had lost all

Fig. 16-16B.

Heliocentric explanation for planetary motions. Mars is used as an example. Orientation: in space looking "down." Observations on the positions of Mars among the stars are plotted for each month. Since the Earth is closer to the sun than Mars, the Earth revolves at a faster rate and covers a greater distance in any one month. For this reason the Earth occasionally overtakes Mars and passes between it and the sun. At such times Mars is seen to shift westward among the stars and follows a looped path (Fig. 16-9). At all other times Mars shifts eastward against the stellar background at rates which vary. For Mars the retrograde motion may last about two months.

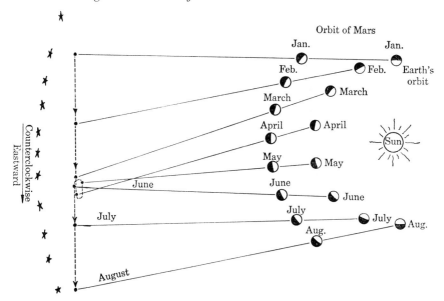

vestige of simplicity. Several dozen epicycles were required to explain the observed motions of the planets. For example, a planet might follow a circular path about an imaginary point, which in turn moved about another point that circled the Earth. The complexity of these epicycles later led Alphonso the Wise (1221-1284) to remark: "Had I been present at the Creation, I would have given some useful hints for the better ordering of the Universe." Yet amazingly accurate results were achieved by the ancient astronomers in calculating the distances from the sun to various planets in terms of the distance from the Earth to the sun (the astronomical unit) and in measuring the sizes of the Earth and moon and the distance between them (pp. 347-350). One is filled with admiration for such intellectual triumphs.

Aristarchus, in the third century B.C., seems to have been the first advocate of the *heliocentric theory*. This mental giant determined that the sun was much larger than the Earth (Fig. 16-17). He reasoned that

Fig. 16-17.

Method used by Aristarchus in obtaining the size of the sun relative to the size of the earth. Aristarchus noted that the moon was highest in the south at sunset when it was exactly in its first quarter phase. Therefore, rays of light must be coming from the sun at the same angle to both the Earth and the moon. In order for the sun's rays to be nearly parallel throughout such a wide area, the sun must be situated at an enormous distance from the Earth. Furthermore, because the moon and sun have nearly the same angular diameter in the sky, the sun must be immensely larger than the moon and the Earth.

At sunset the moon is highest overhead in the southern sky for an observer on the earth

Location of observer on earth at sunset

If sun were smaller, nearer, and located here, the moon would still be in its first quarter phase, but the observer on the earth would not be experiencing sunset

it was simple for the tiny Earth to revolve about the huge sun and to rotate on its axis once each day, whereas it seemed fantastic that the tremendously large celestial sphere could rotate completely in 24 hours. However, the heliocentric concept of Aristarchus and of a few other early astronomers met little acceptance. The geocentric explanation persisted almost without challenge from the sixth century B.C. until the time of Copernicus. The theory lasted so long because it was based on straightforward observation of celestial phenomena, and because, with the aid of this theory, accurate predictions concerning future planetary positions and the times of eclipses could be made. In addition, the explanation appealed to man's sense of importance by locating the Earth at the center of the universe and of all motion.

FOUNDERS OF MODERN ASTRONOMY

Five men had a very powerful impact on astronomy and science in general in the sixteenth and seventeenth centuries—Copernicus, Tycho Brahe, Kepler, Galileo, and Newton.

Copernicus In the sixteenth century Nicolaus Copernicus (1473-1543), a Polish churchman-astronomer, stated the heliocentric (Copernican) theory. The idea had come from the writings of a few ancient philosophers, notably Aristarchus. Consider the radical nature of this concept when it was published shortly before the death of Copernicus. Copernicus believed that the Earth was round, rotated completely on its axis once each 24 hours from west to east, and revolved completely about the sun in a counterclockwise direction each year (Figs. 16-13B and 16-15B). Instead of being the center of the universe, the Earth's status was reduced in the Copernican theory to that of a member of a family of planets which moved about the sun.

This new and startling hypothesis—in direct opposition to a belief which had been firmly established for 2000 years—needed powerful supporting evidence in order to be accepted. Copernicus could not offer convincing data in its favor. He could merely state that the heliocentric theory was simpler, that it seemed logical for the tiny Earth to revolve about the huge sun, and that it was much more comprehensible to imagine the diminutive Earth spinning on its axis than to imagine a complete daily rotation of all the other celestial bodies at their enormous distances from the Earth. As Copernicus believed that the paths which the planets followed about the sun were circular, predictions of future astronomical events were not significantly more accurate than those based on the Ptolemaic theory, and some epicycles were still necessary to explain planetary motions. Copernicus did predict that Mercury and Venus would show phases similar to the phases of the moon (Figs. 16-18 and 16-19), which could not be explained by the geocentric theory; but the accuracy of this prediction was not vindicated until Galileo trained his telescope upon the planets early in the seventeenth century. Copernicus also calculated the distances of

Phases of Venus. Positions of the Earth, Venus, and the sun are shown as viewed from "above." For simplicity in depicting the relative positions, the Earth is shown as stationary in the diagram, and Venus is shown in different positions in its orbit. As Venus moves more rapidly in its orbit than the Earth, it eventually overtakes the Earth, passes between it and the sun, and emerges on the other side.—Like the moon and other spherical bodies in space, half of Venus is always illuminated by the sun's rays, and half is always in darkness. The phases of Venus and of the moon depend upon the proportion of the lighted half which can be seen from the Earth. The apparent diameter of Venus changes (Fig. 16-19). Venus is not visible when it is directly in line with the sun at a "full-moon" position.

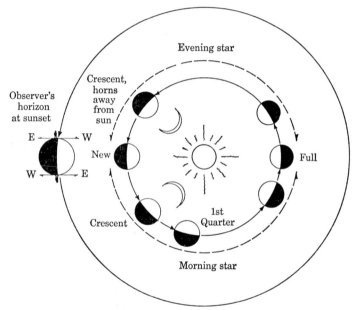

Fig. 16-18.

Mercury and Venus from the sun in terms of the Earth's distance from the sun (Fig. 16-20).

Tycho Brahe This Danish nobleman (1546-1601), was sent to school as a youth to study subjects befitting his status. His tutor was responsible for selecting this curriculum. However, when Brahe was only fourteen years of age, a partial eclipse of the sun occurred. Brahe was amazed that a few men could actually foretell such events by their studies of the heavens, and he developed a great desire to learn about

Venus in different phases as seen through a tele-scope. Although the moon goes through similar phases, its diameter remains nearly the same size, indicating revolution about the Earth. The diameter of Venus appears smallest when Venus is in its full phase and appears about six times as great in the crescent phase. This apparent diameter change is explained readily by the heliocentric theory: Venus appears small on the far side of its orbit from the Earth and large when it is near the Earth.— Mercury goes through phases similar to those of Venus. Planets located farther from the sun than the Earth show chiefly the full phase.

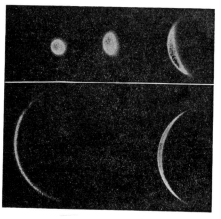

Fig. 16-19.

astronomy. He obtained a copy of Ptolemy's *The Almagest* and some books on mathematics. At first it was necessary for him to read the books secretly, but he soon persuaded his tutor to permit the full-time study of astronomy.

At the age of sixteen, Brahe realized that the Ptolemaic-Copernican controversy could not be resolved without accurate information on the positions of the planets, sun, moon, and stars. Accurate data as a basis for later theorizing, now commonplace in scientific research, was an entirely new technique in the sixteenth century. Brahe was determined to make the necessary observations. After an adventuresome early life in which he married a commoner against the wishes of his parents and lost his nose in a duel (he replaced it with a flesh-colored one made of gold and silver), he received a grant from the king of Denmark with which to construct an observatory. With these funds Brahe built a palatial observatory on the Isle of Hveen and spent the remainder of his life, which ended in Prague, making remarkably accurate observations on the positions of planets and other celestial bodies.

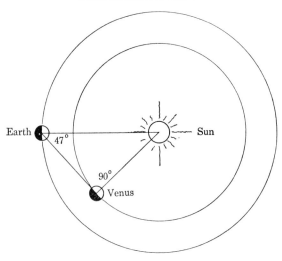

Method used by Copernicus to ascertain the distance to Venus. A right-angle triangle is formed by the sun, Earth, and Venus when Venus attains its maximum angular displacement from the sun.

$$\text{Sine } 47° = \frac{\text{distance of Venus from sun}}{\text{distance of Earth from sun}} = 0.73$$

Therefore distance of Venus from sun = 0.73 times distance of Earth from sun

Fig. 16-20.

Like Aristotle before him, Brahe realized that near objects should show a parallactic displacement against a background of more distant objects if the Earth were revolving about the sun. As he could not find any displacement, he believed that the sun and moon revolved about the Earth. However, he thought that the other planets revolved about the sun. Although Brahe's concept of the universe was not generally accepted, it did constitute a transition from the geocentric to the heliocentric theory. He is remembered principally for his many accurate

Kepler's laws

observations and for his insistence on the need for reliable data as a prerequisite for all theories.

Kepler Johannes Kepler (1571-1630), a German mathematician-astronomer, was a student of Tycho Brahe at Prague and had access to his observations after Brahe's death. These two scientists complemented each other's talents nicely—Brahe the observer and Kepler the theorizer. No hypothesis then known was completely satisfactory in accounting for planetary motions, and Kepler spent many years trying to devise a better explanation. After the expenditure of prodigious mental energy in attempting to reconcile planetary motions with circular orbits, epicycles, and other geometric figures, Kepler finally hit upon elliptical paths as the solution. The following passage describes in his own words the elation he felt at this discovery:*

For, after I had by unceasing toil through a long period of time, using the observations of Brahe, discovered the true distances of the orbits, at last, at last, the true relation of the periodic times to the orbits and, if you ask for the exact time

. . . . though late, yet looked upon me idle
And after long time came;
conceived on the 8th of March of this year, 1618, but unsuccessfully brought to the test and for that reason rejected as false, but, finally returning on the 15th of May, by a new onset it overcame by storm the shadows of my mind, with such fullness of agreement between my seventeen-years' labor on the observations of Brahe and this present study of mine that I at first believed that I was dreaming and was assuming as an accepted principle what was still a subject for enquiry. But the principle is unquestionably true and quite exact: the periodic times of any two planets are to each other exactly as the cubes of the square roots of their median distances. . . .

In the first part of the seventeenth century, Kepler was able to formulate the following three very important laws of planetary motion, for which he earned the epithet, Legislator of the Heavens.

(1) Every planet follows an elliptical orbit about the sun; the sun is located at one focus of the ellipse (Fig. 16-21).

(2) A line joining the center of each planet with the center of the sun sweeps over equal areas in equal periods of time (Fig. 16-22).

* *Harmonice Mundi,* Opera Omnia, Volumen Quintum; translation by Dr. John Walden, 1928.

Kepler's laws

A method of drawing an ellipse. An ellipse can be defined as a closed curve which is the path of a point moving in such a way that the sum of its distances from two fixed points, called foci, is a constant. A string is looped around two fixed pins or pegs, the foci of the ellipse. If this diagram were to represent part of the solar system, the sun would be at one focus and the moving point would describe a planetary orbit. Although the path of the Earth about the sun is an ellipse, it is so nearly a circle that if drawn to scale on the wall of a room, one could not detect its variation from a true circle. The path of the moon about the Earth is also an ellipse.

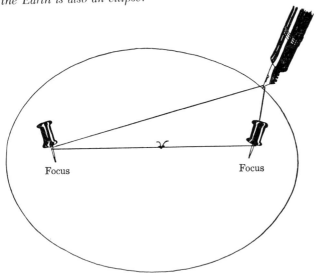

Focus   Focus

Fig. 16-21.

(3) The squares of the periods of revolution of any two planets are in the same ratio as the cubes of their mean distances from the sun:

$$\frac{(\text{Period of revolution of planet } A)^2}{(\text{Period of revolution of planet } B)^2} = \frac{(\text{distance of planet } A \text{ from sun})^3}{(\text{distance of planet } B \text{ from sun})^3}$$

A and B in law (3) may represent any two planets. If B represents the Earth, then both denominators will be equal to 1: the period of revolution of the Earth is 1 year, and its distance from the sun is 1 astronomical unit (93 million miles). Thus, if a new planet were to be discovered at a distance of 4 astronomical units from the sun, its period of revolution could be readily calculated as 8 years. The law indicates that with increasing distances from the sun, planets not only

*Kepler's equal areas law. The shaded parts of the dia-
gram represent areas of space swept over by a line
joining the center of the planet to the center of the sun.
In equal periods of time, the line sweeps equal areas.
As the distance of a planet from the sun varies, the line
will be shortest when the planet is closest to the sun. In
order to cover an equal area of space in this time interval, the planet must move more rapidly when it is close
to the sun than it does when it is farther from the sun.*

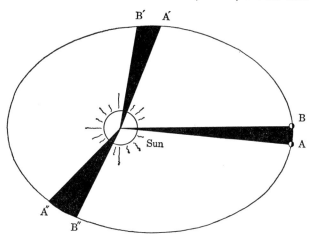

Fig. 16-22.

require longer periods of time to make complete revolutions about the
sun, but also move more slowly in their orbits.

Application of these laws simplified the explanations of planetary
motions, permitted predictions of greater accuracy than was formerly
possible, and thus gave strong support to the heliocentric theory. Later
these laws were shown to hold true also for the motions of the satellites around their planets and for comets about the sun.

Galileo   Galileo Galilei (1564-1642), the Italian astronomer-physi-
ist, was converted to the Copernican system early in his career. A
passage in his book, *Dialogues on the Two Chief Systems of the World,
the Ptolemaic and the Copernican,* published in 1632, illustrates his
reasoning:

I was a very young man. . . . Being firmly persuaded that this opinion
[Copernican] was a piece of solemn folly . . . I began to inquire. . . .
Considering then that nobody followed the Copernican doctrine, who had
not previously held the contrary opinion, and who was not well acquainted
with the arguments of Aristotle and Ptolemy; while on the other hand no-

body followed Ptolemy and Aristotle, who had before adhered to Copernicus, and had gone over from him into the camp of Aristotle; weighing, I
say these things, I began to believe that, if anyone who rejects an opinion
which he has imbibed with his milk, and which has been embraced by an
infinite number, shall take up an opinion held only by a few, condemned
by all the schools, and really regarded as a great paradox, it cannot be
doubted that he must have been induced, not to say driven, to embrace it
by the most cogent arguments. On this account I have become very curious
to penetrate to the very bottom of the subject.

Galileo is perhaps best known for his telescopic studies in astronomy.
Near the beginning of the seventeenth century, he learned that a
Dutch spectacle-maker had constructed an instrument which magnified
distant objects. The value of such an instrument in astronomy was immediately realized by Galileo, and he soon built a telescope of his own.
Imagine the surge of intense interest and excitement which Galileo felt
as he pointed this new instrument at various celestial objects, the first
person ever to study astronomical phenomena with its aid! By this time
he had become convinced of the validity of the Copernican explanation; but he had no proof, and he was even forced to teach the Ptolemaic system at the university where he was stationed. Now the telescope enabled him to gaze upon celestial phenomena which strongly
supported the heliocentric theory. He observed that planets looked
like disks or parts of disks, whereas the stars remained mere pinpoints
of light, as they do today even in the largest of telescopes. The light-
gathering power of the telescope also enabled him to see distant stars
whose light had previously been too faint to affect the unaided eye,
and he discovered that the Milky Way consisted of the combined light
of thousands and thousands of stars, each invisible without optical
assistance. He gives the following account of his discovery of four of
Jupiter's moons: *

On the 7th day of January in the present year, 1610, in the first hour of
the following night, when I was viewing the constellations of the heavens
through a telescope, the planet Jupiter presented itself to my view, and as
I had prepared for myself a very excellent instrument, I noticed a circumstance which I had never been able to notice before, owing to want of power
in my other telescope, namely, that three little stars, small but very bright,
were near the planet; and although I believed them to belong to the number
of the fixed stars, yet they made me somewhat wonder . . . but when on
January 8th, led by some fatality, I turned again to look at the same part of

* The Sidereal Messenger (1610), translated by E. S. Carlos, 1880.

the heavens, I found a very different state of things. . . . I, therefore, waited for the next night with the most intense longing, but I was disappointed of my hope, for the sky was covered with clouds. . . . But on January 10th the stars appeared. . . . These observations also established that there are not only three, but four, erratic sidereal bodies performing their revolutions round Jupiter. . . .

From observation of these motions, Galileo determined that four satellites revolved about Jupiter in the plane of its equator (eight other moons have been found since). Clearly the Earth was not the center of all celestial motion. Furthermore, Jupiter and its moons resembled a miniature solar system. Perhaps the Earth and the other planets moved about the sun in a similar manner.

Other startling discoveries followed at once. Through the telescope, the moon was seen to have an irregular surface marked by craters, mountains, and other topographic features; it definitely was not smooth. Galileo developed a method for measuring the heights of mountains on the moon (Fig. 16-23). On the sun's surface he saw small black spots. During a series of observations these spots moved as a group from one side of the sun to the other (Fig. 21-2). Galileo interpreted this movement correctly as one caused by the sun's rotation. Most devastating to the geocentric theory, however, was Galileo's discovery that Venus and Mercury showed phases (Figs. 16-18 and 16-19) just as Copernicus, about sixty years earlier, had predicted that they would. Moreover, the observation that the diameters of the two planets seemed to change was particularly embarrassing to the Ptolemaic theory which demanded that Venus and Mercury revolve about the Earth in circular paths at unchanging distances from it.

Galileo's support of the Copernican theory eventually led him into conflict with the church, and he is reported to have remarked that the Bible was written to help men get to heaven, not to tell men how the heavens move. Galileo's many telescopic observations, especially those of sunspots, brought him to a state of nearly complete blindness before his death.

Newton It remained for Sir Isaac Newton, whose name is as central in astronomy as in physics and mathematics, to explain why planets follow paths about the sun. The force that keeps the planets moving continuously in their orbits had puzzled inquisitive men for hundreds of years.

Method used by Galileo to measure the heights of mountains on the moon. Orientation: in space looking "down." (The diagram is not to scale.) ABC represents a mountain on the moon; its altitude is greatly exaggerated. At a certain time, an observer on the Earth sees the top of the mountain lighted by the sun's rays. This appears as a tiny white dot isolated in space. The dot grows larger as the moon rotates and more of the mountain is lighted by the sun. The length of AB can be measured in angular degrees. Observation must be made immediately after the moon's rotation has brought the top of the mountain into view as a tiny detached white dot. As the moon's angular diameter and actual size were both known at this time, the actual length of AB could be calculated by a proportion. DB is the hypotenuse of a right angle triangle. As AB and AD (moon's radius) are known, DB can be calculated. AD is a radius of the moon; its length can be subtracted from DB which gives the height of the mountain.—A check on this result can be made by utilizing the length of the shadow cast by the mountain when the sun's rays strike it at an angle which can be determined.

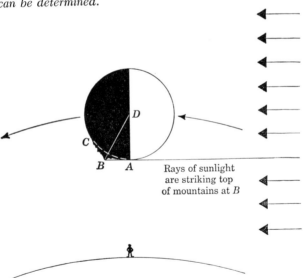

Rays of sunlight
are striking top
of mountains at *B*

Fig. 16-23.

Experience on Earth indicates that objects move only when a force is applied to them. In part, the answer to this problem of planetary motion is given by Newton's first law of motion: every object remains at rest or in uniform motion in a straight line unless it is acted upon by some force (see Chapter 3). In the absence of friction, motion is as natural a state as rest. The planets began to move a long time ago. Presumably the initial impetus is related to the origin of the solar system. As interplanetary space is a nearly perfect vacuum, friction cannot slow celestial bodies as it does all objects on the Earth. Therefore, the planets should continue to move—but in straight lines at uniform rates of speed through space. Instead they follow elliptical orbits about the sun. Here Newton's great unifying principle, the *law of universal gravitation*, proved to be the key: every particle of matter in the universe attracts every other particle with a force which is proportional to the product of their masses, and inversely proportional to the square of the distance between them (see Chapter 4).

The sun exercises a gravitational pull directly toward itself on each planet. The planet's momentum, on the other hand, acts at right angles (tangentially) to this force. The planet follows a compromise path between the two (Fig. 16-24). If the sun's gravitational attraction were

Forces governing planetary orbits.

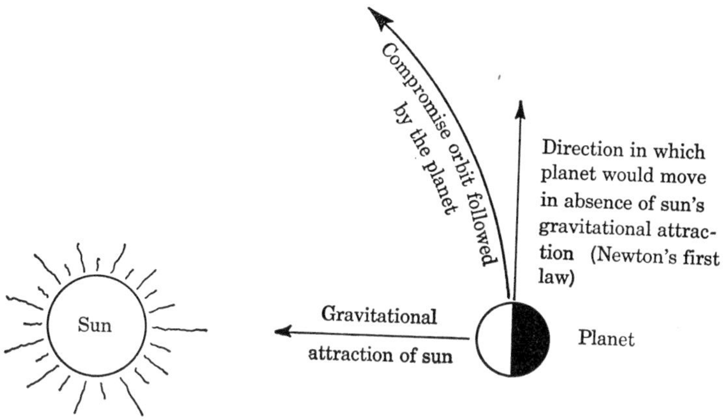

Fig. 16-24.

increased, the Earth should follow a path closer to the sun. If the Earth were stopped motionless and then released, it should move directly toward the sun.

Newton suggested that stars must be situated at tremendous distances from the sun not to be influenced by its gravitational attraction. In addition, he stated that the sun, which he considered a star, would have to be thousands of times as far from the Earth as it is in order to appear as dim as the stars. Newton was thus one of the first scientists to realize the enormous distances which exist between the Earth and the stars.

EVIDENCE SUPPORTING THE LAWS OF KEPLER AND NEWTON

About the middle of the nineteenth century there occurred an outstanding intellectual achievement which was also a striking proof of the law of universal gravitation. The planet Uranus had been discovered more or less by accident in 1781; the discovery was a byproduct of astronomical research and not the result of a planned search. Subsequently, an orbit was calculated for it. For about forty years the location of Uranus in the sky checked accurately with the positions which had been calculated for it. Then Uranus slowly began to deviate from these calculated locations. To be sure, the deviations were slight, but they seemed too large to be mathematical errors. Two explanations appeared possible. Either the law of universal gravitation was not completely accurate or universal, or some unknown body was exerting a gravitational attraction upon Uranus.

Two young men, Adams of England and Leverrier of France, were convinced that an unknown planet, situated at a greater distance from the sun, was causing the deviation in the path of Uranus. They undertook independently the very difficult task of calculating the position of a planet of unknown size and distance whose gravitational pull might be diverting Uranus slightly from its normal path (Fig. 16-25). Still working independently, each was finally able to determine the position of the unknown planet Neptune in space. Both predictions proved amazingly accurate.

Pluto was the last planet to be discovered and was finally located in 1930 after a search lasting twenty-five years. The discovery might have been made some ten years earlier, but a flaw on a photographic film, as well as the proximity of Pluto at that time to a bright star, prevented its detection on a series of photographs taken for this purpose. If perusal of the photographs had shown that one starlike object moved among its neighbors, then that object might have been identified as a planet. Predictions had been made concerning Pluto's existence also, but the discrepancies it caused in the orbit of Neptune were so

The discovery of Neptune. (Diagram is not to scale.) In 1781 Uranus was too far from Neptune to be influenced. But Uranus moves more rapidly than Neptune in its orbit, and as it approached Neptune it began to deviate noticeably from the orbit calculated. The orbit of Neptune is also affected by the gravitational attraction of Uranus.

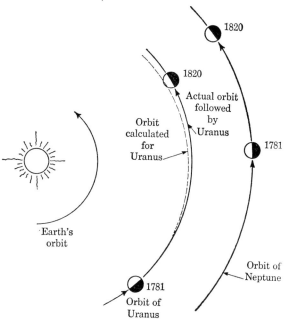

Fig 16-25.

small that its position could not be calculated accurately. Many astronomers now think that additional planets do not exist.

Perhaps the most convincing evidence supporting the validity and accuracy of Kepler's and Newton's laws is the prediction of the positions of celestial bodies for years into the future. These positions are of pinpoint accuracy. For example, astronomers can designate a certain spot on the Earth's surface which will be directly in the path of the moon's shadow during a total solar eclipse that will occur many years in the future. Furthermore, the time for the beginning and ending of the eclipse can be given exactly in hours, minutes, and seconds!

EXERCISES AND QUESTIONS FOR CHAPTER 16

1. According to one explanation of the Christmas Star, a few planets may have seemed so close together in the sky that they appeared to observers

for a short time as one very bright starlike object. Kepler observed such a close approach in the seventeenth century and calculated that a similar close approach occurred about 7 B.C., which may actually be the date of the birth of Christ. Imagine that the planets are Mars, Jupiter, and Saturn and that they appear as one object near the eastern horizon at sunrise. Make a sketch (orientation: looking "down" on the solar system) which shows these three planets and the sun and the Earth in suitable locations.

2. Make a star map which shows the Big Dipper in four positions: (1) as it is now at 9:00 P.M., (2) at 3:00 A.M., (3) at 9:00 A.M., and (4) at 3:00 P.M. Mark these positions A, B, C, and D respectively. Next give the position of the Big Dipper at each of the following times: (1) 3 months later at 3:00 A.M., (2) 9 months later at 3:00 P.M. and (3) 3 months ago at 9:00 A.M.

3. About midnight one evening, you see a bright starlike object high in the sky. A friend states the object is one of the following: (1) Mercury, (2) Venus, (3) Jupiter, or (4) Uranus. Which is it?

4. What is the relationship between the velocity of a planet in its orbit and its distance from the sun? Does the same relationship hold for the moon about the Earth? For comets around the sun?

5. A certain star rises in the east at 6:00 P.M. now. When did it rise in the east 3 months ago? Another star sets in the west at midnight now? When will it set in the west 2 months from now?

6. Distinguish carefully between the actual and apparent motions of the sun, stars, and planets.

7. State the position taken by each of the following concerning the geo-centric-heliocentric controversy and give at least one type of evidence or argument cited by each: Aristarchus, Aristotle, Copernicus, Brahe, Kepler, and Galileo.

8. What measurement can you make on the photograph in Fig. 16-1 to show that the time exposure was approximately 1¼ hours?

CHAPTER 17

The Earth in Space

THE simplicity stressed by Copernicus, the more accurate predictions of planetary positions obtained by using Kepler's laws, the many telescopic discoveries of Galileo, and the unifying explanations of Newton all strongly supported the heliocentric concept. However, actual proof that the Earth rotated on an axis and revolved about the sun was not obtained until the nineteenth century: the pendulum experiment of Foucault in Paris, the first determination of parallax, and the discovery of the aberration of starlight provided final proof. In this chapter, evidence is presented that the Earth is approximately spherical, spins on an axis, and revolves about the sun, and we consider a few methods of measuring sizes and distances in astronomy.

EVIDENCE FOR THE CURVATURE
OF THE EARTH'S SURFACE

When Columbus set sail for the west, most people still believed that the Earth was flat, although learned men from the time of the early Greeks had realized that it was spherical. Ancient astronomers were aware of several lines of evidence which indicate the nearly spherical shape of the Earth.* The shadow of the Earth on the moon during a partial lunar eclipse is curved, and the degree of curvature shows that the Earth's diameter is about four times that of the moon (Fig. 18-10). The early scientists also observed the change in the positions of the stars as the observer travels north or south: the North Star rises

---

* Recent measurements from satellites orbiting the Earth suggest that the North Pole is about 50 feet farther from the Earth's center and that the South Pole is about 50 feet closer to the Earth's center than was previously estimated. A cross section through the Earth at the equator is not a true circle, but an ellipse with one diameter about 1400 feet longer than a diameter oriented 90 degrees to it.

Fig. 17-1.

Light rays from a star are nearly parallel throughout the solar system. Any one who has walked along railroad tracks has had the experience of seeing parallel lines appear to converge in the distance. (Diagram not to scale.)

Light rays from star are
virtually parallel in this area

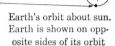

Rays of light from a star   Earth's orbit about sun.
go out in all directions.   Earth is shown on opp-
Two have been projected   osite sides of its orbit
as examples.

Change in altitude of a star above the horizon as the observer's latitude changes. The North Star (Polaris) is directly overhead for an observer at the north pole, on the northern horizon for a person at the equator, and at different angles for observers located between these two places. If the Earth were flat and in the plane of the equator, the North Star would be directly overhead for observers anywhere in the Northern Hemisphere. Polaris is not located precisely at the north celestial pole.

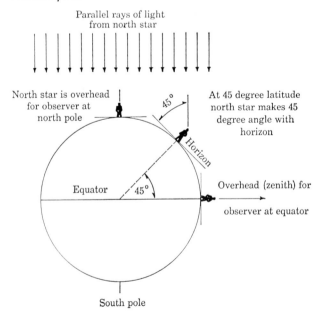

Fig. 17-2.

in the sky as the traveler moves north, and some familiar stars in the southern sky no longer appear at all above the horizon (Figs. 17-1 and 17-2). This observation can be readily explained only if the Earth is spherical. Astronomers also observed the way in which a ship disappears from sight: its deck disappears before its superstructure. If the Earth were flat, the ship would look smaller and smaller with increasing distance from the observer, but all of it would remain visible until it became a mere speck and then disappeared (Fig. 17-3). Still another

Fig. 17-3.

Evidence that the Earth's surface is curved.

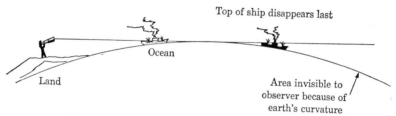

indication of the Earth's shape is the fact that a wider area of its surface is visible from a high altitude than from a low altitude because one can "see over the curvature."

Some of these observations show that the Earth's surface is curved but do not necessarily show that it is spherical. Circumnavigation and photos taken from rockets at very high altitudes also indicate that the Earth's surface is curved (Fig. 17-4). (Circumnavigation could be explained on the basis of a flat Earth.)

Why the Earth Is Spherical   The Earth is not shaped irregularly, nor is it shaped like a cube, cylinder, or tetrahedron, for a definite reason. Its gravitational attraction is a force toward concentrating the greatest amount of matter into the smallest possible volume; the sphere is the most economical space saver of all three-dimensional figures. If some gigantic force could distort the Earth's shape, gravitational attraction would slowly level irregularities and again make the Earth spherical.

The reason why the Earth is not a perfect sphere is that centrifugal force* causes the poles to flatten and the equator to bulge. The magnitude of the centrifugal force is influenced by the speed of motion: if

* Motion along a curved path produces a force which is directed away from the center of curvature and is called centrifugal ("center-fleeing") force. A familiar example is the outward push exerted on a passenger when a car turns a corner.

Fig. 17-4.

Photograph of the Earth from an altitude of 101 miles. Approximately 500,000 square miles of the southwestern United States and northern Mexico are visible in this photograph, which is a mosaic of four photographs made by a rocket-transported camera launched at White Sands, New Mexico. (Courtesy of Naval Research Laboratory, Washington)

Fig. 17-5.

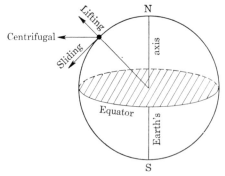

The Earth's rotation at its surface propels an object toward the equator and diminishes its weight. The poles are about 13 miles nearer the center of the Earth than the equator. For this reason one might view motion toward the equator as uphill. The diagram shows why the oceans are not piled up at the poles and why rivers can flow toward the equator.

other factors are equal, centrifugal force is greatest at high speeds. As all parts of the Earth rotate completely about its axis in approximately 24 hours, objects near the equator move very rapidly because they have about 25,000 miles to travel, and objects near the poles move very slowly because they have only a few miles to travel. The centrifugal force is greatest at the equator and least at the poles, and for this reason the Earth bulges at its equator (Fig. 17-5).

Fig. 17-6.

Jolly's method of "weighing" the Earth (1881). A large weight was put in exact balance with an 11-lb spherical flask of mercury. Then a 5-ton lead ball was moved under the mercury. Its gravitational attraction was sufficient to pull the mercury down a short distance, and a small weight was added on the left to restore the balance. Very accurate measurements were required.—The following equations can be set up. As the only unknown, x, is the mass of the Earth, it can be determined:

$$\frac{(\text{Small weight}) \cdot x}{(\text{Earth's radius})^2} = \frac{(\text{mass of mercury}) \cdot (\text{mass of lead})}{(\text{distance between their centers})^2}$$

The lead and the mercury are put into spherical form because the gravitational attraction of a sphere can be considered to be concentrated at the center.

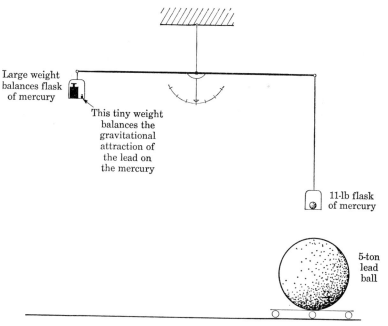

Large weight balances flask of mercury

This tiny weight balances the gravitational attraction of the lead on the mercury

11-lb flask of mercury

5-ton lead ball

Venus rotates more slowly than the Earth and is more nearly a perfect sphere. Jupiter and Saturn, on the other hand, have much greater equatorial bulges than the Earth, largely because they rotate at very rapid rates (about ten hours for a complete rotation for each of them.) Fig. 17-6 illustrates one method of "weighing" the Earth.

EVIDENCE OF THE EARTH'S ROTATION

The spinning of the Earth on its axis from west to east causes the apparent rising in the east and setting in the west of all celestial bodies once in approximately 24 hours. However, as Chapter 16 has shown, this phenomenon cannot be used as evidence that the Earth rotates; it might be explained as an actual westward movement of the celestial bodies.

Historically, it was an experiment performed by Foucault in Paris in 1851 which provided the first actual evidence that the Earth turns on an axis. Foucault suspended a heavy iron ball at the end of a 200-foot wire fastened to the roof of the Pantheon. A pointer was attached to the base of the weight, and a box of sand was placed beneath the pendulum so that lines were drawn in the sand as it swung back and forth. The pendulum's inertia keeps it swinging back and forth in the same plane. However, little by little, the plane of the pendulum's swing appears to turn (as indicated by the line in the sand) in a clockwise direction: the apparent turning is caused by the actual rotation of the Earth in a counterclockwise direction (Fig. 17-7). This phenomenon is most easily understood if we imagine the pendulum to be suspended from a roof at the North Pole: in this case the plane of the pendulum's swing will rotate with respect to the Earth's surface through 360 degrees in about 24 hours. (The same will happen at the South Pole, except that here the plane of the pendulum's swing rotates in a counterclockwise direction with respect to the Earth's surface.) At latitudes below the North Pole, it takes more than 24 hours for the pendulum's plane to rotate through 360 degrees; it takes about 31 hours in Paris. The apparent rotation becomes increasingly slower until finally at the equator there is no rotation at all—that is, the pendulum always swings in the same, fixed plane with respect to the Earth's surface. South of the equator the rotation begins again, slowly, in the opposite (counterclockwise) direction.

All motion is relative. An experience familiar to all of us is that of

Fig. 17-7.

The Foucault pendulum in the U.N. General Assembly Building, New York. The 12-inch sphere is kept swinging by an electromagnet at the center of a 6-foot metal ring. The plane of the swing shifts clockwise, and at this latitude a cycle is completed in about 36 hours and 45 minutes. (Courtesy, United Nations)

sitting in a railroad car at a station beside a second train on the next track: when one of the two trains begins to move, it is often impossible to tell, without using nearby buildings as reference points, which train is actually moving. The sphere of the Earth and the celestial sphere are like the two trains, except that there are no fixed reference points anywhere. Everything on the Earth moves together—air, water, buildings, people—so that even though the rate exceeds 1000 mi/hr at the equator, we have no way of detecting the movement, and therefore it seems to be the celestial sphere which is moving. No wonder the belief in a motionless Earth persisted for more than 2000 years!

Evidence of the Earth's Revolution The eastward shift of the sun against the background of stars (Fig. 16-13B) is explained by the revolution of the Earth about the sun. However, this cannot be used as evidence, because another explanation is possible according to the geocentric theory. As powers of observation grew, revolution of the

343

Earth about the sun was proved by the annual parallactic displacement of near stars against the background of more distant stars (Fig. 16-15B).

SEASONS OF THE YEAR

The seasons of the year—fall, winter, spring, and summer—are caused by the Earth's revolution about the sun and the tilt of its axis to the plane of this orbit (Figs. 17-8 and 17-9). The varying distance of the Earth from the sun, 94.5 to 91.5 million miles, is not an important factor in seasonal changes. As the angle of tilt is maintained throughout

Fig. 17-8.

Winter and summer. Each day the Earth spins completely on its axis. As the direction of rotation for an observer on the Earth is parallel to the equator, summer days are longer than summer nights, and the sun cannot set at either pole during its summer.—The sun's rays are most concentrated when they strike the Earth's surface vertically (AB) and less concentrated when they approach at an angle (CD) because a larger area must be covered with the same amount of energy. The sun's rays may be likened to the water from a garden hose: when the hose is pointed at the ground near one's feet, it strikes a small area with great force, but when the hose is pointed obliquely from the ground, water falls more gently over a much larger area. The beam of a flashlight can be concentrated or spread out in much the same way.

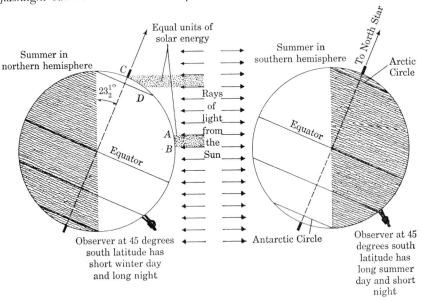

the year, the Northern Hemisphere at one time is tilted toward the sun (its summer season), and six months later when the Earth is on the opposite side of the sun, the Northern Hemisphere is tilted away from the sun (its winter season). If the Earth's axis were perpendicular to

The Earth's orbit inside the celestial sphere (not to scale). The ecliptic is the apparent annual eastward path of the sun among the stars. It may also be defined as the plane of the Earth's orbit around the sun extended to the celestial sphere. Planets are nearly always seen among the stars near the ecliptic. Solstices and equinoxes are shown. The celestial equator is the plane of the Earth's equator extended out to the celestial sphere. The equinoxes are the two opposite points of the celestial sphere where the ecliptic crosses the celestial equator. When the sun appears to be at either of these positions, day and night are equal in length. The solstices are points midway between the equinoxes. For example, the summer solstice is located on the right side of the diagram. The sun appears to be at this point along the ecliptic when viewed from the Earth's position about June 22 on the left side of the diagram.

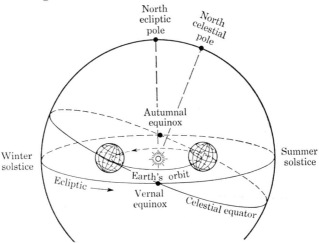

Fig. 17-9.

its orbital plane, there would be no seasons. Each degree of latitude would experience the same sort of weather phenomena all year long—an extended combination of fall and spring. Locations near the equator would be warmest, and those near the poles would be coldest.

Two factors combine to make summer days warmer than winter ones: there are more hours of daylight, and the sun's rays are more direct (Fig. 17-8). Opposite seasons occur simultaneously in the Northern and Southern Hemispheres. The sun is not visible in arctic regions during winter, and perpetual daylight occurs during arctic summers.

CALCULATIONS OF SIZES AND DISTANCES IN ASTRONOMY

Contemplation and measurement of sizes and distances in astronomy are, on the one hand, humbling and awe-inspiring; on the other hand, they are stimulating and intellectually satisfying. At first thought, it seems impossible that man could devise measuring sticks mighty enough to reach into space for distances which are so immense that they can be calculated only in terms of light-years. Yet such triumphs have been achieved, and the first measurements were made hundreds of years ago. It was necessary to begin by measuring the size of the Earth. Completion of this made possible the determination of the distance to the moon and the size of the moon. The next step involved measurement of the distance from the Earth to the sun, the astronomical unit, which is an important yardstick in the scale of celestial distances. The distances between the Earth and some of the nearer stars were calculated next. Several procedures were then discovered which made it possible to figure out the number of light-years between the Earth and remote stars and galaxies. The organization of the following pages parallels this historical development.

Trigonometry—solving triangles—was early applied in the measurement of celestial distances, as well as in the measurements of much shorter lengths on the Earth's surface. To estimate distances in everyday living, the eyes solve triangles. Whenever you pick up an object, your eyes unconsciously estimate the distance of the object by determining the point of intersection of two lines of sight, one from each eye to the object. To illustrate this fact, close one eye and try to pour water from a pitcher into a glass resting upon a table, or attempt to bring the points of two pencils together when a pencil is held in each hand. The wet table and waving pencil points indicate that accurate distance estimates require the services of two eyes and are achieved by locating the apex of a triangle which has as its base the distance between one's eyes. Trigonometric methods allow lengths and distances to be measured by a sort of remote control that involves the solution of triangles (Fig. 17-10).

Fig. 17-10.

Trigonometric method of measuring distance across a large canyon. The surveyor at D wishes to determine the distance across the canyon. He selects a base line (AB) and measures it carefully. Angles A and B are measured next. The distance across the canyon can then be calculated by trigonometry. A base line must be adequate in length for reliable results. If the canyon is nearly 20 miles across, a satisfactory base line would be about 1 mile in length.—Angle C equals the parallax of AB, its angular width, and can be calculated when Angles A and B and the distance AB are known (law of sines). Distances to the nearest stars may be measured by parallax (Fig. 16-15), which is a procedure similar to that above but which utilizes a base line of 186 million miles. Stellar distances are so great that measuring them is similar to measuring the 20-mile distance across the canyon by using a base line only a few inches in length. Thus only the distances to those stars which are located relatively near the Earth can be measured by parallax. (Modified from Skilling and Richardson)

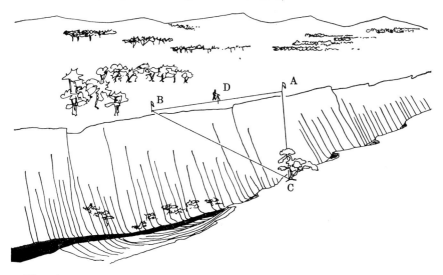

The Size of the Earth The Greek astronomer Eratosthenes first measured the size of the Earth in the third century B.C. As measurement of the Earth's circumference by circumnavigation was out of the question at this time, Eratosthenes used a geometrical approach. He assumed that the sun's rays are parallel, that the Earth is a sphere, and that a plumb line always points toward the Earth's center (Fig. 17-11). He also assumed that his two observation spots (Syene and Alexandria in Egypt) were on the same north-south line. He was aware that a circle can be subdivided into 360 degrees, and that the circumference of a circle can be obtained by measuring the length of 1 degree of arc and then multiplying this length by 360. With this in mind, Eratos-

thenes planned to measure a certain length of arc at the Earth's surface
and then determine geometrically the angle at the Earth's center subtended by this arc. With these data, a simple calculation would give
the Earth's circumference, and from this, its diameter, radius, volume,
and area could be determined.

Fig. 17-11.

*Method used by Eratosthenes, about 235 B.C., to measure the size of
the Earth. (Diagram is not to scale.) The angles shown are equal because if two parallel lines are cut by a third straight line, their corresponding angles are equal.*

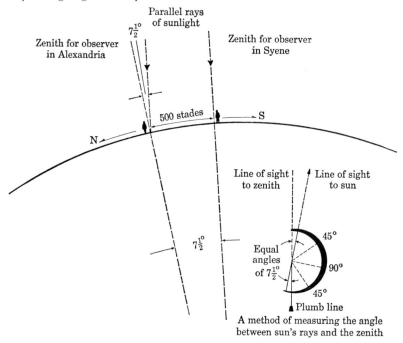

Syene was located a measured 500 stades south of Alexandria. (The
exact length of a stade is uncertain but is thought to equal 6000 feet.)
Eratosthenes knew that the sun was directly overhead at Syene on the
longest day of the year and would shine directly down a well. On this
day he arranged to measure the angle made at Alexandria between
the sun's rays and a plumb bob: this angle was about 7½ degrees. By
geometry (Fig. 17-11) Eratosthenes showed that a 7½-degree angle at
the Earth's center subtended a length of the Earth's circumference

equal to 500 stades. As 360 divided by 7½ is equal to 48, the Earth's circumference equals 48 times 500 or 24,000 stades. This length is somewhat too large—how much depends on the exact length of a stade—but the entire calculation is still remarkably accurate for the third century B.C.

Distance to the Moon and Its Size   About 100 years after Eratosthenes measured the size of the Earth, another Alexandrian astronomer, Hipparchus, calculated the distance to the Moon (Fig. 17-12) and the

Calculation of the distance from the Earth to the moon by parallax. (Diagram is a side view, not to scale; the moon is exactly in the plane of the Earth's equator only at certain times.)—This distance was first calculated by Hipparchus in the second century B.C. For convenience, observers A and B are placed at the same latitudes north and south of the equator, although Hipparchus did not do this. As the latitudes of the observers are known, the size of angle 1 is known (attention is limited to triangles ADC and ADE). The observers take lines of sight on the moon simultaneously to displace the moon by parallax. Next each observer measures the angle between the moon and his zenith point (angle 4). As the approximate size of the Earth was known to Hipparchus, the length of AE its radius was known, and by trigonometric methods all of the angles and sides of the triangles ADC and ADE could then be calculated. The sum of CD and DE is the distance from the center of the Earth to the center of the moon. (Angle 5 can be obtained because the sum of angles 2, 5, and 4 is 180 degrees and angles 2 and 4 are known.)

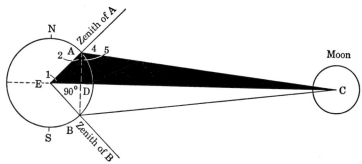

Fig. 17-12.

size of the moon (Fig. 17-13). The distance to the sun—the astronomical unit—cannot be measured as reliably by parallax because its parallax is smaller and because the stars are not visible during the day as a background for reference points. More accurate methods also exist for measuring the astronomical unit.

Fig. 17-13.

A method of ascertaining the size of the moon. (Diagram is not to scale.)
The entire distance around the moon's orbit can be calculated because
the orbit is nearly circular; it is approximately equivalent to the circumference
of a circle whose radius is 240,000 miles. The angular diameter of the moon
in the sky is measured. This is about ½ degree. Measuring the angular di-
ameter of the moon from the Earth's surface rather than from its center
does not make a significant difference in the size of the angle. As the moon's
orbit is very large, an arc of ½ degree can be considered as a straight line
and thus equal to the moon's diameter. Thus:

$$\text{Moon's diameter} = \tfrac{1}{2} \cdot \frac{2\pi r}{360} = \tfrac{1}{2} \cdot \frac{2 \times 3.14 \times 240,000}{360} \text{ miles}$$

which is about 2000 miles. An accurate determination would have to con-
sider the moon's orbit as elliptical, its angular diameter as slightly more
than ½ degree, and certain other refinements.

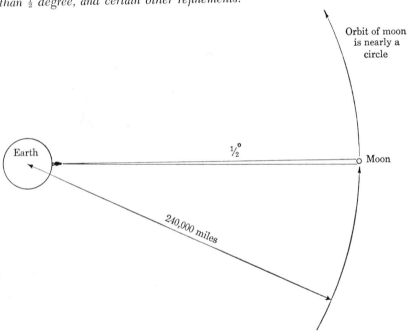

Orbit of moon
is nearly a
circle

Earth   ½°   Moon

240,000 miles

Distance to the Nearer Stars by Parallax   Once the distance from
the Earth to the sun had been determined and powerful telescopes had
been constructed, it became possible to measure the distances to the
nearer stars by parallax (Fig. 16-15B). Astronomers measure parallax
by taking lines of sight to a near star at time intervals of six months
when the Earth is on opposite sides of its orbit. The angle at the star

formed by the intersection of these two lines of sight can be determined (astronomers refer to half of this angle as parallax). Geometrically, the two points on the Earth's orbit and the star form an isosceles triangle in which the length of the base is twice the distance from the Earth to the sun: 186 million miles or 2 astronomical units. This triangle can be subdivided into two equal right-angle triangles in which a side (base) and an angle (the measured parallax) are known. The length of the hypotenuse, or the distance from the star to the Earth can then be calculated. The distance from the Earth to the more distant stars, those 300 or more light-years away, cannot be determined by parallax because the base line of the triangle (diameter of the Earth's orbit) is too small for such measurements.

Distances to Remote Stars.   In modern times, a number of different methods have been used by astronomers in determining distances to remote stars and galaxies. Only one of these is discussed in detail here, that which involves stars known as cepheid variables.

The observed brightness of a star depends upon at least two factors: its actual or intrinsic brightness, and its distance from the observer. Remote stars appear faint even if they are actually very bright, because the intensity of light varies inversely as the square of the distance between the source of light and the observer. This inverse square relationship makes it possible to determine the distance of a remote object by comparing the apparent brightness of the object with its actual brightness which is known or assumed; furthermore, if the distance is known, the intrinsic brightness can be calculated. Consider as an illustration an observer and two assistants having flashlights of identical intrinsic brightness. On a dark night the assistants move away from the observer in opposite directions. If they stop at points equidistant from the observer, the apparent brightnesses of the flashlights will be the same. However, if assistant A moves twice as far away as assistant B, the flashlight of A will show an apparent brightness only one-quarter that of B's. If A moves three times as far away, the apparent brightness of A's light will be only one-ninth that of B's.

It was noticed (by Leavitt and Shapley) that certain stars, subsequently named cepheid variables, changed in brightness systematically over a period of time which in some instances lasted as long as a few months (Fig. 17-14). Careful study showed that the time necessary for the light from such a star to vary from minimum brightness to maximum, and then back to minimum again (its period), is related directly to its intrinsic brightness; the intrinsically brightest stars have the longest periods of variation, and fainter stars have shorter periods of variation (Fig. 17-15). Next, distances to some of the nearer cepheids were obtained by a method not discussed in this text (analysis of stellar motions). The intrinsic brightness of a cepheid could be calculated once its distance and apparent brightness had been measured. Distances to these nearer cepheids were also calculated by using

A cepheid varies in color and spectrum as well as in brightness.

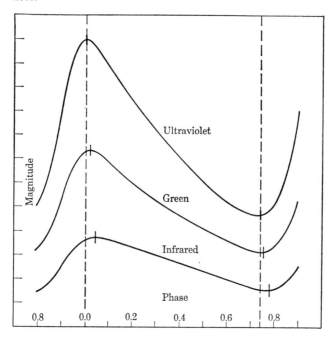

Fig. 17-14.

the inverse square law and the period-luminosity relationship. Many checks indicated that nearer cepheids had periods directly related to their actual brightnesses. This period-luminosity relationship was then assumed to apply to remote stars which were too far away for a direct check by other methods of determining stellar distances. On the basis of this assumption, the distance to a remote cepheid could readily be calculated by astronomers: the period of the remote cepheid and its apparent brightness were measured, the period-luminosity relationship

Fig. 17-15.

Period-luminosity curves for cepheids. The graph shows that the more luminous cepheids have longer periods than the less luminous, and that classical cepheids are more luminous than type II cepheids.

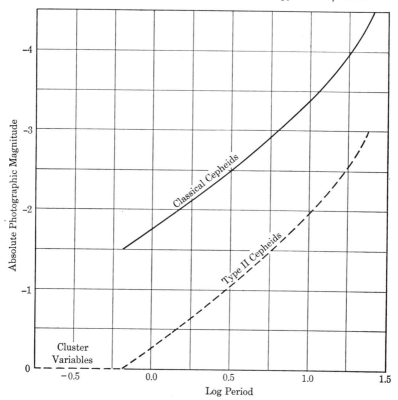

gave its intrinsic brightness, and the distance to the star could then be calculated by applying the inverse square ratio of light intensity to these data.

Distances to Remote Galaxies   Cepheid variables have been discovered in galaxies which are relatively near the Earth (less remote than others) and the distances to these galaxies have been determined on the basis of the assumed period-luminosity relationship. Next the average intrinsic brightnesses of these galaxies are assumed to be representative for all other galaxies. Comparison of the apparent brightness of a remote galaxy with this assumed average intrinsic brightness, and application of the light intensity law, thus gives the distance to the remote galaxy.

Cautions Concerning Stellar Distances Calculations of distances in astronomy involve a number of assumptions which have a tendency to pyramid as distances become greater. The distances to nearer stars are obtained by a method which seems reliable but which depends upon the validity of certain assumptions. These results are then used as a basis for the next method which likewise involves certain other assumptions. For example, in many determinations, light has been assumed to come through space without any diminution of its brightness by intervening dust or gas, an assumption which is undoubtedly somewhat in error and more so in some directions than in others. If light from a star is dimmed by obscuring matter, its calculated distance will be too great; the magnitude of the error depends upon the quantity of obscuring matter. Therefore, opportunity exists for the presence of large errors in these successive extrapolations, and caution should be used in accepting without question the reliability of all stellar distances.

This need for caution has been emphasized in a startling manner recently. Astronomers did not comprehend clearly that two types of cepheids existed until about 1952. One type is at least four times as luminous as the other (Fig. 17-15). All of the cepheids which have been used to obtain distances outside of our galaxy are of the more luminous type. Therefore, if they are actually four times as luminous as they were previously considered, then they must be twice as far away as they were previously thought to be, for their apparent brightness has not changed. Distances to other galaxies and the sizes of these galaxies have all been computed on the basis of the cepheid method, and they are unreliable if the method is not correct. Prior to 1952 a scale of distances had been calculated for the universe; subsequently, all distances and sizes which had been determined for objects beyond our own galaxy were approximately doubled—an error in a calculation had reduced the calculated size of the universe by half its currently accepted figure! (Sizes and distances within our own galaxy were not affected by this correction.) Before 1952, it was believed that the 200-inch telescope at Palomar could see 1 billion light-years into space; astronomers now think that this figure should be increased to 2 billion light-years, or more.

In 1929 the distance to the Andromeda galaxy was determined by the cepheid method to be about 900,000 light-years. In 1944 this calculated distance was reduced to approximately 750,000 light-years by a correction for a dimming of its light caused by obscuring matter (gas and dust) in our own galaxy. In 1952 this revised figure was doubled to about 1.5 million light-years. In 1956-57 the distance was revised again by some astronomers to approximately 2 million light-years, because of the discovery that cepheids in other galaxies are still more luminous even than they were thought to be in 1952.

Surely, we do not yet know the answer to the question, "How big is the universe?"!

EXERCISES AND QUESTIONS FOR CHAPTER 17

1. A new planet is discovered. It is nearly a perfect sphere. What information, if any, does this give concerning the planet's revolution, rotation, composition, and distance from the sun?

2. Explain why the Earth's axis points approximately at the North Star from all positions in its orbit.

3. Explain the probable seasonal or climatic variations which would result from the following: (1) If the Earth's axis were perpendicular to the plane of its orbit about the sun and remained perpendicular in all parts of its orbit; and (2) If the Earth's axis were parallel to the plane of its orbit and pointed always in the same direction in space (the axis of Uranus is nearly parallel to its orbital plane about the sun).

4. If the Earth were to stop rotating, what would probably happen to its shape after the lapse of many years?

5. From the equator where would you look to see the North Star? From the North Pole? From your home town? What is the latitude at each place?

6. What changes occur in the time and place of sunrise and sunset in September? December? June?

7. Explain why planets move in orbits about the sun. State the two laws involved.

8. List some of the changes which have been made in the estimates of astronomical distances in the last few decades.

9. Imagine that you are located at about 50° latitude in the Southern Hemisphere. In what direction is the sun at noon? When will the noon shadow be shortest during the year? When longest?

the brightness of a star is related to the light of its period

CHAPTER 18

The Moon

WITH the exception of the sun, the moon is the most conspicuous of all the celestial bodies and has most influence on the Earth. The light of the full moon was particularly welcome before artificial lighting; the phases of the moon constituted a calendar for early man; and the tidal effects of the moon have always been important in coastal areas.

The moon is the Earth's large satellite. It follows an elliptical path about the Earth at a mean distance of nearly 240,000 miles. Its diameter is about 2160 miles. An average sample of the moon is approximately 3.4 times as heavy as an equal volume of water (the Earth's specific gravity is about 5.5) and its mass is less than 1/81 that of the Earth. The moon acts as a mirror to reflect light from the sun onto the nighttime side of the Earth. The Earth, at times, likewise acts as a mirror to reflect light onto the darkened portion of the moon (earthshine, Fig. 18-1).

The length of the moon's diameter appears to vary as much as 12 percent, indicating that the moon's distance from the Earth varies. In fact, the moon's orbit can be calculated on the basis of this apparent change in diameter: the moon is closest to the Earth when its diameter seems largest. This change in the moon's diameter should not be confused with the apparent increase in size that all celestial bodies undergo near the horizon; that this apparent increase in size is an optical illusion may be proved by photographing an object, such as the moon, both near the horizon and high overhead.

Fig. 18-1.

Earthshine on the moon at the crescent phase in the morning sky—"The old moon in the new moon's arms." The light rays that bring the earthshine to the observer have come from the sun to the Earth, have been reflected to the darkened part of the moon, and then reflected back to the Earth again. Saturn was behind the moon half an hour before the photograph was taken.

PHASES OF THE MOON

The moon's monthly cycle of phases was possibly the first celestial motion to be explained correctly. As the moon is a nearly spherical body in space, one half is always lighted by the sun and the other half is darkened and turned away from the sun. The moon's revolution about the Earth brings varying proportions of its lighted half into view for Earthly observers (Fig. 18-2). New moon occurs when the lighted half is turned completely away from the Earth; full moon occurs a little more than two weeks later when the illuminated half is facing the Earth.

To the earthly observer, the cycle begins about two days after the invisible new moon when a thin crescent can first be seen low in the western sky at sunset. Almost a week later the half-moon (first quarter phase) is high overhead in the southern sky at sunset (Fig. 18-3). At the end of another week, the full moon rises in the east as the sun sinks in the west. At the third quarter phase, the half-moon rises above the eastern horizon at midnight. About one month after the beginning of the cycle, the observer again sees a thin crescent low in the western sky at sunset, and a new cycle has commenced. The length of time spent by the moon above the horizon is inversely proportional to that spent by the sun, a fortunate circumstance for man. During long winter nights, the moon rises earlier, moves higher in the sky, and sets at a later hour than it does during summer months.

The revolution of the moon about the Earth causes it to shift eastward against the background of stars (Chapter 16); hence the Earth's rotation in relation to the moon (lunar day) takes about 24 hours and 51 minutes. Stated another way, the moon rises about 51 minutes later each day (Fig. 18-4). However, the length of the lunar day varies considerably during the year because the moon's orbital plane is in-

Fig. 18-2.

Phases of the moon. Orientation: in space, looking down on the Northern Hemisphere in spring as the moon completes a circuit around the Earth. The phases depend upon the proportion of the lighted half of the moon that can be seen from the Earth. The shaded area indicates the dark half of the moon away from the sun. The pebble-like dots indicate the half of the moon that faces the Earth. An observer on the Earth sees only the lighted part of the moon that contains the dots— the part bordered with heavy lines. A full moon reflects about nine times as much light as a half-moon. The great difference is due partly to the mountains on the moon. These cast shadows when the moon is not full and little light is reflected from surface areas in shadow.

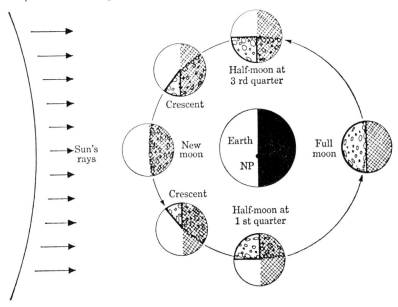

clined to that of the Earth. For example, at the harvest time in the fall, the full moon rises only 20 minutes or so later each night, and so it is visible for a longer time during the early evening hours at this season than it is at other seasons of the year.

The time which elapses between two full moons or two new moons

Location of the moon in the observer's sky during its first quarter. Orientation: in space looking down on the Northern Hemisphere in summer. Three observers are pictured on the Earth. For one it is noon, for the second sunset, and for the third midnight. Each has an eastern and a western horizon. The moon is on the eastern horizon (rising) for the noon observer, high in the south for the sunset observer, and on the western horizon (setting) for the midnight observer. In six hours the Earth's counterclockwise rotation will spin the noon observer into the sunset position, and six hours more will bring him to midnight. Make other diagrams to show the location of the moon in the observer's sky during its other phases. Sunset occurs at different hours at different seasons of the year. The hour of 6:00 P.M. is chosen for convenience of illustration.

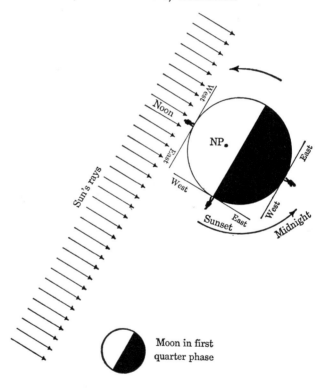

Moon in first
quarter phase

Fig. 18-3.

approximates 29½ days (synodic month). On the other hand, the moon completes its eastward swing among the stars in about 27⅓ days (sidereal month). The orbital movement of the Earth causes this difference (Fig. 18-5).

Fig. 18-4.

The moon rises later each day. Orientation: looking down on the Northern Hemisphere in autumn. The full moon appears above the eastern horizon at sunset on one day for the observer. Next day the Earth's daily rotation has returned him to the sunset position in about 24 hours. Meanwhile the moon has moved forward in its orbit; it is no longer visible at sunset. The Earth must spin 51 minutes longer, on the average, to move the observer into position to see the moon rise in the east again. The amount of movement has been exaggerated. What is the season of the year in the Southern Hemisphere at this time?

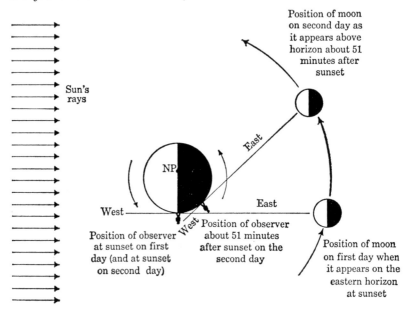

THE MOON'S ROTATION AND REVOLUTION

The moon always turns the same hemisphere toward the Earth; from the Earth one can see the face of the "man in the moon" but never the back of his head. The moon keeps the same face toward the Earth because of two motions: it revolves about the Earth, and it rotates (with respect to the stars) as it revolves; that is, the moon makes one complete rotation in the time it takes to make one complete revolution (Fig. 18-6). Therefore, any specific point on the moon experiences one period of daytime in which the sun is visible (nearly 14 days) followed by a period of nighttime (nearly 14 days) during each sidereal month of $27\frac{1}{3}$ days. To illustrate this phenomenon, try following a circular

Fig. 18-5.

Sidereal and synodic months. Orientation: looking down on the Northern Hemisphere. (1) At the first observation, the moon is in its new phase; the Earth, moon, sun, and reference star are in line in space. (2) About 27⅓ days later, after the moon has revolved through 360 angular degrees around the Earth, the sidereal month is completed. Earth, moon, and reference star are once more aligned—but not so the sun. The moon is a crescent. (3) Approximately two days later, about 29½ days after (1), the synodic month ends. The moon is again in a line between the Earth and the sun in the new moon phase.

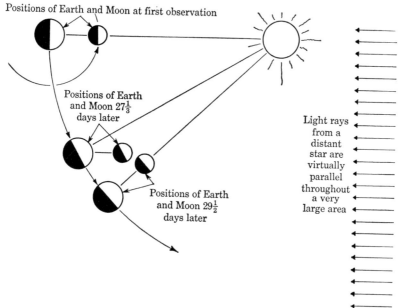

Positions of Earth and Moon at first observation

Positions of Earth and Moon 27⅓ days later

Positions of Earth and Moon 29½ days later

Light rays from a distant star are virtually parallel throughout a very large area

path about a tree, keeping your face turned toward the tree in the center at all times. In order to do this, you will have to rotate once during each complete trip around the tree.

In October 1959 Russian astronomers succeeded in placing a satellite in orbit about the moon and the Earth. Instruments within the satellite, apparently at a command signal radioed from the Earth, turned a camera so that it faced the part of the moon permanently hidden from the Earth and caused photographs to be taken. These were later developed automatically within the satellite and subsequently radioed to the Earth when the satellite had returned to the part of its orbit nearest the Earth. This was a notable, brilliant feat. The photographs suggest that the hidden side of the moon is more monotonous, with fewer

Fig. 18-6.

The moon always presents the same side to the earth. Orientation: looking down on the Northern Hemisphere in summer. Begin with the new moon phase. Point A is in the middle of the hemisphere that is turned toward the Earth. In other phases this same point is indicated at A', A'', and A'''. Points B, C, and D show the positions that would be occupied by point A if the moon did not rotate. The small curved arrows inside the moon show the amount of rotation since the new moon phase. In any period of time, this amount of rotation equals the amount of revolution; e.g., in going from new to first-quarter phase the moon completes one-fourth of its rotation and one-fourth of its revolution. Although approximately the same side of the moon always faces the Earth, any one point on the moon will undergo about two weeks of daytime, in which the sun is visible, and two weeks of nighttime in a single revolution. In the diagram, it is nighttime at point A and daytime at point A''.

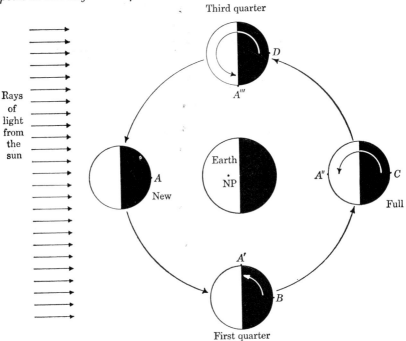

craters and mountains, than the side turned toward the Earth, bu surface details were not clear (Fig. 18.6A).

Earlier in 1959 Russian scientists had fired another satellite int space aimed to collide with the moon. As this satellite approached th moon before crashing into it, data were radioed back to the Eartl which indicated that the moon lacked a magnetic field and radiatio

The other side of the moon as photographed by the Russian interplanetary station Lunic III in October 1959. (Sovfoto)

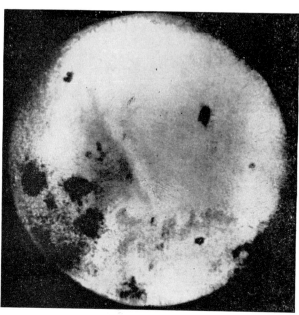

Fig. 18-6A.

belts like those on the Earth. This checked nicely with predictions. The moon's known specific gravity of 3.4 indicated that it probably did not have a core like the Earth's, which some scientists assume is made of iron and nickel. Such a metallic core could be the cause of the Earth's magnetic field and radiation belts. Without a metallic core, such phenomena should be missing on the moon.

One can speculate that the moon formerly rotated much faster, but has been slowed by tidal effects caused by the Earth's gravitational attraction. Tidal friction would have been particularly powerful if the moon had once been fluid. Mercury also always presents the same hemisphere to the sun, perhaps for a similar reason.

The moon's motions are actually among the most complex which astronomers resolve. The moon and the Earth are relatively so close to each other and so far from the sun that the moon's path, like that of the Earth, is always concave toward the sun. The moon and the Earth revolve *around each other*, or rather around the center of gravity in the line that joins them. This center is beneath the Earth's surface, 2900 miles from the Earth's own center. As seen from a point in space,

Fig. 18-7.

The moon's orbit is always concave toward the sun. The movements of the Earth and the moon about the sun have been likened to a celestial race. When the moon is on the far side of the Earth during a two-week period before and after the full moon phase, it travels faster than the Earth, just as the upper side of the wheel of a moving wagon travels forward faster than the lower side. When the moon is between the Earth and the sun for two weeks before and after the new moon phase, it travels more slowly than the Earth. If the paths of the Earth and moon were drawn to scale on this page, they would coincide, for the moon and the Earth are about 400 times farther from the sun than from each other. The Earth moves around the sun at about 18½ mi/sec; the moon moves around the Earth at about ½ mi/sec. Relative to the earth, the moon's path is nearly circular, but relative to the sun it is slightly wavy and always concave toward the sun. The gravitational attraction of the sun on the moon is more than double that of the Earth on the moon. These combined attractions cause the changes in the rate at which the moon moves.

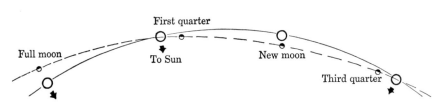

the orbits of the Earth and the moon would thus nearly coincide; the moon would periodically overtake the Earth and would later in its turn be passed by the Earth (Fig. 18-7).

FEATURES OF THE MOON

Atmosphere Considerable evidence indicates that no appreciable sea of air envelopes the moon. No clouds can be seen when the moon is observed through powerful telescopes, nor are there any signs of erosion. Also, the light of a star is blotted out abruptly as it disappears behind the moon, whereas if the moon had a significant atmosphere, the star would be seen through the moon's atmosphere and its light would be dimmed gradually before being completely extinguished. This lack of an appreciable atmosphere is explained by the moon's small gravitational attraction, about one-sixth that of the Earth. If the moon ever did have gas molecules surrounding it, they have long since had the opportunity to escape the relatively slight gravitational pull by virtue of their rapid movement.

However, a Russian astronomer announced recently that he had detected gas which apparently was at that time being erupted during volcanic activity at the moon's surface. This seems to be the first authentic evidence of such activity on the moon.

A hike on the surface of the moon would probably reveal many conditions which differ from those on the Earth. It would be necessary, of course, to supply one's own oxygen and to overcome the effects of low pressure. Dangerous ultraviolet radiations from the sun, which are screened out by the Earth's atmosphere, would have to be guarded against on the moon. Normal conversation would be impossible, for sound waves need a medium for their transmission. Indigenous life apparently would be completely absent. Topography would probably be quite angular and irregular because the softening effects of weathering would be absent. The hiker would weigh about one-sixth of his weight on the Earth and would be able to perform startling athletic feats, such as jumping very high or lifting large objects. Except in the immediate neighborhood of the sun, the sky would be black both day and night (pp. 399-401), and the stars would be visible at all times. The Earth, as a moon in the lunar sky, would go through phases without rising and setting, and would be about 4 times as large and 78 times as bright as the moon appears to an earthly observer. Meteors should pepper the hiker incessantly but would not be visible as "shooting stars" (pp. 391-7). Large variations in temperature (more than 400°F) would occur between day and night. Weather predictions would be simple: two weeks (as measured on the Earth) of fair and hot weather would always be followed by two weeks that would be fair and cold.

Surface Features of the Moon   The most conspicuous topographic features on the moon are its dark areas, craters, and mountains (Figs. 18-8 and 18-9); lesser land forms that are not discussed include rays, rills, and faults. The large dark areas form the so-called lunar seas (*maria*) which make the facial features of the "man in the moon." They are plainly visible to the unaided eye. These relatively smooth, circular regions are confined largely to the moon's Northern Hemisphere. A smooth area tends to reflect rays of light in certain directions,

The moon about two days after the first quarter. The crater Copernicus is a little more than halfway down along the bulging sunrise line. (Yerkes Observatory)

Fig. 18-8.

whereas a rough-surfaced area tends to scatter light in all directions. Therefore, although both types of area may reflect the same amount of light, the smooth area will appear darker than the rough surface unless the observer is favorably located to receive the reflected waves. Through the telescope, the dark areas have the appearance of hardened flows of lava which are peppered with many small craters. The lunar mountains generally are formed in elongated ranges, but isolated peaks also exist, and some of these project as much as 4 to 6 miles above their surroundings (Fig. 16-23). This is a much greater altitude, proportionately, than mountains have on the Earth.

The moon shortly after the full phase. The seas and bright rays are conspicuous, but the mountains are not.

Fig. 18-9.

The thousands of pockmarks on the moon's surface, easily seen with a small telescope, constitute its most intriguing physical aspect. A typical lunar crater is circular in outline and surrounded by a ridge which has a steep inner slope and gentle outer slope. The floor of the crater is lower than the adjoining terrain. According to some estimates, the volume of rocks making up the ridge approximates the volume of the crater itself. A number of the craters contain central peaks and look something like Mexican sombreros. About 30,000 of the craters have been measured; their diameters range from about 140 miles for the largest to a few hundred feet for the smallest visible craters. The origin of the craters constitutes an interesting and, according to some astronomers, as yet unsolved problem. By analogy with such features as Meteor Crater in Arizona (Fig. 19-10), it has been suggested that the moon's craters were formed by the bombardment of huge meteors: the intense heat developed at the moment of impact would have caused the explosion. This explanation is favored at present. However, as lunar craters have shapes which also resemble certain volcanic features on the Earth, such as Crater Lake in Oregon (Fig. 30-10), the hypothesis of a volcanic origin has received support. Other hypotheses have also been suggested.

LUNAR ECLIPSES

Rays of light from the sun are not quite parallel. Therefore, spherical bodies in space, such as the Earth and moon, cast long, tapering,

Fig. 18-10.

Lunar eclipse, January 29, 1953. Exposures were made every five minutes when possible as the moon left the Earth's shadow. The moon is completely eclipsed at the lower left. The shadow's curvature indicates that the Earth is round and about four times the size of the moon. (Photograph by Neil Croom)

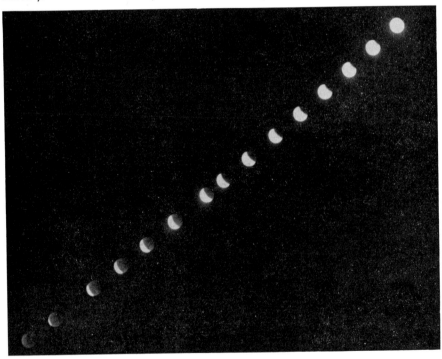

conelike shadows which always point directly away from the sun. The shadows are invisible unless they strike some object and darken it. The moon is eclipsed whenever the Earth comes directly between it and the sun (Figs. 18-10 and 18-11). The moon is always full at the

Fig. 18-11.

Lunar eclipse, I. Orientation: looking down on the Northern Hemisphere in spring. In a and g the moon is shown full, before and after moving through the Earth's shadow. In b and f the moon is in the zone from which some of the sun's light is excluded, but the change in the moon's appearance is not pronounced. In c and e the moon is about half-eclipsed, and in d the eclipse is total. Even when totally eclipsed, the moon is usually visible as a reddish disk, because the penetrating reddish waves in the sunlight are bent inward as they pass through the Earth's atmosphere and thus reach the moon, to be reflected back to the Earth. The sun's rays are nearly parallel but not precisely so. Thus the Earth's shadow is conical rather than cylindrical.

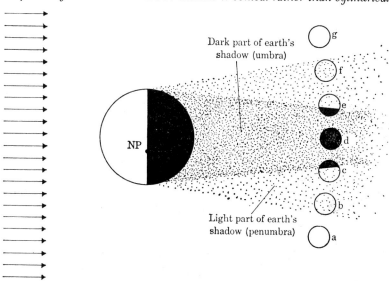

time of a lunar eclipse, and the eclipse is visible to everyone on the nighttime side of the Earth (unless obscured by clouds). For this reason, lunar eclipses are more familiar to the average person than solar eclipses, even though the latter are actually more frequent (about four out of seven). Since the plane of the moon's orbit is inclined approximately 5 degrees to the plane of the Earth's orbit, an eclipse does not occur each time the moon is full (Fig. 18-12). The longest total lunar eclipses last about 1½ hours. As the moon is moving eastward more rapidly than the Earth's shadow, the eastern side of the moon is always darkened first.

It is reported that Christopher Columbus made good use of his knowledge of eclipses at Jamaica on his fourth voyage to the New World. He was sick and hungry, his crew was mutinous, and the Indians refused to furnish food. Fortunately Columbus knew that a total

Fig. 18-12.

Lunar eclipse, II. The Earth and moon are shown in cross section as if viewed from the sun. The dark circle represents the Earth's shadow (umbra) at the moon's distance from the Earth. Since the diameter of the shadow at this distance is about 2½ times the diameter of the moon —5700 miles vs. 2160 miles—total eclipses are possible. Some possible paths of the moon are shown. The different paths occur because the moon's orbital plane around the Earth is inclined about 5 degrees to the ecliptic.

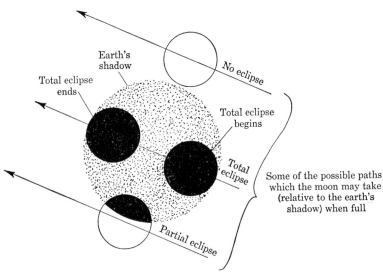

eclipse of the moon was scheduled for a certain evening. He told the natives that God was angry at them for withholding food and would cause a famine, and the light of the moon would be blotted out as a sign of the coming famine. As predicted, the total lunar eclipse took place. Before it was over, however, Columbus reported to the Indians that he had been interceding on their behalf; if they granted the food, the famine would not occur, and the sign for this would be the return of the moon's light. Soon the moon began to shine. Columbus obtained the food.

SOLAR ECLIPSES

A total solar eclipse is a magnificent celestial phenomenon and a rare occurrence in the lives of most of us. Calculations show that an average specific geographic location experiences a total solar eclipse only once in approximately 360 years. Several factors combine to cause this unfortunate situation.

Fig. 18-13.

Solar eclipse. The darker part of the moon's shadow (umbra) covers the region from which a total eclipse is visible. The lighter part of the moon's shadow (penumbra) covers the region from which a partial eclipse is visible.

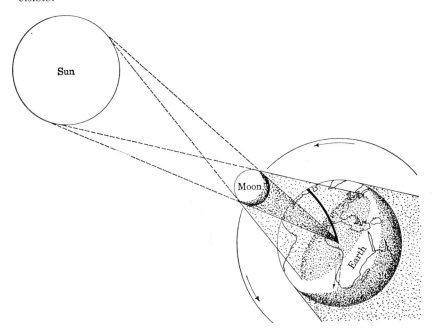

Solar eclipses occur when the new moon comes directly between the Earth and the sun (Figs. 18-13 and 18-14). A solar eclipse does not take place at each new moon for the same reason that a lunar eclipse does not occur at each full moon: the inclination of the moon's orbit to the Earth's orbit causes the tip of the moon's shadow during the new moon phase to sweep above the Earth on some occasions and below the Earth at other times. The moon's shadow has a length of about 232,000 miles. This is about 7000 miles shorter than the mean distance between the moon and the Earth, but because of the eccentricity of the moon's path, the moon is sometimes closer than 232,000 miles to the Earth. The largest shadow it can cast on the Earth is about 167 miles

Fig. 18-14.

The total solar eclipse of June 30, 1954. (Photograph, John R. Winckler, University of Minnesota)

in diameter; usually the shadow is much smaller than this. The shadow moves eastward, the Earth rotates eastward, but the moon's shadow moves more rapidly. When the shadow overtakes the Earth, it passes across the Earth along a path which extends from west to east. The rate at which the shadow crosses the Earth's surface varies from a minimum of about 1000 mi/hr at the equator to a maximum of about 5000 mi/hr at the poles. The length, width, and location of the path traced by the shadow depends upon the moon's distance from the Earth and its location in space. The longest total solar eclipses last about $7\frac{1}{2}$ minutes: this is the time required for the rapidly moving circular shadow, 167 miles or less in diameter, to pass a particular spot on the Earth. A total solar eclipse is preceded and followed by a partial eclipse. Partial eclipses occur more frequently than total eclipses and can be seen from a larger area. At least two partial eclipses of the sun must occur each year.

When the moon comes directly between the sun and Earth but at too great a distance for the tip of its shadow to graze the Earth's surface, a total solar eclipse cannot take place. A person situated on the Earth in the area formed by the projection of this shadow sees an annular eclipse: the dark body of the moon does not completely cover the sun: a thin ring of the sun remains visible. To illustrate this, close one eye and hold a coin between the other eye and something large and round, like a clock. If the coin is close enough to your eye it will completely cover the clock (total eclipse); if the coin is moved farther from your eye, the outer ring of the clock will be visible (annular eclipse).

According to one report (probably unreliable) an eclipse was recorded by the Chinese in 2137 B.C. An interesting story accompanies the report. As day momentarily changed to night during a total solar eclipse, these primitive people believed that a huge monster in the heavens was in the process of devouring the sun. Two royal astronomers were assigned the task of appeasing the monster by performing certain rites. Unfortunately they had become so drunk during a celebration prior to the eclipse that they were unable to perform their duties. For this indiscretion they were punished rather severely: their heads were cut off. The lesson has not been forgotten—no instance has subsequently been recorded of an astronomer who was drunk during an eclipse!

The changes which accompany a total solar eclipse begin with a partial eclipse; the moon's dark body causes a circular indentation on one side of the sun. This indentation grows larger and larger until only a thin crescent of the sun remains visible. The light reaching the Earth is now of a different quality, since it comes entirely from the outer parts of the sun. Just before the sun is completely hidden, the continuous crescentic sliver that remains is subdivided as the sun's light passes only through the lower areas, or valleys, of the moon's silhouette. With increasing darkness, temperatures drop, dew may form, stars become visible, and animals act as if night were approaching. After totality, these phenomena are repeated in the reverse order.

Formerly, the outermost, rarefied part of the sun's atmosphere (corona) was visible only during a total eclipse, but now an instrument (coronagraph) has been developed which blocks out the sun's disk and permits photographs of the corona to be taken at other times.

TIDES

Tides in the Earth's oceans are caused by the gravitational attractions of the moon and the sun, the effect of the moon being more than double that of the sun. It was realized long ago that the phases of the moon and the magnitude of the tides are directly related: the largest tides occur at times of new and full moons; the smallest tides occur during the quarter phases. The time between two high tides or two low tides tends to approximate 12 hours and 25 minutes (the moon rises 51 minutes later each day on the average), but this varies considerably in some coastal areas. Tides in the Earth's solid body are also produced and have been measured, but they can be detected only with very sensitive instruments and are small compared with the tides raised in the waters of the oceans. It is estimated that the surface of the ocean rises and falls from 2 to 5 feet in mid-ocean. However, the funneling effect of bays causes a much greater change in sea level along certain coasts; changes of as much as 70 feet have been reported.

The following explanation of the tides is incomplete and simplified. The moon's pull on the Earth's rigid body acts as if it were all concentrated at the Earth's center, but the waters at the Earth's surface are free to move. Since the moon's gravitational attraction on an object varies inversely as the square of the moon's distance from the object, the moon tends to pull water on the near side of the Earth outward as a bulge (Fig. 18-15)—shortest distance, greatest gravitational attraction, and most movement toward the moon. The whole Earth is pulled a shorter distance toward the moon—greater distance, less gravitational attraction, and less movement toward the moon. Water on the far side of the Earth is pulled toward the moon the shortest distance and so is "left behind" as another bulge—greatest distance, least gravitational attraction, and least movement toward the moon. Thus, the moon causes simultaneous high tides on both the near and the far sides of the Earth. The Earth spins through these tidal areas in its daily rotation. The tides are not exactly 12 hours apart because the moon moves in its orbit, and the places of high tides on the Earth shift with it: the Earth must spin an extra 25 minutes on the average to rotate from one high tide

Fig. 18-15.

The effect of the moon on the tides. Orientation: looking down on the Northern Hemisphere and the moon. The Earth's rotation drags the tidal zones forward a little so that they are not aligned directly with the moon but somewhat east.

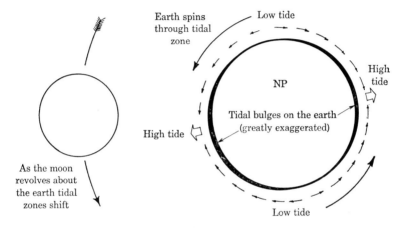

to the next. Although high tides caused by the moon on the near and far sides of the Earth tend to be equal, successive high tides at a particular locality may not be of the same magnitude (Fig. 18-16).

Tidal friction between water and the Earth's crust apparently is causing the Earth to rotate more slowly with the passage of time. It has been estimated that the day may now be approximately 1 second longer than it was 100,000 years ago. At first glance this retardation seems to be too small to be measured. However, a year now would be 365 seconds longer than a year 100,000 years ago, and each of the 100,000 years would have been slightly longer than the preceding year. If a very precise clock had been started 2000 years ago (based upon the Earth's rate of rotation then), it would be ahead of present-day clocks (based upon the Earth's present rate of rotation) by about 3 hours. This change is sufficiently great to be checked by the records of ancient eclipses. Modern astronomers calculated the times and places at which certain ancient total solar eclipses should have occurred. They found that the times and places did not check. For example, according to calculations a total solar eclipse which took place 2000 years ago would have occurred about 3 hours later in the day than the predicted time and at a place which differed about 45 degrees in longitude (in 3 hours the Earth rotates $\frac{1}{8}$ of the angular distance around its axis). Such differences are apparent from ancient records. The times and places of ancient eclipses do check, however, if the gradual lengthening of the day is considered.

Fig. 18-16.

One explanation for the inequality of successive high tides. The earth, seen here from the "side," rotates an observer from A to B in about 12½ hours (with respect to the moon). The high tide experienced by the observer at A is much weaker than that at B. The moon's orbital plane about the Earth is inclined about 5 degrees to the ecliptic, which makes an angle of 23½ degrees with the Earth's equator.

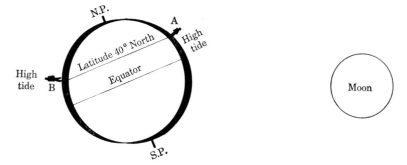

The sun's tide-producing force on the Earth is similar to that of the moon, although smaller in magnitude. The gravitational attraction of the sun on the Earth is about 400 times that of the moon, but tides are caused by the difference in gravitational attraction on the near and far sides of the Earth. The relatively short distance separating the Earth and the moon makes the moon's tide-raising force more than double that of the distant sun. During the times of new and full moon, the tidal effects of the moon and the sun reinforce each other and cause exceptionally great tides (spring or strong tides); during the quarter phases of the moon, the tidal effect of the sun opposes that of the moon and so these tides (neap tides) are weaker.

The size of the tides is also affected by the moon's varying distance from the Earth: tides are greatest when the distance is least. Tides are also affected by the size, shape, and extent of the body of water. The greatest tides occur when the moon is closest to the Earth during its new or full moon phases.

know Keplers laws, page 327

F
. O . A

$e = \dfrac{OF}{OA}$

EXERCISES AND QUESTIONS FOR CHAPTER 18

1. Make a sketch (orientation: looking "down") which shows the following:

   (1) Observer on the Earth at sunset
   (2) Total eclipse of the moon
   (3) Mars in the southwestern sky of the observer.

2. You see the moon in the sky about 9:00 A.M. one morning. What is the approximate phase of the moon? In what direction did you look to see it?

3. One evening shortly after sunset you see a bright starlike object in the southeastern sky. Which one of the following might the object be: Polaris, Mercury, Auriga, Venus, Uranus, Neptune, Mars?

4. What measurements could you make over a period of time which would prove that the moon's orbit about the Earth is not a circle?

5. During a period of about 1½ weeks make a series of semicircular star maps at an early evening hour (orientation: facing south) which shows the moon's different positions against the background of stars as it changes from a crescent to a full moon.

6. Make telescopic observations of the moon when it is in the first quarter and full phases and write descriptions of what you see.

7. In what ways would a hike on the moon's surface probably differ from one on the Earth's surface?

8. Why do lunar eclipses last longer than solar ones?

9. Give a possible explanation why the moon always keeps the same side toward the Earth and Mercury keeps the same side toward the sun.

10. If you were to drive a jeep along the moon's surface, would you leave a trail of dust behind you?

Graft of Planets, size, distances, times or per

CHAPTER 19

The Sun's Family

THE solar family includes the nine known major planets and their satellites, the planetoids (asteroids), comets, and meteors. Important statistics are given for each planet in Fig. 19-1.

Fig. 19-1.

Planetary statistics. Some of the figures are approximations. Mean orbital velocities decrease as distance from the sun increases. Velocities are about 30 mi/sec for Mercury, 18.5 mi/sec for the Earth, and 3 mi/sec for Pluto.

PLANETS	MEAN DISTANCE FROM SUN (in millions of miles)	MEAN DIAMETER (in miles)	MASS RELATIVE TO THAT OF THE EARTH AS 1	SPECIFIC GRAVITY (Water = 1)	PERIOD OF ROTATION	PERIOD OF REVOLUTION	NUMBER OF KNOWN SATELLITES
Mercury	36	2900	0.06	6.1	88 days	88 days	0
Venus	67	7600	0.8	5	About 1(?) month	225 days	0
Earth	93	7900	1.0	5.5	24 hours	365.25 days	1
Mars	142	4200	0.11	4	24.5 hours	687 days	2
Jupiter	483	86,800	318.0	1.4	10 hours	12 years	12
Saturn	886	71,500	95.0	.7	10.2 hours	29.5 years	9
Uranus	1783	29,400	15.0	1.6	10.8 hours	84 years	5
Neptune	2794	28,000	17.0	2.3	15.8 hours	165 years	2
Pluto	3670	Small	0.8(?)	4(?)	?	248 years	?

MERCURY

Mercury, with a diameter of 2900 miles, is the smallest of the major planets, the closest to the sun, and the swiftest (hence its name). It has the greatest density, the longest period of rotation, and the shortest period of revolution of any of the planets. It seems also to have the

378

least atmosphere and probably possesses both the hottest and coldest areas of any planet.

Mercury is too near the sun to be readily observed from the Earth. In fact, Copernicus is reported never to have seen it. Mercury may be an evening star visible in the west just as the sun sets, or a morning star visible in the east just at sunrise (Figs. 16-18 and 16-19). In both cases we see the planet obliquely through a great thickness of the Earth's atmosphere; clouds and dust frequently interfere with clear observation. Some of the ancients believed that there were two planets: Mercury, the evening star, and Apollo, the morning star. Astronomers today obtain their best views of Mercury with a telescope during the day when it is highest above the horizon. Mercury goes through phases similar to those of Venus. Each year Mercury is an evening star three times and a morning star three times.

In a number of respects, Mercury is like the moon. Its diameter is about $1\frac{1}{2}$ times that of the moon. Neither is believed to have an appreciable atmosphere. Each has a period of rotation equal to its period of revolution: 88 days for Mercury and $27\frac{1}{3}$ days for the moon. Therefore, one side of Mercury is always facing the sun. In the absence of an appreciable atmosphere, currents cannot distribute heat from the sun to Mercury's nighttime side, and since probably little heat is conducted through the planet, the temperature on the part that is turned perpetually from the sun may approach absolute zero ($-459°F$). All other planets are farther from the sun, but the sun's energy is distributed over their surfaces by their atmospheres and rotation. Life as known on the Earth could not exist on Mercury.

VENUS

Like Mercury, Venus is both an evening star and a morning star and was given two names by a number of ancient astronomers. The distance between Venus and the Earth varies from about 26 to 160 million miles (Fig. 16-18). When brightest as a thin crescent, Venus is nearly 15 times as bright as Sirius; it causes objects on Earth to show slight shadows at night and can be seen during the day by observers who are aware of its location in the sky.

In both size and mass, Venus is similar to the Earth. The surface of Venus has never been seen because it is perpetually hidden by a thick covering of clouds of unknown composition. The atmosphere above these clouds has a high percentage of carbon dioxide and lacks measurable quantities of free oxygen and water vapor (the absence of water on Venus is puzzling).* The period of rotation of Venus cannot be definitely determined because permanent markings cannot be observed, but it is probably about one month; the nearly spherical shape of Venus suggests a slow rate of spinning. Temperatures at its surface are probably above the boiling point of water, since Venus gets more energy from the sun than does the Earth and also has a better atmosphere for retaining this heat. At such high temperatures, oxygen would be very active chemically and would readily enter into chemical combinations with other elements; perhaps this explains the absence of oxygen in the atmosphere of Venus. The high temperatures and lack of oxygen and water vapor would make Venus quite unattractive for life as known on the Earth.

The orbit of Venus about the sun is very nearly circular. Because of the inclination of its orbit to that of the Earth, Venus transits the sun an average of only two times each century. At such times it can be seen through a smoked glass without a telescope as a round dark spot which moves slowly across the sun's surface. The next transit is predicted for June 8, 2004.

MARS

Mars is the reddish planet named after the bloody god of wars (Fig. 19.2). Its diameter is about half the length of the Earth's. Mars rotates on an axis once in about $24\frac{1}{2}$ hours, and the plane of its equator is inclined about 24 degrees to the plane of its orbit, its axis constantly maintaining the same angle of tilt. The Martian seasons last nearly twice as long as the corresponding seasons on the Earth, because Mars' period of revolution is longer. When closest to the Earth, Mars is about 35 million miles away. Such favorable oppositions (180 degrees from the direction of the sun) occur once every 15 to 17 years, although less favorable oppositions take place every other year.

Mars has two satellites, one of which makes a complete, west-to-east revolution in about $7\frac{1}{2}$ hours. An observer on the more slowly rotating Mars would sometimes see this moon rise in the west and set in the east twice during the same night. No other satellite is known to do this. The effect of Mars on the orbits of these two moons makes it possible for astronomers to calculate the mass of Mars fairly accurately.

* Recent observations from a balloon at an altitude of about 15 miles—above about 98% of the mass of the Earth's atmosphere have indicated the presence of water vapor in the atmosphere of Venus and a surface temperature that may approximate 600°F. The

Fig. 19-2.

Mars. Upper left, September 23; lower left, October 8; upper right, 3½ hours after lower left; lower right, October 19. The polar cap has shrunk considerably in less than 1 month. (Photographed in 1941 by B. Lyot on the Pic du Midi, France)

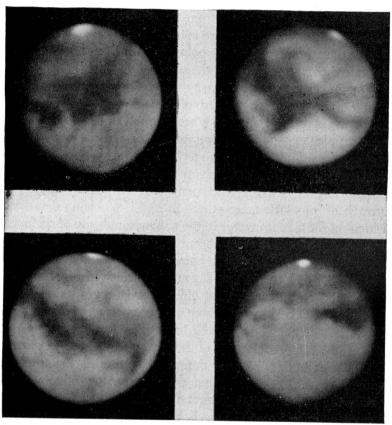

The surface features of Mars can be seen from the Earth more clearly than those of any other planet because of its relative nearness, its rarefied atmosphere, and its lack of frequent clouds. Photographs taken with atmosphere-piercing infrared light show permanent markings. On the other hand, photographs taken on film which is most sensitive to ultraviolet light show a larger, nearly featureless disk because this light is scattered by the outer part of the atmosphere of Mars and does not penetrate to its surface. The atmosphere of Mars is estimated to contain about the same proportion of carbon dioxide as the Earth's atmosphere, but less than 5 percent as much water vapor and 0.1 percent as

temperature of the upper atmosphere—the only part that can be seen—is about −36°F for both sunlit and dark sides. At this temperature most of the water present is probably in the form of ice crystals which do not produce a dark-line spectrum (see p. 410).

much oxygen. The permanent markings are described as blue-green or brown against an orange-red background. White polar caps are present at its north and south poles. These are thought to be less than a few feet in thickness and to consist of ice crystals similar to frost which collects on window panes. As the southern hemisphere is closest to the sun during its summer and farthest from the sun during winter, seasons in the southern hemisphere are more extreme than the corresponding ones in the northern hemisphere. The polar cap in the southern hemisphere may disappear completely during the summer. During the winter each polar cap advances more than halfway toward the equator, a latitude which would be comparable to that of New York City or Chicago. Some astronomers report that blue-green markings become more pronounced near a polar cap in the spring, move toward the equator during the spring and summer, and change into brownish colors during fall and winter. Other astronomers claim that this change is one of intensity rather than of color. The change is attributed by some to seasonal growth of vegetation, by others to chemical changes in certain salts which might take up water in the summer and give it off in the winter, and by still others to changes in the wind direction and fluctuations in volcanic activity. The ruddy background color may be caused by the presence of reddish iron oxides at the surface of Mars in desert areas.

Speculation that intelligent life may exist on Mars has captured the fancy of many persons for whom astronomy is only a casual hobby. The Italian astronomer Schiaparelli innocently instigated this controversy at the favorable opposition of 1877 when he discovered new surface features on Mars which he described as fine dark lines crossing the orange areas. He called them *canali*, meaning "channels." Unfortunately the word was transliterated as the English "canals." An American astronomer, Percival Lowell, believed that these lines were straight and arranged in a geometrical manner and hence were artificially produced by some type of intelligent being. His hypothesis was that these beings would have to live near the equator where it was warmest, and because of the scarcity of water they would be forced to use great irrigation ditches to lead the melting ice and snow in the spring from the polar caps toward the equator. Probably the majority of astronomers doubt whether geometrically arranged lines exist, although they agree that some sort of markings, perhaps discontinuous, are present. Some astronomers ascribe these markings to the presence of vegetation along river channels cut through desert areas; they think the Nile might appear like one of these markings from an observation point 35 million miles away.

In observing Mars from the Earth, we must peer through the sea of air about the Earth which is constantly moving and which thus causes features on the surface of Mars to be somewhat blurred. However, if an observer spends enough time, he may see Mars during an occasional few seconds when the Earth's atmosphere is still and details are clear. The great light-gathering power of the 200-inch Hale telescope may permit short enough time exposures to eliminate much of the blurring. At the close approach of Mars in 1956, the question of the canals could not be definitely settled, but very few astronomers now believe that intelligent beings exist on Mars.

JUPITER

Jupiter (Fig. 19-3) is the largest of the sun's family and is the first of the four giant planets—Jupiter, Saturn, Uranus, and Neptune. Although

Fig. 19-3.

Jupiter. The shadow of a satellite appears in both photographs. (Photographs from Mount Wilson and Palomar Observatories)

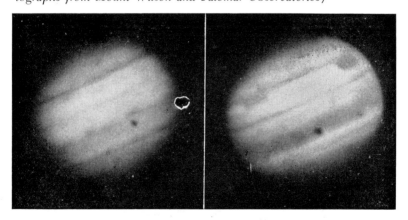

Jupiter's specific gravity is about one-fourth that of the Earth, the total amount of matter in Jupiter is approximately 318 times that of the Earth. Next to Venus, and occasionally Mars, Jupiter is the brightest of the planets; rarely does it scintillate less than Sirius. Its size and satellites make observations exciting with even a small telescope. Of its twelve known moons, four can be seen readily in a small telescope

(Fig. 19-4). They form a sort of miniature solar system and were first observed by Galileo (page 330). The observation of one of these moons in the latter part of the seventeeth century provided the Danish astronomer Roemer with the first means of measuring the speed of light (Fig. 19-5). Low-power telescopic observation also shows other features (Fig. 19-4): Jupiter is flattened noticeably at the poles and bulges at the equator; its satellites are located nearly in the plane of the equator. Reddish and brownish bands parallel to the equator, somewhat analogous to wind belts on the Earth, can be seen against a light-colored background. Minor changes in these belts occur constantly,

Jupiter's four bright satellites. The lower photograph was taken about 3 hours after the upper one. (Photographed at Yerkes Observatory)

Fig. 19-4.

most of the activity occurring at the equator, but the major zones are rather stable. Astronomers believe that they see only the outer part of Jupiter's very dense and thick atmosphere. Jupiter's rapid rotation—about ten hours for one complete rotation at the equator, but different times at different latitudes—apparently is responsible for the polar flattening, the bands, and the minor disturbances (which would actually be gigantic on an earthly scale.) According to some astronomers, Jupiter's low density indicates a relatively small solid core surrounded by an enormously thick atmosphere. Perhaps Jupiter has a rocky core enveloped by a thick layer of ice, which in turn is surrounded by an

Roemer's method of determining the speed of light. Orientation: in space looking "down"; diagram is not to scale. Only one of Jupiter's twelve known moons is considered; this satellite is assumed to revolve around Jupiter once every 24 hours. The observer on the Earth notes that the moon disappears at a certain time on one evening, e.g. 9:00 P.M. By measuring the length of time until it disappears again, the observer determines its period of revolution to be 24 hours. As the moon disappears behind Jupiter at 9:00 P.M. on one night, it should continue to do so on succeeding nights because its period of revolution should be constant. However, it does not do so. Roemer recorded the moon's times of disappearance at intervals of one month as follows: 9:00, 9:03, 9:06, 9:09, 9:12, 9:15, 9:17 (six months later) 9:15, 9:12, 9:09, 9:06, 9:03, and 9:00 (one year later). For the first six months, the moon disappeared a little later each night until the time became about 9:17 P.M.; for the next six months the moon disappeared a little earlier each night until the time again became 9:00 P.M. Roemer explained the 17-minute delay (his figure actually exceeded this by several minutes) at the end of six months by stating that the Earth was on the far side of its orbit at this time, opposite its previous position six months earlier. Therefore, light from Jupiter's moon travels a greater distance at this time to reach the Earth than it did six months before. As the distance from one side of the Earth's orbit to the other was known approximately, the speed of light could be calculated (distance ÷ time = velocity).

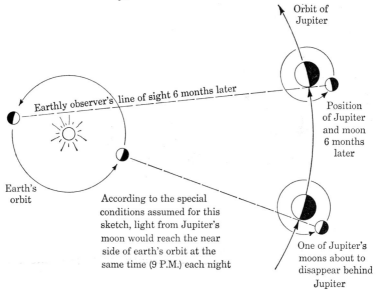

Orbit of
Jupiter

Earthly observer's line of sight 6 months later

Position
of Jupiter
and moon
6 months
later

Earth's
orbit

According to the special
conditions assumed for this
sketch, light from Jupiter's
moon would reach the near
side of earth's orbit at the
same time (9 P.M.) each night

One of Jupiter's
moons about to
disappear behind
Jupiter

Fig. 19-5.

atmosphere containing ammonia and methane. Jupiter has no significant seasonal changes because its axis of rotation is nearly perpendicular to its orbit. Four of Jupiter's more distant satellites revolve in the
retrograde, clockwise direction, as do one of Saturn's, the five known
moons of Uranus, and one of Neptune's two known satellites.

Life on Jupiter, as on Saturn, Uranus, and Neptune, would seem impossible because of exceedingly low temperatures and poisonous atmospheres.

SATURN

Saturn, unique in its possession of a system of rings (Fig. 19-6), is
commonly considered one of the most beautiful of celestial objects
viewable through a telescope. To the unaided eye it appears as a bright
yellowish, starlike object in the night sky. It was the most distant planet
known to ancient astronomers, and it was given the name of the god

*Saturn. Taken with the 100-inch reflector. (Photo-
graph from Mount Wilson and Palomar Observatories)*

Fig. 19-6.

of time for its leisurely (29½ years) revolution through space. Saturn's
diameter is somewhat smaller than Jupiter's but about 9½ times as large
as the Earth's. Saturn is flattened even more noticeably at its poles than
Jupiter, although it spins at approximately the same rate. Its specific
gravity is calculated to be less than 1: that is, if a sufficiently large
ocean could be procured, Saturn, the only planet or satellite believed

to be lighter than water, would float in it. Perhaps Saturn's great equatorial bulge is explained by this very low density. It may have a smaller rocky core and a thicker atmosphere than Jupiter. Like Jupiter, it has belts parallel to its equator, and its atmosphere contains ammonia and methane. Saturn's equator is tilted about 27 degrees to its orbital plane and maintains the same angle of tilt at all times. For this reason an Earthly observer can see the top of the rings for nearly 15 years, and then the bottom (southern) portion of the rings for another 15 years (Fig. 19-7).

Saturn's rings at different angles.

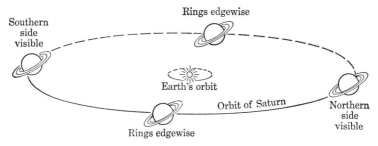

Fig. 19-7.

Saturn has three concentric rings, but the inner one can be seen only in large telescopes. The rings are paper-thin (an estimated 10 to 20 miles) in proportion to their diameters (about 171,000 miles for the outer ring). The rings probably consist of myriads of tiny particles or meteors which revolve as miniature satellites in three orbital groupings about Saturn. Apparently they are not solid because the light of a star, as seen through them, is dimmed but not blotted out; also the inner parts of the rings revolve more rapidly than the outer parts.

One hypothesis on the origin of the rings suggests that they constitute planetary material which was too close to its parent body to consolidate into a satellite. Another hypothesis considers the possibility that a former satellite approached too close to Saturn and was torn to pieces by its gravitational attraction.

URANUS, NEPTUNE, AND PLUTO

In many ways Uranus and Neptune are smaller, cooler replicas of Jupiter and Saturn (minus its rings). They spin rapidly, are flattened at the poles and bulged at the equator, have low density, and possess somewhat similar atmospheres. Each has a diameter about four times that of the Earth and each appears greenish in color in the telescope, perhaps owing to methane in its atmosphere. Uranus can barely be seen by the unaided eye and was discovered by Herschel in 1781. The discoveries of Neptune and Pluto were discussed in Chapter 16. Uranus is unusual in having its equatorial plane tilted more than 80 degrees to the plane of its orbit and also in rotating in the retrograde, east-to-west direction.

Of all the planets, Pluto is the least well known. Its orbit is the most eccentric of all the major planets' orbits and also has the greatest inclination (17 degrees) to the plane of the ecliptic. In fact, at its closest approach to the sun Pluto is actually nearer the sun than Neptune is, but Pluto and Neptune are never very close to each other because of the great inclination of Pluto's orbit. Pluto was probably once a satellite of Neptune.

PLANETOIDS (ASTEROIDS)

Planetoids are minor planets which revolve about the sun. The majority have orbits that are located between Mars and Jupiter. The largest of these bodies is a little less than 500 miles in diameter, and the smallest visible ones are 1 to 2 miles across. Many of them probably have irregular shapes. The orbits of more than 1500 planetoids have been calculated, but thousands more are thought to exist. Their eccentricities and inclinations to the ecliptic plane vary greatly. The total mass of all the planetoids is probably much less than that of the Earth. Perhaps the planetoids represent planetary material which never collected into a major planet, or possibly a former planet may have disrupted into many smaller bodies. Some planetoids approach to within a million miles of the Earth. At such close distances, their geocentric parallaxes can be determined very accurately, which is of great importance in calculating other distances in astronomy.

COMETS

Comets probably constitute the most unusual members of the solar system. They have been aptly described as "flying gravel banks" and

"airy nothings." A well developed comet has a long tail, which always
points away from the sun, and a brighter head section (coma) that
contains a small bright nucleus. However, the tail and nucleus may not
always be present; shapes and masses vary considerably from one close
approach to the next. The most permanent feature of a comet is its
orbit. In size, comets are enormous; the diameters of the heads may
average about 80,000 miles, and the tail sections may extend for millions of miles. In mass, however, they are very small. No comet has
been known to affect the orbit of a planet or a satellite, although comets
themselves have been influenced greatly by these bodies. The light of
a star is barely dimmed behind the tail of a comet. Apparently the Earth
has passed through a comet's tail with no noticeable effect. Comets are
quite different from meteors in appearance. A bright comet covers a
large part of the sky, appears to be nearly motionless in space except
for the daily east-to-west movement, and may be visible on successive
nights for weeks, or even months.

The nucleus of a comet may be a porous structure consisting of a
swarm of small meteorlike solids embedded in ices of methane, ammonia, and water. As a comet approaches the sun, it commonly increases in size, becomes brighter, and develops a tail (Fig. 19-8). Increased heat from the sun probably expels gases and dust explosively
from the ices and meteoric particles in the head; this material diffuses
into space to enlarge the head and form a tail. The comet as a whole is
loosely held together by the mutual gravitational attraction of its particles. Radiation from the sun exerts pressure which is insignificant on
large objects but which is greater than the opposing gravitational attraction on very tiny objects. Therefore, as a comet approaches the sun,
corpuscular and electromagnetic radiations repel tiny particles in the
tail and cause it to point away from the sun (Fig. 19-9). Material ex-
pelled from the head of a comet to its tail cannot be recovered because
the comet's gravitational attraction is too weak to sweep it up. It must
continue to revolve in orbits about the sun as would a feather or a handful of powdery snow under similar circumstances. Friction is so common on the Earth that the picture of light, diffuse material revolving
permanently in orbits about the sun is startling at first, but friction is
practically nonexistent in space. If a comet approaches too close to the
sun or to a large planet, it may be disrupted into a number of smaller
comets. In fact, meteoric swarms probably originate in this manner.

The light of a comet is partly reflected sunlight and partly re-radiated sunlight.

According to present estimates, most comets probably belong to the solar system, but many have orbits which cause them to exist for long

Fig. 19-8.

Halley's Comet. Fourteen successive views from April 26 to June 11, 1910. (Photographs from Mount Wilson and Palomar Observatories)

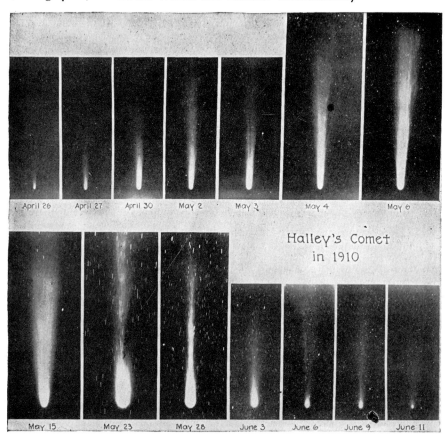

periods of time far out in space; comets adhere to Kepler's laws and travel most slowly when farthest from the sun. Comets that can be seen by the unaided eye average about one in every ten years; The Arend-Roland comet, visible in the spring of 1957, is a recent example. Spectacular comets are much less common. Probably Halley's comet is the

The tail of a comet points away from the sun. The tail commonly is curved and longest when closest to the sun.

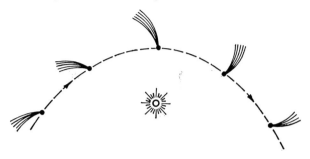

Fig. 19-9.

most famous; records indicate that it has been observed many times at intervals of about 75 years, perhaps since 240 B.C. It is scheduled to reappear about 1986.

METEORS

For the souvenir-collecting inhabitants of the Earth, meteors should be prized possessions. A sentimental public that collects tiny cakes of soap from hotels, pebbles from a beach, or bits of wood from a famous ship should be fascinated by material which comes to the Earth from outer space. Meteors are the familiar objects known as "shooting stars," a misleading term because they are very unlike stars. Most meteors are solid particles about the size of sand grains or pebbles and travel in orbits about the sun or elswhere in the solar system. However, some meteors weigh many tons; no arbitrary limit separates large meteors from small planetoids. Meteors are invisible until they enter the Earth's atmosphere and are heated to incandescence by the friction created by their collision with air molecules. Temperatures rise high enough to vaporize most meteors completely, and the brighter ones leave trails of gases which may remain visible for a number of minutes. Apparently the air through which the meteor travels is ionized and thus made luminous. We see the cylindrical trail left by a meteor, not the meteor itself. Most meteors become visible at altitudes of 60 to 70 miles and disappear at altitudes of 40 to 50 miles; their average speed is about 26 mi/sec. Millions of meteors may enter the Earth's atmosphere daily, but most of them are completely volatilized before they reach the Earth's surface. The Earth's inhabitants are indeed fortunate to have an air umbrella.

That stones can fall from the skies has been generally accepted for about 150 years. A notable fall of a few thousand stones in France about 1800 was studied by a commission and contributed greatly to this acceptance. However, when a smaller fall in Connecticut was described by two members of the Yale faculty, President Jefferson is quoted as saying: "I should rather believe that those two Yankee professors would lie than to believe that stones fell from heaven." At that time people failed to understand what force could keep a stone floating in the sky. Today this is explained by the law of universal gravitation; distant stones have no weight and no tendency to approach the Earth, and near stones must travel close to the Earth before the Earth's gravitational attraction causes them to enter the atmosphere.

The term *meteorite* refers to the solid object that has reached the Earth's surface. About three-fourths of the known elements have been identified in meteorites. Commonly they are either metallic or stony,

Fig. 19.10.

Meteor Crater, Arizona. It is 4200 feet in diameter and 570 feet deep. Living cedar trees on the site show that the meteor fell at least 700 years ago. (Photograph by John Forrell, Fort Worth, Texas)

or both. Metallic meteorites consist largely of iron with some nickel; stony meteorites are somewhat similar to dark-colored, heavy, igneous rocks found on the Earth. An interesting problem is suggested by the composition of meteorites. If the material of meteors is representative of the material of the planets, then nearly half of the Earth should be composed of iron and nickel. Since these materials are not present at the Earth's surface, perhaps they are concentrated at the center. Other evidence seems to indicate that the Earth has a core about 4300 miles in

Fig. 19-11.

A few of the Carolina bays. Nineteen bays are recognized here, eighteen in a strip about a mile wide, extending northwest-southeast through picture. Some overlap. Light-colored areas are sand rims which are best developed on south-eastern sides. (Courtesy, Professor C. E. Prouty, Michigan State University)

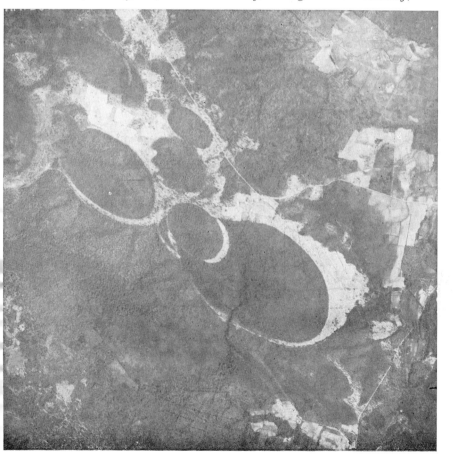

diameter which is heavier and different from the material above it. According to some recent research, sufficient gold may be present in the Earth's core to form a 3-foot layer completely covering the Earth's surface, and platinum may be twice as abundant as gold. These speculations are based on the percentages of gold and platinum found in about 100 sample metallic meteorites, and on the assumption that the same percentages would exist in all metallic meteorites and also in the Earth's core.

Meteor colors. Meteors travel both clockwise and counterclockwise in orbits about the sun at rates which may be faster or slower than the speed of the Earth. The rate at which a meteor descends through the Earth's atmosphere determines the amount of friction and heat developed: high speeds produce great friction, high temperatures, and bluish-white colors; slower speeds cause less friction, lower temperatures, and reddish colors. Most meteors noted by an observer in the early evening hours are traveling more rapidly than the Earth and in the same direction. Thus the "front end" of the meteor collides rather gently with the "rear bumper" of the Earth and a reddish meteor results. On the other hand, in the hours immediately preceding sunrise, an observer sees meteors which are traveling in the opposite direction from the Earth. There is head-on collision, and bluish-white meteors result. Meteors moving more slowly than the Earth and in the same direction are exceptional. Their light is reddish. Some meteors, also exceptional, have orbits at angles to the Earth's orbit.

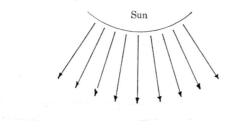

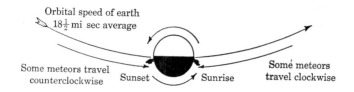

Fig. 19-12.

Metallic meteorites are more readily recognized than nonmetallic ones because they have an unusual composition and a high specific gravity. The majority of museum specimens are metallic. However, spectroscopic identification of meteors as they volatilize at high altitudes indicates that stony meteorites are actually more numerous than metallic ones. Characteristically, meteorites have a thin, blackened crust pitted with irregular holes that look something like thumb prints and were caused by differential fusion. The freshly ground surface of a stony meteorite commonly shows a light grayish color and metallic specks. Surprisingly, most meteorites are not at high temperatures when they strike the Earth's surface. They come from the bitter cold of outer space, and only their surfaces are heated as they penetrate the Earth's atmosphere. According to some estimates, any meteor exceeding 10 pounds in mass has a good opportunity of passing through the air without volatilizing completely.

No human being is known to have been killed by a meteorite, and the chances that an individual might be hit are extremely slim, although some animals have been killed and buildings have been hit. One example of a near miss occurred in 1924, when a funeral procession in Colorado just passed a certain stretch of highway before the road was struck

Fig. 19-13.

The radiant of a meteor shower. The meteors seem to come from one spot in the sky (radiant) for the same reason that railroad tracks seem to diverge from a distant point. However, meteors in a swarm travel together along parallel paths unless they are deflected.

Fig. 19-14.

The great iron-nickel meteorite found at Cape York, Greenland, by Admiral Peary in 1895. It weighs about 36½ tons. (Courtesy, American Museum of Natural History)

by a 14-pound stone. That meteors can be frightfully devastating was shown by the fall of June 30, 1908, in Siberia. It is reported that the blast was heard 400 miles away, windows were broken at a distance of 50 miles, trees were blown over within a radius of 20 or more miles, and several hundred reindeer were killed. A number of craters, the largest 150 feet across, dot the site of that fall. Some Russian scientists stated recently that a nuclear explosion, not meteors, caused the destruction in 1908. Again in 1947 an uninhabited area in Siberia was hit by a swarm of meteors.

Meteor Crater in Arizona (Fig. 19-10) undoubtedly was made by the impact of a large meteor or a group of smaller ones. Chubb Crater in northern Canada, about 2½ miles in diameter, likewise shows indications of a meteoritic origin. A multitude of depressions (Fig. 19-11) in the Carolinas and adjoining coastal areas to the north and south may also have been caused by meteoritic bombardment. Temperatures at the moment of impact of large swift meteors are probably high enough to volatilize completely the rocks, soil, and water at such spots. The great expansion necessitated by the change to a gaseous state causes the explosion. The column of air directly in the path of a meteor does not have time to move completely aside; it is compressed into an air-shock wave that affects a much larger area than the area actually hit by the meteorite.

Usually more meteors are visible in the early morning hours than are visible before midnight. Meteors seen after midnight tend to be bluish-white in color and to have short trails; they are vaporized rapidly by the intense heat generated by their hurried passage through the Earth's atmosphere (Fig. 19-12). Early evening meteors tend to be reddish and to have longer trails. Occasionally showers of meteors are visible (Fig. 19-13). A very large meteorite is shown in Fig. 19-14.

EXERCISES AND QUESTIONS FOR CHAPTER 19

1. Make a sketch (orientation: looking down) which shows the following:

    (1) Observer on the Earth at sunrise
    (2) Moon causing an annular eclipse
    (3) Mars near observer's western horizon
    (4) Venus as a morning star in observer's sky (through a telescope it appears as a crescent).

2. Can Mercury and Venus cause eclipses of the sun when they are located directly between the Earth and the sun?

3. Compare and contrast the phases of the moon and Venus.

4. A friend tells you that Mercury is a morning star visible each morning for a slightly longer time before sunrise. What is the approximate phase of Mercury?

5. Observe each of the planets visible this term in the telescope. If Jupiter is visible, how could you prove that its four easily seen moons are not nearby stars?

6. Make a series of semicircular star maps spanning several weeks which prove that planets are "wanderers."

7. Which of the planets other than the Earth has the most favorable conditions for life as we know it?

8. List as many unique features for each of the planets as you can.

CHAPTER 20

Tools of the Astronomer

IN AN ordinary conversation about his favorite subject, an astronomer might make a few statements such as any of the following: The planet Venus has considerable carbon dioxide in its atmosphere The sun is an average star about 93 million miles from the Earth and about 864,000 miles in diameter. Stars consist of the same materials as the sun, although the elements may occur in different proportions and the surface temperatures may be different. Millions of galaxies exist in the universe at distances of millions of light-years and all of them seem to be moving away from us.

Such remarks would be commonplace among astronomers, but reaching the ears of the intellectually curious nonastronomer, they cannot but cause wonder and skepticism. Information about celestial objects has been obtained largely through a study of light, and chiefly by means of three instruments—the telescope, the camera, and the spectroscope.

Although light is the source of our information about the stars, the source of light itself is still something of a mystery. According to the wave theory, the light which we can see consists of electromagnetic waves which move in a straight line at the rate of about 186,000 mi/sec through a vacuum (see Chapter 8). The wave lengths of visible light are incredibly short, and the number of vibrations per second fantastically large.

COLOR

Ordinary white light is the combination of the different wave lengths which the human eye can see individually as the different colors of the rainbow: red, orange, yellow, green, blue, indigo, and violet. With a simple prism, white light (sunlight) can be separated into its component colors (Figs. 8-1 and 8-2): the red waves are longest and the violet ones shortest. Long waves penetrate the atmosphere better than short waves since short waves tend to be scattered by dust particles and air molecules (Fig. 20-1).

Blue sky and reddish sunsets. Orientation: looking "down" on the sun and the Earth. One observer is experiencing noon on the Earth, and another is at his sunrise position. The longer red waves penetrate the atmosphere more readily than the shorter blue and violet waves, which are scattered easily by gas and dust in the air.— As the sun's light comes through the Earth's atmosphere, some of the shorter waves are scattered, and hence the sun looks yellowish or reddish instead of white. The scattering is greatest at sunrise and sunset, when the sun's rays come through the Earth's atmosphere at the greatest slant. The scattered light waves, predominantly blue and violet, are reflected by the dust particles in the atmosphere and make the sky look blue.—When there is a great deal of dust in the atmosphere near the horizon, then reddish colors are prominent in the sunset. Occasionally at midday, when considerable dust and haze intervene between the observer and the sun, the sun takes on an orange hue.

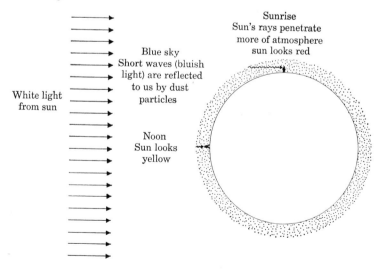

Fig. 20.1

If an object is not itself a source of light, it is visible because it reflects or refracts light from another source; the color of such an object depends on which wave lengths it reflects, and hence does not absorb. The color of an object which is the source of light, however, depends upon the temperature of the object. If a piece of metal is heated gradually, it feels warm before any change in color can be detected; the warmth is caused by the radiation of invisible infrared electromagnetic waves. As the temperature increases, red light predominates among the radiations, and the metal is seen to glow. At still higher temperatures the radiations become stronger and the color changes in turn to orange, to yellow, and then to green. Highest temperatures produce radiations which are strongest in the blue and violet wave lengths. The relationship between temperature and color enables astronomers to determine the surface temperatures of the stars. Yellowish stars like the sun have surface temperatures of approximately 6000°C (10,000°F); the surface temperatures of reddish stars are lower, and those of bluish stars are higher.

Daylight is the reflection of sunlight by the particles in the Earth's atmosphere. As seen from a space rocket flying high above the Earth's

Celestial objects are elevated by atmospheric refraction. Atmospheric refraction makes an object appear higher above the horizon than its actual position; this effect increases greatly near the horizon. Therefore, the bottom portion of a large object such as the sun appears to be elevated more than the top portion, and it looks flattened. No distortion occurs in a horizontal direction.

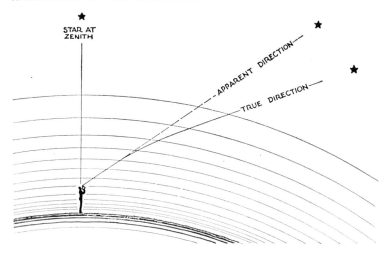

Fig. 20-2.

atmosphere, the sky approaches the black of interstellar space even if the sun is visible. Similarly, from the airless moon, the sky would be black.

ATMOSPHERIC REFRACTION OF LIGHT WAVES

We are all familiar with the apparent bend in a straight object when part of it is seen under water. The bending of light waves (refraction) as they penetrate the Earth's atmosphere is similar, and causes an apparent increase in the altitude of celestial objects (Fig. 20-2). The light from an object on the horizon has a larger amount of atmosphere to penetrate than does the light from objects at higher altitudes: the amount of refraction decreases as the altitude of the object increases. Refraction of light on the horizon amounts to approximately half a degree: because of this, the sun is visible about two minutes before it actually rises above the eastern horizon and after it actually sets below the western horizon.

THE TELESCOPE AND CAMERA IN ASTRONOMY

The light-gathering power of the 200-inch telescope, the world's largest telescope, is about 360,000 times that of the human eye. Objects much too faint to be seen by the unaided eye are brilliantly visible in this telescope. The telescope acts like a funnel by collecting beams of light from a wide area and focusing them at one point (Fig. 20-3). This light-gathering function is much more important than magnification. Radio telescopes are discussed briefly in the next section; they are much larger than the optical telescopes considered here.

The camera in astronomy has the advantage of providing a permanent record of what is seen, unbiased by any personal prejudice. Also, many of the celestial objects which astronomers want to study are too distant for the eye to see even through the 200-inch telescope; here the camera makes its primary contribution by extending outward the boundaries of the visible universe. Light from a very distant star funneled through a telescope onto a film may be too faint to create an image in a minute, or an hour, or sometimes even in a night, but if the time exposure is continued for a few nights, the star's photograph may eventually be obtained. General fogging of the entire negative limits the length of time a film may be exposed.

Sketch of the path of light waves in the 200-inch Hale reflector. This telescope is large enough to place an operator inside the tube. In small reflecting telescopes a mirror is oriented at a 45 degree angle at the principal focus (position of operator above), and light is reflected to an eyepiece attached to the side of the telescope. A third arrangement is possible in larger reflectors: light is reflected from a small mirror at the principal focus back down the tube through a hole in the center of the large concave mirror to an eyepiece located below and entirely outside of the telescope. Inside the tube four rods at 90-degree angles to each other support the smaller mirror and cause the four lines which are sometimes seen projecting from stars in photographs.—Refracting telescopes have a lens at the mouth through which light passes on its journey to the eyepiece at the opposite end. All large telescopes (more than 40 inches in diameter) are reflectors, for a number of reasons: as light does not pass through the mirror, its quality does not have to be so nearly perfect as in a refractor; the mirror can be supported on the back; light is not separated into its different colors by reflection from the surface of the mirror.

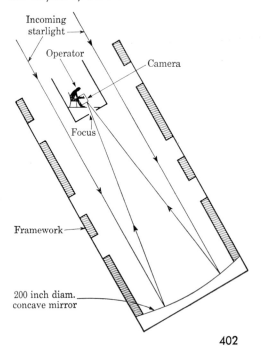

Incoming starlight
Operator
Camera
Focus
Framework
200 inch diam. concave mirror

Fig. 20-3.

402

An electronic device, called an image converter, has recently been constructed which is much more sensitive to light than any known film and which may increase by many times the distance that the telescope can now reach. It is thought that a 20-inch telescope with this attachment may be able to see as far as a 100-inch telescope without it, or possibly even as far as the 200-inch one. If this proves correct, the importance of this device in astronomy can hardly be exaggerated.

Large telescopes are oriented on axes and electrically operated so that they can be centered exactly upon any celestial object and follow it, without deviation, on its daily east-to-west journey across the skies. Astronomers use a system of coordinates similar to terrestrial latitude and longitude to locate celestial bodies. The position of the desired object in the sky is obtained from a set of tables. The telescope is turned a certain number of angular degrees in one direction, then the designated number of degrees along a second axis at right angles to the first, until it points directly at the target. The astronomer does not need to look in the sky for the object to guide the movement of the telescope.

The Hale Telescope Few scientific projects ever stimulated the imagination and interest in science of quite so many people as did the 200-inch telescope at Palomar (Figs. 20-4 and 20-5). The history of the big telescope is closely related to the life of Dr. George Hale. As a boy, George Hale became interested in astronomy and persuaded his father to purchase a telescope for him. Later as a professional astronomer, Dr. Hale realized that certain problems could not be solved until observations farther into space were possible. Therefore, he was instrumental in having a 40-inch refracting telescope built for the Yerkes Observatory in Wisconsin (still the largest refractor in the world). With the help of this instrument, some of the questions astronomers were asking could be answered, but more questions were raised than were answered. A still larger telescope was needed. Again Dr. Hale provided the driving force which finally resulted in the construction of the 100-inch reflecting telescope at Mt. Wilson in California. Again, the increased range of visibility aided in solving some problems, but many new questions were raised; again a larger telescope was needed. In 1928 the construction of the 200-inch telescope was planned; for this project Dr. Hale obtained financial backing from the Rockefeller Foundation.

The motto of the builders of the 200-inch telescope was "The impos-

sible is that which we have not yet learned to do." First, a materia
other than glass was needed for the mirror, because glass expands anc
contracts too much with temperature changes occurring during a
night's operation in an open-air observatory. For three years quartz

Fig. 20-4.

*The Hale Reflector. An astronomer is preparing to enter the cage (in-
visible in this sketch) inside the telescope. (From a drawing by Russell
W. Porter)*

mirrors were cast experimentally, but the result was always failure.
Following this, Pyrex was tried and proved satisfactory. Experiments
began with small Pyrex blocks at Corning, New York. As difficulties
were overcome, larger and larger blocks were cast. One of these ex-

Fig. 20-5.

Dome of 200-inch telescope on Palomar Mountain in California, seen by moonlight. The entire top part of the dome can move on tracks so that the telescope may be pointed at any part of the sky. (Photograph by Mount Wilson and Palomar Observatories)

perimental blocks has been used for the mirror of the 120-inch Lick reflector, the second largest telescope in existence. Finally, a 200-inch Pyrex block was produced, but it developed a flaw, and a second block of Pyrex had to be poured. This was cooled successfully during the year that followed. In 1936 the many-ton mass of Pyrex, about 17 feet across, was fastened firmly to a railroad car and sent westward. Special routing was necessary to avoid certain low underpasses. Holidays were declared at a number of towns along the way, schools were dismissed, and teachers and pupils watched as the big block of Pyrex moved by.

Grinding and polishing of the mirror took place in California and were not completed until 1947. Years of careful, painstaking work were required to produce a nearly perfect surface that could bring to a focus all of the light rays falling on it. A self-taught optical expert, formerly a truck driver at the Mt. Wilson Observatory, directed this work. New inventions and techniques were needed in many aspects of the construction. The mirror was supported by a metal framework ingeniously designed to eliminate much sagging. The huge 50-ton mass is balanced so evenly that a tiny electric motor moves it readily. Dr. Hale unfortunately did not live to see the dedication in 1948. It is known as the Hale telescope.

This telescope is now in operation at the Palomar Observatory in California. The three largest telescopes in existence are all located in California: large observatories are commonly located in areas far from city lights and smoke, in climates that permit "good seeing" on many nights, and in high altitudes above the dense atmosphere of sea level. The maximum range of the Hale telescope may be as much as about 6 billion light-years, and its primary function is to determine the structure and composition of the universe. Several of the photographs reproduced for this text were taken through the Hale telescope.

RADIO ASTRONOMY

In addition to the visible electromagnetic waves, invisible waves of longer wave lengths are also produced by stars, star groups, and galaxies. These waves are intermediate in length between light waves and standard radio waves. They are being studied at present by radio telescope (Figs. 20-6 and 20-7), a new and rapidly developing research technique in astronomy which has already furnished much valuable information to astronomers. A national radio astronomy observatory has been set up by the United States Government in West Virginia, and construction of a huge radio telescope (Fig. 20-7) is scheduled. Smaller radio telescopes are in operation at present.

The radio telescope has certain advantages over the optical telescope. Since radio waves readily penetrate the Earth's atmosphere and clouds of gas and dust in space, the radio telescope may be used in cloudy weather and thus permits "full-time" astronomy. The radio telescope can also penetrate farther into space than the optical telescope and hence may "see" objects which are too cool to give off visible light. However, the target objects are never actually seen, they are difficult to locate precisely, and many of them at present are of unknown origin. Already credited to the radio telescopes are: (1) the discovery of galaxies in collision (Fig. 20-8), (2) additional information about

Fig. 20-6.

The 250-foot steerable radio telescope at Jodrell Bank Experimental Station, University of Manchester, Great Britain. (Courtesy, A. C. B. Lovell)

the size, shape, and number of spiral arms of our own and other galaxies, (3) a navigational sextant which can be used in fog, and (4) the surprising discovery that the amount of matter scattered in clouds of gas and dust in spiral galaxies may constitute only 1 to 2 percent of all the matter in the galaxies instead of the previous estimate of half of that total.

Fig. 20-7.

The 50-foot radio telescope at the Naval Research Laboratory, Washington. This is something like a reflecting telescope, but a "dish" of metal sheet or wire mesh is substituted for the mirror. The radio waves from the part of the sky toward which it is pointed are focused on the rod. The waves are then conveyed to a sensitive receiver where the strength of the signal is recorded in a selected wave length by a registering meter. The record must then be interpreted.

THE SPECTROSCOPE IN ASTRONOMY

Spectra and the operation of the spectroscope are discussed in Chapter 8. Here we deal with the instrument as it finds application in astronomy. A spectroscope is an instrument designed to study light by passing it through a glass prism and separating the different waves

Fig. 20-8.

Colliding galaxies, NGC 5128. A spiral seen edgewise seems to be colliding centrally with a large galaxy which is intermediate in type between elliptical and spiral. The discovery of these colliding galaxies is credited to radio telescopes. The galaxies constitute a very powerful source of radio waves. The Hale telescope was called on to photograph this part of space to identify the source of the radio emission. (Photograph from the Mount Wilson and Palomar Observatories)

(Figs. 8-3, 8-4, and 20-9). Solids, liquids, and compressed gases of all known materials, when heated to temperatures high enough to make them luminous, show continuous spectra; that is, a continuous band of colors like the rainbow is visible. Furthermore, experimentation has shown that the color and intensity of the radiation changes with different temperatures. Therefore, the spectroscope can be used to measure the temperature of a glowing object in the laboratory or of a star thousands of light-years away. Even a casual look at the sky on a dark clear night will show that stars vary in color from blue, through white and yellow, to red. Differences in the colors of glowing objects may also be caused by differences in their chemical compositions. However, the colors of stars seem to be due almost entirely to temperature differences.

Research has also shown that each of the elements, when in the form of a noncompressed gas hot enough to glow, produces a bright-line spectrum—a number of colored lines against a dark background (Fig. 8-5). Furthermore, each element in this state always produces the same characteristic pattern of bright lines; the numbers, locations, and intensities of the lines are different for each element. Thus, elements can be identified in the laboratory on the basis of their bright-line spectra; each has a distinguishing set of "fingerprints." For example, the bright-line spectrum of sodium vapor contains only two lines, each in the yellow part of the spectrum. In contrast, the bright-line

Fig. 20-9.

Paths of light waves inside a spectroscope. Highly schematic. Careful study of the sketch should show how a spectroscope functions in spreading apart the light waves which enter it so that they may be studied individually. Many shades of each color occur, and the statement that all waves of red light are focused at one point should be interpreted broadly. It should be apparent that dark lines will occur in the spectrum if certain wave lengths (colors) are missing.

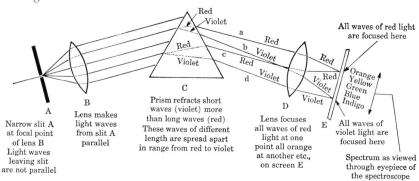

spectrum of hydrogen shows four prominent lines in the visible region, one in the red, one in the blue, and two in the violet part of the spectrum. The dark background is caused by the absence of waves in those parts of the spectrum.

Elements can also be identified in the sun and the stars by the characteristic spectra they produce; but the spectra produced by the sun and most stars are dark-line spectra—that is, the characteristic pattern of an element appears as dark lines against a continuous colored background (except for the dark lines). The two lines of sodium vapor, for example, would appear as dark lines against the yellow part of the spec-

Doppler effect

trum. Two prerequisites are necessary for the production of a dark-line spectrum: the light must come from a continuous source, and it must pass through a cooler gas before reaching a spectroscope. The cooler gas absorbs from the light the same waves it would emit if it were hot enough to emit a bright-line spectrum (Fig. 8-5). The dark-line spectrum thus shows the composition of the cooler medium located between the source and the spectroscope. Sunlight is considered to come from hot compressed gas which gives all of the visible waves. Some of these waves are absorbed by cooler gases in the sun's atmosphere (p. 416) as the light passes through it. The effect of the cool gases in the Earth's own atmosphere must also be considered. The chemical compositions of the atmospheres of the planets can be determined spectroscopically because light from the sun passes through these atmospheres before it is reflected to the Earth; in this case astronomers must separate the dark-line spectra produced by the sun's atmosphere, the atmosphere of the planet, and the atmosphere of the Earth.

In addition to determination of the temperature, chemical composition, and structure of a distant star, its spectrum also apparently shows the direction and rate of movement of the star relative to the Earth (Fig. 20-10). Comparisons of dark-line spectra produced in the laboratory with those from different stars have shown that the dark lines characteristic of certain elements may all be shifted the same amount toward one end of a star's spectrum. This shift is a form of the Doppler effect.

One form of Doppler effect with which we are all familiar is the drop in pitch of a car horn as the car passes us on the road. The sound waves seem to be shortened as the car approaches, raising the pitch of the horn; as the car recedes, the sound waves seem to be lengthened and there is an immediate drop in the pitch of the horn.

There is a similar interpretation for the shift in the dark lines of a star spectrum. If a star is moving away from the Earth (lower star in Fig. 20-11), then fewer light waves reach the spectroscope per unit of time and so each of the waves appears longer. But a change in the wave length of light means a change in its color: red is the longest visible wave length and violet is the shortest. Therefore, each of the dark lines in this spectrum is shifted the same amount toward the red end. Similarly, if the distance separating the star and the Earth is decreasing (upper star in Fig. 20-11), each wave seen or photographed in the spectrum appears to be shorter, and each of the dark

Fig. 20-10.

Doppler effect explained according to wave theory of light. Wave fronts are moving out periodically from the source area in all directions. An observer is stationed at A. The wave fronts are assumed to move forward at the rate of six each second. During one second, therefore, waves 9, 8, 7, 6, 5, and 4 pass by the observer. However, if the observer during that second moves from A to B, waves 3 and 2 will also pass by him. Thus eight wave fronts move by the observer during this second, and each wave seems to be reduced in length. If the observer remains at B, the rate returns to six per second.—On the other hand, if the observer moves to D during the second, waves 4 and 5 will not reach him, and the rate is reduced to four waves each second. To the observer, each wave seems longer. Thus a decrease in distance (between source and observer) seems to decrease wave lengths, whereas an increase in distance appears to increase wave lengths. This apparent lengthening or shortening of waves can be produced by movement of the observer, the source, or both. The magnitude of the apparent change in wave length is directly proportional to the rate at which the distance is changing. For example, if the observer moves more rapidly in a second and travels from A to C instead of from A to B, nine waves will reach the observer during this second and the waves will seem shorter than they did at the rate of eight each second.—An apparent change in the wave length of visible light produces a corresponding change in its color. Motion toward a spectroscope seems to shorten all of the visible waves and shifts the color of each a bit toward the violet end of the spectrum. On the other hand, motion away from the spectroscope seems to increase the length of each wave and thus shift it toward the red end of the spectrum.

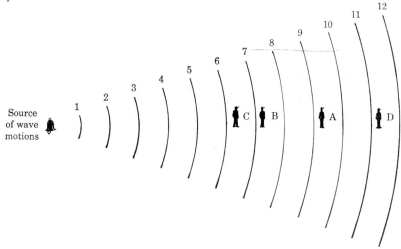

lines is shifted an equal distance toward the violet end of the spectrum. The rate of movement is calculated from the magnitude of the shift.

A certain prominent physicist, too anxious to reach his destination, is reported to have been detected by a policeman driving through a red light. For this indiscretion he received a ticket and the opportunity to meet a judge. Not wishing to pay the fine, the physicist had recourse to his knowledge of the Doppler effect and began a learned discourse on the properties of light. He told the judge that green waves are

Fig. 20-11.

Doppler displacements in dark-line spectra. The red end of the spectrum is toward the right. Bright comparison lines above and below each dark-line stellar spectrum are spectra of the iron arc as produced in the laboratory. Light from this laboratory source illuminated the top and bottom portions of the slit of the spectroscope, whereas light from the star passed through the middle portion of the slit. Therefore, the positions of the lines could be compared precisely and photographed on the same film. At the left are the ultraviolet dark-line spectra of Alpha Cygni (above) and Betelgeuse (below). At the right the dark lines of sodium in the yellow region of the stars' spectra appear between bright comparison lines of sodium. Here the Doppler displacements are clearly shown: the red shift in the lower photograph indicates that the distance between the Earth and Betelgeuse is increasing; the violet shift in the upper photograph indicates that the distance between the Earth and Alpha Cygni is decreasing. (Photographed at Mount Wilson Observatory)

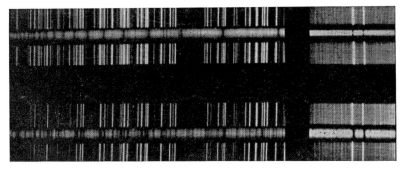

shorter than red ones, and that driving toward the source would have the effect of shortening the wave lengths. Therefore, to the driver, the red traffic light would appear to be green. The judge was about convinced that the physicist's explanation was correct when a student in the courtroom (who had been flunked by the physicist on an exam the week before) whispered to the judge to ask the physicist how fast he would have to drive in order to change red light into green. As a result of his answer, the physicist was fined, not for passing through a red light, but for speeding!

EXERCISES AND QUESTIONS FOR CHAPTER 20

1. List some favorable, some unfavorable, and some unique features of reflecting, refracting, and radio telescopes.

2. Two stars have the same intrinsic (actual) luminosity. However, one star is three times farther from an observer than the other. How will their luminosities compare?

3. Three persons wearing white, yellow, and blue shirts respectively enter a room illuminated entirely by yellow light. Are their shirts the same color in this room?

4. How is a bright-line spectrum produced? What is the significance of a bright-line spectrum? A dark-line spectrum?

5. Explain how the following information is obtained about stars: (1) chemical composition, (2) motion, (3) temperature, and (4) distance.

6. Describe favorable conditions for the location of a large reflecting telescope; of a large radio telescope.

7. How do astronomers determine the chemical composition of the atmosphere of a planet like Venus?

CHAPTER 21

Sun, Stars, Galaxies — The Universe

THE SUN

IF A fast jet plane could travel at 750 mi/hr right from the Earth to the sun, a distance of almost 93 million miles, the trip would take about 14 years and 2 months. By terrestrial standards, therefore, the sun is tremendously distant, but by astronomical standards it is our neighbor—the only star close enough to have a visible disk, and close enough to be studied in detail. Fortunately the sun seems to be an average type of star, perhaps somewhat smaller than most, and information obtained concerning it is probably applicable in varying degrees to

Fig. 21-1.

A solar prominence. (Photographed by R. B. Dunn with the 15-inch camera, Sacramento Peak Observatory)

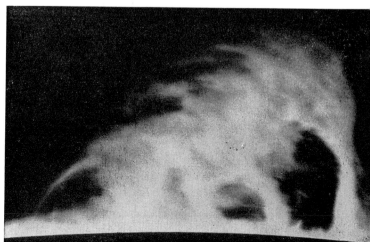

other stars. The sun's mass shapes the orbits of the other members of the solar system and keeps them moving about it.

Approximately 699/700 of all the matter in the solar system is concentrated in the sun, and much of the remainder is present in Jupiter. The sun's mass is about 332,000 times that of the Earth, and its volume is about 1.3 million times that of the Earth. If the Earth were the size of a grapefruit, the sun would be about 50 feet in diameter and about a mile away.

The sun, as a hot gaseous body, has no physical features corresponding exactly to the solid body and atmosphere of the Earth. Direct radiation from the sun seems to come from the photosphere, the visible surface approximately 864,000 miles in diameter which forms the disk of the sun. Below this surface, which is not a sharp boundary, gas particles are dense enough to be opaque. Above the photosphere, a progressively thinner gaseous atmosphere extends outward for several million miles and may, according to information obtained during the International Geophysical Year, even permeate the space between the sun and the Earth. The pearly white corona forms the outer part of the sun's atmosphere and by far the largest portion of it. The density of gases in the corona is so low that comets passing through it have not been seen to slow down. Temperatures in these diffuse gases may be very high. To the unaided eye, the sun's atmosphere is visible only at times of total solar eclipses (Fig. 18-14) when the brighter light from the sun's disk is hidden behind the dark body of the moon. Also seen during total solar eclipses or in the coronagraph are the prominences, great clouds of flaming gas which may erupt from the sun to great altitudes (Fig. 21-1). Prominences are puzzling: occasionally they seem to form high above the sun's disk, and downward moving material appears to be more abundant than material that has erupted visibly. Through the telescope the sun's yellowish disk is visibly darker around the edges; light from the edges of the photosphere travels to us obliquely through the sun's atmosphere, and hence more of the waves are absorbed by it.

The temperature of the photosphere is estimated to be about 6000°C. Temperatures presumably increase downward in the sun's interior, and some calculations indicate that they may attain magnitudes of millions of degrees near the sun's center. Such extreme temperatures are considered necessary to prevent the sun from collapsing under the tremendous pressure of its huge mass. At such temperatures, atoms probably are stripped of their electrons or gain and lose electrons rapidly.

Their volumes are thus greatly decreased, because atomic nuclei are very tiny in relation to the size of whole atoms (like a two-carat diamond in the center of a huge auditorium). Densities, therefore, can be enormously increased even though the material remains essentially a gas. The spectroscope indicates that the sun's atmosphere consists chiefly of hydrogen and helium; however, more than sixty of the elements known on the Earth have been detected in the sun. Since large-scale circulation from the sun's interior to the surface and back again presumably occurs, the composition of the sun's atmosphere may be representative of the sun as a whole.

Fig. 21-2.

Sunspots as evidence of the sun's rotation. This group lasted 95 days and made four transits. It attained a very large size and could be seen without a telescope. (Photographs from the Mount Wilson and Palomar Observatories)

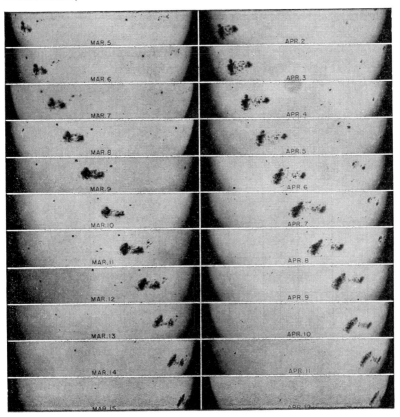

The movement of sunspots and the Doppler effect (Chapter 20) both provide evidence that the sun rotates on its axis. The equatorial region requires about 25 days for one complete spin, whereas the polar areas need around 34 days; this difference indicates a gaseous condition for the sun's surface. The Doppler effect is noted when light from opposite sides of the sun is examined in a spectroscope: a red shift shows up in the dark-line spectrum of one side (spinning away from us) and a violet shift shows up in the dark-line spectrum of the other side, indicating that the sun turns on an axis. Sunspots moving from one side of the sun to the other also indicate that the sun is rotating (Fig. 21-2). These were first observed by Galileo through his telescope. Galileo considered it unlikely that the sunspots moved across the surface of a motionless sun, and so he deduced that the sun was spinning.

Viewed through a telescope, sunspots appear as relatively small, irregularly shaped dark areas chiefly located within the sun's equatorial regions. The largest of the spots rival Jupiter in size. The temperatures of sunspot centers may be about 4000°C, approximately 2000°C lower than the sun's surface elsewhere; therefore, sunspots appear dark against the brighter, hotter background. The number of sunspots varies somewhat periodically; a maximum number of spots occurs about every eleven years on the average (Fig. 21-3). The International Geophysical

Fig. 21-3.

Sunspot cycle. Each point represents the number of sunspot groups observed during the year. (From data by Seth B. Nicholson, Mount Wilson Observatory)

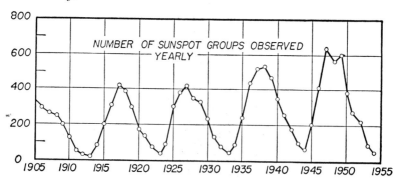

Year was chosen to coincide with a time of maximum solar activity. Half of all sunspots exist for four days or less, but some have lasted several months. Although sunspots are commonly described as violent storms at the sun's surface, there seems to be little evidence for this explanation; in fact, it has been suggested recently that sunspots may be calm areas surrounded by turbulent regions. Their origin is unknown. During sunspot maxima the aurora borealis is pronounced, and magnetic storms may occur which are powerful enough to interfere with radio and television reception.

The solar system appears to be moving toward the constellation Hercules at about 12 mi/sec relative to the 8000 or so stars visible to the unaided eye. The evidence of this motion is based on a familiar phenomenon: as one drives toward a group of houses, they seem to spread apart; as one drives away, they appear to come together again. Stars in the vicinity of Hercules appear to be diverging, whereas stars on the opposite side of the sky seem to be converging. Furthermore, most of the stars in the vicinity of Hercules show violet shifts in the spectroscope; red shifts are common for stars in the opposite direction.

Some Solar-Terrestrial Relations   Terrestrial effects of solar activity are known to increase in number and intensity at sunspot maxima. Radio fade-outs may occur throughout the lighted half of the Earth whenever a solar flare occurs near the sun's meridian (waves which move vertically outward from the sun will then strike the Earth). Long-distance radio reception is possible because radio waves are reflected back to the Earth's surface by ionized layers in the Earth's atmosphere (ionization is discussed on p. 257). Ionized layers apparently are created by the action of ultraviolet light from the sun on rarefied gases in the Earth's upper atmosphere. Therefore, the extra amount of ultraviolet light associated with the flare and traveling at about 186,000 mi/sec changes the ionized layers sufficiently to produce the radio fade-outs.

Protons, electrons, and perhaps other charged particles from the sun may cause ionospheric storms which influence radio reception all over the Earth and may last for days. The particles take about one day to move from the sun to the Earth.

Such streams of charged particles from the sun seem also to offer at least a partial explanation for the northern and southern lights (aurora borealis and aurora australis). The particles evidently follow lines of force in the Earth's magnetic field (Fig. 10-13) downward through the Earth's atmosphere toward the north and south magnetic poles. As the charged particles pass through the atmosphere, they ionize some of the atoms in their path; these give off the varicolored lights observed in the aurora. The magnetic north pole is about at latitude 70 degrees north. Occasionally an aurora can be seen as far away as 40 degrees of latitude from the north magnetic pole.

Source of the Sun's Energy   Each square foot of the sun's surface is estimated to radiate heat and light energy at about 8000 horsepower. According to one estimate, the amount of energy received by the Earth in three days from the sun is approximately equivalent to the total amount of energy available to man in the Earth's crust as fossil fuels or nuclear resources. Geologic history seems to show that the Earth exceeds three billion years in age and that the energy production of the sun has not varied greatly in much of that time; otherwise the effects of drastic climatic changes should have been detected in the geologic record.

Nuclear reactions (p. 288) are presumably the source of the sun's energy; other sources such as burning or contraction appear impossible or inadequate. A possible type of reaction involves a series of changes during which hydrogen is metamorphosed into helium. During the transformation some matter is changed to energy: Einstein's famous equation ($E = mc^2$) indicates that annihilation of a tiny quantity of matter results in the creation of a tremendous amount of energy. For such nuclear reactions (fusion) to take place on the Earth, small positively charged nuclei are crashed against each other at high speeds in large "atom smashing" machines. The entire interior of the sun can be considered a gigantic "atom smasher."

If this concept is correct, the mass of the sun is slowly decreasing at an estimated rate of approximately eight billion pounds of matter per second. However, calculations indicate that enough hydrogen is present to stoke the solar furnace for billions of years in the future. The fraction of this energy received by the Earth is very small, equivalent perhaps to the sun's loss of four pounds of matter per second, and about one-third of this energy is wasted by being reflected back into space.

STARS

Stars are other suns—large hot gaseous bodies shining by their own light. They are so remote that they appear as mere points of light even in the largest of telescopes. The number of stars visible with the aid of a large telescope is practically limitless; but to the unaided eye, not more than 8000 are visible in the entire celestial sphere, and an observer does well to distinguish several hundred stars at any one time. The fact that only twenty known stars (counting multiple stars, described below, as one) are located within a dozen light-years of the Earth emphasizes the isolation of stars in space.

We can speculate that families of planets move about many of these distant suns, and that some of the planets are favorably situated for the existence of conditions similar to those on the Earth. No telescope is powerful enough to prove or disprove this conjecture. However, a method of checking it has been suggested. If a star like the sun should be eclipsed by a planet like Jupiter, the dimming of the star's light might be measurable with a modern photoelectric photometer. Whether or not other stars also have sunspots, prominences, coronas, and similar phenomena cannot be ascertained by observation.

Stars vary widely in size, temperature, brightness, density, and mass. Giant stars apparently have densities approaching that of a well-developed vacuum produced on the Earth. On the other hand, calculations indicate that some stars, appropriately termed dwarfs, may approximate the Earth in size and have densities exceeding 1 ton/cu in. Probably dwarfs are composed chiefly of fast-moving atomic nuclei which have been stripped of their space-consuming electron shells. Certainly the term gas was not intended originally for such material. Stellar volumes vary much more than stellar masses: stars are rare which contain more than ten times the matter present in the sun or which have less than one-tenth this quantity.

Stellar spectra indicate that surface temperatures of stars vary from a maximum in the neighborhood of 50,000°C (blue stars) to a minimum of about 2000°C (red stars). More stars are closer to the minimum than to the maximum. The radiation from a star whose surface is less than 2000°C would be too weak to detect visually unless the star were relatively very close. Such stars may exist unknown to us.

The diameter of a star can be calculated indirectly if the temperature and the intrinsic brightness of the star are known. The temperature of the star controls the amount of light given off by a unit area of its surface. Therefore, if the temperature and the total amount of light radiated by the star are known, its surface area and its diameter can be determined. Thus a highly luminous red star with a low surface temperature must be very large because the amount of light radiated by a star depends upon its size and temperature; conversely, a very hot white star with low absolute luminosity must be small.

A special instrument (stellar interferometer) used with the largest of telescopes makes possible the measurement of the angular diameters of some of the largest of the stars. The actual diameter can be calculated from this if the distance to the star is known. These two independent methods of calculating the diameters of stars give results which are reasonably compatible.

Multiple and Variable Stars   With the aid of the telescope and spectroscope, it has been shown that many apparently single stars actually consist of two or more stars that mutually revolve about some center and are separated by relatively small astronomical distances. The second star from the end of the handle of the Big Dipper and the star Sirius are good examples of double (binary) stars. True binaries should be distinguished from two stars which *appear* close only because they are almost on the same line of sight from the Earth. In some instances, the orbits of double stars are so oriented that one periodically eclipses the other. If the stars are of different brightnesses, the eclipse caused by one star differs from that caused by the other, and a change occurs in the amount of light received from the stars (Fig. 21-4). The

Fig. 21-4.

Light curve and system of Algol. This star is in the constellation Perseus. The size of the sun is shown on the same scale. (Determined by Joel Stebbins)

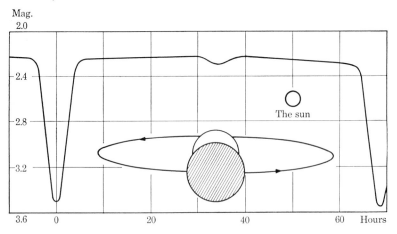

time of a complete revolution can thereby be determined. Cepheids are another type of variable star (p. 352). Double stars are of great importance in astronomy because they provide a means of estimating the mass of a star: the gravitational effect of one star on the other can be calculated when their period of revolution and the distance between them have been determined.

Novae or "new" stars have been observed a number of times in the history of astronomy. Tycho Brahe's star in Cassiopeia in 1572 is a famous example of an exceptional type called a *supernova*. At its brightest, this star was visible during the day. Calculations indicate that a supernova located a few light-years away would be hundreds of times as bright as the full moon. Apparently such stars were too faint for easy observation before their tremendous, sudden increase in energy output. After a year or so of vastly increased brightness, each of these stars returned to its former inconspicuous place in the universe. It has been suggested that the outer layers of novae become unstable and are blown off explosively (Fig. 21-5).

Fig. 21-5.

Expanding nebula around Nova Aquilae, 1918. (Photographed with the 100-inch telescope, Mount Wilson Observatory)

Stellar Spectra A star may be classified by its spectrum (Fig. 21-6) which is determined by the star's temperature, chemical composition, and physical structure. Six types (B, A, F, G, K, and M) include nearly all of the thousands of stars whose spectra have been studied. Typical members of each type are distinctive from those of other types, but gradations exist between them; members of one type have temperatures, colors, and spectral lines which are transitional to those of neighboring types.

Evidently the temperature of a star is the most important reason for

Fig. 21-6.

Classification of stars according to spectral types. From top to bottom the stars decrease in surface temperature and increase in redness. The stars were originally classified according to spectral types alphabetically from A through P. Subsequently some letters have been dropped, and others have been added. Thus the present system of letters is somewhat haphazard. The following mnemonic should be of assistance in remembering the order of the most abundant spectral types: Be A Fine Girl, Kiss Me.

TYPE	APPROXIMATE SURFACE TEMPERATURE (FAHRENHEIT)	COLOR	TYPICAL STAR	SPECTRUM
B	40,000	Blue-white	Spica	Helium lines
A	20,000	White	Sirius, Vega	Hydrogen lines, metals appear
F	14,000	Yellowish-white	Procyon	Metals stronger
G	11,000	Yellow	Sun, Capella	Metallic lines numerous and conspicuous
K	8,000	Orange	Arcturus	Calcium lines strong
M	5,000	Red	Antares	Titanium oxide lines prominent

its having a certain color and belonging to a certain spectral group, since two stars which seem identical except for surface temperatures have quite different spectra. Some spectral lines are prominent at low temperatures; others stand out at higher temperatures. The chemical compositions of stars appear to be more or less the same: hydrogen is the most abundant element in stars, helium is next, and together these two elements appear to make up all but a tiny portion of stellar matter.

Fig. 21-7 shows the commonest spectral types of stars plotted graphically according to their luminosities. Approximately two-thirds of all the known spectral types, the main sequence of stars, cluster about a line extending on the diagram from the upper left to the lower right. Most of the remainder of the stars that have been plotted are grouped somewhat loosely about a line which leads from the main sequence toward the upper right. The reddish stars on the right side of the diagram are readily subdivided into two groups, one of much greater luminosity than the other. This dichotomy of one stellar type

Russell diagram. Stars of type-I population are plotted
graphically according to their luminosities and spectral
types. The sun is a type-G star with an absolute visual
magnitude of about 5. Hipparchus, about 150 B.C., divided stars into six classes in order of their brightness
as seen from the Earth. Class 1 was the brightest; class
6 was the faintest. Subsequently the classification has
been modified and extended in each direction. Stars
with zero or minus magnitudes are brighter than those
with plus magnitudes. A star of one magnitude is 2½
times as bright as a star of the next higher magnitude.
Absolute magnitudes are the magnitudes which stars
would have at a distance of 32½ light-years or 10 par-
secs. One parsec is the distance to a point that would
have a parallax of 1 second of arc as measured from
the ends of a 93,000,000-mile base line. In a similar
diagram for stars of population II, the whole upper part
of the main sequence for population I would be absent.
This part apparently represents stars too youthful to
be extant in a population-II group. (Diagram by W.
Gyllenberg, Lund Observatory)

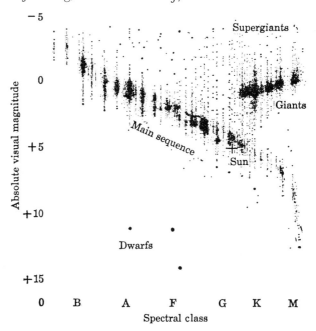

Fig. 21-7.

into two groups of different brightnesses is increasingly less distinct
toward the left side of the diagram. The difference in luminosity is
interpreted as a difference in size. For example, a very bright class M
star is probably a giant or supergiant; although the amount of radiation

per unit area from such a star is relatively small, its volume is so large that a tremendous amount of illumination is given off.

Unusual stars known as white dwarfs are situated in the lower left part of the diagram. Few have been discovered, perhaps because they are very faint and are visible only if located relatively close to the Earth. The white color of these stars indicates a high temperature and much radiation per unit of area, so their low intrinsic brightness is probably due to very small size. White dwarfs may have densities of the order of 1 ton/cu in.

In general along the main sequence in the Russell diagram, large hot stars occur at the upper end on the left side of the diagram, and small cool reddish stars are located in the lower right. Gradations occur between these two groups. The sun is a G-type star belonging in the main sequence.

Evolution of Stars   It has been suggested that stars originated at different times in the past and that each is evolving through stages which can be characterized as youthful, mature, and old. Thus, stars have absolute ages (the number of years since they formed) and genetic ages (the present stages in their evolutionary cycles). According to this hypothesis, a star begins as a huge, cool, diffuse mass of gas and dust whose only heat comes from contraction caused by the mutual gravitational attraction of the entire mass. Temperatures in the interior of the shrinking mass eventually become high enough for nuclear reactions to begin: at this stage contraction ceases, the mass begins to give off light, and it is said to become a star.

The amount of matter in the contracting mass is very important, since the rate at which a star consumes its nuclear fuel (chiefly hydrogen) apparently increases as the cube of its mass. A large amount should produce a very hot star, whereas a small original mass should never reach high temperatures. Therefore, large luminous stars such as the blue supergiants probably have absolute ages which are relatively quite short. Furthermore, such stars apparently go through their evolutionary cycles rapidly. They exist only in regions of space where gas and dust (the parent materials of stars) are present. The time involved in the evolutionary cycle of a star is probably inversely proportional to the square of its mass.

If the mass is too small, contraction cannot raise temperatures to the point at which nuclear reactions can begin; such masses may form planets instead of stars. On the other hand, if the mass is very large, clusters of stars may form. Each star in the cluster has approximately the same absolute age, but the stars have different genetic ages. The stars farthest along in their evolutionary cycles are those which originally had the most mass; they consume this matter most rapidly. The heat energy produced by one type of nuclear transformation would tend to prevent contraction until its ingredients were used and the reaction stopped; then the star might shrink again until still higher temperatures were attained and a type of nuclear reaction that involved different elements could begin. At these higher temperatures the region in which fusion occurred might be enlarged and the outer parts of the star might be expanded until it became a giant.

According to one hypothesis, the sun will eventually become a red dwarf near the end of its stellar career. However, it is speculated that this will not happen until much of the sun's available hydrogen has first been changed into helium and the sun has become so large and hot that the existence of life on the Earth would be impossible. Fortunately, this event is not expected to take place for several billion years.

According to another hypothesis, stars in their development may move horizontally from right to left across the Russell diagram. Perhaps the period of development represented by main-sequence stars is relatively slow, so more stars at any given time are in this main sequence stage than in either the preceding (youthful) or following (old) stages.

NEBULAE

Astronomers use the term nebula for any celestial object that forms more than a pinpoint of light in the telescope. The term covers several highly diverse kinds of objects. Some nebulae are part of our galaxy and are caused by the presence of dark or light clouds between the Earth and distant stars (Figs. 21-8, 21-9, 21-10, and 21-11); others are galaxies situated at remote distances beyond the Milky Way.

GALAXIES

Stars are not scattered uniformly through space. The known universe or cosmos consists of vast aggregates of stars called *galaxies* or *extragalactic nebulae*. Our solar system is located in a galaxy whose central plane seems to be marked by the Milky Way (Figs. 21-9 and 21-11),

Fig. 21-8.

Nebulae surrounding stars of the Pleiades. Contrast this telescopic view with that of the unaided eye. (Photographed by E. E. Barnard)

Fig. 21-9.

Great rift in the Milky Way from Cygnus to Scorpius. Dark areas apparently are caused by clouds of gas and dust which hide the light of stars behind them. (Mosaic from the Atlas of the Northern Milky Way)

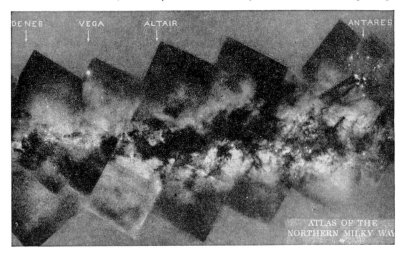

that faint band of light which crosses the sky in the neighborhood of constellations such as Auriga, Perseus, Cassiopeia, Cygnus, Sagittarius, and Scorpio. The light of the Milky Way is produced by the combined radiations of millions of stars, each too faint to be visible to the naked eye. Most stars seen as individuals in the telescope are part of our galaxy.

Planetary nebula in Aquarius. Photographed with the 200-inch Hale reflector in red light. Note the peculiar spokelike details near the inner rim of the ring. Like similar ring nebulae, it is illuminated by a very hot central star (Photograph from the Mount Wilson and Palomar Observatories)

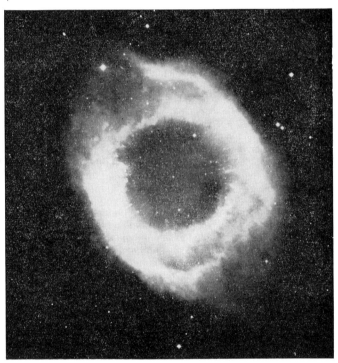

Fig. 21-10.

Determination of the shape of our galaxy is a difficult task, somewhat like trying to get an over-all view of a house from a single spot in one room; the Earth is situated inside the galaxy whose shape is to be determined.

Two methods suggest themselves: (1) star counts may be made at progressively greater distances in various directions; and (2) comparison may be made with what appear to be similar galaxies located far away in space. If a telescope is pointed toward the Milky Way and a series of photographs are taken with longer and longer time exposures (a way of increasing the distance which can be observed each time), stars are found to remain abundant in this direction. In fact, stellar density appears to be greatest in the general vicinity of Sagittarius.

Fig. 21-11.

The southern Milky Way centered on the star Antares. Note the striking resemblance between this photograph and that of a spiral galaxy such as is shown in Fig. 15-3. This is a side view of the central part of our galaxy, showing the concentration of obscuring matter along the central plane. (Photographed by Arthur D. Code at Bloemfontein, South Africa, with a Henyey-Greenstein wide-angle camera)

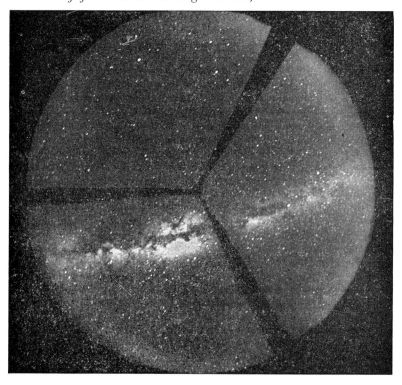

If the telescope is turned at right angles to the Milky Way and a series of photographs are again taken with longer and longer time exposures, stars are seen to become progressively less numerous at approximately equal distances on either side, and eventually no additional stars belonging to our galaxy are encountered. According to these data, our galaxy is a flattened structure (Fig. 21-12). Within this flattened structure, stars seem to be more numerous in certain areas than in others. Figs. 15-4 and 21-14 suggest that the Milky Way galaxy may form a sort of enormous pinwheel with arms spiraling outward from the center. The galactic center seems to be located in the direction of

Schematic diagram of our galaxy based upon data available at present. Most of the billions of stars in the galaxy are probably grouped along its central plane, although some outlying stars are scattered around the main structure. Dark obscuring matter is shown concentrated along the central plane (Milky Way). Globular clusters form a sort of spherical halo around the galaxy. No attempt has been made to show spiral arms in section.

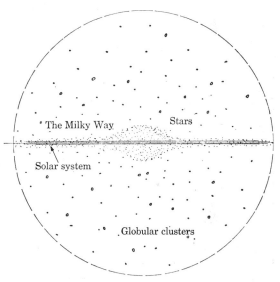

Fig. 21-12.

Sagittarius; Auriga is situated in the opposite direction. Our galaxy is currently estimated to have a diameter of the order of 100,000 light-years and a maximum thickness at the center of about one-tenth this figure. No one has seen through the center to the other side because concentrations of gas and dust—like a cosmic smog—along the Milky Way obscure vision; however, such a symmetrical shape appears logical. Recent peepholes discovered in the vicinity of Sagittarius have permitted observations into the central portion of the galaxy for the first time. The solar system appears to be located in the central plane of the galaxy in one of the spiral arms, perhaps 25,000 to 30,000 light-years outward from the center. Radio telescopes may be able to penetrate through the nucleus to the other side of our galaxy.

Theoretically, the Milky Way galaxy should be spinning on an axis, otherwise the mutual gravitational attraction of its members should cause it to collapse. Evidence indicates that this is the case. Astronomers have calculated that about 200 million years are required for one complete rotation at the distance of the solar system from the center.

Fig. 21-13.

Globular cluster M 13 in Hercules (Photograph from the Mount Wilson and Palomar Observatories)

Objects nearer the center probably complete their swings in shorter periods of time.

A *globular cluster* is a compact spherical aggregate of tens of thousands of stars that resembles somewhat a swarm of bees in shape and movement (Fig. 21-13). About 100 globular clusters have been discovered in space around the outer boundaries of our galaxy (Fig. 21-12). Globular clusters are likewise known to be associated with other galaxies. The stars within a globular cluster are probably less than 1 light-year from their neighbors, but collisions are probably rare.

The Andromeda nebula (Fig. 21-14) is perhaps the most famous

Fig. 21-14.

Great spiral galaxy in Andromeda, Messier 31. Two elliptical galaxies can be seen in the photograph: one is directly above the nucleus; the other is to the left of the nucleus. (Photographed with the 48-inch Schmidt Telescope, Palomar Observatory)

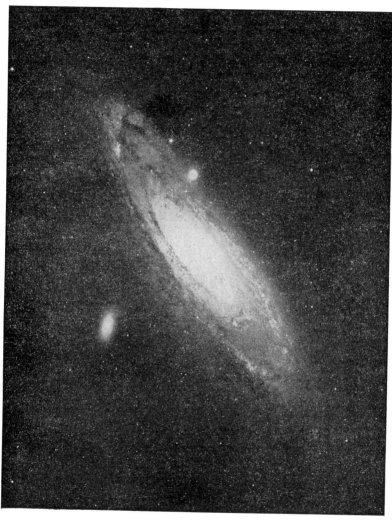

galaxy other than our own. It is visible to the unaided eye on a clear dark night as a faint patch of light located in the direction of the constellation Andromeda (Fig. 15-6). If all the galaxy were visible to the unaided eye, it would cover about 4 degrees of space. To observe it, we must look through the stars which are part of our galaxy far into space—perhaps 2 million light-years away. It is the most remote object visible to the unaided eye. In it astronomers have been able to discover individual stars, cepheid variables, globular clusters, novae, various spectral types of stars, and obscuring matter—in other words, it seems to be a galaxy similar to our own.

Studies of our galaxy and of others indicate that the distribution and abundance of stars of certain types vary within a galaxy. Accordingly, two broad groupings have been recognized: Population I and Population II. Stars of Population I characteristically occur in the spiral arms of galaxies and in regions where dust clouds are abundant. The sun belongs to this group (Fig. 21-7). The brightest stars of Population I are the blue supergiants. Cepheids (p. 352) of this group are four or more times as bright as those in Population II. (This discovery was responsible for a recent revision in the scale of distances in the universe.) The stars of Population II are located in regions of space where interstellar gas and dust are absent: in the central portions of galaxies, in the area surrounding the main parts of the galaxies, and in globular clusters. Red supergiants are the brightest stars of Population II.

The Population I group of stars apparently includes most types of stars, whereas the Population II group lacks some of the types present in the Population I group, such as the blue supergiants. In other words, the majority of the stars in the two groups are similar and the Population II group is notable chiefly for the types of stars which are missing. The blue supergiants of Population I evidently have relatively brief absolute ages and evolutionary cycles; they can be found only in regions of space which have enough gas and dust so that new stars can form. Dark concentrated areas noted by astronomers in some dust clouds may be the beginning stages in the formation of stars. All of the stars in a Population II group apparently formed at the same time in the past; and no new stars can form, since the necessary gas and dust material is absent.

Additional populations, transitional between Population I and Population II, have been recognized recently by some astronomers.

Astronomers estimate that millions of galaxies exist in the universe (Fig. 21-15). They are thought to be comparable in size to our galaxy, and separated from each other by average distances which may exceed their diameters by a few tens of times. Photographs show that galaxies have different shapes (Fig. 21-16). A few are irregular in structure, but most have a bright nucleus and a regular symmetrical form which indicates rotation. Regular galaxies vary in shape from spherical or ellipsoidal to flattened disks. Some of the disks have great arms which extend outward from the nucleus like the arms of a huge pinwheel.

Fig. 21-15.

Part of a cluster of galaxies in Coma Berenices. A sceptic may wonder how many specks of dust on a film have been counted as remote galaxies. Resurveys of certain areas with newer and larger telescopes have shown that perhaps 3 to 4 percent of the galaxies counted on earlier photographs have actually been dust specks. However, enough new galaxies were discovered through the more powerful telescopes to replace the dust-speck galaxies erroneously counted in such regions. (Photographed with the 200-inch Hale Telescope, Palomar Observatory)

These are called spirals. Knowledge of the different shapes has given rise to the speculation that galaxies too may evolve, starting as slowly spinning globular masses, then shrinking, spinning more rapidly, and flattening. Eventually material would be pushed from the nucleus into spiral arms, which would increase in size until the nucleus disappeared altogether and an irregular nebula resulted. Some astronomers hypothesize that this evolution takes place in the reverse order.

If a man were to walk through a forest during an afternoon, he could observe trees in different stages of their life cycles: seeds, tiny saplings, young trees, big trees, dead trees, and partly decayed logs. The observer could not watch a tree evolving through its cycle during that afternoon, but he might be astute enough to deduce such a cycle from his observations of different trees in different stages of their life cycles. So it may be with astronomers and galaxies and stars.

Fig. 21-16.

Galaxies have elliptical, spiral, and irregular shapes. Messier 51 in Canes Venatici is shown here. Spiral galaxies are shown in Figs. 21-16A through D. Figs. 21-16E and F are of elliptical galaxies; and Fig. 21-16G is an irregular galaxy. (All of the photographs are reproduced through the courtesy of the Mount Wilson and Palomar Observatories except 21-16G, which was photographed at the Union Observatory, Johannesburg, South Africa)

The recent discovery that the gas and dust from which stars form is apparently nearly exhausted in the spiral galaxies as well as the ellipsoidal ones has profound implications concerning the future evolutionary development of these galaxies. Star formation must be nearing its end in the spiral galaxies; it probably ended billions of years ago in the ellipsoidal galaxies which are practically free of gas and dust. Thus the brightness of galaxies will probably decrease with time since new stars cannot form to replace the "burned-out" stars after the gas and dust is exhausted. Since this dimming of galactic light is an exceedingly slow process, it should continue for billions of years.

THE EXPANDING UNIVERSE

Intriguing data have been obtained by spectroscopic examination of the light received from galaxies located in various parts of the universe. The dark lines in the spectra of most galaxies show a shift toward the red end of the spectrum. Furthermore, the amount of the red shift is roughly proportional to the distance of the galaxy from the Earth: a "near" galaxy shows a small red shift, a moderately distant galaxy has a medium red shift, and a remote galaxy shows a large red shift. One interpretation of this red shift is that each galaxy may actually be moving away from the Earth, and that the magnitude of the shift is directly proportional to the rate of recession. In other words, the red

Fig. 21-16A.

NGC 4594 in Virgo

shift is considered a Doppler effect (Fig. 20-10) which indicates moving apart; a large shift is thought to show a very rapid rate of movement— thousands of miles per second.

Assuming that this interpretation is correct and that the galaxies have continued to move at their present rates, astronomers calculate that all of the galaxies may have begun to move away from the same general location in space some 5 to 6 billion years ago.* A number of different types of evidence from the fields of geology and astronomy suggest very tentatively an age for the universe of 5 to 6 billion years. In combination they seem to point to some unique event or cataclysm which may have occurred at that time in the past. Some astronomers refer to this as the "big bang" hypothesis.

* Some astronomers suggest a revision to 10 billion ± 3 to 4 billion years.

According to this concept, the material from which the galaxies later developed probably began to move outward at the same time but in different directions and at different rates. Since objects in space should continue to move at uniform velocities in straight lines in the absence of other forces, galaxies with slow velocities have traveled shorter distances than those with rapid velocities. Since galaxies seem to be distributed in space in clusters, the expansion is probably between

Fig. 21-16B.

Messier 33 in Triangulum

clusters; the distances separating galaxies within a cluster are probably not increasing.

According to one astronomer, a "big squeeze" may have preceded the "big bang." The mutual gravitational attraction of material in space caused it to contract and collapse into a relatively small region of space. The speculative nature of such ideas should be obvious.

Although, according to this interpretation, most galaxies are moving away from us, the position of our galaxy may not be unique. If a balloon (universe) covered by uniformly spaced dots (galaxies) were inflated, not only would each dot move away from its neighbors, but from any one dot all other dots would appear to be receding. Similarly all galaxies may be moving away from each other.*

ORIGIN OF THE SOLAR SYSTEM AND THE UNIVERSE

The problem of origins is a stimulating one but also frustrating, since no definite answers seem possible. Many hypotheses have been suggested for the origin of the solar system, but none is entirely satisfactory. Nearly all hypotheses conclude that the regularity and uni-

Fig. 21-16C.

Barred spiral NGC 1300 in Eridanus

formity exhibited by planetary motions indicate that the planets originated at more or less the same time and in the same general manner. All hypotheses involve the rearrangement of matter and energy previously in existence, and in many hypotheses the material of the planets was once part of the sun, of material which subsequently formed the sun, or of a companion star of the sun.

The nebula hypothesis of Kant and Laplace was considered by many

* According to the competing, steady-state universe hypothesis, the universe had no beginning, will have no end, and is uniform in time and space. As expansion occurs, new matter (hydrogen) is created to maintain a uniform density. New stars and galaxies form and evolve from this new matter and replace those that have expanded outward. Thus individual stars and galaxies change, but the over-all nature of the universe remains uniform.

Fig. 21-16D.

Andromeda, showing individual stars

during the nineteenth century to be a satisfactory explanation of the origin of the solar system. According to this hypothesis, the solar system was once a great cloud of hot, gaseous, and slowly rotating material; as it cooled it shrank and spun more and more rapidly until the equatorial bulge became so large that it became detached and formed a ring. The process was repeated, and a new ring was formed for each planet (Fig. 21-17). These rings, in turn, became globular gaseous

Fig. 21-16E.

NGC 4278

Fig. 21-16F.

NGC 3115 in Sextans

Fig. 21-16G

Large Magellanic cloud

masses which cooled, shrank, and threw off more rings to form the satellites. Thus the planets were first gaseous, then liquid, and finally solid. A number of serious objections have since been raised to this hypothesis: if it were correct, then the sun should be spinning rapidly and preparing to cast off another ring, and all satellites should be revolving in the same west-to-east direction.

The nebular hypothesis of Laplace. The gaseous rings later contracted into planets. (Courtesy, Scientific American)

Fig. 21-17.

During the present century a number of hypotheses have been presented which attempt to explain the origin of the planets by the ejection of material from the sun or from a companion star of the sun. The tide-producing effect of a passing star is important in some of these hypotheses. However, all encounter one serious difficulty: material ejected from the interior of the sun should be so hot that it would disperse explosively into space. Some of the most recent hypotheses are variations of the original Kant-Laplace idea.

CONCLUSIONS AND CAUTIONS

One is quite likely to complete a study of astronomy with mixed emotions. On the one hand we cannot but be amazed at man's ingenuity in attaining the knowledge that has been accumulated about the universe. On the other hand, the tiny inconspicuous role which has been assigned to the Earth, and the fundamental unanswered questions of the origin of the universe, its nature, and its ultimate destiny, cannot but fill us with humility, wonder, and awe.

The dynamic and hypothetical nature of many astronomical concepts should be kept conspicuously in mind at all times. In all the sciences and in all periods there have been ardent advocates of concepts which later had to be abandoned as new information became available. Astronomical data, concerned as they are with the structure, composition, life cycle, and motions of celestial objects so remote that their distances must be measured in hundreds, thousands, and even millions of light-years, must necessarily remain tenuous and subject to constant check and revision. Hypotheses and theories in science lay down directions for research and thus serve a useful function even when they have to be entirely abandoned soon after they are propounded. But the hypothetical nature of some of these concepts should be given much greater emphasis than it often is in textbooks and in scientific periodicals. The fact that the amount of matter calculated to exist in the universe was recently revised upwards to ten times the previously estimated amount, and that the calculated size of the universe was recently revised upwards to more than double its previously estimated size, should help us to recognize the hypothetical nature of many new theories and to accept them with caution. Although a number of astronomers now consider the concept of an expanding universe as rather well established, this theory has not been proved and other interpretations of existing data may be possible.

The current dynamic nature of astronomy, particularly of its astrophysical aspects, was strikingly pointed out by Dr. Gamow in reviewing a recent book. He pointed out that the book was outmoded before publication. Very rapid changes in the field of astrophysics had made it obsolete during the short interval between the time it was written and the time it was published.

EXERCISES AND QUESTIONS FOR CHAPTER 21

1. Give two different types of evidence that the sun is (1) moving toward Vega (Hercules) in space and (2) rotating on an axis.

2. Give at least two different reasons why one star may be brighter than another in the sky.

3. What is a probable account of how stars produce energy?

4. Why are stars thought to pass through an evolutionary sequence?

5. Give two different types of evidence which aid astronomers in determining the shape of our galaxy.

6. What evidence supports the "big bang" hypothesis?

7. Refer to Chapter 17 and the discussion of the recent revisions which have been made in the scale of sizes and distances in the universe. What effect did each change in distance have on the estimated age of the universe according to the "big bang" hypothesis?

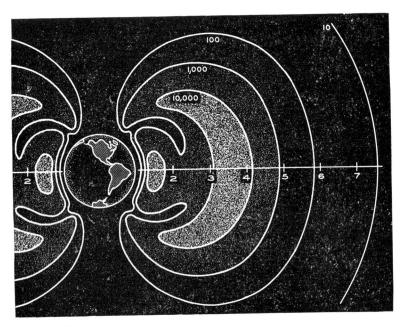

Fig. 21-18.

The Van Allen Radiation Belt. Distances are given in earth-radii. Radiation intensities, represented by the contours, are in Geiger counts per second. This diagram appeared in Sky *and* Telescope *for June, 1959.*

CHAPTER 22

Weather: Air, Heat, and Water

BENJAMIN FRANKLIN once said, "Some people are weatherwise, but most are otherwise." There is much talk about the weather, and much adaptation to changes in it; yet to many of us weather changes continue to seem highly mysterious. Chapters 22 and 23 attempt to remove as many readers as possible from the "otherwise" category. Weather affects man's daily life so intimately that a functional grasp of its concepts would be welcome to us all. Fortunately, although explanations for local, specific weather phenomena may often be complex, a general understanding of the weather and an appreciation of the limitations of weather forecasting are well within the range of most of us.

What is the significance of the daily weather map, with its lows, highs, fronts, and air masses? Will a raincoat be needed today? Will tomorrow be suitable for sailing? Is a frost likely tonight? Is rain-making successful? Why do crisp clear days alternate with warmer, cloudy, drizzling ones? Are people limited merely to discussion of the weather or can they actually influence and partially control it? Answers to some of these questions will be attempted in the following pages.

Rain, snow, hurricane, tornado, gale, frost, dew, hail, clouds, fog, wind, and sunshine are all manifestations of the weather. An understanding of them depends upon a knowledge of air, heat, and water as they function on a rotating, revolving, sun-warmed Earth. Let us consider first the air.

THE ATMOSPHERE

The atmosphere is the sea of air which surrounds the Earth; it extends in appreciable quantities for several hundred miles above the surface, probably 700 miles and more, but a distinct outer boundary

The Earth and atmosphere, drawn approximately to scale. The chemical composition of pure dry air is indicated above, but in nature air normally contains other substances such as water vapor, dust, and carbon dioxide. The Earth's atmosphere lacks a distinct outer boundary. Some molecules occur thousands of miles above the surface. Recent discoveries suggest that an exceedingly dilute gas may exist in the space between the Earth and the sun. If this is correct, the outer part of the sun's corona may actually envelope the Earth. During the recent International Geophysical Year, the two Van Allen high-energy radiation belts which ring the Earth were discovered unexpectedly and are known to extend outward some 20,000 to 30,000 miles from the Earth's surface.

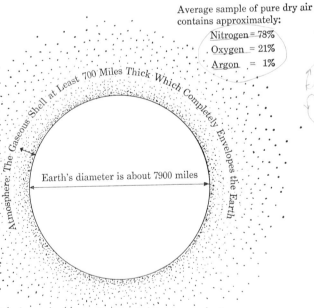

Average sample of pure dry air contains approximately:

Nitrogen = 78%
Oxygen = 21%
Argon = 1%

Atmosphere: The Gaseous Shell at Least 700 Miles Thick Which Completely Envelopes the Earth

Earth's diameter is about 7900 miles

Fig. 22-1.

is lacking. This gaseous envelope is held to the Earth by gravitational attraction. In it man lives and breathes. Because of it rain falls, vegetation grows, and rocks decay. The importance of the atmosphere to man cannot be exaggerated.

Nitrogen and oxygen make up most of the atmosphere's gaseous mixture; nitrogen is nearly four times as abundant as oxygen in dry air (Fig. 22-1). This proportion seems to extend with little variation throughout the first 100 miles or more of the atmosphere. Water vapor (up to 4 or 5 percent), carbon dioxide, and dust particles are present in small, varying, but important amounts.

Atmospheric pressure is simply the weight of the mass of air, several hundred miles thick, which presses down on the Earth's surface. The atmosphere is densest at the Earth's surface and thins out rapidly upward; atmospheric pressure is small at high altitudes. Estimates indicate that about one-half of the total mass of the atmosphere is present in the first $3\frac{1}{2}$ miles above the Earth's surface; approximately 97 percent of the entire mass is found within 18 miles. Man is not crushed by the atmosphere because the pressure inside his body is equal to the pressure outside. Atmospheric pressure at sea level is nearly 15 lbs/sq in,

Fig. 22-2.

Atmospheric pressure. The pressure is reduced by about one-half for each $3\frac{1}{2}$ mile increase in altitude. For example, the first $3\frac{1}{2}$ miles of the atmosphere exerts a pressure of $7\frac{1}{2}$ lb/sq in. The pressure of the rest of the atmosphere (perhaps 20,000 miles thick) also approximates $7\frac{1}{2}$ lb/sq in.

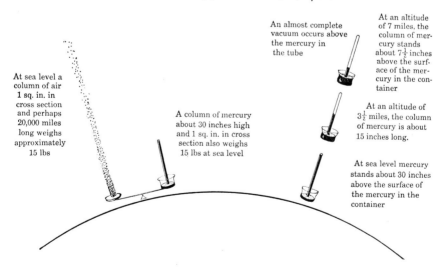

At sea level a column of air 1 sq. in. in cross section and perhaps 20,000 miles long weighs approximately 15 lbs

A column of mercury about 30 inches high and 1 sq. in. in cross section also weighs 15 lbs at sea level

An almost complete vacuum occurs above the mercury in the tube

At an altitude of 7 miles, the column of mercury stands about $7\frac{1}{2}$ inches above the surface of the mercury in the container

At an altitude of $3\frac{1}{2}$ miles, the column of mercury is about 15 inches long.

At sea level mercury stands about 30 inches above the surface of the mercury in the container

or more than 1 ton/sq ft. In a barometer (p. 97) at sea level, the pressure of the atmosphere is sufficient to support a column of mercury 29.92 inches (76 cm) in height (Fig. 22-2). The barometer is the most important weather instrument. It functions as well inside of a building as outside.

Barometric pressure is commonly shown on weather maps in millibars. A millibar is 1/1000 of a bar, which is defined as a pressure of 1 million dynes/sq cm. A sea level barometric reading of 29.92 in. of mercury equals 1013.2 millibars.

Layers of the Atmosphere   Nearly all weather phenomena—storms, clouds, convectional circulation, and the like—are confined to the layer which rests upon the Earth's surface and is called the *troposphere*. The troposphere (Fig. 22-3) is thickest at the equator (about 11 or 12 miles) and thinnest at the poles (4 to 5 miles). The greater thickness at the equator is probably a result of turbulence produced by intense solar heating. Temperatures decrease upward in the troposphere. Lower temperatures occur at the top of the troposphere above the equator ($-120°F$) than above the poles ($-75°F$). Winds tend to increase in velocity upward in the troposphere.

The *stratosphere* extends from the top of the troposphere (the *tropopause*) to an altitude of about 20 miles, although an upper boundary at 50 to 60 miles has been suggested by some meteorologists. Horizontal movements of air predominate in the stratosphere, and the skies are nearly devoid of dust, clouds, and water vapor. Temperatures vary little in the lower part of the stratosphere, but increase upward. Flying in the stratosphere is possible over the polar regions where the troposphere is thinnest, but more difficult at lower latitudes.

At present, meteorologists do not agree concerning terminology for the divisions of the atmosphere above the troposphere. However, some facts are known. A warm layer occurs at altitudes of about 25 to 40 miles, and maximum temperatures in this zone exceed those near the Earth's surface. The high temperatures may be caused by the selective absorption of ultraviolet radiation by ozone.

There is a so-called *ozone layer* in the stratosphere. Ozone, the three-atom molecule of oxygen, occurs in greatest abundance at altitudes below 20 miles. However, ozone is produced and destroyed at the greatest rate in the warm layer above the stratosphere. Though it con-

Fig. 22-3.

Structure of the atmosphere. (*After Cecilia Payne-Gaposchkin, Introduction to Astronomy,* Prentice-Hall, 1954)

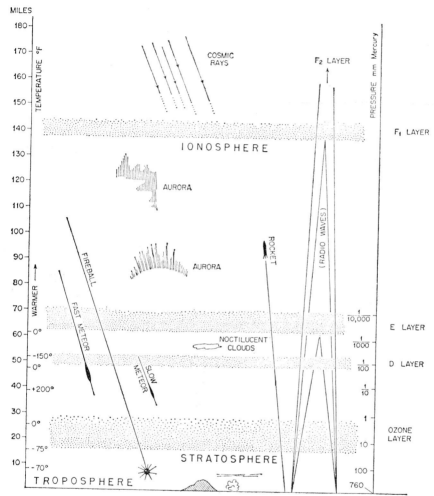

stitutes only a small proportion of the gases present, if the ozone layer were missing, our skins would be burned and our eyes would be blinded by the ultraviolet waves it now absorbs.

The next principal layer of the atmosphere, the *ionosphere*, lies above the warm layer and begins at altitudes of 50 miles or so where the effects of the ionization (p. 257) of gases in the atmosphere can be observed. Several ionization layers exist in the ionosphere and are important to man because they reflect certain radio waves back to the Earth's surface and make long-distance radio reception possible.

Heating of the Atmosphere   The temperature of an object is related directly to the rate of movement or vibration of the atoms and molecules which compose it (p. 103). An increase in the rate of movement raises the temperature, a decrease lowers it. For example, the temperature of hot water is higher than that of cold water because its water molecules are moving more rapidly. In the language of molecules, one desires a drink of slowly moving water molecules on a hot day and longs for rapidly moving air molecules during cold winter months. A person feels warm on a hot day partly because air molecules are bounding against his body with greater force than on a cold day.

The Earth's atmosphere is heated somewhat indirectly by energy which comes from the sun, largely in the form of short electromagnetic waves such as visible light. At the Earth's surface the short waves are absorbed and later reradiated as longer electromagnetic waves (Fig. 22-4). These longer waves can be absorbed by certain molecules in the atmosphere—chiefly carbon dioxide and water vapor. Absorption of the waves causes these molecules to move faster; in turn they bump

Fig. 22-4.

Heating of the Earth's atmosphere. Solar energy passing through the air is reflected and absorbed so that less than half reaches the ground surface. Percentages vary considerably from place to place and from day to day.

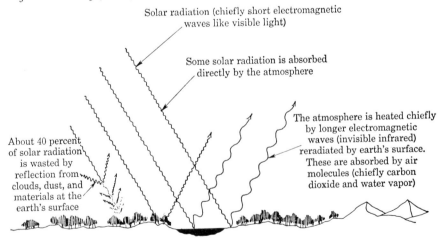

Solar radiation (chiefly short electromagnetic waves like visible light)

Some solar radiation is absorbed directly by the atmosphere

The atmosphere is heated chiefly by longer electromagnetic waves (invisible infrared) reradiated by earth's surface. These are absorbed by air molecules (chiefly carbon dioxide and water vapor)

About 40 percent of solar radiation is wasted by reflection from clouds, dust, and materials at the earth's surface

into nitrogen and oxygen molecules and gradually raise the temperature of the entire atmosphere. Heat may be transferred by conduction, convection, and radiation (Fig. 22-5).

Fig. 22-5.

Heat is transferred by conduction, convection, and radiation.

The "greenhouse effect" may be explained in a similar manner (Fig. 22-6). Short waves of sunlight can penetrate the glass windows enclosing a greenhouse. Materials inside the greenhouse absorb the light waves and reradiate longer electromagnetic waves which cannot penetrate the glass. These are trapped inside and increase the temperature. This phenomenon is familiar to anyone who has entered a car which has been parked for some time in sunshine with its windows closed.

A number of weather phenomena can now be explained readily. Temperatures commonly are lower at increased altitudes because distance from the heat source (Earth's surface) is greater; in addition, fewer molecules are present in the rarefied upper atmosphere to absorb the radiations. The average decrease in temperature at increasing altitudes (the lapse rate) is about $3\frac{1}{2}°F$ per 1000 feet. Extreme temperature changes from hot days to cold nights are common in desert areas

View of a functional house with large windows facing south. As the sun is high in the sky at noon during the summer, its rays cannot enter the house. However, during the winter when the sun is low in the sky at noon, its rays can strike the far wall of the house and aid considerably in heating it. The difference in altitude of the noon sun at the latitude of New York is 47 degrees; 73½ degrees above the horizon on June 22 and 26½ degrees above the horizon on December 22.—If deciduous trees are planted to the south and west, they will provide desired shade in the summer and block little sunlight in the winter.

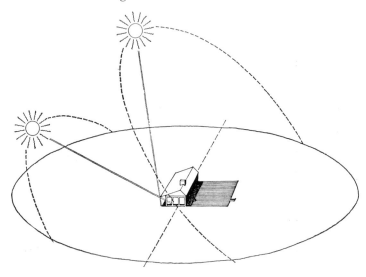

Fig. 22-6.

because little water vapor is present in the atmosphere to make the air an efficient blanket for trapping the Earth's heat (Fig. 22-7). Frosts are more likely on clear nights than on cloudy ones for a similar reason. The ground steadily loses heat by radiation until it reaches a lower temperature than the air immediately above it. Subsequently this bottom air loses heat to the ground and becomes cooler and heavier than the air above it. Therefore, on a clear calm night a thin layer of cold air may accumulate in contact with the ground and beneath warmer air above it. This cool heavy air may drain down slopes and collect in depressions and produce frosts. For this reason citrus orchards in California and coffee plantations in Brazil are located on sloping land rather than in depressions, where frosts are more common.

Temperature Variations. During the night in the absence of solar radiation, the ground continuously loses heat by reradiation, and the coolest part of the day normally occurs around sunrise. On the other hand, energy received from the sun is at a maximum at noon when the rays of sunlight are most direct. But radiations from the sun continue to add more energy than is reradiated into space for approximately three hours after the noon maximum. The warmest part of the day normally occurs at about 3:00 P.M. for a land area.

Fig. 22-7.

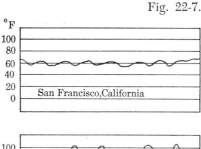

One-week temperature records. The moderating effect of the ocean makes temperature fluctuation at San Francisco small. The daily variation in the Arizona desert is striking. (Modified from U.S. Department of Agriculture.)

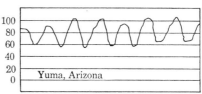

For similar reasons the coolest month of the year for a land area normally is January in the Northern Hemisphere and the warmest month is July. Over the oceans the moderating effects of the water shift the coolest and warmest months to February and August. The greatest known temperature variation during the year is experienced in the huge land mass of northern Siberia. The least temperature range during the year occurs over the oceans. A record high temperature of 136°F (not in direct sunlight) was recorded in the Sahara in September 1922. Record low temperatures occur in Antarctica (below −100°F). Temperatures sometimes differ considerably at locations that are not far apart. One record showed a variation of 28°F within a distance of 225 feet on a steep hillside.

Water in the Air   The presence and amount of water vapor in the air is of tremendous importance to man. It affects the temperature by absorbing waves radiated from the Earth, and it determines the quantity of precipitation. However, the total amount of water in the gaseous, liquid, or solid state in the atmosphere at any one time is surprisingly small. If all of it were to be precipitated as rain onto the surface of the Earth at one time, the average accumulation would approximate 1 inch. Therefore, for large amounts of rain to fall, the air over an area must be replaced many times. The amount of water vapor in the air influences the physical comfort of man and furnishes latent energy for the development of storms and the circulation of the atmosphere.

Water has a number of remarkable properties. It reaches its greatest density at 4°C and expands upon freezing. Therefore, lakes freeze from the top rather than from the bottom as they would if ice did not float. The amount of heat energy involved in changing the temperature of water (specific heat) is very high relative to other substances. Likewise the heat of fusion and the latent heat of vaporization are also very high. To change 1 gram of water at 100°C into 1 gram of water vapor at 100°C requires 540 calories. (One calorie approximately equals the amount of heat energy needed to raise the temperature of 1 gram of water 1 centigrade degree.) When water vapor returns to a liquid state, 540 calories of heat energy are released per gram. When considerable quantities of water vapor condense, enormous quantities of energy are released.

Temperature has an important effect on the amount of water vapor which is present in the atmosphere. A rise in temperature increases the capacity of air to take up water vapor; in other words, warm air can hold more moisture than cool air. This becomes understandable if one recalls that air expands when heated, and its molecules become separated more widely. Additional space is thus available among the air molecules for water vapor particles. A drop in the temperature of the air causes the air molecules to crowd together and leaves less space for water vapor particles; condensation occurs if water vapor and suitable nuclei are present, and the air is chilled sufficiently.

To illustrate that warm air can hold more moisture than cool air, a simple experiment may be performed with a dry glass container. Water vapor can be added to the air in this container by breathing into it enough times to cause condensation; a film of water vapor forms on the glass sides. The container should then be covered quickly. If the air in the covered container is later warmed, perhaps by setting it in the sun for a time, the film of water vapor disappears. However, the film reappears if the air in the container is then chilled.

Condensation cannot begin until the air has become saturated with water vapor. The critical temperature at which saturation occurs is called the _dew point_ and depends upon the amount of water vapor in the air. If much water vapor is present, the dew point is high. Condensation from the gas to the liquid occurs if the temperature is above 32°F, whereas sublimation (direct change from water vapor to ice) may occur if the temperature is below 32°F. However, supercooled clouds in which water droplets exist at temperatures below freezing are common.

Condensation may be accomplished by chilling the air, thus decreasing the amount of water vapor which can be held, or by increasing the quantity of water vapor in the air. In molecular terms, condensation may be pictured as a grouping of water vapor molecules around suitable nuclei into clusters which are large enough to be visible. Cooling causes a decrease in molecular motion; thus molecules cohere more readily to each other and adhere to some nucleus upon collision. If many water vapor molecules are present in a certain amount of air, chances are opportune for numerous collisions and for the development of clusters. On the other hand, a rise in temperature increases the rate of molecular movement and tends to disrupt visible clusters of water vapor molecules into invisible individual particles. Tiny invisible salt crystals and particles from the combustion of coal, oil, and gas seem to form the most satisfactory nuclei which occur in nature.

According to these principles, ready explanations are available for such commonplace phenomena as the fogging of the bathroom mirror when one takes a shower, seeing one's breath on a cool morning, jet trails, the presence of tiny water droplets on the outside of a cool glass of liquid on a hot humid day, and the "sweating" of pipes in the summer. Fog, dew, clouds, rain, hail, sleet, and glaze result from condensation; that is, from the clustering of water vapor molecules into visible droplets, commonly because air has been chilled. _Precipitation_ is the general term for moisture which has condensed from the air and fallen through it as rain, snow, hail, or sleet.

Dew, Frost, Fog, and Smog If air is cooled below the dew point by contact with a cold surface, water vapor will condense as dew directly upon that surface—rock, grass, tractor, or building. If the temperature is below 32°F, delicate feathery white frost crystals form by sublimation. If the temperature falls below freezing after dew has formed, the water drops freeze into tiny pellets of ice.

Fog is essentially a cloud which rests upon the Earth's surface. To a man at a low altitude, the peak of a mountain appears covered by clouds; for a mountain climber standing on the same peak, fog blankets the surface. Commonly fogs consist of very small droplets of water (about .001 inch in diameter) which remain suspended in the air, but some fogs consist of tiny ice crystals. Fogs have been classified as radiation, advection (meaning: carried in from elsewhere), evaporation, and upslope.

Radiation fogs may develop along the ground during clear calm evenings when much of the radiation from the Earth's surface is able to escape upward through the atmosphere. (Cloudy air, on the other hand, tends to trap the radiations.) Air in contact with the cool ground is chilled and condensation occurs. Fogs tend to develop over low-lying areas because cool heavy air at night moves down slopes to collect along the bottoms of depressions. In addition, air tends to obtain water vapor by evaporation more readily from low-lying areas. The next morning the sun shines on the fog, warms the air, and the fog disappears.

Advection fogs form over the oceans if air blows from a warm current over a cool current. A familiar example is furnished by the Grand Banks off Newfoundland, where the cold Labrador Current and warm Gulf Stream meet. Favorable conditions for such fogs also result wherever warm moist air moves across cool or snow-covered ground. A light wind may mix the air sufficiently along the ground for a thick fog to result.

Evaporation fogs occur when cool dry air moves across a water body and sufficient evaporation takes place to saturate the lower layers. Such fogs are also called steam fogs, as they give the appearance of steam rising from the surface of the water. Upslope fogs form wherever air moves along a surface which increases in altitude. Condensation occurs because lower temperatures at higher altitudes cause saturation. Fogs may also be produced if air along the Earth's surface is saturated by rain drops which fall from higher altitudes.

Smog is a combination of fog and smoke and is a nuisance and hazard for man. Tiny particles put into the air by the various activities of a large city furnish innumerable condensation nuclei for the origin of fog. The smog will persist if it prevents the sunlight from reaching and warming the ground and thereby the air above it. Thus cool, heavy, stable, smog-filled air tends to blanket the Earth's surface until moved along by strong winds. Conditions favorable for fogs (cool stable air along the ground) are unfavorable for precipitation (unstable rising air masses).

CLOUDS

Clouds (Fig. 22-8) consist of moisture which has condensed from the air as tiny water droplets or sublimated as small ice crystals. Only slight upward currents are necessary to prevent these from falling. Clouds are of two general types: *stratus* (layered, blanketlike) and *cumulus* (globular, heaped masses). Other terms used in cloud descriptions are *cirrus* (curl), *alto* (high), and *nimbus* (rain cloud). Clouds form when air is forced to rise to higher altitudes and is cooled by expansion (*adiabatic cooling*, Fig. 22-9). As air rises it must push upward or aside the air which it replaces. This requires energy and is obtained at the expense of lowering the molecular activity of the rising air. An average rate of cooling of rising air is about 5.5°F per 1000 feet of upward movement. However, if moisture condenses in the rising air, large quantities of energy from the latent heat of vaporization are released. This latent energy decreases the rate at which cooling occurs to about 3.2°F per 1000 feet and provides energy for continued upward movement.

Upward movements of air have three principal causes in nature:

(1) *Convection*—One area of the Earth's surface may be heated more strongly than adjoining sections. The air above this area becomes warmed and expands. It is then pushed upward by adjoining cooler heavier air. Bare soil or a paved runway surrounded by vegetation or a land area adjoining a water body illustrate suitable conditions. Convection may be on a local or global scale.

(2) *Orographic movement*—Prevailing winds may move air along the Earth's surface and upward over mountain barriers (Fig. 22-10).

(3) Upward movements are associated with low-pressure areas (p. 488).

The standardized classification of clouds with abbreviated definitions which appears below has been reproduced from a weather map published by the U.S. Weather Bureau on January 24, 1946:

In the International System there are ten principal kinds of clouds. Their names, classification and mean heights are shown in the following table. The mean heights are for temperate latitudes and refer not to sea level but to the general level of land in the region. There is nearly always some variation

Fig. 22-8.

Basic clouds at average altitude levels.

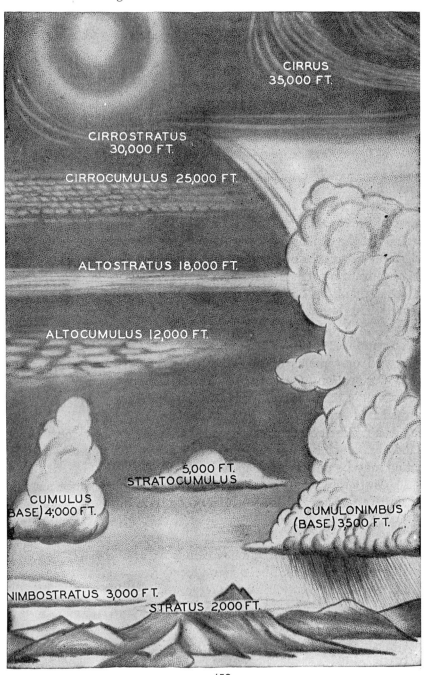

Fig. 22-9.

Effect of increase in altitude on air and water. (After Neuberger and Stephens)

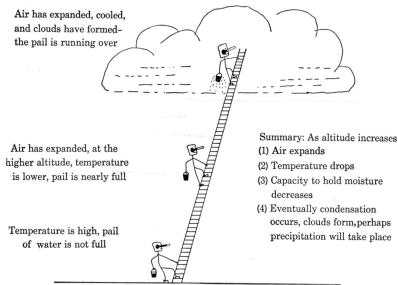

Air has expanded, cooled, and clouds have formed— the pail is running over

Air has expanded, at the higher altitude, temperature is lower, pail is nearly full

Summary: As altitude increases
(1) Air expands
(2) Temperature drops
(3) Capacity to hold moisture decreases
(4) Eventually condensation occurs, clouds form, perhaps precipitation will take place

Temperature is high, pail of water is not full

from the mean height, and in certain cases there may be large departures. Thus, cirrus clouds may sometimes be observed as low as 10,000 feet in temperate regions and at lower levels in higher latitudes.

Family A: HIGH CLOUDS (mean lower level, 20,000 feet)
  1. Cirrus (Fig. 22-11A)

> *More precipitation occurs on the windward side of a mountain than on the leeward side. A rain shadow may occur on the lee side of the mountain. The north-south mass of the Sierra Nevada in California furnishes an excellent illustration. Prevailing moisture-laden westerly winds are forced to climb upwards more than two miles to cross the higher parts of the range. Much precipitation occurs on the western slopes. But as the air descends to lower altitudes to the east, very little precipitation occurs. This is the desert region of eastern California and Nevada.*

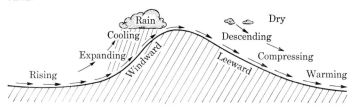

Fig. 22-10.

2. Cirrocumulus (Fig. 22-11B)
3. Cirrostratus (Fig. 22-11C)

Family B: MIDDLE CLOUDS (mean upper level 20,000 feet; mean lower level, 6500 feet)
4. Altocumulus (Fig. 22-11D)
5. Altostratus (Fig. 22-11E)

Family C: LOW CLOUDS (mean upper level 6500 feet; mean lower level, close to surface)
6. Stratocumulus Fig. 22-11F)
7. Stratus (Fig. 22-11G)
8. Nimbostratus (Fig. 22-11H)

Family D: CLOUDS WITH VERTICAL DEVELOPMENT (mean upper level, that of cirrus; mean lower level, 1600 feet)
9. Cumulus (Fig. 22-11I)
10. Cumulonimbus (Fig. 22-11J)

CLOUD DEFINITIONS

Abbreviated *

1. CIRRUS—Detached clouds of delicate and fibrous appearance, usually without shading, generally white in color, often of silky appearance. They are always composed of ice crystals.

2. CIRROCUMULUS—A layer or patch composed of small white flakes or of very small globular masses, which are arranged in groups or lines, or more often in ripples resembling those of the sand on the seashore. (Cirrocumulus clouds are rare. They should be associated with cirrus and cirrostratus clouds and are smaller and higher than altocumulus clouds with which they are commonly confused.)

3. CIRROSTRATUS—A thin whitish veil which does not blur the outlines of the sun or moon, but usually gives rise to halos. (Cirrostratus clouds may give the sky a milky look. They are thicker and lower and form a more uniform sheet than cirrus clouds. If cirrostratus clouds are observed a few hours after cirrus clouds, precipitation will probably occur within the next 24 hours.)

4. ALTOCUMULUS—A layer (or patches) composed of rather flattened globular masses, the smallest elements of the regularly arranged layer being small and thin. These elements are arranged in groups, in lines, or waves, following one or two directions and are sometimes so close together that their edges join. (Altocumulus clouds may or may not show shadows and are commonly associated with fair weather. They grade toward altostratus clouds when they are packed closely and toward cumulus clouds when they

* Material in parentheses has been added by the authors.

Fig. 22-11A.

Cirrus. (*H. T. Floreen*)

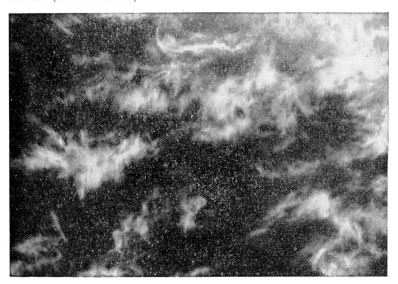

Cirrocumulus. Cirrostratus in lower right. (*H. T. Floreen*)

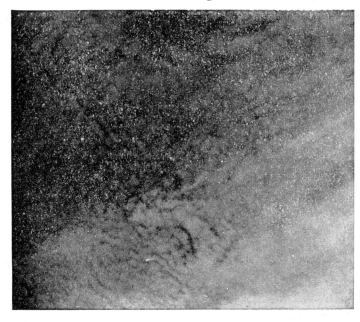

Fig. 22-11B.

Cirrostratus showing a halo. (G. A. Clarke)

Fig. 22-11C.

Altocumulus. (C. F. Brooks)

Fig. 22-11D

Altostratus (above). (U.S. Weather Bureau)

Fig. 22-11E.

Fig. 22-11F.

Stratocumulus. (W. J. Humphreys)

Stratus. (C. A. Clarke)

Fig. 22-11G.

Nimbostratus, above, with roll of cumulus. (J. C. Hagen)

Fig. 22-11H.

Cumulus. (*H. T. Floreen*)

Fig. 22-11I.

Cumulonimbus with rain shower at base. (*U.S. Navy*)

Fig. 22-11J.

show vertical development. Altocumulus clouds may form a dense layer showing definite relief on its lower surface.)

5. ALTOSTRATUS—Striated or fibrous veil, more or less gray or bluish in color. This cloud is like thick cirrostratus, but without halo phenomena; the sun or moon shows vaguely, with a faint gleam as though through ground glass. (If altostratus clouds are observed soon after cirrus and cirrostratus clouds, precipitation is probable within the next 12 hours. Altostratus clouds commonly form by a lowering of cirrostratus clouds; they hide the sun and the moon only in their darker portions. Nimbostratus clouds are darker than altostratus clouds and hide the sun and moon in all parts.)

6. STRATOCUMULUS—A layer (or patches) composed of globular masses or rolls; the smallest of the elements are fairly large; they are soft and gray with darker parts. The elements are arranged in groups, in lines, or in waves, aligned in one or two directions. Often the rolls are so close that their edges join. (Stratocumulus clouds may cover the entire sky and are most common in winter. They may form from stratus clouds by increased convectional circulation or vice versa.)

7. STRATUS—A low uniform layer of cloud resembling fog but not resting on the ground.

8. NIMBOSTRATUS—A low, formless, and rainy layer, of a dark color, usually nearly uniform; when it gives precipitation it is in the form of continuous rain or snow.

9. CUMULUS—Dense clouds with vertical development; the upper surface is dome shaped and exhibits rounded protuberances, while the base is nearly horizontal.

10. CUMULONIMBUS—Heavy masses of cloud with great vertical development, whose cumuliform summits rise in the form of mountains or towers, the upper parts having a fibrous texture and often spreading out in the shape of an anvil.

In attempting to identify clouds, one should remember that all types of gradations occur, that more than one kind of cloud may be in the sky at one time, and that clouds tend to form and disappear rapidly. Identification may also be difficult unless one has been observing the development of the clouds and is aware of the physical conditions involved in their formation.

Clouds may disperse for several reasons: precipitation may remove surplus water; the clouds may be warmed by radiations from the sun or Earth which decrease the relative humidity; surrounding drier air may mix with the clouds, especially near the margins; if downward air currents develop, the air will be warmed by compression.

Clouds are important as weather indicators and show air movements. A cloud will appear white to a distant observer if it reflects all of the sunlight falling on it. However, the same cloud will be gray or black to an observer beneath it from whom the sunlight is largely or entirely obscured.

RAIN, SLEET, GLAZE

Meteorologists are somewhat uncertain concerning the origin of *raindrops*. Probably they form in different ways under different conditions. Tiny water droplets or snow and ice crystals in clouds must grow large enough that they cannot be kept suspended by upward-moving air currents. How do thousands or millions of tiny cloud droplets coalesce into a raindrop in a short time? According to one hypothesis, some raindrops were once ice crystals which acted as condensation nuclei for the accumulation of water vapor molecules. These melted as they fell to lower warmer altitudes. However, this cannot explain rains which occur in the tropics from clouds which have temperatures above the freezing point. According to another hypothesis, small droplets tend to collide and coalesce as they fall; larger droplets would be most effective in collecting smaller ones. If strong updrafts are present as in cumulus clouds, coalescence may occur in a different manner. After a few raindrops form in the cloud, they remain suspended or fall slowly, and the tiny cloud droplets stream upward past them. Collisions and coalescence follow. When a raindrop reaches a certain size, it subdivides into two smaller drops, which in their turn grow larger and subdivide again. This type of chain reaction may produce many raindrops in a short time. Evaporation on the way down may prevent some rain or snow from reaching the Earth's surface.

Sleet is frozen rain. It forms when raindrops fall through colder layers of air closer to the Earth's surface and change to ice beads. These bounce when they hit the ground and may form a white layer. *Glaze* is an ice coating, not a type of precipitation, which forms when raindrops hit colder objects near the Earth's surface and freeze into clear ice. Occasionally ice storms (Fig. 22-12) cause considerable damage.

Some of the heaviest observed amounts of rainfall reported by the U.S. Weather Bureau follow: 12 inches at Holt, Missouri, on June 22, 1947; 62.4 inches at Baguio, Philippine Islands, on July 14-16, 1911; 102 inches at Cherrapunji, India, in four days in June 1876; and 884 inches at Cherrapunji during six months in 1861, April to September.

Fig. 22-12.
After an ice storm in New York in January 1943.

HAIL

Hail consists of rounded particles of ice which form in cumulonimbus clouds that contain powerful upward currents of air. According to one hypothesis, hailstones develop when raindrops are carried to high altitudes by powerful upward air currents and frozen into pellets of ice. At these high altitudes they may become coated with snow and become heavy enough to fall. During descent the snow may melt and additional water droplets may be collected. Another powerful upward current may cause freezing again. Repetition of this process produces hailstones with successive layers and onionlike structures (Fig. 22-13). Hailstones as large as grapefruit were reported from Nebraska in July 1928 but such huge stones are rare. Hailstones cause thousands of dollars worth of damage to agricultural crops and the possessions of man each year.

Fig. 22-13.

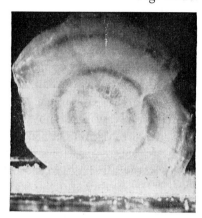

*A hailstone. Note the layers of snow and
ice. This hailstone fell in Iowa in June 1940.
(Courtesy, U.S. Weather Bureau)*

SNOW

Snow consists of ice crystals which developed in the air by sublimation: water vapor changed directly into solid particles at temperatures
below freezing. Most snow crystals are six-sided in design, but some are
three-pointed. Thousands of variations on this general design have been
observed (Fig. 22-14). Most snowflakes consist of aggregates of ice

*Snow crystals photographed through a
microscope. (Courtesy, U.S. Weather
Bureau)*

Fig. 22-14.

crystals. If flakes fall through warmer air they may melt together to
form large clots. According to Tannehill, huge clots of snow, 15 inches
across and 8 inches thick, fell in Montana in 1887! Temperatures are
never too low for snow to form, but very cold air contains little moisture.

On the average, about 10 inches of snow will melt to 1 inch of water. Although the term *blizzard* is popularly applied to any heavy, somewhat windy snowfall, a blizzard is officially defined as "a violent, intensely cold wind, laden with snow mostly or entirely picked up from the ground." It may or may not snow during a blizzard. According to the U.S. Weather Bureau, the greatest recorded seasonal snowfall is 884 inches at Tamarack, California, during the winter of 1906-07. During the New York snowstorm of December 26-27, 1947, 26 inches of snow fell in 24 hours, a record for the city. More than $8,000,000 were spent in removing the snow from the metropolitan area. Additional heavy snowfalls include the 60 inches which fell at Giant Forest, California, in one day and the 96 inches which accumulated at Vanceboro, Maine, in four days.

HUMIDITY

Absolute humidity refers to the amount of water vapor actually present in the air. On the other hand, a relative humidity of 75 percent means that the air contains three-fourths of the total amount of moisture that it can hold at that temperature. Humidity may be less than 100 percent during a rainstorm because rain is falling from a saturated cloud situated a few thousand feet above the surface. Air nearer the ground through which the raindrops move is not saturated with water vapor. High humidity is uncomfortable on warm days because the rate of evaporation, which is a cooling process, becomes slow when the air is nearly saturated with water vapor.

To understand the cooling which results from evaporation, consider a container of water. Molecules in the liquid are in constant motion, and some are moving much more rapidly than others. The fastest moving molecules near the surface of the water tend to escape into the air to become a gas. As heat is directly related to the rapidity of molecular motion, removal of the fastest moving molecules leaves behind a concentration of slower moving molecules at a lower temperature. When evaporation occurs from a person's skin, the molecules of the skin move more slowly because they must share their energy of motion with the slowly moving water molecules which remain.

A breeze aids evaporation by preventing saturated air from stagnating. A windy cold day feels particularly chilly because the rate of evaporation of moisture from one's skin is increased. A swimmer feels chilly as he steps out of the water and rapid evaporation occurs. However, he feels quite comfortable a moment later after a brisk rub with a towel has removed excess water. In the heating of buildings, lower temperatures and higher humidity are less expensive and healthier than higher temperatures coupled with low humidity. The air in some homes during the winter is so dry that rapid evaporation occurs and one feels cool despite rather high temperatures.

Humidity may be measured by a hygrometer which uses strands of human hair as an essential element. The hairs become shorter in dry air and longer in humid air. (Girls who curl their hair know what happens to curls when hair becomes wet.) Humidity may also be measured by a pair of thermometers (Fig. 22-15) one of which has a wet cloth

Fig. 22-15.

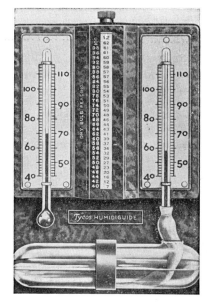

Stationary wet-bulb and dry-bulb thermometers. For accurate readings, a fan should be operating to keep the air from stagnating about the bulbs. (Courtesy, Taylor Instrument Companies)

around its bulb. If the humidity of the air is 100 percent, evaporation does not occur, and the temperature readings of the two thermometers will be the same. However, if humidity is not 100 percent, evaporation and cooling take place. Dry air causes a considerable drop in the temperature around the bulb of the wet-bulb thermometer. Thus the difference in the readings of the wet- and dry-bulb thermometers can be calibrated in such a manner that the humidity of the air is directly indicated.

The *infrared absorption hygrometer* is a new and superior method of measuring the moisture content of the air. It utilizes a beam of light containing two wave lengths. One type of wave is absorbed by water vapor in the air, whereas the other is unaffected. Therefore, the ratio of energy transmitted in the two wave lengths indicates the quantity of water vapor present in the air sample in the path of the waves.

WEATHER MODIFICATION—RAINMAKING

Recent attempts at weather modification have received a good deal of publicity and the results obtained are still controversial. For example, in 1950 New York State hired an expert (a meteorologist) to make rain; subsequent claims filed against it by irate persons who had wanted clear skies at certain times when rain fell forced the state to employ other experts (lawyers) to try to prove that the rainmaking attempts were unsuccessful. Rainmakers theorize somewhat as follows. At times clouds may contain moisture under conditions of supersaturation; that is, temperatures are below the condensation point, but no condensation takes place. In fact, such supercooled clouds seem to be common in middle latitudes, perhaps for lack of enough ice crystals to act as condensation nuclei. If a supercooled cloud contains both water droplets and ice crystals, the crystals will grow by addition of molecules from the droplets and may join to form a snowflake which melts as it falls and forms a raindrop. Silver iodide crystals (commonly spread from generators on the ground) can act as condensation centers; they resemble ice crystals in structure. Dry Ice pellets—solid carbon dioxide—dropped from a plane (Fig. 22-16) chill the air in their paths to produce ice crystals as condensation nuclei.

In experiments performed on Mt. Washington, New Hampshire, handfuls of dry ice were tossed into supercooled clouds moving across the summit, and snow was observed to fall from the clouds immediately downwind. Experimentation and statistical studies will probably have to continue for a number of years before definite conclusions can be reached concerning the results of rainmaking attempts. For example, cloud seeding is commonly done under conditions in which precipitation is possible. If precipitation does result, one must still wonder whether the rain or snow would have fallen naturally without artificial stimulation by man. Experiments in which silver iodide generators were operated only on alternate days indicated an influence on the weather. A periodicity could be detected in weather patterns in downwind areas. Other experiments are reported to have resulted in increased rainfall of a certain percentage in test areas during the same time intervals that surrounding areas have had normal or below normal amounts of precipitation. Such tests indicate that man can modify the weather

Fig. 22-16.

Results of cloud seeding. The L-shaped hole in the supercooled clouds is 15 miles long and 3 miles wide. It was produced by seeding the clouds with dry-ice pellets. The dark area at the right is the wing tip of a plane. (Courtesy, U.S. Army Signal Corps)

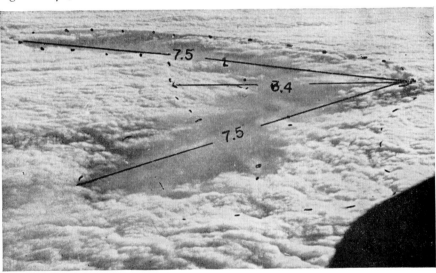

to some extent. However, one must be uncertain of the degree of success achieved by man in modifying the weather until complete reports are available which list failures as well as successes.

Perhaps hail can be prevented by seeding clouds which are potential producers of hailstones. If premature precipitation results, this may prevent the subsequent formation of hail. A hail-suppression program in the Hudson Valley region of New York met with some success in 1956 but was discontinued in 1957 following a damaging hail storm which occurred at night.

CIRCULATION OF THE ATMOSPHERE

Three factors are of paramount importance in explaining the circulation of the Earth's atmosphere.

(1) Heated air expands and is pushed upward by nearby cooler, heavier air (Fig. 22-20).

(2) Air moves horizontally from high to low pressure areas.

(3) Moving objects are deflected to the right in the direction of movement in the Northern Hemisphere but to the left in the Southern Hemisphere (the Coriolis effect).

An experiment may be readily performed which shows that warm air is lighter than cold air (Fig. 22-17). According to the molecular

Fig. 22-17.

Cold air is heavy and sinks; warm air is light and rises. In A, one covered glass bottle contains cold air, the other contains warm air. In B, smoke has been puffed into the square bottle containing cold air. This makes it visible. In C, the two bottles are placed mouth to mouth, the warm air on top, and the covers have been removed. No mixing occurs. In D, the cold-air has been placed on top. The cold air (smoke) has moved to the bottom, and the warm air has risen to the top.

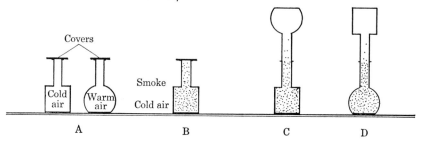

theory, molecules are closer together in cold air than in warm at equal atmospheric pressures and give it a greater density. Precise laboratory measurements prove that air has greater density at lower temperatures. To air a room quickly in cool weather, one makes use of this principle by opening windows from both top (warm stale air leaves) and bottom (cold fresh air enters).

Along the Earth's surface, air moves from high to low pressure areas and is called wind. Winds are designated according to the direction from which they are blowing; for example, a north wind blows from the north. A generalized explanation of the wind systems of the Earth is relatively simple; local details may be quite complex. The sun may be considered the engine of this circulation and the rotation of the Earth the steering mechanism.

Circulation begins at the equator where solar radiation is most intense and air rises (Fig. 22-18). The air cools gradually during its

Generalized diagram of atmospheric circulation. The rotating Earth is shown without continents for simplicity. After Bjerknes, Bergeron, Rossby, and Haynes. (Courtesy, A. N. Strahler, Physical Geography, John Wiley & Sons, Inc., 1951)

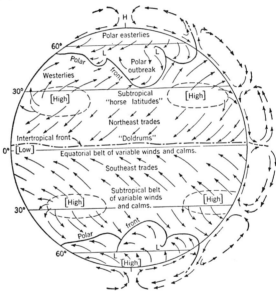

Fig. 22-18.

ascent. Eventually at a high altitude, some of the air heads northward, some southward. Along the Earth's surface, winds move toward the equator and replace the rising air. If the Earth were not rotating and if complicating continental masses were not present, a huge simple convection current would develop. Air would rise at the equator, sink at the poles, and move horizontally between these two areas. However, the spinning Earth deflects to the east much of the air that rises at the equator and starts northward or southward at high altitudes (Fig. 22-19). As this air arrives at about the 30 degree latitudes, it is moving almost due eastward and high above the Earth's surface. Gradually the air descends to the Earth's surface to form high pressure belts at latitudes from 30 to 40 degrees (the horse latitudes). However, these areas of high pressure are not continuous; they are subdivided into large cells centering over the oceans.

Deviation of projectiles produced by the Earth's rotation. The heavy lines show the direction of firing; the broken lines, the direction of flight as modified by the Earth's rotation. Arrows indicate the difference of the Earth's rotational velocity at various latitudes. Whether the projectile is fired north or south, east or west, it is always deviated to the right in the Northern Hemisphere and to the left in the Southern Hemisphere. (Courtesy, Cecilia Payne-Gaposchkin, Introduction to Astronomy, Prentice-Hall, 1954)

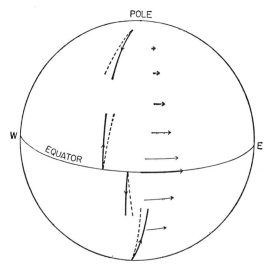

Fig. 22-19.

In the Northern Hemisphere, air returns from these cells along the Earth's surface to the equator. On the return journey, it is deflected to the right (west) to form the northeast tradewinds. Air also moves from the horse latitudes along the Earth's surface toward the north. Deflection produces the belt of westerlies. Cold air moving southward along the Earth's surface from the high-pressure polar area is deflected to the right (west) and forms a belt of polar easterlies. These meet the belt of westerlies at latitudes of about 55 to 60 degrees. Along this boundary upward movements of air create a low-pressure zone.

Similar circulation in the Southern Hemisphere, combined with a deflection to the left, produces comparable belts of trade winds, westerlies, and polar easterlies. All of the pressure belts shift somewhat with the seasons and are influenced by local topographic conditions. The pressure belts and wind systems are better developed in the Southern Hemisphere than in the Northern Hemisphere because of the greater proportion of water to land.

Much of the preceding explanation concerning the global circulation of the Earth's atmosphere is theoretical, especially that concerning the movements of air masses high above the Earth's surface. Evidence for a convectional cell on either side of the equator seems reliable. Some evidence is available for convectional cells in the belts of westerlies. However, some meteorologists think that polar cells do not exist.

Atmospheric circulation aids in causing certain kinds of climate at certain places on the Earth's surface. At the equator warm moist air rises, expands, and cools. Heavy precipitation, high temperatures, and gentle variable winds are common. At the horse latitudes, relatively dry air descends and is warmed. Its capacity to hold moisture is thereby increased, and little precipitation results. The world's desert areas are situated at latitudes of about 25 to 35 degrees. In the trade-wind belts, winds blow constantly in one direction, temperatures are high, and little precipitation takes place unless air is forced locally to climb over mountain barriers.

Weather in the belts of westerlies is noted for the regularity with which it changes from fair to stormy and back again (p. 484). Mark Twain had these middle latitudes in mind when he said, "If you do not like our weather, wait five minutes."

The jet streams are powerful, little-known, high-altitude winds which commonly blow eastward in great snakelike curves near the top of the troposphere. The jet streams have widths up to 300 miles and more but have thicknesses of a few miles or less. They shift northward and southward with the seasons. Speeds up to 200 to 300 mi/hr have been measured in their centers, but velocities decrease rapidly away from the centers. The winds blow in gusts. The importance of the jet streams in high-altitude flying is obvious. Planes which fly eastward in the jet streams may have their speeds increased by 150 mi/hr. The exact relationship between the jet streams and changes of the weather is still uncertain. Three or four jet streams have been discovered in the Northern Hemisphere and one has been detected in the Southern Hemisphere.

HEATING OF LAND AND WATER

A number of weather phenomena can be explained by the fact that land heats up and cools off more quickly than water (Fig. 22-20). To illustrate this, a simple experiment can be performed. Two dishes at the same temperature, one containing soil and the other water, are

Fig. 22-20.

Land gains and loses heat more rapidly than water. The isolated white clouds hailed with joy by the shipwrecked sailor are interpreted by him as signs of a land mass. The island gains heat more rapidly than the surrounding water. Thus, during the day the strongly heated air above the island expands and rises. Air moves in horizontally from the water to replace it. The air is cooled during the upward movement; its capacity to hold water vapor decreases; and condensation occurs to form clouds. (Modified from Schneider)

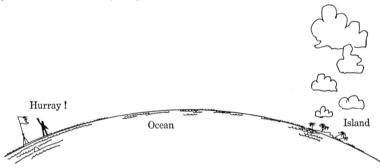

Hurray !

Ocean   Island

placed in sunlight for a short time. If each material is then touched by the hand (a thermometer, of course, is more accurate) the surface of the soil is found to be warmer than the upper portion of the water. In like manner, the two dishes may be chilled in a refrigerator; this time the surface of the soil feels cooler to the hand. Only the surface of the soil heats up or cools off more rapidly than the water. Circulation causes the temperature of the water to be nearly uniform throughout, and evaporation cools the surface. In addition, more heat energy is required to raise the temperature of a certain volume of water a specific number of degrees than is needed to raise the temperature of an equal volume of soil an equal number of degrees (the specific heat of water is high). Furthermore, darker-colored objects like soil tend to absorb more of the sun's rays than lighter-colored materials like water.

In coastal regions a breeze commonly blows from the sea to the land during the day (Fig. 22-21); at night the wind direction may be reversed and blow from land to sea. During the day air over coastal areas commonly becomes warmer than air above the adjoining water because land is heated more quickly than water. Cooler air above the surface of the ocean moves inland to push upward the warmer lighter air over the land. The more rapid cooling of the land at night chills the air above it. This cooler heavier land air tends to move seaward

The sea breeze. Cause: land gains heat more quickly than water.

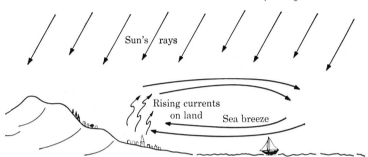

Fig. 22-21.

to push up lighter warmer nocturnal air which is rising above the surface of the water. However, local exceptions to this general process are not rare.

The monsoon seasons of India and of other areas may be explained in a somewhat similar manner. During hot summer weather, air above India and the great land mass of central Asia is heated strongly and is pushed upward by moisture-laden air which moves northward from the Indian Ocean across the land. Altitudes increase gradually in the direction of the massive Himalaya Mountains. The moist northward-moving air, therefore, must rise higher and higher into regions of lower temperatures. Chilling of the air at higher altitudes results in enormous quantities of precipitation—more than 1000 inches of water per year have fallen on Cherrapunji, India. However, Cherrapunji averages only 1 inch of rainfall per month during December and January. In contrast, the average rainfall for the United States is approximately 30 inches per year.

Mountain and valley breezes also occur. Cold heavy air may move down a mountain slope at night. A narrow valley between high mountain slopes will experience a pronounced mountain breeze. During the day the air above the surface of the valley may become much warmer than that on the adjoining high land areas and move convectionally up the slopes.

EXERCISES AND QUESTIONS FOR CHAPTER 22

1. Which weather instrument operates about as well inside a house as outside? Name several which do not. Why?

2. Identify the clouds in the sky every day of the week at some particular time of the day—say, just prior to a class meeting or at noon. Record your identifications and check their accuracy periodically.

3. Describe key ideas and data involved in weather modification. Why is evaluation of weather modification controversial?

4. Why do jets leave trails in the sky? Why do water pipes "sweat" in the summer?

5. Two air masses are rising. They are identical except that one has more water vapor than the other. Which should rise higher? Why? Which should cool more rapidly? Why?

6. Why does one feel more comfortable in a breeze on a hot humid day than in still air?

7. Why do deserts exist in eastern California and Nevada?

8. Why are conditions favorable for the formation of dew and frost unfavorable for precipitation?

9. Distinguish between altostratus and nimbostratus clouds.

10. What conditions seem necessary for precipitation to occur?

11. Why is mercury used in most barometers instead of some liquid like water?

12. Why do more abrupt and greater changes in temperature occur on Mars between night and day than on the Earth?

13. Assume that an air mass at a temperature of 80°F moves from an altitude of 1000 feet across a mountain barrier 10,000 feet high and descends to an altitude of 1000 feet on the lee side. Assume further that condensation and precipitation begin at an altitude of 5000 feet, continue

to the top, and that all of the water vapor is precipitated from the air by the time it reaches the top of the mountain. What is the temperature of the air mass when it reaches an altitude of 1000 feet on the lee side of the mountain? What effect does the presence or absence of moisture (as cloud droplets) have upon temperature changes during ascent and descent? Use 5.5°F/1000 feet as the dry adiabatic rate and 3.2°F/1000 feet as the wet adiabatic rate (during condensation or evaporation).

14. Which has a higher specific gravity, a gallon of dry air or a gallon of moist air? Assume that pressure and temperature are the same. Hint: the same number of molecules occur in each gallon.

15. If a pail of water were emptied from the top of a skyscraper, what would be experienced by persons on the street directly below? (Assume that the water does not evaporate before reaching the ground.)

CHAPTER 23

Weather: Air Masses, Fronts, Storms, Pressure Systems, and Forecasts

AIR MASSES

Until the technique of air-mass analysis (which was developed after World War I) clarified weather phenomena greatly, explanations of weather changes seemed confusing and uncertain to most people. If a pronounced weather change occurs abruptly—for example, a cool crisp clear day follows a series of hot cloudy rainy ones —air-mass analysis has a ready explanation. Different kinds of air are known to exist in different parts of the world; as an illustration, one mass of air may be colder, heavier, and drier than another. The type of air above an area is of chief importance in determining the kind of weather which the area experiences.

Air masses normally are not stationary. They are especially mobile in the belt of westerlies where the dominant direction of air movement is from west to east. If the type of air above an area one day has moved eastward by the following day, it may have been replaced by a noticeably different kind of air, causing a rather sudden change in the weather conditions in that locality—that is, in temperature, humidity, pressure, wind, clouds, and precipitation.

An air mass constitutes a huge section of the Earth's atmosphere which has nearly uniform properties such as temperature and humidity in a horizontal direction; it tends to be homogeneous parallel to the Earth's surface, but it may be heterogeneous in a vertical direction. Four types of air masses are of particular importance in causing weather changes in the middle latitudes: polar continental, polar maritime, tropical continental, and tropical maritime. These terms indicate the chief physical properties of the air masses: hot if tropical, cold if polar, moist if the air accumulated over water (maritime), and dry if the source region was a land area.

Source regions of air masses are of two main types. Circulation of the Earth's atmosphere may cause large volumes of air to stagnate frequently for a time in certain areas and to take on properties characteristic of such areas. If air moves across a large area with uniform surface conditions, it may reach fairly complete equilibrium with the surface beneath it in a few days or a week or two. Further changes in the air mass are very slow. Equilibrium is attained more rapidly over a warm surface than over a cold surface because of mixing produced by convection. Such air masses may subsequently move hundreds and even thousands of miles from their source regions and still retain enough of their original characteristics to be recognizable.

For example, in North America during the winter, a source of polar continental air is the entire area north of 55 degrees latitude, from Labrador in the east to Alaska in the west. Because of the prevalent snow and ice, this nearly stationary air becomes intensely chilled, particularly near the ground. As the air is coldest and heaviest along the ground, it is stable; little tendency for upward movements exists, and condensation and clouds are not common.

When Polar Canadian air leaves its source area to travel southward into the United States, its arrival can be recognized readily by the nonmeteorologist. It produces a cold wave in the winter and sends fuel trucks scurrying quickly from one house to another. In the summer its vigorous gusty arrival from the northwest may herald a welcome relief from the preceding heat wave. Occasionally tongues of polar continental air reach southward into Florida. The Earth's surface in the United States commonly is warmer than such air. As a result, the bottom air is heated and rises, not uniformly, but in great ascending bubbles something like the boiling of water on a Gargantuan scale. A typical spring day in New York inside a mass of Polar Canadian air would dawn with cloudless sparkling blue skies. During the morning, solar radiation becomes increasingly intense and initiates the upward movement of large blobs of air. These upward-moving air currents become visible when they reach altitudes at which condensation occurs; white cottony puffs of cumulus clouds develop. By late afternoon the sky may be nearly covered by such clouds. However, after sunset, the upward movement decreases, the clouds disappear, and a brilliant, cool, starlit evening results.

Pilots and their passengers know when they fly through such currents by the upward bump as they enter and the sudden drop as they leave. Glider pilots can attain great altitudes by circling within these rising air bubbles. Dust is carried upward and a clear sparkling day results. Precipitation is not common from such clouds, for little moisture is present. However, cumulonimbus clouds and thunderstorms may develop.

A different reaction is involved when tropical maritime air moves northward and northeastward from the Gulf of Mexico into the United States. The ground in winter is colder than such an air mass, the bottom air becomes chilled, and stability develops. Moisture readily condenses into clouds of the stratus type, and precipitation is common.

Air-Mass vs. Frontal Weather   In the middle latitudes in North America, the prevailing wind direction is from west to east. North of this belt of westerlies, the polar easterlies pile up polar continental air toward the south. Pressure at latitudes of about 55 to 60 degrees periodically becomes great enough to push a huge tongue of this cool dry air southward into the United States (Fig. 22-18). On the other hand, south of the belt of westerlies, winds blowing from the horse latitudes (about 30 to 35 degrees) tend to push tropical maritime air to the north. Periodically, pressure detaches a great mass of this warm moist air and moves it northward into the United States. Once these air masses have reached the United States, they tend to move across it from west to east. Thus, periodic movements of different kinds of air are important in causing the weather cycle of the belt of westerlies—a few days of polar continental weather tend to alternate with a few days of tropical maritime weather. Polar maritime air and tropical continental air affect the weather of the eastern part of the United States as a whole less frequently than do the polar continental and tropical maritime air masses.

As air masses are very large, they may require a few days to pass over any given locality. During this time, one experiences "air mass weather"; the same general weather conditions are repeated each day during this part of the weather cycle. Major weather changes occur as the leading portion of an air mass moves past a given place. The forward margin of a mass of polar air is aptly termed a cold front, and the front edge of a tropical air mass is called a warm front. Fronts may be pronounced and persistent or weak and evanescent.

FRONTS

Certain weather changes characteristically are associated with the advance of a cold front (Figs. 23-1 and 23-2). As cold air is heavier

Fig. 23-1.

A vertical cross section through a cold-front cloud system and its air masses.

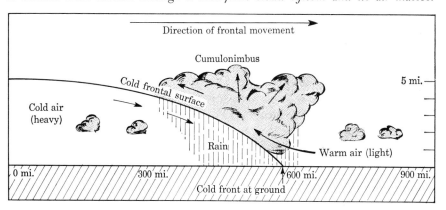

than warm air, it stays near the surface and shoves warmer air forward and upward like the action of a snowplow. As the warmer air is forced to rise, it expands and cools, and cumulus and cumulonimbus clouds develop. Precipitation may develop at higher altitudes. Sudden heavy precipitation is characteristic of the passage of a cold front. The slope in a cold front averages 1 mile in a vertical direction to 40 or 80 miles along the Earth's surface. Cold fronts tend to move southeastward into the United States. The amount of precipitation and turbulence associated with the arrival of a cold front depends upon the nature of the two air masses involved. Extreme conditions result if warm moist air is underrun by very cold air. Although clouds commonly develop all along

Photograph of a cold front. This dust storm occurred at Manteer, Kansas, in April 1935. The dust was picked up by the advancing cold air. (Courtesy, U.S. Weather Bureau)

Fig. 23-2.

a cold front because of the upward moving air currents it causes, actual precipitation may be localized in scattered areas.

Showers and turbulence associated with nimbostratus and cumulonimbus clouds may also develop in advance of the actual arrival of the cold front along the ground. Friction may slow the rate of movement of the cold air along the Earth's surface and permit cold air at higher altitudes to move ahead of it. The presence of such overrunning

Fig. 23-3.

A vertical cross section through a warm-front cloud system and its air masses.

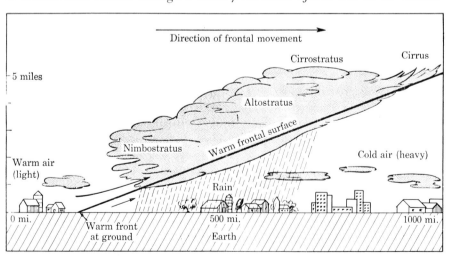

cold air above warmer surface air produces very unstable conditions, and a line of showers and thunderstorms may develop (squall line). Newspapers may report erroneously that such showers have "cooled the air" instead of stating correctly that the arrival of cooler air has caused precipitation.

On the other hand, as warm air is lighter than cool air, the forward part of an advancing warm air mass must rise over cooler air in its path and push the cool air forward. Certain weather changes are commonly associated with a well-developed warm front (Fig. 23-3). The slope along a warm front approximates 1 to 100 or 1 to 200. Thus if the cirrus clouds of the frontal surface are at an altitude of 5 miles, the base of the frontal surface along the ground may be 500 to 1000 miles to the rear.

Fig. 23-4.

Formation of an occluded front. An airplane flying at a high altitude would pass through three kinds of air masses and two types of fronts.

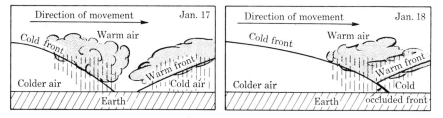

Cold fronts commonly move faster than warm fronts and may overtake them. When this occurs, the entire warm air mass is lifted above the Earth's surface forming a third type of front, the occluded front (Fig. 23-4).

PRESSURE AREAS

Barometric readings from widely scattered stations show that atmospheric pressure varies considerably at any one time at different stations and at any one station over a period of time. When lines (isobars) are drawn on a map through the locations of stations which have the same barometric pressure, definite centers of low or high pressure commonly appear. Variations in pressure caused by altitude differences are eliminated by certain corrections which reduce all of the readings to sea level. These pressure systems may span several hundred miles from one side to another. The lows (cyclones) and highs (anticyclones) have characteristic conditions of wind, temperature, clouds, and precipitation associated with them. They appear to be caused by the movements of air masses.

A low-pressure center may develop along the boundary of two moving masses of air: for example, polar continental to the north and tropical maritime to the south (Fig. 23-5). The air masses do not mix

Fig. 23-5.

Development of a typical middle-latitude low. Six stages are shown. As the cold front moves faster than the warm front, the area of warm air in the system becomes narrowed until occlusion occurs. The whirling counterclockwise circulation then weakens in the cold air. Variations of this manner of formation are common. (Courtesy, U.S. Weather Bureau)

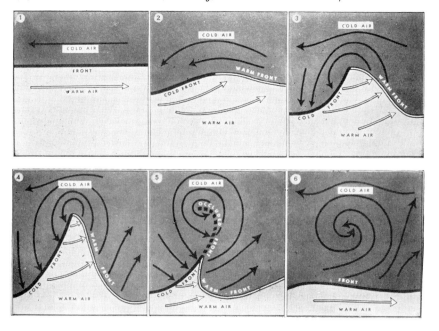

readily. Cold dense air may push under the warm light air somewhere along the boundary at a minor irregularity and cause it to move upward. The cold air north of the front pushes southward forming a cold front; the warm air from the south moves northward and upward forming a warm front. The rising current of warm air in the center produces low barometric pressure.

At locations away from the center, air moves inward along the

Earth's surface and is deflected to the right in the direction of movement in the Northern Hemisphere. Thus a counterclockwise circulation originates about the low-pressure area, and winds spiral inward and upward toward the center. Lows tend to be elliptical in shape and elongated in a northeast-southwest direction. Eastward and northeastward movement of lows in the United States averages about 20 mi/hr in the summer and 30 mi/hr in the winter.

High-pressure areas are commonly much larger than low-pressure areas. In a high-pressure system, air moves along the Earth's surface outward from the center; it is deflected to the right and spirals outward and around the center in a clockwise circulation in the Northern Hemisphere. As air moves horizontally from high- to low-pressure areas because of the pressure differential, winds are strong when the difference in pressure is great. If the pressure lines (isobars) are close together on a map, winds are strong, and the pressure system is well developed. On the other hand, if the pressure lines are far apart, winds tend to be gentle, and the pressure system is not intensively developed. Winds tend to blow at acute angles to the pressure lines. The contrast between lows and highs is less distinct in the summer than in the winter. In the Southern Hemisphere, movement of air in the low- and high-pressure systems is reversed—clockwise in a low, and counterclockwise in a high.

Figure 23-6 relates pressure systems, air masses, fronts, and characteristic weather conditions as they tend to develop in the United States. An observer is located in the eastern part of the United States. A low-pressure center has developed along the boundary separating polar continental from tropical maritime air. On Monday the low-pressure center is situated about 600 miles west of the observer. A warm front extends southeastward from the center, and a center of high pressure is located to the northwest in the polar continental air mass. The tropical maritime and polar continental air masses, their accompanying warm and cold fronts, and the low- and high-pressure centers are all moving to the northeast. Weather data collected during preceding years suggest that the center of the low will pass north of the observer's location. A movement of about 600 miles per day for the pressure systems is typical.

A person at the observation point commonly experiences the following weather changes during the summer months. First, certain phenomena take place which are associated with the approach of a warm

Fig. 23-6.

*The diagrammatic weather map below shows polar continental and tropical
maritime air masses associated with well-developed high- and low-pressure
areas with accompanying cold and warm fronts. The future path of the low-
pressure center is plotted, with its probable location the next day marked.
The high-pressure center will move southeastward and then follow the low
to the east. Note the counterclockwise circulation which has developed
around the low-pressure system and the clockwise circulation around the high.
AB is a cross section through the cold and warm fronts. The cold front commonly overtakes the northern part of the warm front, thereby forming an
occlusion.*

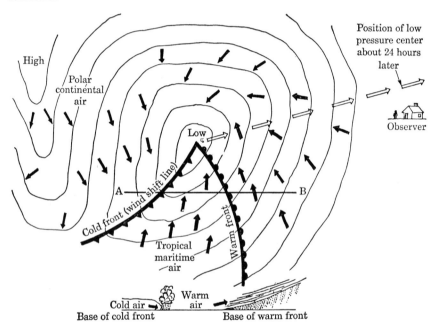

front: the barometer falls slowly; temperature and humidity rise gradually; winds are from the east or southeast; and a few high harmless-look-
ing clouds (cirrus) appear in the west. Several hours later the clouds
are thicker and lower. Later the sky becomes completely overcast, and
a light rain falls steadily for a number of hours. A warm front may
extend for several hundred miles from its foot at the Earth's surface to
its top where a few wisps of cirrus clouds are visible.

On Tuesday the lower part of the warm front passes over the observation point. It is warm and humid, and the sky may clear. The barometer is low and steady, and the wind blows from the south or southwest.
At a later hour on Tuesday the cold front approaches the observer. Its

presence is heralded by a high cloud bank capped here and there by huge towering masses (cumulonimbus) which appear in the west and move eastward. Thunderstorms and brief heavy downpours are common as the cold front passes over an area, although the storms may be scattered here and there along the front.

By Wednesday the sky has cleared, and by afternoon it contains great white scattered puffs of fair-weather clouds (cumulus) which sparkle against the blue background. The barometer is rising, and humidity is low; it is cool, and the wind blows vigorously from the northwest. The observer can now predict with some confidence that he will experience these same general weather conditions (air-mass weather) for another day or so as the polar continental mass moves by, although each day should be a little warmer than the previous one. However, a watchful eye should be kept on the barometer, the wind, and on the southwest sky for the first signs of the approach of the next low.

Many variations centering about these general weather changes are possible, and the changes may be quite different locally from those described. The fronts may move at different rates of speed in different directions; the low- and high-pressure systems may be weakly or strongly developed; and the air masses themselves may vary in physical properties. For example, in the Kansas flood of 1951, the front part of a cold air mass remained nearly motionless over Kansas for about 4 days instead of moving eastward as normally happens. During this time, warm moist air from the Gulf of Mexico moved northward and upward over the cold air, shedding torrents of rain on the surface below.

The belt of westerlies has been likened to a huge river which flows in an easterly direction across the United States. In this river, low- and high-pressure systems are like gigantic eddies with their counterclockwise and clockwise circulations. In fact, the eddies may be so numerous that they obscure the general eastward movement of the river itself. The eddies develop somewhat periodically and follow each other eastward, some persisting much longer than others. This eastward procession of lows and highs and the passage of large masses of different kinds of air cause the alternation of weather conditions common to the middle latitudes. For this reason, a telephone call concerning the weather to a friend located some distance to the west will often aid one in predicting the type of weather which is headed eastward and which is due to arrive in one's local area several hours later. Although the general trend of movement is eastward, from the Mississippi basin the most frequented tracks of the weather disturbances are northeastward across the New England states or northeastward to the Great Lakes and then along the St. Lawrence Valley (Fig. 23-7). Some storms cross the Atlantic and travel eastward as far as Siberia.

Principal tracks of lows in the United States. The lows tend to form in the southeast, the southwest, or the northwest. Their paths tend to converge on the northeastern part of the United States. (Adapted from U.S. Weather Bureau map)

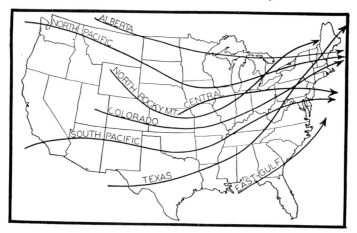

Fig. 23-7.

WEATHER FORECASTING

Weather forecasting is based upon information concerning the whereabouts of different air masses, pressure systems, fronts, and their movements at any one time (Fig. 23-8). The most important elements of the weather are (1) temperature of the air, (2) atmospheric pressure, (3) direction and speed of the wind, (4) humidity, (5) type and amount of cloudiness, and (6) amount of precipitation. This information is then interpreted in the light of past experience which indicates the paths followed most frequently by low- and high-pressure systems and the rates at which they commonly travel at different times of the year. In addition, the characteristic reactions of different air masses to various ground conditions must be known by the weather forecaster if he is to predict future weather changes with some accuracy. In general, accurate predictions depend upon speedy interpretations by experienced

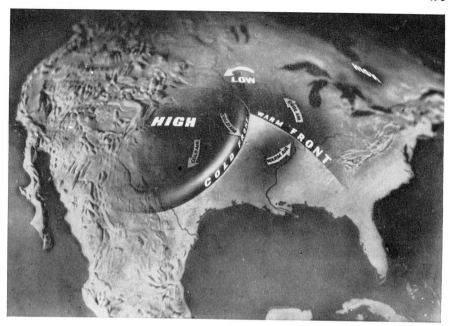

Fig. 23-8.

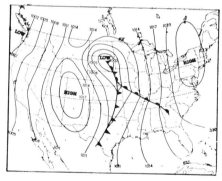

Weather map. If air masses were visible, the frontal system drawn on the small map might appear as shown in the three-dimensional illustration. A cold-front type of occlusion has been created north of the surface junction of the two fronts. (Courtesy, U.S. Weather Bureau)

observers of a large amount of weather data which has been collected rapidly from a wide area.

THE GRASSHOPPER

One of the most interesting of recent weather instruments is a self-contained automatic weather station called the Grasshopper. This instrument may be parachuted from a plane to inaccessible areas. An automatic clock is started before the weather station is dropped, and

(A)

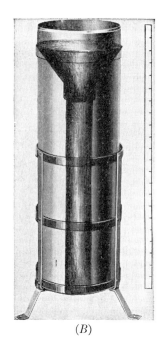

(B)

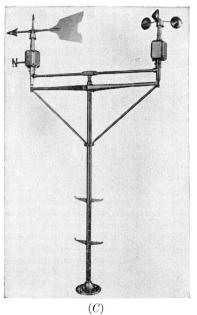

(C)

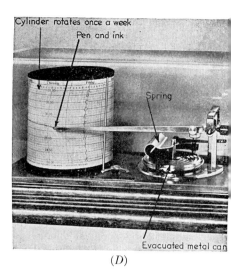

Cylinder rotates once a week

Pen and ink

Spring

Evacuated metal can

(D)

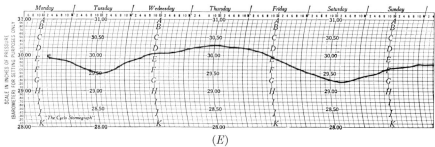

(E)

this clock controls all future activity. A small explosive disengages the parachute after the landing. Six other charges cause legs attached to springs to stick out and place the weather station in an upright position. Another explosive sends up a 20-foot antenna. Weather-responsive devices then function to turn a radio transmitter on and off. A receiving station can change the radio signals into temperature, pressure, and humidity readings. The automatic weather station can also be used as a radio beacon. Other weather instruments are illustrated in Fig. 23-9.

STORMS

Thunderstorms Estimates suggest that more than 40,000 thunderstorms may occur during an average day on the Earth and that from 1500 to 2000 may be in existence simultaneously. Most thunderstorms result from strong upward currents of air and are characterized by local extent, short lifetime, electrical discharges, and heavy falls of large raindrops. The upward currents may originate as part of a convectional circulation within an air mass caused by intensive solar heating of a localized area (Fig. 23-10). Such thunderstorms are most common in the afternoon in the warmer months of the year. The upward movements of air may also be associated with the arrival of a cold front or by passage over a mountainous area. Such storms may occur at any time of the year, although they are not common in winter.

Fig. 23-9.

Weather instruments: (See opposite page) A. Radiosonde. The soldier is about to release the radiosonde. At the right is radar equipment which automatically follows the flight of the balloon and gives the direction and velocity of the upper winds. During its rise and descent via parachute after the balloon has expanded and burst, the radiosonde automatically transmits signals which indicate the temperature, pressure, and humidity of the air it is moving through.—B. Standard rain or snow gauge. (Courtesy, Friez Instrument Division)—C. Wind instruments. The support has a standard three-cup anemometer and wind vane indicating a north wind. (Courtesy, U.S. Weather Bureau)—D. Barograph. (Courtesy, Taylor Instrument Companies) E. Barograph record at New Paltz, New York, for the week ending April 7, 1957. Considerable fluctuation in atmospheric pressure is illustrated. A low-pressure center, accompanied by an occluded front and precipitation, moved past New Paltz on Tuesday. Wednesday and Thursday were generally fair with high pressure. On Friday and Saturday a well-developed low-pressure system passed New Paltz on its northeastward journey. However, the center of the low was northwest of the New Paltz area. Warm, cold, and occluded fronts accompanied the low. Precipitation occurred on Friday and Saturday.

Most thunderstorms have several cells in different stages of development. Each cell consists of an updraft, commonly associated with a downdraft. A cell develops as a rising column of moist air which expands, is cooled, and produces a cumulus cloud. Condensation re-

Fig. 23-10.

Structure of a thunderstorm.

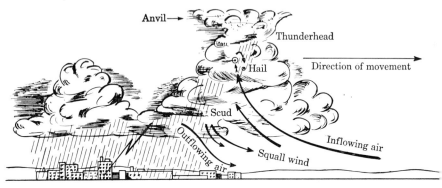

leases considerable energy (latent heat of vaporization) which continues the upward movement and results in the development of a cumulonimbus cloud. Thunderstorms are accordingly more common in the warmer months, since their energy is derived chiefly from heat energy released during condensation; air must be warm to hold large quantities of moisture. As rain falls, it cools the air, causing a downward movement. The cell dissipates as the cool heavy air spreads out along the surface and stops the updraft.

The electrical and sound phenomena associated with thunderstorms may be quite violent. Lightning is like a huge electric spark, and thunder is the sound produced by heated, rapidly expanding air in the vicinity of the lightning flash. As sound travels about 1 mile in 5 seconds, the distance to the lightning flash may be calculated by measuring the time which elapses between the flash and the arrival of the sound. Thunder should not be feared; if you hear it, the lightning flash which caused it is over, and you are safe so far as it is concerned.

Hurricanes   Hurricane, typhoon, and tropical cyclone are synonyms for relatively small, very intense, low-pressure areas which may extend a few hundred miles from one side to another. As a hurricane is quite thin relative to its breadth, it somewhat resembles a whirling phono-

;raph record. Hurricanes which influence weather in the United States
)riginate near the equatorial doldrums and tend to move northwesterly
mtil they reach the belt of westerlies, where they assume a northeast-
,vard movement (Fig. 23-11). This direction of movement is caused by

*Common path of tropical hurricanes northward along
the Atlantic.*

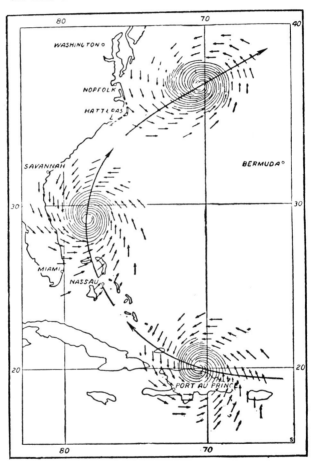

Fig. 23-11.

winds which spiral in a clockwise direction outward and around a
nearly permanent center of high pressure in the Atlantic at latitudes of
about 30 to 40 degrees. A hurricane may move an average distance of
300 to 350 miles per day. However, winds spiraling counterclockwise
toward the low-pressure center have attained speeds of 150 mi/hr and

Fig. 23-12.

Flying above a hurricane. The eye around which the clouds circle is just above the tail of the Navy plane. (Official U.S. Navy Photo)

more. The center or eye of the storm is calm (Fig. 23-12). As a hurricane approaches a certain area, winds of increasing intensity blow in a certain direction, and dark clouds and heavy rains materialize. Calm settles over the area when the center of the storm reaches it. Exhausted birds may land upon ships at sea. Barometer readings below 27 inches of mercury have been recorded, but pressures below 28 inches are not common. As the rear of the storm passes by the observer, winds again become violent, but this time in the opposite direction, and the rain and clouds are repeated. The West Indian hurricanes are most numerous in late summer and early fall.

The exact manner of origin and development of hurricanes is uncertain. More than a dozen West Indian hurricanes may develop during a year and an occasional storm will reach the northeastern part of the United States. During an unusual year several hurricanes may damage eastern sections of the United States. For example, the New England hurricane of 1938 caused an estimated property loss of a few hundred million dollars. The right side of a hurricane in the Northern Hemisphere is more severe than the left, because the forward motion of the storm (averaging 10 to 15 mi/hr) is added to the inward-spiraling winds. Most of the deaths attributed to hurricanes have been caused by inundations of coastal areas by high waves. A rainfall of more than 20 inches in 24 hours has been recorded in the United States. In the Philippines, records show as much as 46 inches of rainfall in 24 hours and 88 inches in four days. Thunder and lightning are associated with some hurricanes but are obscured by other noises such as the roar of wind and waves, the crashing of buildings, and falling raindrops. Hurricanes become weaker as they move across land for two reasons: (1) friction between the winds and the irregular surface, and (2) a decreasing supply of moisture, reducing the huge quantities of latent energy released by condensation of water vapor.

Tornadoes   The tornado or twister is a very small, very powerful, low-pressure system which may be less than half a mile in diameter

Whirling funnel-like cloud of a tornado in Kansas. (Courtesy, Ira B. Blackstock from U.S. Weather Bureau)

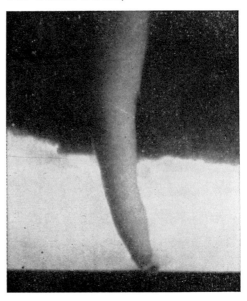

Fig. 23-13.

(Fig. 23-13). Tornadoes in the United States commonly move from southwest to northeast at the rate of 20 to 40 mi/hr. The path of a tornado along the Earth's surface may extend for a few hundred feet or

for a few tens of miles. Winds spiral in a counterclockwise direction
toward the center of the storm at rates which sometimes exceed 200
mi/hr. Updrafts of 100 to 200 mi/hr occur at the center. The base of
the dark funnel-shaped cloud, which is suspended from a large cumulonimbus cloud, may move along the Earth's surface and destroy all
the buildings in its path. However, here and there along its havoc-
wreaking trail, the bottom of the storm may rise momentarily above
the surface and spare the buildings beneath it. The destruction is
caused by the power of the winds, the explosive effect of the sudden
drop in atmospheric pressure outside buildings, and the tremendous
lifting effect of the updrafts. Tornadoes probably originate as whirling
upward currents of air along the contiguous margins of very cold and
very warm moist air masses. Conditions are particularly favorable if
the cold air at higher altitudes overruns warm air along the Earth's
surface. Tornadoes are most common in the United States (the annual
average is 145) and Australia. In the United States most tornadoes
occur in the spring and summer in the Mississippi Valley region.

Many weird events happen in tornadoes. Horses and cars have been
picked up by these violent storms and carried some distance before
being dropped more or less undamaged. Roosters perched in trees are
reported to have lost all of their feathers but to have remained otherwise unharmed.

Nearly 600 tornadoes, a record number, occurred in the United
States in the first half of 1957. More than half of these formed in the
southern Great Plains, a region plagued by drought for the preceding
seven years. The drought was broken in one of the most extended
periods of storm turbulence experienced recently by any area in the
United States: dust storms, blizzards, torrential rains, floods, and tornadoes.

EXERCISES AND QUESTIONS FOR CHAPTER 23

1. Arrange a number of weather maps in chronological order with the
   youngest on the bottom. Examine the top map and predict the changes
   which you think are likely to occur in the next one, then check, and
   repeat the procedure. You will probably make many mistakes, and
   unpredictable weather changes may have occurred. However, you
   should learn a good deal about weather changes. Daily weather maps
   can be obtained from the U.S. Weather Bureau (an annual subscription
   cost $9.60 recently).

2. With a group of three or four fellow-students, make yourself responsible for a week of observations of weather phenomena and their explanation. At the time of the week's report by your group, make a weather prediction.

3. If an automatic recording barometer is available, mark on each week's record the weather changes which have occurred. Is there a correlation between highs and lows and certain weather changes?

4. What special influence, if any, does your local topography have on weather phenomena?

5. Make a collection of weather sayings and criticize them. Which ones have a meteorological basis?

6. Check the accuracy of weather forecasts for a time and assign an accuracy percentage. Remember that a forecast covers a wide area.

7. Describe two different reasons why hurricanes tend to become weakened overland.

8. Point B is 1500 miles due east of point A in the Southern Hemisphere. The center of a large, well-developed high-pressure system is located midway between A and B. Advise the pilot of an airplane the best route to fly from A to B and return.

9. You are located in a car in the central United States at the intersection of roads leading north, south, east, and west. A tornado is approaching. What should you do?

10. Why does weather in the middle latitudes vary so frequently?

11. What is the common path of lows in the United States? What is their average speed?

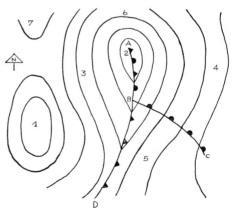

12. The weather map shown above is for the central or central-eastern part of the United States. Seven weather stations are located by numbers from 1 to 7 on the map. Certain weather phenomena are associated with the letters A, B, C, and D.

(1) Name an occluded front; a warm front; a cold front.

(2) Locate the weather station with highest barometric reading.

(3) Which station most likely has winds blowing from the southeast?

(4) If you were the owner of a store selling umbrellas and raincoats, where would you like most to be located now?

(5) Which station probably has brisk northwest winds?

(6) Which station (or stations) probably has nimbostratus clouds? Cumulus clouds? Altostratus clouds?

(7) Which station probably has the highest temperature reading? The lowest?

CHAPTER 24

Sermons in Stones

And this our life, exempt from public haunts,
Finds tongues in trees, books in the running brooks,
Sermons in stones, and good in everything.
—As You Like It: *Act II, Scene I*

GEOLOGY is concerned with the Earth, its origin, and the countless changes that have occurred in its surface features, physical conditions, and living inhabitants during the millions of years of its existence. Geology will always have a fascination for those who are curious about the globe they live on—people who want to know why a geyser erupts and why a volcano spews forth hot molten material; who wonder why the Earth trembles violently and frequently in some parts of the world, causing death and destruction; who ask themselves Why? When? and How? as they view a valley sculptured by the erosive action of running water, as they wander through caverns produced by solution out of limestone and see the queer-shaped objects formed by dripstone, or at a museum as they study the life forms preserved in fossils from the rocks of the Earth's crust.

Mountains, hills, plateaus, and valleys are not permanent features of the Earth's surface but only temporary forms in an ever-changing pattern. Rocks are not dead, inert, and unchanging; they are alive with messages about a geologic history that seems to stretch backward into time for many hundreds of millions of years. There really are "sermons in stones" for anyone who knows how to decode the records.

A hike along trails close to home will mean so much more if one

503

can stop here and there to win from the rocks tales of events that occurred long, long ago. Perhaps exposed on a slab of sedimentary rock
will be raindrop prints which record the impact of the last drops of a
storm which occurred millions of years ago; nearby may be birdlike
three-toed footprints informing the observer that a dinosaur once

*Outdoor bathtub formed by a dinosaur footprint. The track
holds 18 gallons of water and is located in a Cretaceous
(Mesozoic) formation in Texas. (Courtesy, Roland T. Bird
and American Museum of Natural History)*

Fig. 24-1.

walked by (Fig. 24-1). Sandstone layers encountered along the way
may contain abundant fossils of animals whose present relatives live
only in the ocean. This "sermon" indicates that many years ago the area
was covered by marine water, sand was carried by rivers from nearby
lands to this sea and deposited, and that shelled animals were buried in
the accumulating sand and later fossilized. Subsequently the sediments

became hard rocks which were eventually uplifted to their present positions where erosion has now exposed them to view (Fig. 24-2).

Utilitarian Aspects of Geology In today's civilization, which relies so heavily upon the natural resources of the Earth, geology is an exceedingly utilitarian science. For such essential materials as uranium, iron, copper, lead, zinc, tungsten, manganese, oil and coal, geology must furnish answers for important questions. Where can suitable deposits be found? How can these best be exploited? What are the reserves of these materials? Geologists likewise aid in the search for deposits of more prosaic materials—clay or shale for bricks, limestone for cement or building materials, and sand, gravel, and traprock for road-building materials. Diamonds, rubies, and other precious stones excite everyone's admiration, but many persons are ignorant of their origin and mode of occurrence.

THE EARTH

Geology begins with the Earth at the point where astronomy leaves off. (The Earth in the astronomical universe is discussed in Chapter 15.) The Earth is spherical in shape, though somewhat flattened at the poles and bulging at the equator. It measures about 7900 miles in diameter and 25,000 miles in circumference. An average sample of it weighs about 5½ times as much as an equal volume of water. This is about double the specific gravity of rocks at the Earth's surface and indicates that materials in its interior are quite dense.

Materials constituting the outer part of the Earth are gathered into three spheres: the atmosphere, the hydrosphere, and the lithosphere— the sphere of air, the sphere of water, and the sphere of stone.

The *atmosphere,* which is the major subject of Chapters 22 and 23, is also of great importance as a geologic agent. Wind—i.e., air in motion along the Earth's surface—causes erosion* directly by blowing sand grains and other fragments against obstructions and rock surfaces. Moving air masses transport rock fragments from one area to another— witness migrating sand dunes and dust storms. As winds produce waves and currents at sea, they are the indirect cause of marine erosion. The atmosphere is the agent which transports inland much of the water

---

* Erosion includes all the processes of loosening, removal, and transportation which tend to wear away the Earth's surface.

(A)

(B)

(C)

Fig. 24-2.

What happened from the time an animal was buried during the Cenozoic era until its discovery: A. A flood carries sediment which is deposited on the flood plain.—B. The flood recedes, and a drowned animal's bones lie on the ground.—C. Sediments from successive floods bury the skeleton, which becomes

506

(D)

(E)

(F)

fossilized.—D. The fossil is buried far below the surface; the mountains are worn down by erosion.—E. Uplift of the region results in erosion of the area.— F. After deep erosion, a man finds the fossil projecting from a rock layer. (Copyright, Chicago Natural History Museum. Drawings by John Conrad Hansin)

507

vapor evaporated from the surfaces of the oceans by the sun's energy. Over the lands, condensation of the water vapor leads to precipitation such as rain or snow, much of which is returned eventually by rivers to the oceans. The atmosphere is thus indirectly responsible for all of the eroding and transporting activities of running water. As a direct agent in the weathering (breaking up and decay) of rocks, different gases in the atmosphere may react chemically with rock materials.

The *hydrosphere* is the discontinuous envelope of water covering parts of the Earth's surface. It includes the oceans which submerge nearly three-fourths of the Earth's surface, lakes, rivers, and underground openings filled with water. If irregularities, such as continents and ocean basins, did not exist, water would completely cover the outer part of the Earth to an estimated depth of more than $1\frac{1}{2}$ miles.

The *lithosphere* is the solid part of the Earth. The *crust* is the outer part of the lithosphere on which we live; it is more or less accessible to direct study. "Crust" is a useful but misleading term. It is a holdover from a time in the past when the whole interior of the Earth was believed to be molten beneath a thin solidified portion which had crusted over. Bedrock (Fig. 27-5) is the name used by geologists for the outer part of the crust which may be covered by water, loose rock fragments, soil and vegetation, or directly by the atmosphere. Wherever the soil is penetrated deeply enough (commonly a few tens of feet or less), bedrock is found beneath.

The deepest known part of the ocean, off the Philippine coast, is about $6\frac{1}{2}$ miles deep; the highest known mountain, Mt. Everest in the Himalayas, is approximately $5\frac{1}{2}$ miles in altitude. Thus the Earth's greatest relief (vertical distance between the highest and lowest points) is about 12 miles. On a sphere with a diameter of about 660 feet, this would correspond to a distance of approximately 1 foot.

The Earth's surface has two well-defined levels: the continental platforms and, about 3 miles lower, the floors of the ocean basins (Fig. 29-3). The continental platforms on the average rise more than half a mile above sea level and occupy about one-third of the 197 million square miles making up the Earth's surface. The origin of the continental platforms and deep sea basins is one of the fundamental problems of geology. Were they formed early in the Earth's history? Have they persisted more or less in their original shapes? Do continents shift their positions?

The deepest parts of the oceans, particularly in the Pacific and Indian oceans, occur as long, narrow troughs bordering the continents. Since these deeps are not filled by sediments washed outward from the lands, they may be of comparatively recent origin. Numerous powerful earthquakes occur in these areas and indicate that crustal movements are still taking place. Part of the sea floor apparently is subsiding at the same time that nearby coastal regions are being uplifted.

By direct observation, man has access to only a very thin outer part of the lithosphere: the deepest mines penetrate less than 2 miles beneath the surface, and the deepest wells about 5 miles. However, geologic records indicate that certain rocks now exposed at the surface may once have been buried several miles below it.

MATERIALS OF THE EARTH'S CRUST

Chemical analyses have been completed for various types of rocks, and an estimate has been made (Clarke and Washington) of the relative proportions of the elements in the outer 10-mile zone of the crust. Eight elements—oxygen (most abundant), silicon, aluminum, iron, calcium, sodium, potassium, and magnesium (least abundant)—are thought to constitute more than 98 percent by weight of this 10-mile zone. Of these, oxygen and silicon together may make up about three-fourths of the total. The following mnemonic expression puts these eight elements in the order of their relative abundance: "Only Silly Artists In College Study Past Midnight." If the materials in the atmosphere and hydrosphere are added to those of the 10-mile zone, percentages are changed only slightly.

Minerals Minerals are homogeneous units from which the rocks of the Earth's crust are fashioned. As aggregates of minerals, rocks tend to be heterogeneous materials. Most minerals consist of elements combined as chemical compounds, although a few may occur as native elements: for example, gold, silver, copper, and carbon (diamond and graphite). Each mineral possesses physical characteristics and a chemical composition which distinguish it from all other minerals. One mineral may be different from another because it breaks in a special manner, develops with a distinctive shape, or has some unique property such as a peculiar taste, feel, or magnetism (Figs. 24-3 and 24-4). Although hundreds of mineral species are known, only two dozen or so are important as rock-making or ore minerals. As examples of minerals

Fig. 24-3.

Minerals crystallize with different shapes. Top left, *quartz*—Top right, *garnet*—
Lower left, *pyrite*—Lower right, *Tourmaline.* *Note the six-sided pyramids cap-
ping the quartz crystals and the pyrite cubes.* (*Photographed by Neil Croom*)

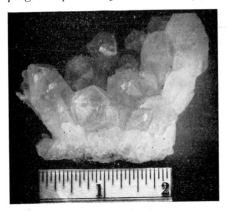

Fig. 24-4.

*Minerals cleave in different ways. Top left: Mica illustrates nearly perfect cleavage
in one direction. Top right: Galena and halite cleave (i.e., break along smooth,
flat surfaces) in three directions which are oriented at right angles to each other.
Check this the next time you have access to a salt shaker. The tiny salt cubes
resulting from the three-directional cleavage are apparent even without a magnifying glass. Lower left: Calcite also cleaves in three directions, but the intersections
do not form 90-degree angles. Lower right: Fluorite cleaves in four directions.
(Photographed by Neil Croom)*

we may cite feldspar, quartz, mica, pyrite, and limonite. These and others are discussed briefly in Chapter 26.

Most minerals originate by precipitation from solution, in much the way that rock candy is made or the way that salt crystals form from a water solution (Fig. 24-5). The amount of a substance which may be

Copper sulfate crystals. The crystals were made in the laboratory by precipitation from a saturated solution of copper sulfate. If the process had taken place more rapidly, individual crystals would have been smaller and more numerous. Minerals form in nature in a similar manner. Salt and sugar are materials readily available for crystal growing. (Photographed by Neil Croom)

Fig. 24-5.

dissolved in a solvent depends of course on what it is and what the solvent is, but also on physical factors like temperature and pressure. Ordinarily the lower the temperature, the smaller the amount of the substance that can be dissolved. Thus as high-temperature solutions rise from the depths along cracks or other passageways in rocks and reach zones of lower temperatures nearer the Earth's surface, precipitation may occur. If several materials are dissolved, the least soluble substance crystallizes first and the most soluble substance is precipitated last. In this manner the walls of a crack in bedrock may be lined with various kinds of minerals (Fig. 24-6). Molten rock-making material like that erupted at volcanoes is the type of solution (magma or lava) from which the great bulk of minerals have formed. Hot-water solutions are another type from which many minerals have been precipitated.

Fig. 24-6.

Geode lined with agate and quartz crystals. Geodes are formed by the deposition of mineral matter upon the inside of rounded or irregular cavities in rocks. Note that the crystals point inward, indicating that the cavity was previously filled with liquid. If the rate of deposition of silica is rapid, a fine-grained variety of quartz (agate in the picture) is deposited in alternating colored layers. Minute amounts of iron oxide impart the colors. The channel through which the solutions entered is shown. (Courtesy, Branson, Tarr, and Keller, Introduction to Geology, McGraw-Hill Book Company, Inc., 1952)

Rocks The majority of rocks are heterogeneous aggregates of more than one kind of mineral, but some rocks consist largely of a single kind of mineral. Some geological processes make rocks; others break them up and destroy them. Products formed by the destruction of one kind of rock may later be combined into a new rock type in a cycle that is continuous (Fig. 26-2). Rocks are discussed in some detail in Chapter 26.

Igneous Rocks Igneous rocks are produced by the cooling and crystallization of molten rock-making material called magma or lava. The hardening process may occur within or upon the Earth's crust (Fig. 24-7). Granite and basalt are familiar examples of this group. The minerals in igneous rocks occur in characteristic assemblages of certain mineral types, and the individual mineral grains (particles) are shaped and oriented so that they mutually interlock. Single grains are large enough to be visible in granite but too small to be readily distinguished by the unaided eye in basalt (Fig. 24-8). Feldspar, pyrobole, quartz, and mica are common minerals in igneous rocks. Variations in

Two buried lava flows in Yellowstone National Park. Sedimentary rocks such as sandstone and shale occur above and below the flows. The following events are recorded: (1) deposition of sediment, (2) lava flow, (3) deposition of additional sediments, (4) another lava flow, (5) sedimentation again, and (6) erosion which results in a valley and the exposure of these rocks along one side of the valley. (Photographed by Richard J. Ordway)

Fig. 24-7.

the proportions of such minerals produce light, medium, and dark colors.

Sedimentary Rocks   Sedimentary rocks consist of consolidated rock and mineral fragments which have been transported and deposited by such geologic agents as running water, waves, wind, and ice. Some of the fragments may be rounded; others are angular. Such features depend upon the length of transportation and other factors. Sediments also include matter carried in solution and later precipitated in oceans or lakes. Loose sediments may be changed into solid sedimentary rocks by pressure from overlying strata which are deposited later and by the precipitation of cementing material as a binder around individual grains (Fig. 24-9).

The presence of different layers, beds, or strata constitutes an outstanding feature of most sedimentary rocks and serves to distinguish them from many igneous and metamorphic rocks. Layers result from changes in conditions as deposition takes place. For example, velocities of the transporting medium may be increased or decreased so that

Fig. 24-8.

Igneous, sedimentary, and metamorphic rocks. Top left: The conglomerate specimen (sedimentary) was once a gravel, as is shown by its rounded pebbles. Top right: Schist is a metamorphic rock which tends to break into thin slabs. Note the parallel orientation of the mica flakes which causes this. Lower left: Obsidian is natural glass; it is formed when lava cools very quickly. Lower right: The volcanic bomb originated when a clot of lava was hurled high into the air by a volcanic explosion. The outside cooled and hardened, thus trapping bubbles of gas inside; the lava later solidified around the gas bubbles. The shape of the bomb resulted from its twisting and turning passage through the air. When the bomb hit the ground, it broke and the interior was exposed as shown in the photograph. (Photographed by Neil Croom)

larger or smaller particles are dropped at a certain spot. Fossils (Figs. 24-10 and 24-11) are the remains or traces of prehistoric life which have been preserved in rocks. They are abundant in some sedimentary rocks, thus readily distinguishing them from the igneous and meta-

Fig. 24-9.

Cementation of sand as seen under the microscope. a, Loose sand from an Oregon beach; b, partially cemented sandstone from a Brazilian coral reef; and c, completely cemented sandstone from Ohio. (From Principles of Geology by Gilluly, Waters, and Woodford, 2d edition, 1959. W. H. Freeman and Company)

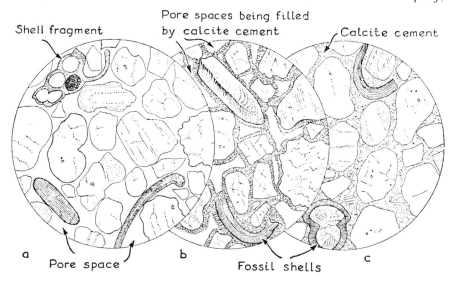

morphic groups. Fossils "label" the rocks in which they occur and yield much information about the past.

Conglomerate, sandstone, and shale—formerly gravel, sand, and mud or clay, respectively—are common types of sedimentary rocks. Limestones, which consist chiefly of the mineral calcite, are likewise common. The calcite may have formed by precipitation from solution or by the accumulation of shell fragments previously produced by various organisms from calcium carbonate dissolved in water.

Metamorphic Rocks This group has formed by the changing of older sedimentary or igneous rocks into notably different types. New kinds of minerals, or mineral particles with different shapes or orientations, can be produced in the crust by heat, pressure, and the chemi-

Fossils in sandstone. Among the fossils are brachiopods, gastropods (snails), and the tail of a trilobite. (Photographed by Neil Croom)

Fig. 24-10.

Fig. 24-11.

Skeleton of a Jurassic ichthyosaur. This remarkable fossil contains parts of several skeletons of unborn young. It is about 12 feet long. (Courtesy, American Museum of Natural History)

cal action of solutions. Some metamorphic rocks are characterized by the segregation of different kinds of minerals into bands (gneiss) and others (schist and slate) by a tendency to break along closely spaced parallel surfaces into flat slabs (foliation). Marble is a recrystallized limestone which has neither banding nor foliation. The study of metamorphism has been aided greatly by observations of rocks at stages that represent gradual changes between nonmetamorphosed and completely metamorphosed rocks in the field (out of doors in contrast to the laboratory or classroom). Recognizable features in the original rocks are seen to become fainter and new minerals or structures to become better developed as the metamorphic rocks are approached.

READING SERMONS IN STONES

How do we read the "sermons in stones"? As a model of geologic history Hotchkiss traced the story of a millpond. The story begins with an unusual happening in the history of a stream. A dam is built across it and a pond develops on the upstream side of the dam. For a number of years the stream and pond lead normal lives. The stream carries sediment obtained from the wasting away and destruction of rocks and drops this material in the quiet waters of the pond. Larger pieces are deposited first near the edge of the pond, and smaller ones are dropped farther out in deeper, more quiet water. Water flowing over the dam is thus clear and relatively free of sediment. The story closes with a second unusual event. A powerful flood destroys the dam and pond and carves out a 6-foot trench in the sediments which had been deposited in the pond during the preceding years.

If no written records or eyewitness accounts were available for this short history, what information could be won from the sediments concerning events which took place during this time? First, the sediments exposed in the gully are examined and are found to consist of layers which differ in thickness, color, and particle size. These sediments suggest the former presence of a pond since they occur in thin uniform layers unlike those deposited in the channel of a stream, and remnants of the dam suggest how the pond formed. Certain layers contain abundant leaves, apparently indicating that they were deposited during the fall. A count of the total number of layers containing abundant leaves, each separated from the next by layers deposited at other times of the year, might indicate approximately how long ago the dam was built. Careful study of the layers shows that some are thicker, coarser, and lighter colored than others which are thinner, finer, and dark colored. The "sermon" recorded here seems to be that thick layers were formed during spring and early summer when the volume of water was great and the stream carried much sediment. However, when the pond was covered by ice during the winter, few particles were added to the quiet waters. At this time the finest sediments were deposited. Previously they had been kept in suspension by agitation in the higher waters during warmer weather. A higher percentage of organic matter produces darker colors in these layers (Fig. 24-12).

Varved clay from a former lake bed in Massachusetts. Each couplet of dark and light layers represents one year. (Courtesy, Professor R. F. Flint.)

Fig. 24-12.

Two layers with abundant leaves separated by exceptionally thick, light-colored beds containing some sand and small pebbles seem to imply an exceptionally wet year. On the other hand, two beds which contain abundant leaves and are separated by relatively thin, fine-grained layers indicate a rather dry year. Examination of all the layers should therefore yield the succession of wet, normal, or dry years which have occurred since the dam was built. A check on our findings might be obtained by cutting down a nearby tree and studying its rings—

wide rings would indicate rapid growth during favorable wet seasons, and narrow rings would show less growth during dry seasons.

To draw an analogy between the pond and a geologic epoch: The effect of the dam might correspond to that of a slowly sinking area that allows the sea to spread thousands of square miles over once dry land.

Fig. 24-13.
Amethyst Cliff in Yellowstone National Park. The cliff is about 2000 feet high. The black objects are petrified trees which resemble the living redwoods; many are stumps still located in the positions in which they grew. The organic matter once present in the trees has been removed by solution and replaced by mineral quartz. Tree rings in some of the petrified logs indicate that they lived for more than 1000 years. Eighteen buried forests are shown. One cannot fail to be impressed by the amount of time represented here by the following processes, each repeated eighteen times: (1) The slow formation of soil from the volcanic debris which fell on this area; this probably required hundreds or thousands of years. (2) Growth of a forest; the fossilized trees may not have been the first generation to grow here. Since this cliff is exposed along one side of a valley, the valley had to be produced by erosion subsequent to all the activity of (1) and (2). Yet the geologic history of Amethyst is a relatively recent event. For example, all of the rocks exposed in the Grand Canyon region (Fig. 25-3) are older. The sketch is highly schematic. (Courtesy, U.S. Geological Survey)

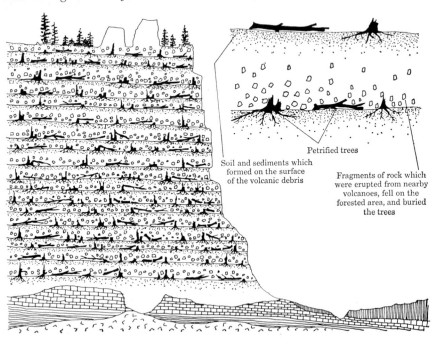

Petrified trees

Soil and sediments which
formed on the surface
of the volcanic debris

Fragments of rock which
were erupted from nearby
volcanoes, fell on the
forested area, and buried
the trees

Upon the subsiding floor of this sea, sediments are deposited in thicknesses which may eventually total hundreds and even thousands of feet—mud, silt, sand, and gravel which later become sedimentary rocks. Animals live and die in the sea and on the sea bottom, and their bones and shells are buried by the sediments. Some of them are preserved as fossils. Rocks, and the fossils they contain, record events taking place in that part of the Earth's surface when they originated. The geologic epoch might end with a slow upward movement of the entire area so that the former sea bottom becomes land once more. Running water and other agents of erosion would at once begin to carve hills and valleys in its surface.

The story of the stream and the millpond can illustrate several points. Erosion, transportation, and deposition are important geologic processes that occur today and seem to have occurred throughout the millions of years of geologically recorded history. Principles and techniques learned by studying the sediments deposited in the mill pond can be applied to studies of the rocks of the Earth's crust. "Sermons" recorded in the millpond sediments have been repeated, with wide variations, many times in the past. Geologists enjoy attempting to decipher their messages. A particularly striking illustration of rock-recorded geologic history is shown in Fig. 24-13.

EXERCISES AND QUESTIONS FOR CHAPTER 24

1. List some of the ways in which geology is of economic and intellectual value to man. Why is geology likely to be of greater economic importance to man in the future than in the past?

2. Grow artificial crystals in the laboratory or at home. Vary conditions (the rate of cooling) so as to produce large crystals at one time and small ones at another time. A simple experiment can be performed by dissolving sugar in hot water until a thick syrupy solution results. Allow this to cool. Suspend a string in the solution so that some of the crystals will attach themselves to it. They will be better developed than those which form on the bottom of the container. Why?

3. Explore your neighborhood or be on the lookout as you travel for geologic features that seem to tell a story: e.g. rock outcrops, hills, stream valleys, clay pits, volcanoes, mines, lakes, and coastal areas. Can you develop the geologic history that each such feature records? If you are unsuccessful now, try later on when your knowledge of geology has increased.

4. Examine the material from a salt shaker and describe the shapes of the salt particles. What mineral property is illustrated? A magnifying glass is useful but not essential.

5. Visit a nearby museum and study the minerals, rocks, fossils, and other exhibits.

6. Give brief descriptions of the Earth's three spheres.

7. A certain town is located on a hill near a steep cliff which has been used as the town dump—waste materials have been transported to the cliff and pushed over the edge to pile up on lower ground below. Included among the waste products have been automobiles made in the 1920's; 1930's, 1949, 1954, and 1959. Make a sketch (do you have a sense of humor?) which illustrates what an observer would see in the sides of a valley subsequently eroded through this dump by a stream. If the observer were acquainted with ancient model automobiles, could he date the different zones in the dump? Do you detect any similarities between this illustration and a pile of sedimentary rocks containing fossils?

CHAPTER 25

Crustal Movements and Geologic Time

THE GRAND CANYON

T HE Grand Canyon of the Colorado River is some 200 miles long and has an average depth of about 5000 feet. Its width from rim to rim varies from 4 to 18 miles (Figs. 25-1, 25-2, and 25-3). As for the spectacle from the brink of the inner gorge, it is one of the wonders of the world, and the feelings that overwhelm a visitor have never found adequate expression in words. But always among these feelings there arises an urgent desire to know about the causes of so vast an opening in the Earth's crust and the history that produced it. Here the geologist can help with the answers he has learned through a study of the record in the rocks. He can point out that in the long geologic history of this region the canyon is only the most recent of six immense chapters of geologic change.

The story begins more than a billion years ago with the origin of the ancient metamorphic and igneous rocks (Precambrian: Archeozoic) now exposed in the inner gorge. Similar rocks are found today only in mountainous regions or in areas that once were mountainous ("stumps" of mountains). Thus the presence of such rocks seems to imply the former existence of a range of mountains in this area long before the origin of the Colorado Plateau and Colorado River (Fig. 25-4A). Since some of these ancient metamorphic rocks seem once to have been sedimentary, and since sedimentary rocks are made of fragments of

Fig. 25-1.

The Grand Canyon district. In the drawing, a view east-northeast across the mouth of the canyon where it cuts through Grand Wash Cliffs and enters the lower country to the west of the Colorado Plateau. The Grand Canyon proper extends to the mouth of the Little Colorado River, above which the gorge is called Marble Canyon as far as Echo Cliffs, and above that, Glen Canyon. (After Lathrop Douglass)

still older rocks, the history of the Grand Canyon begins after geologic processes had been in operation for some time.

The upper parts of these Precambrian rocks everywhere are beveled to a remarkably flat surface (Fig. 25-4B), apparently the end product of a very long period of erosion during which the mountains were worn down to an approximately level surface (a *peneplane*) near sea level.

Chapter Two in the geologic history of the Grand Canyon deals with the tilted layers of sedimentary rocks (Precambrian: Proterozoic) which rest unconformably (p. 704) upon the older metamorphic rocks

Figs. 25-4C and D). These tilted sedimentary beds likewise are very
ncient. They originated with the gradual subsidence of the area after
t had been peneplaned. Upon this sinking surface was deposited a
hickness of more than 12,000 feet of sediments which later hardened
nto sedimentary rocks. Geologists believe the strata were deposited
•riginally in a nearly horizontal position (witness similar beds being
ormed today). Later they were broken into separate blocks along
;reat fractures (faults) in the Earth's crust. One side of each block
vas pushed upward a great distance, whereas the other side was tilted

Fig. 25-2.

'he Grand Canyon of the Colorado
River in Arizona. (Photograph by
Richard J. Ordway)

lownward. The rocks thus appear as a record of the former presence of
a second generation of mountains in this area, perhaps similar to fault-
block mountains which exist today in various parts of the world. Exposures along the sides of the canyon show that these tilted blocks of
sedimentary rocks likewise are beveled across their tops by a second
widespread, remarkably smooth surface (a second peneplane: Fig.
25-4E). Again the rocks record a long, long period of time during
which this second generation of mountains in the Grand Canyon area
was destroyed by erosion.

The third great chapter (Paleozoic) in the geologic history of the

Grand Canyon begins with the formation of the horizontal strata, about 4000 feet thick, which today rest unconformably upon the older rocks below (Figs. 25-3 and 25-4F). A number of these beds contain abundant fossils of marine origin; other layers include fossils of land organisms; still others—the white sandstones exposed in the 300-foot cliff near the top of the canyon—seem identical with wind-blown sands which accumulate in dunes in desert areas today. Apparently, the

Fig. 25-3.

Structure section of the Grand Canyon region. In a structure section part of the Earth's crust is shown as it would probably look if a great ditch were dug through the area and an observer could see the rocks exposed in one wall of the ditch. The sketch is quite generalized and not to scale. The distance from the Grand Canyon in Arizona northward to the Pink Cliffs in Utah is about 80 miles. The vertical scale particularly has been distorted—e.g., the Canyon averages 12 miles in width and 1 mile in depth, yet it is shown nearly as deep as it is wide. Additional rock outcrops occur in tributary valleys which trend at right angles to the Grand Canyon and assist geologists in making the structure section. Precambrian, Paleozoic, Mesozoic, and Cenozoic are eras of geologic chronology (p. 750). The total thickness of the Paleozoic, Mesozoic, and Cenozoic strata is about 3 miles.

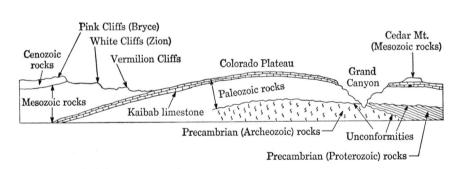

North
(in Utah)

South
(in Arizona)

Pink Cliffs (Bryce)
White Cliffs (Zion)
Cenozoic rocks
Vermilion Cliffs
Colorado Plateau
Cedar Mt.
(Mesozoic rocks)
Grand Canyon
Mesozoic rocks
Kaibab limestone
Paleozoic rocks
Precambrian (Archeozoic) rocks
Unconformities
Precambrian (Proterozoic) rocks

Grand Canyon area was covered by the sea on several occasions during the long period of time represented by the formation of these sedimentary rocks. Dry land arose again whenever the sea receded from the area; and once the region may have been a desert.

Chapters Four and Five of our story must be compressed here. They tell of the origin of the Mesozoic and Cenozoic sedimentary rocks now exposed in the spectacular scenery of Zion and Bryce canyons.

Fig. 25-4.

Five stages in the Precambrian history of the Grand Canyon region. The view is northward, and the sections represent an east-west distance of about 15 miles. The solid black shading in block D represents alluvium. The great wedge of Proterozoic formations near the right end of block F is shown in Fig. 25-3.— A. Precambrian Archeozoic rocks are formed by sedimentation, folding, metamorphism, and igneous activity. Mountains result.— B. Peneplanation leaves only stumps of the mountains.— C. Precambrian Proterozoic sedimentary rocks are formed.— D. Mountains are produced by faulting.— E. Peneplanation occurs and again only the stumps of the mountains remain. In fact, in some parts of the Grand Canyon region all of the Proterozoic rocks have been eroded away.— F. Sedimentation is resumed at the start of the Paleozoic era. (After C. O. Dunbar, Historical Geology, 1949, John Wiley & Sons, Inc.)

A. Folding and metamorphism forms the Precambrian (Archeozoic) rocks

B. Peneplanation leaves only the roots of the Archeozoic mountains

C. Precambrian (Proterozoic) sediments are deposited

D. Block mountains form by faulting

E. Near peneplanation brings the Precambrian era to a close

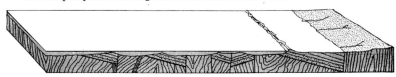

F. Cambrian submergence marks beginning of Paleozoic era

The present-day topographic features of the Grand Canyon region were produced by erosion and uplift during Chapter Six. Mesozoic rocks like those in Cedar Mountain now rest as erosional remnants on the Colorado Plateau. They indicate that the entire region was formerly blanketed by these Mesozoic strata (this follows the so-called *principle of original continuity*, p. 542) and perhaps by some of the Cenozoic rocks also. During a time picturesquely named "the Great Denudation" these strata, hundreds of feet in thickness, were stripped from above the Paleozoic rocks that now form the surface of the Colorado Plateau. As erosion wore away the rocks toward the north, the edges of resistant beds formed cliffs and the steplike topography shown in the Pink, White, and Vermilion Cliffs today. The quantity of rock debris transported from the area during the Great Denudation exceeds that removed from the region during the origin of the Grand Canyon itself.

The river now called the Colorado began to flow across this region when the surface was still at a low altitude. As the region was gradually uplifted some 1 or 2 miles to form the present dome-shaped plateau, the river flowed more swiftly. Like a saw cutting through a board, the river eroded downward in its channel through the central portions of the rising dome. As evidence, the river now flows from lower ground in the north, through the elevated plateau region, into lower ground to the southwest. If the plateau had been in existence first, the river would have flowed around and not across it. Downcutting by the river enabled various types of mass-wasting (p. 597) to widen the canyon.

As geologic time is measured, the uplift and canyon cutting occurred only a short time ago. The Grand Canyon itself is still a youthful valley in terms of the amount of erosion yet to be done to wear the area down near sea level. As one stands on the brink of the canyon, he finds it hard to realize that the tiny-appearing, muddy stream in the bottom of the canyon has performed such a prodigious amount of erosion. Yet it is estimated that the Colorado River carries an average of about a million tons of sediment through the canyon every 24 hours.

In volume, this tonnage is approximately equivalent to 12 million cubic feet of the average kind of rock making up the Earth's crust: for example, a solid that is 300 feet long, 200 feet wide, and 200 feet high. If erosion were to continue at this rate for about three centuries and a half, the Colorado River would have carried the equivalent of 1 cubic mile through the canyon. Of course, this material comes from the entire drainage area of the river, not from the Grand Canyon alone.

Many of the Paleozoic, Mesozoic, and Cenozoic strata bear fossils. For
xample, trilobites (extinct members of the phylum Arthropoda—p.
55) and certain kinds of primitive fish are found only in the Paleozoic
ocks, whereas dinosaur fossils are confined to Mesozoic beds. Thus the
ocks of the Grand Canyon region also furnish a thick picture book of
he life of the past (p. 750).

PROBLEMS AND PRINCIPLES

Two disturbing questions are sharply pointed up by the story of the
Grand Canyon. First, does the Earth's crust actually move this much?
Iave areas that once were beneath the surface of the ocean actually
een lifted upward for two or more miles? What have geologists dis-
overed about crustal movements? Certainly no one living has seen the
rust move such great distances. Does the movement occur suddenly,
r is it a gradual upwarping or downward sinking? Second, is the Earth
eally as old as the history of the Grand Canyon seems to indicate—
undreds of millions of years during which the various geologic agents
ave been functioning? Is the Earth so ancient that a river, enlarging
s valley little by little, actually has sculptured out such a vast opening
1 the Earth's crust as the Grand Canyon? Yet geologists speak of this
s a "recent" event! What is the evidence for the great antiquity of the
:arth?

Skepticism is natural and healthy at a first encounter with geologic
rocesses involving great crustal movements and time measured not in
enerations or centuries or even thousands of years, but in millions and
undreds of millions of years. In the study of geology these two pro-
ound implications of geologic facts must be grappled with at once.
'he origin of a great mountain system cannot be understood without
ome idea of the magnitude of crustal forces. Nor can glacier ice form,
rind slowly and ponderously over a third of the Earth's land surface,
nd then shrink back, without the passage of a much longer period of
me than is often associated with the Earth's existence. Appropriately,
herefore, the study of geology is introduced by a discussion of great
rustal movements and the enormous length of geologic time.

In summary:

A number of fundamental geologic ideas are lodged in the story of
he Grand Canyon.

(1) Rocks have formed at different times, in different places, and in different ways.

(2) Rocks are the written records of geologic history ("sermons in stones").

(3) Fossils furnish much information about the Earth's history—about physical changes such as the advances and retreats of ancient seas as well as about biological changes.

(4) The Earth is very old.

(5) Forces within the Earth cause the crust to move.

(6) As sediments pile up parallel to the Earth's surface in nearly horizontal layers, they constitute a gigantic rock calendar. The youngest rocks occur at the top of a pile, the oldest rocks at the bottom.

(7) Surface and climatic conditions in any given area have varied greatly at different times in the past.

INSTABILITY OF THE EARTH'S CRUST

The notion of a *terra firma* is incompatible with geology and would not be subscribed to by the average person in regions familiar with earthquakes and volcanoes. Evidence indicating that the Earth's crust does move and has moved greatly in the past can be separated into three groups: (1) Present-day movements and movements which have occurred in the immediate past. Newspapers, radios, and periodicals provide sources of information. (2) Movements for which evidence comes from man's historic records. (3) Movements for which evidence comes from rocks in the Earth's crust.

The term *diastrophism* encompasses all movements of the Earth's crust which involve changes of position and rock deformation, whether large, small, quick, slow, up, down, or sideways.

In order to measure upward or downward changes in position, a reference surface is needed. Sea level is satisfactory for this purpose because the oceans are interconnected, and mean tide is nearly level throughout the world. Sea level may be projected inland as an imaginary surface; for example Mt. Washington in New Hampshire is 6288 feet above sea level. Sea level is not a perfect measuring surface because the total volume of water in the oceans has not been constant throughout the geologic past. Furthermore, great crustal warpings of the ocean floors and the addition of sediments to the ocean basins have undoubtedly caused changes in sea level in the past. However, such changes are thought to be slow and nearly uniform throughout the world.

Recent Movements of the Earth's Crust An earthquake (p. 710) is a trembling, vibrating, quaking motion in the ground caused commonly by a sudden movement of the Earth's crust (Fig. 25-5). On almost any

Fig. 25-5.

A fault scarp which formed suddenly at the time of the Japanese earthquake of 1891. (After Koto)

day of the year a newspaper somewhere in the world carries an account of an earthquake which affected the Earth's surface in its vicinity or was of sufficient magnitude to be of world-wide interest. No part of the Earth's surface is immune to earthquakes, though certain regions have many, whereas others have few. Even New England, which is not considered an earthquake area, has experienced an average of at least one shock a year during the past 300 years or so. However, most of New England's earthquakes have been so slight that they were detected only by sensitive instruments.

In the issue of *The New York Times* for August 27, 1950, there appeared the following account of a major earthquake:

In reporting a great earthquake twelve days ago, seismologists used such words as "terrific," "dizzy," and "colossal." But the region hit by the quake —Northern India and Tibet—was so remote that just what happened there was unknown. Last week the Indian Air Force disclosed the results of a survey it had made of the Indian territory affected. This is what the survey showed: The entire geography of the area was changed. Roads and rivers have disappeared and sections of railway have been left hanging in midair. Hundreds of square miles are covered by new lakes. Thousands of acres of land have been laid waste by yawning fissures. Sulphur has polluted the water of some rivers and fish are piling onto the crumbled banks as if trying to escape. More than 100,000 homes have been wholly or partly destroyed, 50,000 head of cattle killed and 5,000,000 persons in all affected. It will be weeks or months before all the destruction can be measured.

Earthquakes can produce notable geologic changes. In 1899 in the Yakutat Bay region of southern Alaska, several great earthquakes resulted from the sudden lifting of part of the coast a vertical distance of nearly 50 feet. Simultaneously another part of the same coast was moved downward. After an earthquake in Chile in 1882, coastal towns were found to be located 3 to 4 feet higher above sea level than before the shock.

In the area around New Madrid, Missouri, a number of earthquakes occurred in 1811 and 1812. The shocks resulted from movements involving sections of the Mississippi River flood plain. Parts of the area were lifted up, other parts were moved downward. The downward movement caused flooding of large areas and the formation of lakes, some of which exist today. In the greatest quakes the ground is reported to have moved up and down in waves, causing fissures to open and close in the soil and trees to tilt at various angles.

In April 1906 the San Francisco Bay region of California experienced a violent earthquake. Sudden movements occurred on opposite sides of a great vertical crack (fault) in the Earth's crust. Most of the movement was in a horizontal direction. Roads, fences, pipes, and houses were offset a maximum distance of 22 feet along the fracture (Fig. 31-18), and the ground was torn apart. Movement occurred throughout a distance of some 250 miles along the fault. The greatest destruction in San Francisco was caused by fire, which spread quickly from damaged buildings. A second destructive earthquake, less violent than that of 1906, occurred in 1957. Additional movements will probably occur in the future.

A very powerful earthquake shook the Hebgen Lake region of southwestern Montana about 11:40 P.M. on August 17, 1959. Irving J. Witkind, a geologist camped about a mile from the lake at this time, reported his conviction that the center of the earthquake was a few yards directly below his trailer and not 20 miles away and 20 miles below the surface as later determined. Witkind's first reaction was that his trailer had broken loose and was bumping downhill. After he had scrambled outside and saw trees swaying in the absence of wind, he knew the cause. Subsequent investigation has revealed small cliffs (fault scarps) up to 20 feet high produced by the faulting which caused the earthquake. These cliffs represent renewed movement along old faults. The crustal movement caused a tilting of the valley of Hebgen Lake so that one shoreline was submerged about 10 feet and the opposite shoreline emerged about 10 feet.

According to Jarvis B. Hadley, another geologist present in the area, the most disastrous effect of the earthquake was a gigantic landslide in the canyon of the Madison River 6 miles below Hebgen Dam. In a minute or so, 35 million cubic yards of broken rock slid into the canyon and covered the river and highway for nearly a mile to a depth of 100 to 300 feet. Three weeks later a lake 175 feet deep and nearly 6 miles long had formed upstream from the landslide area. The walls of the gorge are steep and had foliation and other surfaces which slanted steeply toward the river and along which weathered rocks near the surface could slide. The slide started about 1300 feet above the river, swept downward and across the valley, and at its maximum extended 400 feet above the river on the opposite side. From this unstable position, some debris subsequently slid back into the valley. A number of people lost their lives in this disaster.

In the Baltic area man has measured crustal movements by means of marks placed along the coast. The presence of many marine shells on land surfaces bordering the coast had suggested that uplift might be taking place. Some of the stakes which were located formerly at mean tide level are now several feet above sea level and more than a mile inland from the present shore line. A maximum uplift in northern Sweden of 7 feet in the last 175 years has been ascertained. Movement is so slow that inhabitants in the area cannot detect any change in the position of the Earth's surface.

Many similar examples could be cited showing how the Earth's crust has moved in both vertical and horizontal directions. To be sure the magnitudes are quite small when compared with movements recorded by rocks in the Grand Canyon, but happening so quickly they make us keenly aware of crustal movements.

Evidence of Crustal Movements from Historic Records A classic example of movement of land with respect to sea level is the Temple of Jupiter Serapis, built about 2000 years ago by Romans along the seashore west of Naples. Three columns of this building, each about 40 feet high, remain standing today. The bottom 20 feet or so of each of the columns contain holes which were bored by small marine mollusks. Shells remain in some of the holes. How can these facts be interpreted?

The floor of the building was originally constructed above sea level and is above sea level now. Mollusk shells found in the holes belong to animals whose living relatives exist only in the ocean. Similar clams living less than 2000 years ago likewise must have existed only in the sea. These facts suggest strongly that the land must have been submerged until nearly 20 feet of sea water covered the base of the columns. Afterward the land emerged again above sea level.

It might be deduced that sediments would have been deposited in this area west of Naples when the temple was partly submerged. These sediments should now be visible and should contain the shells and bones of marine animals. The next step is to check this deduction against field evidence. Sedimentary deposits up to 20 feet in thickness are exposed today in the vicinity of the columns. In fact, the three columns were discovered in the latter part of the eighteenth century and had to be excavated from sediments which had buried the bases of the columns. The sedimentary deposits corroborate nicely the evidence from the columns.

Was this movement an actual sinking of the land followed by a later uplift, or did sea level rise and then fall? What sort of evidence will aid in the decision? If sea level rose and fell through a vertical distance of approximately 20 feet within the last 2000 years, the evidence should be world-wide, because the oceans are linked together. A check readily reveals the local nature of the movement and indicates that the land itself must have moved.

Ancient docks built on the Isle of Crete in the Mediterranean about 2000 years ago are today as much as 27 feet above sea level. However, other structures are below sea level today. Thus the Isle of Crete shows evidence of local crustal warping within the last 2000 years— some parts up, other parts down.

Crustal movements involving vertical distances of 27 feet in 2000 years, may be plausible. But how can such tiny distances aid in the comprehension of vertical uplifts of 2 miles or more? A simple proportion may help. What will be the altitude of the Cretan docks if their upward movement continues at the same rate for a million years? (One million years in geology is thought to be a mere fraction of the total length of time available.) Let x be the unknown distance upward. Then $27 : 2000 = x : 1,000,000$

$$x = 13,500 \text{ feet}$$

The proportion exemplifies an important fundamental principle in geology. If relatively small movements or the action of apparently tiny forces act through a very long period of time, they produce major results.

Rocks Show Evidence of Crustal Movements Along the seacoast, certain features of the landscape (Fig. 25-6) are associated closely

Fig. 25-6.

Cliffs and terraces result from wave erosion. The broken line shows the profile of the coast before erosion. A beach may be located at the base of the wave-cut cliff. Waves erode the land like a horizontal saw.

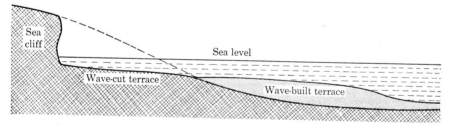

with sea level: beaches, cliffs cut by the waves, and smooth beveled rock surfaces (wave-cut terraces) sloping gently out to sea. Erosional remnants (stacks) may project above the surface of the wave-cut terrace. A study of shells and animal remains found along the shore line and of others found inland shows that recognizable differences exist between marine and nonmarine forms. A check with other observers in different parts of the world substantiates the conclusion that certain types of animal life live only in the sea and that certain topographic features form only along the coast line near sea level. If such features are found today above sea level (Fig. 25-7), their present location implies changes in the relative positions of the land and sea.

Unconsolidated sands, silts, and muds containing the shells and bones

Fig. 25-7.

Uplifted beaches in Alaska on Middleton Island. The lines of low bluffs are old sea cliffs. The upper part of the inclined strata has been cut off by wave erosion. (Photo by S. R. Capps, U.S. Geological Survey)

of marine organisms can be found today a hundred or more feet above sea level in some areas. If such deposits are found near existing coastal areas, one does not hesitate to conclude that the land was elevated after deposition of the sediments. Consolidated sedimentary rocks containing similar marine fossils can be found at elevations of hundreds and even thousands of feet above sea level (3 to 4 miles in the Himalayas). Were such areas also formerly beneath the surface of the ocean? The difference between the two examples is one of magnitude only. The evidence seems conclusive that some movements of the Earth's crust have been very great.

Where sediments such as sand or mud are being deposited today on the Earth's surface, invariably they form beds which are nearly horizontal. Yet ancient sedimentary rocks, like sandstone or shale, can be found cropping out at the surface with their layers tilted at a steep angle to the horizontal or perhaps even standing vertically (Fig. 25-8). Apparently such rocks have been tilted after deposition by powerful crustal movements.

Such facts and principles seem disarmingly simple, but their implications concerning the magnitude and number of crustal movements in the geologic past are so profound that it was many years before they were accepted.

The discovery of sedimentary rocks which have been bent, folded,

Vertical Paleozoic strata in the Dry Lake Mountains near Las Vegas, Nevada. A playa lake can be seen in the distance. After an infrequent heavy rain, water collects in the lower part of the area and produces a lake in which sediments collect. Rapid evaporation soon dries up the lake. (Photographed by Richard J. Ordway)

Fig.   25-8.

and twisted (Fig. 25-9) is probably even more amazing than the finding of marine sedimentary rocks on a high mountain top. Furthermore, rock formations have been broken and offset along great fractures in the crust (Fig. 25-10). Previous examples have dealt chiefly with vertical movements. But some folds and faults result from great compressive forces in the crust.

Another type of evidence indicates that the Earth's crust has moved greatly in the past. If erosion has been taking place unendingly upon the Earth's surface since the first rains fell, why have the continents not been worn down to a relatively smooth surface near sea level? Forces must exist which oppose those of erosion and act to increase and elevate the land areas.

Sufficient evidence has probably been presented in the preceding sections to show that the Earth's crust moves now and has moved greatly in the geologic past. The next problem is the magnitude of time in-

Fig. 25-9.

Large anticline. The rocks record folding, uplift, and erosion. Note the triangular "flatirons" produced by erosion between two stream valleys and the undercutting which is taking place along the outside of the bend of the main stream. The fold

Fig. 25-10.

Airphotograph of a fault. The view is toward the southwest along the south side of Macdonald Lake near Great Slave Lake. The fault separates ancient Precambrian granite on the left from less ancient Precambrian sedimentary rocks on the right. (Courtesy, Royal Canadian Air Force)

volved in the Earth's history. How long have geologic forces been operating on the Earth?

THE PROBLEM OF GEOLOGIC TIME

The time and manner of the Earth's origin pose questions upon which men of all centuries have expended much in the way of speculation and ingenuity. Estimates of the age of the Earth have ranged from a minimum of about 6000 years to eternity. Unfortunately, the 6000-year figure gained authority in the seventeenth century as the actual age of the Earth. For 150 years or so, attempts were made to explain all of the Earth's features in terms of 6000 years or less. The past had to be credited with a succession of great catastrophes which had no counterparts in the present. Streams flowed in valleys formed by the sudden opening of great fissures in the Earth's crust; mountains were formed by quick cataclysmic upheavals; great floods covered large portions of the Earth, leaving behind huge boulders which the raging waters had picked up and carried. As these catastrophes were not occurring during the present age, men believed they could explain the Earth's history best by speculations conceived while sitting at their desks rather than by actual study of the Earth in the field.

Near the end of the eighteenth century, James Hutton, a Scottish farmer-physician, introduced a point of view which radically changed all geologic thinking. Hutton was an observer of nature. It was only after years of careful, patient field work that he published in 1785 the book embodying his principle: *The present is the key to the past.* Hutton argued that the study of processes now operating on the Earth would yield information for unraveling the mysteries of the Earth's past. According to this principle, agents now at work shaping the Earth's surface have been functioning throughout the Earth's history. Today winds blow, rains fall, water flows down hill, volcanoes erupt, sediments are deposited, shells are buried, the earth quakes, rocks crumble and decay, snow changes to ice, and coastal areas are eaten away by wave action. Of course these processes have not always functioned at the same rate as they do at present. Volcanic activity, for example, was probably more pronounced in some periods of the past than it is today. Yet the study of today's volcanoes is our guide in interpreting ancient volcanic activity. Given time enough, processes of the kinds that we are familiar with in the present can account for most of the Earth's features.

Key Concepts in Geology   Hutton's inductive reasoning was a far cry from the preceding years of speculation. Perhaps his greatest contribution to geology was this emphasis upon painstaking field observation as opposed to armchair deduction. Concerning the Earth itself, Hutton stated that he could "find no vestige of a beginning . . . no prospect of an end."

Hutton's motto—*The present is the key to the past*—was later championed by the great British geologist Charles Lyell and remains fundamental in geology. It is a specimen of what may be called *key concepts.* These are principles that guide research and give a structure to the separate facts of science. They have been called part of the tactics and strategy of geology. Other key concepts are to be met in these pages —among them, the concept of the cyclic development of topography

(p. 610), isostasy (p. 735), the evolutionary development of life forms (p. 747), and the principle of original continuity mentioned on p. 528 and discussed below.

MEASUREMENT OF GEOLOGIC TIME

If crustal changes are to be accounted for by processes that we are familiar with today, they must have come about slowly, over immense epochs of time. This immensity was for many years a stumbling block to the acceptance of Hutton's principle, but the evidence in favor of it has been overwhelming.

A number of methods for estimating geologic time have been applied, and we will discuss three of them. All methods have certain features in common. They all depend on (1) fixing attention upon some change or process which is taking place on the Earth at present, (2) the assumption that this change has been going on uniformly since the origin of the Earth, (3) measurement of the total change, and (4) determination of the amount of the change which occurs in one year. Dividing the total change by the annual change then gives the age of the Earth.

Accumulation of Sediments A very fruitful effort to measure geologic time proceeded from studying the accumulation of sediment on the Earth's surface. Sediments are transported by streams to places of deposition where they pile up layer upon layer. Eventually the sediments are consolidated into hard sedimentary rocks. Field work by many investigators in all parts of the world has shown that the total thickness of known sedimentary rocks deposited on the Earth's surface is about 100 miles. Of course, this is a composite record; only a small fraction has accumulated at any one place. The principles used by geologists in putting together the scattered fragments of this sedimentary record are worth a few words of description, since they belong to the tactics and strategy of geology mentioned above.

Superposition In many places on the Earth today, sediments are being deposited layer upon layer. Geologists make the very reasonable assumption that sediments accumulated in the same manner in the past. Thus, the strata in a pile of sedimentary rocks are apparently arranged in chronological order; the oldest layer is at the bottom, and the youngest layer is at the top. This concept may at first appear too obvious to be considered as a key principle. Yet general recognition that rocks had formed at different times in the Earth's history, not simultaneously, developed only about 150 years ago. Exceptionally, crustal movements have overturned layered rocks and the oldest stratum is no longer on the bottom. However, intense rock deformation found in such areas warns the geologist to expect the unusual.

Original Horizontal Orientation of Strata   At present, sediments are deposited in layers which tend to parallel the Earth's surface at places of deposition and are nearly horizontal. Presumably they were deposited in a similar manner in the past. Many ancient sedimentary rocks are found in a crumpled or tilted condition today. According to the concept of original horizontality, these ancient strata were approximately horizontal when they formed, but subsequent crustal movements have changed their original attitude. Acceptance of this principle was postponed for some time by the sheer immensity that had to be ascribed to crustal forces if they were to produce the deformation.

Original Continuity of Strata   Sedimentary layers that are being formed today commonly do not end abruptly as, for example, do the beds exposed on opposite sides of the Grand Canyon (Fig. 25-2). In-

Fig. 25-11.

Truncation by erosion or dislocation. The sketch is highly diagrammatic. The layer of conglomerate exposed in the hill at the left once extended unbroken toward the right where it changes to sandstone. Erosion has truncated the strata along the slopes of the hills and removed the large volumes of rock which once existed in the spaces separating the hills. Truncation by dislocation (faulting) is shown at the right. Even if mantle obscured the actual trace of the fault at the Earth's surface, a geologist could deduce by matching the offset layers that a fault existed.

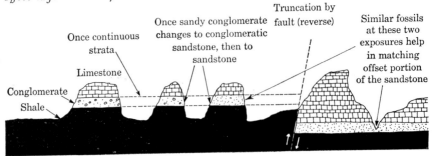

stead they tend to thin or pinch out gradually. If strata are found to terminate abruptly today, it is assumed that erosion or offsetting by faulting has caused this truncation (Fig. 25-11). In the Grand Canyon, the series of sedimentary beds which are now exposed along the north and south rims must formerly have extended unbroken from one side to the other. Erosion has produced a great gorge where part of a plateau once existed.

Fossil Succession Fossils can be found in sedimentary beds that have been piled one on top of the other. According to the concept of superposition, these fossils represent organisms that lived at different times during the past. The oldest organisms must have been in existence when the bottom layer was deposited, but the youngest organism could not have come into being until much later, when the top layer was formed. When fossils are collected from such rocks and arranged chronologically from oldest to youngest, a striking feature is noted. The youngest fossils resemble today's organisms more closely than do the oldest fossils, and gradations occur between them (Fig. 25-12). In fact, many of the older forms long ago became extinct. In general, the changes are from more simple to more complex forms. The horse series is a well-known illustration. Such fossil collections strongly support the concept of evolution (p. 747). Animals and plants which existed during any one interval of geologic history apparently had reached more or less similar stages in their development in most parts of the Earth. They possessed characteristic features which differed from those of their ancient relatives and from those of the generations which followed them. Some forms evidently evolved slowly through millions of years, whereas other forms changed rapidly. It seems to follow that sediments deposited more or less simultaneously in various parts of the world should contain fossils which are somewhat similar. Thus, sedimentary rocks are tagged by the fossils which they contain, and scattered outcrops may be matched or correlated on the basis of these labels.

William "Strata" Smith, an English surveyor, is generally given credit for this discovery. Smith observed layers of sedimentary rocks in excavations and natural exposures in the areas in which he worked. As a hobby he collected the fossils which were so abundant in these strata. Near the end of the eighteenth century he was able to arrive at two important conclusions: (1) In a certain area individual layers always

Fig. 25-12.

Evolution of the horse. Contrary to popular belief, the evolutionary development of the horse was not a straight-line, undeviating, progressive development which began with a small, four-toed, browsing animal that gradually became larger, lost all but one of its toes, and developed teeth suitable for grazing. Several varieties of horses apparently existed simultaneously, and of these all but one type subsequently became extinct. For example, three-toed browsing horses lived at the same time as one-toed grazing horses; the one-toed horse evolved toward the present-day horse, whereas the three-toed horse became extinct. Some varieties of horse became smaller rather than larger. Furthermore, rates of evolutionary development apparently differed at different intervals during the Cenozoic.

Tertiary and Quaternary refer to periods in the Cenozoic era and are terms, along with the name of the epoch called Recent, which some geologists would like to eliminate.

(*After W. D. Matthew*, American Museum of Natural History Journal)

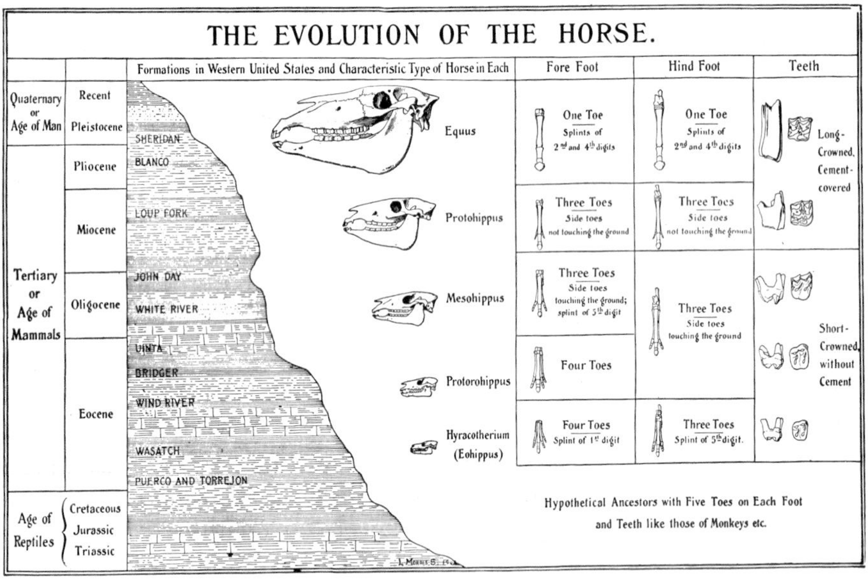

THE EVOLUTION OF THE HORSE.

Formations in Western United States and Characteristic Type of Horse in Each				Fore Foot	Hind Foot	Teeth
Quaternary or Age of Man	Recent			One Toe	One Toe	Long-Crowned, Cement-covered
	Pleistocene	SHERIDAN	Equus	Splints of 2nd and 4th digits	Splints of 2nd and 4th digits	
	Pliocene	BLANCO				
	Miocene	LOUP FORK	Protohippus	Three Toes Side toes not touching the ground	Three Toes Side toes not touching the ground	
Tertiary or Age of Mammals	Oligocene	JOHN DAY	Mesohippus	Three Toes Side toes touching the ground; splint of 5th digit	Three Toes Side toes touching the ground	Short-Crowned, without Cement
		WHITE RIVER				
	Eocene	UINTA	Protorohippus	Four Toes		
		BRIDGER				
		WIND RIVER				
		WASATCH	Hyracotherium (Eohippus)	Four Toes Splint of 1st digit	Three Toes Splint of 5th digit.	
		PUERCO AND TORREJON				
Age of Reptiles	Cretaceous			Hypothetical Ancestors with Five Toes on Each Foot and Teeth like those of Monkeys etc.		
	Jurassic					
	Triassic					

occur in the same succession at each outcrop; for example, a gray cherty limestone would always underlie a cross-bedded white sand-stone. (2) Each kind of sedimentary rock has a distinctive set of fossils which distinguishes it from all other kinds. Smith amazed his fossil-collecting friends by his ability to examine their collections and tell them the locations and strata from which each of the fossils came.

Correlation of different sedimentary rocks on the basis of their fossil content is complicated by the fact that most living organisms are con-fined to certain distinctive environments. For example, certain types of marine animals dwell on sandy bottoms today, a different group lives on muddy bottoms, and only a few species live in both environments. Identical fossil forms, therefore, cannot be found in sedimentary beds which formed simultaneously in different environments. However, the age equivalence of the different fossil types can be determined by trac-ing the strata involved from one area to another. A series of sandstone beds may crop out in one area, and layers of shale may be exposed a few miles away. As a geologist walks from one area to the other, he may be able to observe that the sandstone changes gradually to shaly sand-stone, then to sandy shale, and finally to shale. The age equivalence of fossils found in the sandstone and the shale thus seems to be demon-strated. A geologic chronology based on world-wide fossil collections has enabled investigators to put the Earth's history more or less into chronological order (p. 750). Unfortunately, fossils are lacking in some sedimentary rocks.

Shallow Seas Once More Extensive   Marine waters at one time or another in the past have covered most areas which are now dry land, commonly more than once. Geologically speaking, the coast line which separates land from sea has proved to be an extremely flexible and movable boundary. Local sinking of the land or world-wide rise in sea level causes ocean water to advance inexorably on continental areas. A rise in sea level is caused by the displacement of sea water by sedi-ments, by eruptions of lava on the sea floor, by upward movements of the sea floor, and by the melting of glaciers. If the floor of a shallow sea subsided continuously, space was made available for thick accumula-tions of sediments. Land areas of the Earth today appear to be much higher and more extensive than they were for most of the geologic past.

Patching Together the Sedimentary Record   Sites of deposition have shifted from one area to another throughout geologic time, and erosion commonly has begun as soon as deposition ceased. As erosion went on in a region, previously formed rocks were destroyed together with their record of the Earth's history. In addition, no sediments were deposited in that region as permanent records of the events which were then taking place. Thus the determination of the Earth's geologic history must be based upon the matching together of many scattered fragments into a more complete composite record. Arranging the numerous separated sequences of sedimentary beds into their chronological order and deciphering the messages they contain have proved to be a monumental task made feasible only by world-wide cooperation (Fig. 25-13).

How is the age of the Earth measured by using the accumulation-of-sediments method? The 100-mile column mentioned above is composed of shales, sandstones, limestones, conglomerates, and similar rocks. If an average annual rate of deposition could be determined, the length of time involved in the formation of these rocks could be calculated. The Earth would necessarily be older than this figure. Can an average rate of accumulation of sediments be calculated?

In the fifth century B.C., the Greek historian Herodotus observed that the Nile River annually spread a thin layer of silt and mud over its flood plain. He recognized that deposits at the mouth of the Nile had been formed in this manner, and he estimated that the process must have taken thousands of years. Quantitative determination of the rate of accumulation became possible in 1854 when a statue of Rameses II was found with its base buried beneath about 9 feet of river-laid sediments. As the statue was some 3200 years old, the annual rate of accumulation of sediments during that period averaged 1 foot every 355 years. When this rate is applied as a yardstick to the 100-mile thick geologic column (total ÷ annual) a length of nearly 180 million years is indicated.

How accurate a yardstick is a rate of 1 foot every 355 years? If this rate of accumulation of sediments were representative for the entire Earth at the present time, how accurate is it when applied to all of geologic time? Unfortunately, it is not accurate at all. A foot of sand may accumulate in one place in the same interval that twenty feet of gravel and one-tenth of an inch of calcareous material pile up elsewhere. Research concerning the rate at which calcareous material is accumulating upon ocean bottoms today indicates that thousands of years may be

Fig. 25-13.

Composite nature of the sedimentary record. The sketch is highly diagram-matic. Layers of sedimentary rocks are exposed along the slopes of mountains in New York, Texas, and France. Strata numbered 1 through 8 in New York are shown by fossils to be the oldest of the three groups of rocks illustrated.—Stratum 8 in Texas contains fossils which are nearly identical with those found in bed 8 in New York. Thus the organisms probably lived at about the same time in the past and the strata in which they are found were probably deposited about simultaneously in terms of geologic time. (This does not, of course, indicate that layer 8 was once continuous from New York to Texas.) Therefore, beds numbered 9 through 16 in Texas apparently are younger than the rocks exposed in New York.—In a similar manner, layers 15 and 16 in France seem to have been deposited at the same time as beds 15 and 16 in Texas. Therefore, beds numbered 17 through 23 in France form the youngest group of sedimentary rocks in the three areas. During deposition of the youngest strata in France, erosion may have been taking place in New York and Texas.—Thus the composite thickness of sedimentary rocks for the time interval represented by the three groups of rocks equals the combined thicknesses of the three groups minus the overlapping layers, a total of 2000 feet. Of two layers deposited at the same time, the thicker is counted in the composite geologic record. Thus layer 8 in New York and layers 15 and 16 in France were included in the total thickness.

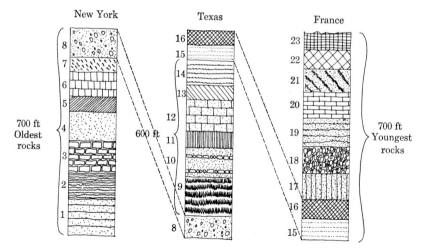

necessary for each foot of thickness of an extensive marine limestone. Since land areas apparently are higher and more extensive today than they were in most of the past, the present rate of accumulation of sediments must be much more rapid than the average rate for all of geological time—perhaps ten or fifteen times more rapid. High lands speed up the processes of erosion and deposition. In addition, great breaks (unconformities) still occur in the geologic record; they represent long periods of time for which no deposits have yet been found. Furthermore, many of the oldest rocks known are metamorphic ones which originally were sedimentary strata. No estimate is possible for their thickness.

One must conclude that the rate of accumulation of sediments indicates that the Earth is very ancient, but does not permit an accurate estimate in terms of millions of years.

Sodium in the Sea as a Measure of the Earth's Age   The oceans contain approximately $3\frac{1}{2}$ percent by weight of dissolved material. About three-fourths of this is common salt (sodium chloride). This material has apparently been dissolved from the rocks of the Earth's crust. Much of the rain or snow which falls on the Earth's surface is returned to the sea by running water. On its journey, the water picks up the dissolved products of weathering (including sodium) and carries them along. Some of this water is then evaporated from the surface of the ocean, carried inland as water vapor, and precipitated again over the lands. However, the dissolved sodium remains in solution because the oceans are not saturated with it. This cycle (Fig. 28-1) apparently has been going on ever since the first rains fell on the Earth's surface. Thus the oceans are becoming saltier every hour. It is a strange paradox that additions of fresh water from the lands cause the annual increase in the salt content. (However, fresh water is not pure water. It contains dissolved mineral matter even when the concentrations are too small to be noticeable.)

If the total amount of sodium in the oceans could be measured and divided by the amount added each year, the age of the oceans would be obtained. This would be a minimum figure for the age of the Earth. Surprisingly, these two measurements can be made within reasonable limits of error. The total amount of water in the oceans can be calculated approximately. Analysis of sea water shows that the sodium content is relatively constant. Thus, the total amount of sodium in the oceans can be obtained by multiplying the total volume of marine water by the percentage of sodium in it. This figure has been estimated as about 16×10^{15} tons (National Research Council investigation). The annual increment of sodium may be estimated by determining the volume of water added to the oceans each year by certain rivers and by measuring the sodium content of these rivers. Calculations based upon data obtained in this manner provide an estimate of the amount of sodium brought to the oceans annually. This total is thought to approximate 16×10^7 tons. The annual increment cannot be obtained by measuring the salinity of the oceans in successive years; the change is much too small.

$$\frac{\text{Total sodium in oceans}}{\text{Annual sodium increment}} = \frac{16 \times 10^{15}}{16 \times 10^7} = 1 \times 10^8 = \text{about 100 million years}$$

This method of measuring the age of the Earth was first used in 1899. For a number of years afterward, the Earth was considered by many to be approximately 100 million years old, much older than previously imagined.

Some criticism of the accuracy of the method is in order. Three assumptions have been necessary: (1) the original ocean consisted of fresh water; (2) all of the sodium brought to the oceans has remained in solution; (3) the annual increment of sodium at present is a fair average for all of geologic time. The first assumption seems reasonable. However, not all the sodium that has been brought to the oceans has remained there. Although marine water is not nearly saturated with sodium, parts of the sea have occasionally been separated from the main body in climates which caused rapid evaporation and the precipitation of sodium chloride and other salts. Some of this salt is mined, used by man, and returned as waste to the seas. Other salt may be blown inland from the oceans as spray and be returned later to the sea. Such "cyclic" salt has been to the oceans before and should not be counted in the present annual increment. On the other hand, the total sodium content of the oceans should be increased by the amount of sodium which now constitutes part of sedimentary beds of salt or is trapped in marine water in the pore spaces of other sedimentary layers. In addition, the present annual rate of erosion is probably far above the average for the geologic past. Therefore, the present annual addition of sodium is probably much too high for an all-time average. How much, can only be guessed. These corrections decrease the annual increment and increase the age of the ocean. For example, if it were found that the annual average increment should be only one-fourth of its present amount, then the estimate of the age of the ocean would be increased four times to a total of 400 million years. In any event, the method indicates that the oceans and the Earth are very old.

Determining Geologic Time by Radioactivity   The nuclei of a number of elements are radioactive naturally; they undergo a spontaneous metamorphosis or change, give off invisible radiations, and transform themselves into atoms of different elements. (Atomic structure and transformations are discussed in detail in Chapters 13 and 14.) Up to the present time, no experiments by man, involving very high or low temperatures, pressures, or various chemical associations, have altered the rate of this spontaneous disintegration. Radioactive decay for any given weight of a radioactive element seems to proceed at a uniform rate.

Uranium and thorium are important radioactive elements used in determining the ages of rocks. In nature, uranium is found as a constituent of certain kinds of minerals which originated by precipitation from solution. Commonly the solution was magma (liquid rock), but sometimes it consisted of hot water. At the time the uranium-bearing mineral formed,* the uranium was spontaneously undergoing a series of changes—the decay series—which resulted in the formation of fourteen new substances: the fourteenth is lead, which is stable. As uranium appears to change into lead via these fourteen substances at a known uniform rate, the proportion of uranium to lead in a rock measures the age of that rock.† The oldest rocks have the highest proportion of lead.

The rate of disintegration can be determined in several ways (p. 235). In approximately $4\frac{1}{2}$ billion years, one-half of the uranium atoms (U^{238}) in any given quantity will have disintegrated into the atoms of other elements; a large portion will be lead. One-half of the remainder will be changed in another $4\frac{1}{2}$ billion years and so on. This relationship is known as the half-life period. For example, a rock which contained only one-half of its original content of uranium would have formed $4\frac{1}{2}$ billion years ago.

The problem of determining the age of the uranium-bearing rock is something like that of finding out how long a coal-burning furnace, now burning steadily away, has been in operation. Beside the furnace there

* The uranium was disintegrating into lead previous to its crystallization, but this lead was scattered about in the magma or hot water. Determination of the original quantity of uranium which produced that amount of lead is therefore not possible. Naturally, a large amount of uranium would produce a relatively large quantity of lead during the same time interval that a small amount of uranium would produce only a small quantity of lead.

† If the decay series is in equilibrium, the age of a uranium-bearing mineral can be determined by the ratio of any one of the series to the end product. The ratio Pb^{206} (end product) to Pb^{210} (member of the decay series from U^{238} to Pb^{206}) has given excellent results recently which substantiate earlier age determinations.

stands a huge coke pile, and we know that coke is one of the end products of coal burning in a limited supply of oxygen. By keeping a record
of the furnace in operation over a short interval we can establish the
rate at which it is using up coal and the proportion of coke it is producing. Now we can measure the size of the large coke pile. Using
this figure in calculations based on the rate of coal consumption and
coke production, and assuming that these rates have not changed, we
can soon tell how long ago the furnace started operation.

In much the same way the original quantity of uranium in a rock
formation can be determined by adding the number of uranium atoms
in the rock being tested to the total number of atoms in the specimen
which result from the disintegration of uranium. Each of these atoms
was once a uranium atom. Of course, one must take care at this point.
We might go wrong if we included in our count common lead—the
kind used in pipes and storage batteries—which formed by precipitation from solution as part of a mineral not containing uranium (galena
is the chief ore mineral). Fortunately, radioactive lead and common
lead can be distinguished. On the other hand, some of the lead atoms
formed in the specimen may have left it. Lead can be dissolved out
during weathering. If we include any common lead that has been added
to the radioactive lead, our reckoning will assign too long an age; and
if any radioactive lead has been dissolved and removed, our reckoning
will assign too short an age. To avoid such errors, the best specimens to
use for determining the age of a formation are single unweathered
crystals of uranium-bearing minerals. The lead atoms which form by
disintegration of the uranium are trapped in the crystal.

Careful measurement of the age of a uranium-bearing mineral is a
costly and tedious undertaking and few determinations have been
made. Tests of various uranium-bearing minerals from different locations have given results which range from a few million years to many
hundreds of millions of years. This spread suggests that uranium-bearing minerals have formed at many different times in the past. The oldest rocks yet measured by this method are about 3 billion years old.*
Perhaps older rocks will be found in the future. Radioactive age determinations thus indicate that the Earth has a minimum age of about
3 billion years. Other kinds of evidence, such as age determinations of
meteorites, suggest that the Earth and other planets in the solar system
may have originated 4 to 5 billion years ago.

Recent major advances have been made in the radioactive technique

---

* Samples of ancient rocks from South Africa have recently been dated as about 4 billion
years old, but some uncertainty exists concerning the reliability of the results.

of measuring the ages of rocks. Radioactive isotopes (p. 286) of elements such as potassium and rubidium can now be used in these measurements and the age of almost any igneous and metamorphic rock can be calculated in millions of years.

The immensity of geologic time is quite unimaginable, but the relative length of its epochs can be grasped with the help of analogies. Imagine that you are walking into the past at the rate of 100 years for each 3-foot step. Walking a mile (1760 steps) on this scale would be the equivalent of going back 176,000 years into time. The first step takes you back to about the Civil War, the second step approximately to the Revolutionary War. Eighteen more steps would total 2000 years and carry you back to the time of Christ. Now to walk into time far enough back to see a dinosaur (at the end of the Mesozoic Era) would require a 400-mile hike! For the next 700 miles or so you would be passing through the Mesozoic Age of Reptiles. A total of about 3000 miles, roughly the distance from New York to San Francisco, would have to be walked to arrive at the beginning of the Paleozoic era, some 550 to 600 million years ago. On the scale we have chosen, 3 billion years is the equivalent of about three round trips from the Atlantic to the Pacific—each 3-foot step equivalent to 100 years!

Again, suppose that all of the Earth's 3 billion years of conjectured history is compressed into 1 year. On this scale, the Paleozoic era, which contains the oldest rocks with abundant fossils, would not even begin until 10 months had passed. Mammals would appear on the scene about the second week in December. Apparently man would arrive around 11:45 P.M. on December 31. All of recorded history would be represented by the last 60 seconds.

There is an interesting check on the accuracy of the radioactive method of measuring the age of rocks. Uranium-235, uranium-238, and thorium (see Chapter 14) are radioactive and disintegrate into lead. Each changes into its own special kind of lead at its own rate. All three have been found in a single specimen, though this is rare. Thus three independent age determinations were made for the same rock. The three results were in reasonably close agreement and strongly support the accuracy of the method. This is analogous to three different clocks which give the same time. One's faith in the correctness of that time is much stronger than it would be on the basis of the reading of a single clock.

The remarkable discoveries made since the turn of the century in the fields of atomic structure and radioactivity have had their impact on geology as well as on other sciences. The first radioactive determinations of mineral age were made shortly before World War I. For the first time in the history of geology, ages of minerals could apparently be measured accurately in actual millions of years. The Earth was found to be much older than had previously been believed. Prior to the discovery of radioactivity, it had generally been thought that the Earth was cooling off by the gradual loss of heat residual from its fiery origin. Now, the heat which is known to be given off during radioactive disintegration has made it uncertain whether the Earth is cooling off or warming up. This problem has an important bearing on fundamental geologic processes.

The Carbon-14 Method of Measuring the Age of Dead Organic Matter

Akin to the methods of measuring geologic time, an exciting technique has been developed to measure the age of dead organic matter. This method is applied to once-living matter and indicates, apparently with a high degree of accuracy, the number of years which have elapsed since the source organism stopped living. The technique was discovered somewhat incidentally, as so many other important techniques in science have been. It is an outgrowth of research by Libby and others on cosmic radiation. It was learned that cosmic rays, during their bombardment of the Earth, are changing nitrogen in the atmosphere into a heavy type of carbon atom which is radioactive. This carbon isotope has an atomic weight of 14, whereas common carbon has an atomic weight of 12 and is not radioactive. Although a single carbon-14 atom does not exist long (it disintegrates into nitrogen), additional carbon-14 atoms are constantly forming in the air.

Libby theorized that a constant ratio of carbon-14 atoms to carbon-12 atoms should be present in the atmosphere and in all living organisms including man. He reasoned somewhat as follows: Carbon-14 is forming continuously everywhere in the Earth's atmosphere; some of it unites with oxygen to form carbon dioxide; plants assimilate carbon dioxide during their life functions; and animals eat plants. The hypothesis was at once tested. Samples of such diverse organic matter as sewage, trees, seal oil, and sea shells were obtained from all parts of the Earth and checked. The proportions of carbon-14 to carbon-12 were found to be approximately the same in all instances.

The testing involves vaporization of a carefully measured quantity of carbon, and the determination of the proportion of carbon-14 in this by testing the radioactivity of the sample with a Geiger counter (p. 235). The radioactivity is directly proportional to the quantity of carbon-14 atoms present in the specimen.

Now a second hypothesis was formulated. In living organisms, a constant proportion of carbon-14 to carbon-12 is maintained because new supplies of carbon-14 are continuously being taken in to replace those lost by disintegration. But after death, replenishment ceases, whereas disintegration continues. Recent measurements of the period of carbon-14 indicate a half-life of about 5600 years. The proportion of carbon-14 left in a dead organism should indicate, then, the length of time that has gone by since the organism died. A small proportion of carbon-14 to carbon-12 would show that the organism died long ago.

This hypothesis was tested against known historic records. For example, tests were made on wood taken from coffins that contained Egyptian mummies, the dates of whose deaths were known. (Presumably the wood for a coffin was cut at about the time the death occurred.) The carbon-14 age determinations corresponded closely to the dates based on recorded history. The oldest checks that historical evidence permits were in the neighborhood of 5000 years. Another method of checking has apparently doubled this figure. Geologists have believed that ice sheets advanced and retreated simultaneously in both Europe and North America during the recent Ice Age (p. 645). Tests on a number of samples from trees buried by the last advance of the glaciers in both regions gave results in reasonably close agreement in the vicinity of 10,000 years. Thus, tests of various kinds seem to confirm the accuracy of the carbon-14 method of measuring the time that has elapsed since a given organism stopped living.

To be sure, the method requires some precautions. Cosmic radiation may have varied in intensity in the past. Apparently certain chemical changes can occur after death and these affect the ratio and the accuracy of the age determination, for example, the addition of carbon-12 to the organism. The carbon-14 method has a time limitation, though further refinements may be expected to keep lengthening this. Carbon-14 has a half-life period of less than 6000 years. Too little of it remains for testing, by present methods, after 50,000 to 70,000 years have elapsed. The method itself is time-consuming and costly. In spite of limitations, a number of testing centers have been started, and hundreds of samples have been tested. Research workers can submit samples whose age determinations would make the greatest contribution to their scientific work.

Imagine the eagerness with which an archaeologist, for example, might wait for the results. Perhaps he submitted a sample of charcoal from an ancient campfire around which he had found the bones of a few extinct animal species and the arrowheads and artifacts of prehistoric human culture. Before the discovery of the carbon-14 method, an exact age determination would have been impossible. Now the date when the campfire was built (actually when the firewood was cut) is determinable within a small percentage of error. For example, charcoal from an ancient campfire on Santa Rosa Island off the coast of California has been found in association with the fossils of dwarf mammoths and suggests a successful hunting expedition about 30,000 years ago.

Sandals made from sagebrush bark were found in an Oregon cave. When tested, an age of about 9000 years was indicated. Since many sandals were found in the same cave, we have evidence of an American cobbler of 7000 B.C. or so.

A few years ago some herdsmen camped for the night near a spring in Palestine. They noticed a small opening in the ground nearby. Investigating, they found a cave and in it a number of sealed earthen jars. In their rage at finding rolls of parchment in the jars rather than gold coins, the herdsmen destroyed most of the material. Fortunately they carried away a few rolls and these passed from hand to hand until at last one of the parchments reached a scholar capable of recognizing its importance. It proved to be a scroll almost 25 feet long which contained a nearly complete version of the Book of Isaiah. Since the present text of Isaiah has been taken from a copy of a still older version in the 1600's, the date of this new discovery was quite significant to biblical scholars. The amount of carbon-14 present in the linen wrappings of the parchment indicates that the scroll was written about 1900 years ago. The ancient and modern versions proved nearly identical. Fortunately, many more of these Dead Sea scrolls have since been discovered in other caves and are being studied.

METHODS AND VIEWPOINTS OF GEOLOGY

Geology is primarily a field study with the whole outdoors for a laboratory. The basis of modern geology has been laid by detailed, painstaking field observations made mainly during the last century and a half by numerous diligent investigators. It has been said that one can learn geology only through his feet, and it is difficult to see how a satisfactory understanding of geology can be achieved without emphasis upon field observations. Countless pairs of shoes and boots have been worn out by geologists slogging through mud, climbing over rocks, and walking up hill and down in search of information relating to the Earth's history! Although photographs and diagrams can help bring the outdoors within fours walls, laboratory work and field trips remain essential features of the study of the science.

Data painstakingly collected from thousands of sites are recorded on geologic maps which show kinds, distribution, and attitudes of rock formations at the Earth's surface (Fig. 25-14). Often a study of scattered outcrops will justify a confident prediction that a certain rock formation will be found buried beneath loose mantle here, or another one there. Such predictions do not rely upon any mysterious powers but upon a knowledge of rocks. For instance, even vegetation can furnish a clue: it may be different on opposite sides of the boundary between two different kinds of rock. Surface details—*topography*—depend largely upon the distribution of resistant and weak rock formations and can aid in the detection of hidden rock types. Mines and wells aid in the study of rocks beneath the Earth's surface. Even the material brought to the surface by burrowing animals may be of value.

All of this evidence amassed so carefully shows that change is the keynote of the Earth's history. Changes and processes which now act on the Earth are studied, and the information thus obtained is applied to the past. The aim is to read all of the sermons which are written in the rocks. Rocks originate and break up, and their remains go into the formation of new rocks. Erosion may wear down continental areas to fairly smooth surfaces near sea level. Crustal forces later elevate the lands and cause the forces of erosion to begin their task of leveling all over again. Today's surface features have evolved from different forms in the past and will themselves change in the future. Evidence has been presented which shows that the Earth's crust can move, has moved, and is moving, and that geologic processes apparently have been active for some three billion years.

It is a pleasant task now in the succeeding chapters to try to answer some of the following questions: How do valleys and mountains form? Why did a recent Ice Age occur and what happened during it? Why

Fig. 25-14.

Association of the three major rock groups. The intrusive mass of igneous rock in the central part of the map has penetrated a folded series of sedimentary rocks which have been metamorphosed along the contact with the intrusive. A geologic map is shown above; a structure section along the line AB is shown below.

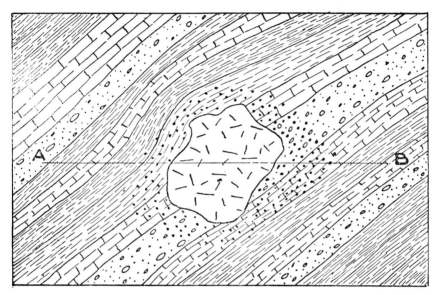

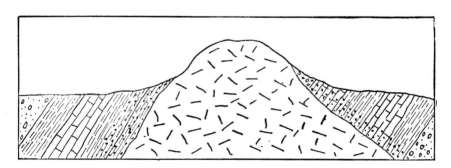

do volcanoes and geysers erupt? Where does magma come from? What sort of animals and plants have been alive during the three billion years of earth history? What makes the Earth quake at times, and why are earthquakes and volcanoes more abundant in some areas than in others? Why do oases exist in desert areas? Some of these questions have answers based on facts; others can be answered only in the realm of hypothesis and speculation. Geology is a young and growing science. It has many fundamental problems which still must be solved, and it is everywhere necessary to separate fact from guess.

Exercises and Questions for Chapter 25

1. Give the evidence and/or supporting argument for each of the following statements concerning the geologic history of the Grand Canyon:

   (A) Archeozoic igneous and metamorphic rocks probably represent the "stumps" of mountains.
   (B) An uplift of about $1\frac{1}{2}$ miles has occurred.
   (C) A thick blanket of Mesozoic rocks has been stripped by erosion from much of the surface of the Colorado Plateau.
   (D) Climatic conditions have varied in the past in this area.

2. Make a point of seeing films such as *In the Beginning* and *Riches of the Earth*. Observe color slides of the Grand Canyon and other areas, and be on the lookout for faults, folds, and other geologic features.

3. Interpret the "sermons" in each of the following:

   (A) A bed of coal in a mine at a depth of 2000 feet below the surface. The coal bed occurs in a thick sequence of horizontal Paleozoic strata. Brachiopods and trilobites occur in some of the layers above the coal.
   (B) Steeply tilted sandstone beds with dinosaur footprints and ripple marks.

4. Choose five of the fundamental principles of geology and give the evidence and/or supporting argument on which each is based.

5. Make your own illustration to show the enormous extent of geologic time.

6. Why is there a time limit on age determinations made with the carbon-14 method? How was the accuracy of the method checked?

7. Give an example of the integration (overlapping) of several different sciences.

8. Describe briefly three possible causes of a rise in sea level.

9. What is probably the most serious error in age determinations made with the sodium-in-the-sea and accumulation-of-sediments methods?

10. The questions below refer to the accompanying figure:

a. Why do the ridges and valleys have their present locations and shapes?

b. The figure illustrates two different methods of measuring the thicknesses (vertical distance between top and bottom) of strata. One method involves geometry and surface measurements, the other is obvious. Describe the two methods.

c. Describe changes in ancient geography as shown by the succession of rock types.

d. The gray limestones in Nos. 1 and 6 are very similar. Describe two possible methods of identifying a certain outcrop of gray limestone as No. 1 or No. 6. You may do field work in the vicinity of the outcrop.

e. Describe the sequence of geologic events which have occurred in this area. Proceed chronologically from the oldest event (origin of No. 1) to the youngest event (erosion and origin of mantle and soil).

f. Draw lines showing the probable location of the boundaries (contacts) between Nos. 6 and 7. These boundaries are buried by the mantle.

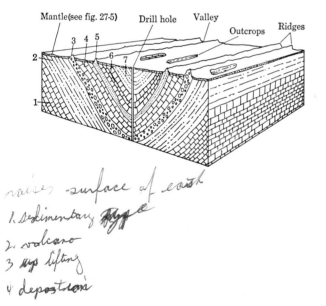

Mantle
(see fig. 27-5)

350	7. Red shale (land fossils)
150	6. Gray limestone (marine fossils)
75	
250	5. Sandstone (no fossils)
100	4. Bluish limestone (no fossils)
300	3. Conglomerate (land fossils)
	2. Black shale (marine)
450	1. Gray limestone (marine)

Local geologic
column 1675 ft

Mantle(see fig. 27-5)   Drill hole   Valley

Outcrops   Ridges

2-

3 4 5

6   7

1-

CHAPTER **26**

Minerals and Rocks

MINERALS are natural inorganic substances that have characteristic physical properties and chemical compositions. Rocks are aggregates of minerals. The atoms and atomic groups which make up most minerals are arranged according to a definite three-dimensional pattern (Fig. 26-1). This internal structure is the most important feature of a mineral.

Fig. 26-1.

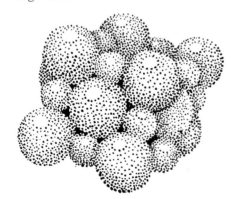

Model of halite (salt). The model shows the relative size and arrangement of the atoms (ions) of sodium (small spheres) and chlorine (large spheres) in a crystal of salt. (Courtesy, C. Compton, Introduction to Chemistry)

An analogy of Trefethen's may clarify the distinction between a rock and a mineral. A building is constructed of wood, bricks, cement, nails, and the like, just as a rock is composed of different minerals. Different buildings (rocks) result from varying proportions of these building materials (minerals) and the methods of combining them. A cement

560

basement may underlie a mansion or a three-room bungalow; nails used in repairing the White House may be identical in composition with those in the local hardware store. Some types of houses, such as the Cape Cod, have characteristic shapes and materials, although considerable variation occurs. Analogously, each type of rock has a typical assemblage of minerals which is arranged in a certain manner. The chance association of several minerals which were precipitated from solution in a cavity does not produce a rock. Rocks tend to form large portions of the Earth's solid crust, whereas mineral deposits may be quite small. Certain types of houses are suited to certain climates. One should not expect to find a tropical-type house within the Arctic Circle. Neither should one expect to find some types of rocks in certain environments of the Earth's crust. For example, horizontal sedimentary rocks are uncommon in the center of a great mountain chain.

MINERALS

Four mineral groups are estimated to constitute more than 90 percent of the minerals of the Earth's crust: feldspars (about 60 percent), pyrobole (*pyro*xene and amphi*bole*), quartz, and mica. These are compounds of oxygen and silicon with different proportions of aluminum, iron, calcium, magnesium, sodium, potassium, and minor amounts of other elements. A few minerals occur as single elements.

Mineral Properties Each mineral has a distinctive set of physical properties (Table 26-1). Commonly a combination of two or three of these properties easily and rapidly distinguishes one mineral from another. The principal useful properties for field identification are color, streak, hardness, luster, crystal form, cleavage or fracture, and miscellaneous characteristics involving taste, feel, odor, magnetism, and specific gravity. Diamond and graphite illustrate distinctive physical properties of the kind that mark most minerals. Each is composed of carbon, yet one is the hardest of known minerals and transparent, whereas the other (graphite) is one of the softest, is opaque, and marks paper.

Color and Streak The color of a mineral is probably its most obvious physical property and may be useful in mineral identification—or it may be deceptive. An inherent color depends upon the kinds and

Table 26-1 PROPERTIES OF SOME COMMON MINERALS

Only the more diagnostic properties are listed. Most minerals can be identified by means of two or three of the properties listed below. In some minerals color is important; in others, cleavage is characteristic; and in others, the crystal shape identifies the mineral.

NAME AND CHEMICAL COMPOSITION	HARDNESS	COLOR	STREAK	CLEAVAGE	STRUCTURE	REMARKS
Graphite (C)	1–2	Silvery to black	Black to med. gray	Good, 1 direction	Foliated, scaly, granular	Greasy feel, marks paper; constitutes the "lead" in a lead pencil
Diamond (C)	10	Colorless, red, yellow, green, black	—	Excellent, 4 directions	Some 8-sided crystals	Hardest of all known minerals
Sulfur (S)	1.5–2.5	Yellow	—	—	Granular, earthy	Color and hardness are important
Copper (Cu)	2.5–3	Copper red	—	—	Scales and branching masses	Metallic luster on fresh surface; heavy
Gold (Au)	2.5–3	Gold	Reddish	—	Grains and lumps	Malleable, ductile; heavy
Hematite (Fe_2O_3)	Varies	Reddish	Reddish	—	Earthy, granular	Streak important; heavy
Limonite (hydrous iron oxide)	Varies	Yellowish brown	Yellowish brown	—	Earthy, granular	Streak important; common stain on rocks (rust)
Magnetite (Fe_3O_4)	5.5–6.5	Black	—	—	Granular; 8-sided crystals	Black, heavy, and magnetic
Galena (PbS)	2+	Bluish lead gray	Lead gray	Excellent, 3 directions at 90°	Cleavable masses and cubic crystals	Heavy; cleavage shows stairlike arrangement
Sphalerite (ZnS)	3.5–4	Yellow to black	—	Good, 6 directions	Crystals and cleavage fragments	Cleavage, resinous luster, color important
Pyrite (FeS_2)	6–6.5	Brass yellow	—	—	Cubic crystals and granular masses	Crystals often show parallel scratches; hardness important
Chalcopyrite ($CuFeS_2$)	3.5–4	Gold yellow	Greenish black	—	Massive, granular	Softer than pyrite
Feldspar (silicate)	6	Varies—white and flesh-colored	—	Good, 2 directions about at 90° angles	Granular masses	Hardness and cleavage important
Pyrobole (complex silicate)	5.5–6	Dark	—	Good, 2 directions	Crystals and granular masses	Name = *pyroxene* + *amphibole*; specimens often show a "grain," because of cleavage
Quartz (SiO_2)	7	White to black	—	Curved fracture	Crystals and masses	Crystals are capped by 6-sided pyramids; common
Mica (complex silicate)	2–3	White to black	—	Excellent, 1 direction	Crystals and cleavage fragments	Flakes elastic; thin films can be peeled easily
Calcite ($CaCO_3$)	3	Varies	—	Excellent, 3 directions, not at right angles	Crystals and cleavage fragments	Fizzes in dilute hydrochloric acid; cleavage very important
Dolomite $CaMg(CO_3)_2$	3.5–4	Varies	—	Good, 3 directions, not at right angles	Crystals, granular	Powdered mineral fizzes in dilute hydrochloric acid; cleavage surfaces curved

Mineral	Hardness	Color	Streak	Cleavage	Crystal form	Distinguishing characteristics
Chalk ($CaCO_3$)	1	White, also gray or yellowish	—	—	Powdery	Fizzes in dilute hydrochloric acid
Chlorite (silicate)	1–2.5	Greenish	White	Excellent, 1 direction	Scaly, micaceous	Nonelastic flakes
Talc (hydrous magnesium silicate)	1+	White, green, gray	White	Good, 1 direction	Foliated and granulated masses	Flakes are nonelastic and have a greasy feel
Gypsum (hydrous calcium sulfate)	2	White, yellowish, reddish	—	3 directions, 1 excellent	Foliated and massive	Can be scratched easily with fingernail
Halite (NaCl)	2–2.5	White, colorless (also colored)	—	3 directions at 90°	Granular, cubic crystals	Taste, cleavage, hardness
Olivine (iron-magnesium silicate)	6.5–7	Yellowish, greenish	—	—	Granular masses	Green, glassy, granular
Garnet (complex silicate)	6.5–7.5	Red, brown, yellowish	—	—	Crystals common; also granular masses	Crystals distinctive in shape
Fluorite (CaF_2)	4	Varies	—	Excellent, 4 directions	Cubes and 8-sided crystals, granular	Cleavage important
Tourmaline (complex silicate)	7–7.5	Varies	—	—	Elongated, striated crystals with triangular cross section	Hardness and shapes of crystals distinctive
Corundum (Al_2O_3)	9	Gray, brown, dark	—	Parting resembles cleavage	Barrel-shaped, 6-sided crystals	Parting tends to produce elongated crystals with flat ends
Beryl (beryllium silicate)	8	Greenish	—	—	6-Sided crystals	Hard greenish crystals
Topaz (complex silicate)	8	Varies	—	1 distinct crosswise	Crystals and granular masses	Crystals commonly striated lengthwise
Opal ($SiO_2 \cdot nH_2O$)	5.5–6	Varies	—	—	—	Breaks with curved surfaces; glassy and pearly lusters

arrangement of the atoms in the mineral and is diagnostic for some minerals. Examples are the brass-yellow of pyrite, the rich golden yellow of chalcopyrite, the azure blue of azurite, and the bluish lead-gray of galena. Colors of other minerals vary widely because they depend upon the chance presence of impurities or of fractures. Examples are quartz and calcite, which may be colorless, white, yellow, red, green, blue, amethyst, brown, or black. The color of a surface alteration should be distinguished carefully from the true color of the mineral.

The color of a mineral in powdered form is called its *streak*. A streak may be obtained by rubbing the mineral specimen on a hard, somewhat rough surface. Commonly a piece of unglazed porcelain (a streak plate) is used. Some specimens of hematite and limonite are black in color and identical in appearance; but the streak of hematite is always reddish, whereas the streak of limonite is yellowish brown. The color of the streak tends to be more constant than the color of the mineral. Streak is not important in the identification of a number of minerals, particularly those which are quite hard.

Luster   This is the appearance of a mineral in ordinary light. Some minerals such as pyrite and galena, have a metallic luster (like a metal); others have nonmetallic lusters—glassy, dull, greasy, or pearly.

Hardness   The hardness of a mineral is its resistance to abrasion or to scratching. The characteristic hardness of a mineral makes possible a simple test readily applied in the field. In a simplified scale of hardness* there are three labels: soft, medium, and hard. A soft mineral can be scratched with the fingernail. Hard minerals scratch glass and cannot be scratched with a knife. Minerals with medium hardness can be scratched with a steel nail or knife blade, but not with the fingernail. They do not scratch glass. Skill in determining the ease with which glass is scratched can be acquired and will help in distinguishing among several hard minerals.

A soft mineral may leave a mark on a hard mineral, but this mark

* A hardness scale (Moh's) has mineral representatives from 1 to 10; diamond is number 10. These are: talc, gypsum, calcite, fluorite, apatite, feldspar, quartz, topaz, corundum, and diamond. On this basis, the fingernail is about 2 to 2½, the glass is 5½, and the knife blade is 5½ to 6. Although the minerals are spaced as uniformly as possible, the jump from corundum to diamond (9 to 10) is as large proportionally as the jump from talc to corundum (1 to 9).

can be rubbed off. A true scratch can be detected with the fingernail as a tiny groove.

Crystal Form   A crystal is a solid bounded by smooth plane surfaces called faces which depend upon the internal atomic arrangement. According to an old joke in crystallography, the beauty of a crystal depends upon the "planeness" of its faces. If space is available during crystallization, most minerals are precipitated with characteristic external shapes (Fig. 24-3).

Cleavage or Fracture   The manner in which a mineral breaks may be very useful in identification. If the break produces one or more smooth plane surfaces, the specimen is said to have cleavage (Fig. 24-4). Fracture results in irregular surfaces. Different types of cleavage and fracture occur. A single mineral may cleave in one direction but fracture in others. Mica illustrates practically perfect cleavage in one direction. Calcite has three cleavage surfaces which do not meet at 90-degree angles, whereas galena and halite break along three smooth surfaces mutually at right angles. Quartz does not possess cleavage but commonly breaks with a fracture that is greatly curved and undulating.

The presence or absence of cleavage can be recognized most readily by observing the manner in which light is reflected as a specimen is rotated. If cleavage surfaces are present, light will flash as if a number of tiny mirrors were oriented at definite angles to each other. The distinction between a cleavage surface and a crystal face is sometimes difficult. Crystal faces always occur on the exterior of a mineral; whereas cleavage surfaces originate when the mineral is broken, and the interior is exposed. As a last resort, the specimen can be broken. However, a cleavage surface commonly shows a number of stairlike treads and risers which were produced when the break shifted from one plane of cleavage to another. Galena is an excellent example (Fig. 24-4). Crystal faces tend to be smooth and flat.

Miscellaneous Properties   Halite (salt) may be readily identified by its taste. Magnetite is attracted by a magnet. Test for magnetism by balancing the magnet so that it teeters on the edge of a table. Next, bring the specimen beneath and close to the unsupported end of the magnet. For smaller specimens or scattered magnetite grains in a large specimen, break off a few specks and test with the magnet. Graphite has a greasy feel. Some minerals have characteristic odors. The specific gravity of a mineral specimen may be distinctive; most metals are heavy, whereas most nonmetals have a low specific gravity.

SEDIMENTARY ROCKS

The Rock Cycle   Fig. 26-2 illustrates the rock cycle which was prob-ably initiated by igneous rocks. Sedimentary rocks obtain source ma-

The rock cycle. If sedimentary rocks are buried so deeply that they melt, perhaps they change to metamorphic rocks before the melting occurs.

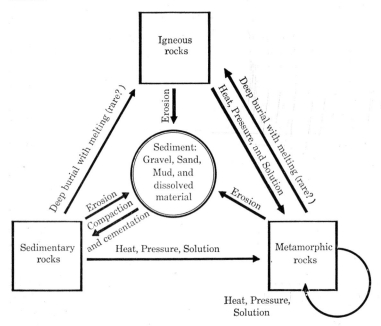

Fig. 26-2.

terials from all three groups, any of which may later be metamor-phosed. Deep burial of igneous, sedimentary, or metamorphic rocks may result in fusion and the subsequent formation of igneous rocks upon cooling (many geologists believe this process to be somewhat rare). Thus rocks may change from one type to another more than once and in more than one kind of sequence.

Importance of Sedimentary Rocks   Sedimentary rocks (Fig. 26-3) are important to man for a number of reasons. They are estimated to underlie about 75 percent of the Earth's land surface and constitute about 5 percent of the outer 10-mile zone of the Earth's crust by weight. If one were to parachute at random over the continental areas of the Earth, three times out of four on the average he would land on sedimentary rocks or find them directly beneath the soil. This group

Fig. 26-3.

Sandstones and shales. Note the resistant layer of sandstone which forms the top of the falls. Mount Marion formation (Devonian) at High Falls, New York. (Photograph by Neil Croom)

constitutes a thin, ragged skin resting everywhere upon underlying igneous and metamorphic rocks. Commonly man lives and moves on sedimentary rocks. Thicknesses of 6 to 8 miles or more of sediments have accumulated at different times in the past and at present, but these greatly exceed average thicknesses. Oil and gas are closely associated with sedimentary rocks; coal and many important iron ore deposits are special kinds of sedimentary rocks. Water resources of the Earth's crust are affected greatly by the kinds and structures of sediments and sedimentary rocks present in various areas.

Rocks contain sign-language records to inform man of such past events as advances and retreats of ancient seas, glaciation, and the former existence of some remarkable organisms. Sedimentary rocks furnish the most detailed and abundant information concerning this history. To decipher the sign language is a fundamental geologic objective.

Sediments are produced by the erosion of rocks. They include all fragments and all dissolved materials which have been transported and later deposited. A huge glacial boulder, tiny mud particles, and pieces of shells are examples. Sedimentary rocks may be subdivided into fragmental (Fig. 26-4) and precipitated groups, although some rocks are a combination of the two.

Conglomerate near Las Vegas, Nevada. (Photograph by Richard J. Ordway)

Fig. 26-4.

Fragmental Sedimentary Rocks   These are subdivided into rock types chiefly on the basis of particle size (Table 26-2).

If mixtures of different sizes make classification uncertain, terms such as "sandy shale" or "conglomeratic sandstone" can be used. In conglomerate and sandstone, angular or rounded individual grains can be seen readily; in shale, however, individual fragments are too small to be seen with the unaided eye.

Shapes and degree of rounding of individual particles depend upon

Table 26-2 FRAGMENTAL SEDIMENTARY ROCKS

SEDIMENTS	CONSOLIDATED ROCK EQUIVALENT	DIAMETER SIZES IN MILLIMETERS
Gravel	Conglomerate (Fig. 24-8)	Greater than 2 mm (= 1/12 in.)
Sand	Sandstone (Fig. 26-3)	2 mm to 0.2 mm
Mud or clay	Shale (Fig. 26-3)	Smaller than sand (the size between sand and mud is silt)

a number of factors, such as type and structure of the material and length of transportation. In general, the greater the distance a fragment is carried, the more rounded it becomes. If the fragment is composed of homogeneous rock material, a spheroidal pebble or sand grain is eventually produced by the bumps and scratches of other fragments or rock surfaces along its path. If the original fragment had a tabular shape, a rounded disk-like form finally results.

Near source areas, sediments include both weak and resistant materials. As distance from the source increases, less and less of the weak material remains in the larger sizes (Fig. 26-5). Quartz is abun-

Fig. 26-5.

Size gradation is from coarse to fine away from the source area. The thickness of individual beds is greatly exaggerated in this highly diagrammatic sketch. One type of rock grades gradually into the next as the formations are followed from west to east across the area. The conglomerate and sandstone are composed chiefly of well-rounded particles of quartz.—Several events in geologic history apparently can be interpreted from the rocks. Since the particles become finer grained toward the east, streams which deposited them probably flowed from a source area in the west. Evidently the site of the source area was some distance away, because the particles are well rounded and almost entirely quartz. Furthermore, the size of the pebbles in the conglomerate implies a moderately high land mass such as could give streams flowing down its slopes sufficient velocity to transport the pieces. The source area has subsequently been destroyed by erosion. The sedimentary rocks in the sketch are the only evidence of its former existence.

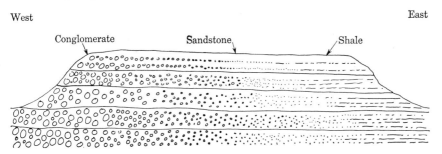

West   East

Conglomerate   Sandstone   Shale

dant in the Earth's crust and resistant to both chemical and mechanical action. Therefore, many sandstones are composed chiefly of quartz particles. On the other hand, flaky minerals such as mica make up a large part of most shales because the tiny flakes tend to float beyond places of accumulation of sand grains. Deposition is brought about by a decrease in the velocity of the transporting agent. The sea floor is the greatest area for deposition of sediments, and marine sedimentary rocks predominate over all other kinds.

According to some estimates, three types of sedimentary rock—shale, sandstone, and limestone—make up about 99 percent of all sedimentary rocks. Of these, shale is the most abundant (nearly one-half) and limestone is the least abundant. Such an abundance of shale is understandable if one recalls that feldspars and pyroboles make up the bulk of most rocks. These minerals change to clay upon weathering.

Precipitated Sedimentary Rocks Dissolved materials—chiefly calcium carbonate, silica, and sodium chloride (an estimated $11\frac{1}{2}$ percent)—are brought to the oceans each year by rivers. Sea water contains about $3\frac{1}{2}$ percent by weight of dissolved materials; approximately three-fourths of it is sodium chloride (common salt). The discrepancy between the percentages of dissolved materials in river and ocean water is explained by the action of shell-making organisms which use calcium carbonate and silica but not sodium chloride.

If water containing various dissolved salts is evaporated, the least soluble salt will be precipitated first and the most soluble salt last. Many valuable deposits have been made in this manner. When the volume of sea water is reduced about one-half by evaporation, calcium carbonate (limestone) is precipitated. On the other hand, sodium chloride (common table salt) is not precipitated until the volume has been decreased to approximately one-tenth of the original amount. Beds of salt (Fig. 7-12) seem to imply the existence of an arid or semiarid climate at the time of their formation.

Limestones Limestones are made almost entirely of calcite (calcium carbonate). The source of the calcite may be shell fragments or material precipitated from solution by chemical and/or organic processes. Calcium carbonate remains in solution only if dissolved carbon dioxide is present. Deposition is caused by the life functions of plants and animals which withdraw carbon dioxide from water.

Many limestones are so fine-grained that individual particles cannot be seen with the unaided eye. Other limestones are composed of larger calcite grains and look somewhat like marble. Limestones are scratched easily by a knife and effervesce readily in cold dilute hydrochloric acid (a slight reaction occurs with lemon juice or vinegar). Limestone may be almost any color, but grays are common. Limestones grade into fragmental rocks, such as shale or sandstone. Such rocks can be given names like "calcareous shale" or "shaly limestone." Limestones do not break into flat slabs as readily as shale.

Properties of Sedimentary Rocks   Sedimentary rocks are composed of layers (Fig. 26-6) which differ from each other in color, texture, or

Tilted Paleozoic strata near Indian Springs, Nevada. The total thickness of the Cambrian rocks exposed here is about 1½ miles. Joshua trees grow on the alluvium-filled valley in the foreground. (Photograph by Richard J. Ordway)

Fig. 26-6.

composition, or in all of these. Layered rocks break most readily along bedding surfaces. Change is the keynote of stratification, one of the two outstanding properties of sedimentary rocks. Presence of fossils is the other (Fig. 24-10). The type of sediment deposited at any one place remains uniform as a single bed is built up. Conditions must change for a second bed to form above the first one. This change may be accomplished by a sudden influx of sediment of a different color or composition, or shifting currents may alternate the deposition of large and small grains.

The colors of sedimentary rocks vary widely. Furthermore, the color of an outer weathered surface should be distinguished carefully from the color of a fresh surface—the "true" color of the rock. For example, a chamois-colored exterior may coat a dark blue limestone, or a red coating may hide a pure white rock. Carbonaceous matter gives rocks dark colors; iron oxides tend to color rocks yellowish brown or red. Only a small percentage of the coloring agent is necessary; a red sandstone, for example, may contain as little as 1 percent of finely divided hematite.

Almost everyone has seen mud cracks formed by the drying and shrinking of sediment as a puddle of water evaporates. Similar cracks have formed many times in the past (Fig. 26-7). Large mud cracks

Mud cracks on a playa lake near Las Vegas, Nevada. See also Fig. 25-8. (Photograph by Richard J. Ordway)

Fig. 26-7.

may reach a width of several inches across the top and attain a depth ten times greater. Sand and silt blown by the wind may fill the cracks before the next layer of sediment is spread above, thus preserving them. Mud cracks are common along the flood plains of large rivers and in semiarid areas where shallow lakes form during heavy rains and dry up afterward. They indicate that the enclosing sedimentary rocks

Tops vs. bottoms in steeply dipping sedimentary rocks. Costly mining exploratory work may fail or succeed depending upon the accuracy of the interpretation. Some of the signs to be noted are shown in the sketch above.— Another method involves the matching of the sequence of beds at one site with undisturbed layers some distance away. Graded bedding can be illustrated by tossing a number of handfuls of mixed sand, silt, and gravel into a deep pool of water. The coarser pieces commonly reach the bottom first.

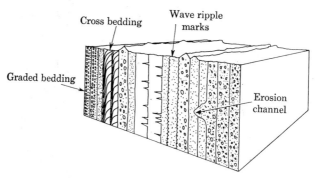

Fig. 26-8.

formed in shallow water. Since mud cracks are wedge-shaped in cross section, the point of the wedge toward the bottom, they are useful in telling tops from bottoms in steeply dipping sedimentary rocks (Fig. 26-8). Ripple marks (Fig. 26-9), rain-drop prints, and animal trails may form in a similar manner.

Ripple marks and dinosaur footprints. The tilted sandstone layers are located in Dinosaur National Monument, Utah. (Photograph by Richard J. Ordway)

Fig. 26-9.

Some sedimentary rocks have a conspicuous minor layering oriented at an angle to the main trend of the beds. This feature is called *cross-bedding* (Fig. 26-10). It may form in the bed of a stream where a depression is being filled rapidly by deposition from upstream. Al-

Cross-bedding in sandstone, Kanab, Utah. (Photograph by Richard J. Ordway)

Fig. 26-10.

though the main volume of sand dropped by the stream in this channel has a horizontal trend, the surface along which the sand is deposited is tilted. Cross-bedding is very well developed in some dune sands and in deltaic deposits made by rivers, but it may form wherever sediments are deposited rapidly over fairly steep slopes. Cross-bedding may be measured in fractions of an inch or in tens of feet.

IGNEOUS ROCKS

These once-molten, "fire-made" rocks (Figs. 26-11 and 24-8) probably compose the great bulk of the Earth's crust, although sedimentary rocks are much more abundant at its surface. Fluid rock-making material may harden on the Earth's surface (extrusive igneous rocks) or below the surface (intrusive igneous rocks). Intrusive types are seen at the surface today because their former covering of other rocks has been removed by erosion.

Chemical Composition   Below the Earth's surface, molten igneous material is called *magma* (Greek; "dough"); above the Earth's surface this same material, minus some of its dissolved gases, is termed *lava*.

The hardened rock is sometimes also called lava. Magma and lava are mutual solutions of all rock-making ingredients plus dissolved volatile substances such as steam (which predominates), carbon dioxide, sulfur, chlorine, fluorine, and boron. The volatiles do not enter into the composition of rock-forming minerals. However, these dissolved gases perform a number of important functions. They increase the fluidity of magma, cause explosive activity at volcanoes, and concentrate valuable metals formerly scattered in tiny amounts throughout the magma.

Fig. 26-11.

Igneous rocks: Top, *gabbro*—Middle, *diorite*—
Bottom, *granite.* (*Photograph by Neil Croom*)

Silica (SiO_2), aluminum, iron, calcium, magnesium, sodium, and potassium are the abundant ingredients in magma and lava. The silica content of igneous rocks varies from about 40 to 80 percent. If a magma is high in its silica content (some 70 percent or more), its percentages of iron, calcium, and magnesium are correspondingly low; on the other hand, a low-silica magma (some 50 percent or less) is high in its percentages of iron, calcium, and magnesium. The percentage of aluminum is nearly constant. Low-silica magmas are fluid and produce dark-colored rocks, whereas high-silica magmas tend to be viscous and to produce light-colored igneous rocks.

Texture   The shapes, sizes, and arrangement of individual mineral grains in a rock determine its texture. Texture depends upon a number of factors. Some dissolved substances in magma are more soluble than others. As magma cools, the least soluble substances crystallize first as solid grains, whereas the most soluble substances crystallize last. Accordingly, the first mineral grains crystallizing in a liquid medium develop with their characteristic shapes; the next mineral grains to form have somewhat modified crystal shapes; and the mineral grains precipitated last are formless masses filling all remaining spaces. An interlocking texture is characteristic. In a simplified order of crystallization, pyroboles and dark mica tend to form first, feldspars next, and quartz last.

Pyroboles are made of iron, calcium, and other elements combined in definite proportions with silica. Commonly pyroboles crystallize from magma first and extract from it all of the silica they need to combine with their other ingredients. Therefore, abundant pyrobole can form only from a low-silica magma having a high proportion of these other materials. Pyrobole cannot form if one of the necessary elements is missing. Feldspars make the next demand on the silica supply. Thus quartz, which is free silica and crystallizes last, can be present in an igneous rock only if the original magma had a high percentage of silica. As pyrobole tends to be dark colored and feldspar and quartz are light colored, low-silica magmas commonly produce dark-colored igneous rocks. Some silica combines with iron, calcium, and magnesium to form dark-colored pyroboles; the remaining silica is taken up by feldspar, and no silica is left over to crystallize out as light-colored quartz. On the other hand, high-silica magmas that contain relatively small amounts of iron, calcium, and magnesium can produce only limited quantities of pyroboles. In such high-silica magmas abundant feldspar forms next, and enough silica remains for the precipitation of a substantial quantity of quartz. Thus, a light-colored igneous rock is produced. Low-silica igneous rocks have specific gravities of about 3.0 in contrast to the 2.7 of high-silica igneous rocks.

Sizes of individual mineral grains in igneous rocks are influenced by a number of factors. Slow cooling under a thick cover of rocks produces large mineral grains, whereas the sudden chilling of lava as it reaches the surface results in the formation of many small particles. In general, intrusive rocks are coarse grained, and extrusive rocks are fine grained. However, some intrusive bodies are fine grained—for example, sills and dikes (Fig. 30-12) which were injected as thin streams of magma along cracks in cold rocks. In other dikes and sills, the magma flowed long enough to heat the wall rocks, and the eventual cooling was a slow process. Many large intrusive masses have fine-grained borders, whereas thick flows of fluid low-silica lava may have medium-grained interiors. Natural glass (obsidian) results when lava or magma is chilled so rapidly that individual atoms and atomic groups do not have time to unite into mineral grains. Obsidian is a frozen sample of the original molten material. Pumice is obsidian which is so full of gas bubble holes that it is light enough to float in water.

Some igneous rocks are composed of mineral grains of two sharply different sizes, one much larger than the other. Such a texture is called porphyritic (Fig. 26-12). One manner in which porphyritic texture

Porphyritic texture in extrusive igneous rock.

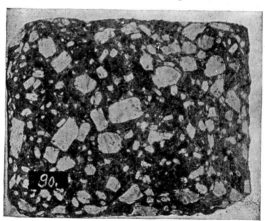

Fig. 26-12.

may develop involves two stages of cooling. A rising magma may stop far below the surface and cool slowly. The first-formed minerals grow into large grains which float in the fluid magma. Later the magma may resume its rise toward the surface and be erupted as a lava. Upon the Earth's surface the lava cools rapidly. Many small particles crystallize and surround the larger ones (phenocrysts) which had formed previously below the surface.

The diamond pipes of South Africa may illustrate porphyritic texture. These pipes are cylindrical intrusive igneous rock bodies which crystallized from a very low-silica magma. Diamonds occur as well-developed crystals scattered here and there in the igneous rock. According to one explanation, the diamonds crystallized first far below the surface. Later they were carried upward by the magma to their present locations where the remaining material solidified. A striking bit of evidence supporting this concept comes from one of the South African mines. Two broken parts of a rodlike diamond crystal were found at different levels in the mine. The two parts are said to have fitted together perfectly. Apparently the crystal, formed below, was broken as it moved upward, and one part rose higher than the other.

Classification of Igneous Rocks Igneous rocks differ in texture and mineral composition and are classified by these criteria. As with sedimentary rocks, however, the problem of arbitrarily subdividing a continuous series is encountered. Table 26-3 offers a simplified version of

Table 26-3 SIMPLIFIED FIELD CLASSIFICATION
FOR IGNEOUS ROCKS[a]

Texture[b]	High silica (70-80%) Light-colored rocks Minerals: Feldspar and quartz with some pyrobole and/or mica		Medium ⟷ Feldspar and pyrobole	Low silica (40 to 50%) Dark-colored rocks Pyrobole and feldspar
GRANULAR—particles readily visible—commonly intrusive	Granite	Syenite (no quartz, otherwise like granite)	Diorite	Gabbro
APHANITIC—particles invisible or tiny specks— commonly extrusive	Felsite			Basalt
GLASSY—no mineral particles	Obsidian (commonly the chemical equivalent of a granite)			

[a] Distinct boundaries between these types do not occur in nature, and specimens have been found which represent all possible gradations in texture and mineral composition.
[b] All of the rock types listed above may have porphyritic texture. If so, they can be given names like "porphyritic granite."

a classification of igneous rocks which is readily applicable in the field or laboratory without the use of chemical analyses or a powerful microscope. Of the hundreds of igneous rocks that have found names, fortunately only a few are common.

Granite is a granular light-colored igneous rock which contains feldspar (about 60 percent), quartz (about 30 percent), and dark minerals or mica. It crystallized as an intrusive igneous body from high-silica magma. Rocks which have the appearance of granite but were formed in another manner are discussed elsewhere (p. 685). Felsite contains the same minerals as granite, syenite, and some diorites but has an aphanitic texture (with particles invisible or visible as tiny specks). Typically, felsite occurs in extrusive igneous rocks, in small intrusive bodies, or around the margins of larger intrusives. Obsidian commonly has a chemical composition similar to that of granite. Syenite is a granular, light-colored igneous rock lacking quartz. Otherwise syenite is similar to granite. The quartz and feldspar in a granite commonly have different colors. Therefore, granites tend to have three colors, whereas syenites tend to have two colors. In some granites and syenites the feldspar is reddish, and the rocks are darker than average in color.

Gabbro is a granular, dark-colored igneous rock containing more than 50 percent pyrobole; the rest is largely feldspar. It crystallized from a low-silica magma, commonly as an intrusive. Diorite contains more feldspar than pyrobole and is intermediate in color between granite and gabbro (Fig. 26-11). As the term is used here, *basalt* is a group name for fine-grained, dark-colored igneous rocks, the chemical equivalents of gabbro and some diorites. The modes of occurrence of basalt and felsite are similar.

The great diversity of igneous rocks is due in large part to the chance combination of two independent variables: different kinds of magmas and different methods of cooling and crystallizing.

Granites and rocks like granite are estimated to constitute about 95 percent of all intrusive rocks; on the other hand, basalts and basaltic types probably make up more than 95 percent of all extrusive rocks. Geologists do not yet understand why this distribution exists.

METAMORPHISM

Many persons are familiar with the concept that living organisms become adapted to their environments. Few persons are aware, however, that rocks also become adapted to their environments. During this adaptation, which is a slow and sometimes incomplete process, older rocks are changed into new, notably different kinds of rocks; they are metamorphosed (Fig. 25-14) until they attain a more or less stable form capable of resisting further change under the conditions of their environment.

Changes Produced by Metamorphism   These transformations* involve the development of new textures, new structures, new minerals, or any combination of these. Original characteristics of a rock may be destroyed completely by metamorphism.

Great heat and pressure may cause the atoms present in a rock to be regrouped into new minerals. Commonly these are dense, space-saving minerals which are stable in the new environment. Certain minerals are found only in intensely metamorphosed rocks; others are limited to mildly metamorphosed rocks. Such minerals constitute valuable "geologic thermometers" which measure the degree of the metamorphic changes.

Rounded pebbles and boulders in a conglomerate have been metamorphosed into elongated, roughly cylindrical shapes which may be an inch or more in diameter and exceed 12 inches in length. Commonly the pebbles are elongated parallel to each other. They furnish a striking example of a change in texture. Obviously, enormous forces were necessary to twist, pull, and squeeze rock fragments into such shapes.

Agents Causing Transformations   Heat has a major role in metamorphism because a rise in temperature makes most chemical changes proceed at a faster rate. Furthermore, certain chemical reactions can occur at high temperatures which are impossible at lower ones.

Pressure is another factor in metamorphism. Powerful forces may crush, pulverize, and break rocks by squeezing and twisting them. In addition, great pressures applied slowly may deform rocks plastically; a slow permanent change in shape is produced without rupture.

Solutions aid in the formation of new minerals by adding and removing various substances or by facilitating the recrystallization and rearrangement of mineral materials already present. Many chemical

---

* Metamorphism deals with the formation of new rocks from old rocks; the bulk of the rock materials remains solid at all times. Thus, changes which occur when a loose sediment becomes a consolidated sedimentary rock or which take place during the weathering of rocks are not considered metamorphic.

reactions are slow or impossible between dry substances but take place rapidly when a little water is added.

Contact Metamorphism In Glacier National Park, dark sills of diorite approximately 50 to 100 feet thick have been intruded into a gray rock similar to limestone (dolomite). Distinct white bands 10 to 20 feet thick occur above and below the sills. Individual particles can be seen in the hard white rock but not in the softer dolomite. Traces of bedding surfaces are visible in the white bands. Evidently this material was once gray dolomite before its metamorphism to marble. During the metamorphism the tiny grains in the dolomite recrystallized and combined into the larger particles seen in the marble. Heat from the once-molten diorite apparently caused the metamorphism, because the changes decrease gradually in intensity away from the margins of the sill. Such transformations are called contact metamorphism because they occur along the contacts of igneous bodies. In its simplest manifestation, contact metamorphism results from increased temperature alone, but gases may escape from the magma into the enclosing rocks and aid the process.

Foliation Foliation (Latin: "leaf formation") or rock cleavage refers to the capacity of a metamorphic rock to split into thin slabs along closely spaced parallel smooth surfaces (Fig. 26-13). Metamorphic rocks may be subdivided into two groups by the presence or absence of foliation. Slate, schist, and gneiss are common examples of foliated metamorphic rocks; hornfels, marble, and quartzite represent nonfoliated types.

Sedimentary rocks such as shale are not in fact foliated, though they break along bedding surfaces to produce thin slabs. A bedding surface should be distinguished from a foliated surface. Shale consists chiefly of tiny flakes of minerals which were deposited with their flat sides in alignment. When shales are broken, they split along flat surfaces which parallel the sides of these tiny flakes.

When shale is squeezed by great compressive forces during one kind of metamorphism, the layers are bent and folded. During this folding, existing mineral grains are granulated, recrystallized, and reoriented. In addition, new platy or elongated minerals may develop. Most of the resulting flaky mineral particles are lined up parallel to each other and at right angles to the axis of compression. The resulting metamorphic rock is a slate. The microscope has shown that the excellent foliation of slate is the direct result of the combined cleavages of its tiny flaky constituents.

All traces of the original stratification have been destroyed in many slates. However, gradations between shale and slate are known in nature. Such partially metamorphosed rocks provide valuable clues which enable geologists to understand how slates and other metamorphic rocks originate.

Fig. 26-13.

Slate vs. shale. Relics of original bedding are shown in the slate. Before metamorphism the rock would have broken into flat pieces parallel to the stratification. After metamorphism the rock breaks parallel to the foliation. The enlargement shows small offsets along the foliation (rock cleavage) surfaces. (From Principles of Geology by Gilluly, Waters, and Woodford, 2d edition, 1959, W. H. Freeman and Company)

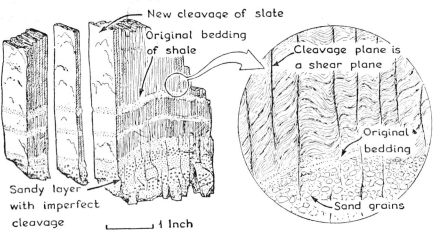

When shale is metamorphosed by heat and/or solutions in the absence of compressive forces (greater pressure in one direction than in others), parallel orientation of platy minerals is lacking and the resulting rock has no cleavage. This rock is called a *hornfels*. It may form from other rocks than shale. If rocks made up of nonplaty or nonelongated mineral grains are squeezed and metamorphosed, nonfoliated rocks result, because foliation is impossible without the presence of platy minerals. Thus sandstones (chiefly quartz) and limestones (calcite) change to quartzites and marbles which are nonfoliated.

Some Common Metamorphic Rocks   *Slate* is a well foliated rock which can be split into thin smooth slabs for blackboards, roofing, and a number of other purposes. Commonly its mineral grains are too tiny to be seen with the unaided eye. The distinction between shale and slate is sometimes difficult (Figs. 26-13 and 26-14). Traces of the

Fig. 26-14.

Two metamorphic rocks. Shale (sedimentary, shown in the middle) tends to break with a gently curved surface, whereas slate (shown at the left) tends to break with a smooth flat shiny surface. Gneiss, at the right, shows banding. (Photographs by Neil Croom)

original sedimentary layers oriented at an angle to the foliation may be found in the slate and make identification certain. However, bedding and foliation may be parallel, or no traces of the original stratification may remain. In these cases, the following criteria are helpful, although exceptions are known for each: Slates tend to break with flat surfaces, whereas many shales split along gently curved surfaces. Slates may have a higher luster than shales. In addition, slates may ring under the blow of a metallic object, whereas shale gives a dull sound. Commonly, slates are blue-black in color.

Schist (pronounced "shist") is a coarse-grained foliated metamorphic rock which breaks easily into thin flakes and slabs (Fig. 24-8). Individual mineral grains can be seen with the unaided eye. Schists appear to be composed almost entirely of the parallel micaceous minerals exposed along their wrinkled, foliated surfaces. However, observation of a specimen in cross section shows that other minerals are present. A shale may be metamorphosed first to slate (low rank); later the slate, by further metamorphism, may be changed to schist (high rank).

Gneiss is a coarse-grained metamorphic rock which has poorly developed foliation and a banded, streaked appearance (Fig. 26-14). Gneisses and schists are high-rank metamorphic rocks which grade into each other. They result from the metamorphism of a variety of other kinds of rocks. The streaked appearance of a gneiss (pronounced "nice") depends upon the segregation of its materials into bands which commonly are crumpled and contorted. Many gneisses were once granites.

Hornfels is a dense nonfoliated metamorphic rock which resulted from the thorough recrystallization of older rocks, commonly around the margins of igneous intrusives. The compression necessary to produce parallel orientation of platy or elongated minerals was absent. Hornfelses may be fine grained or have a sugary texture visible to the unaided eye. They are hard and tough and vary in color. Some hornfelses break with a smooth, curved fracture and closely resemble other kinds of rocks (limestone, felsite, and basalt) and some varieties of quartz. Identification of certain specimens is not possible without the microscope. However, field relationships may furnish important clues.

Quartzite is a nonfoliated metamorphic rock which consists of quartz grains cemented so firmly together that the rock breaks through, not around, the individual grains. Recrystallization tends to produce an interlocking texture. Quartzites commonly have smooth, glassy surfaces. In contrast sandstones break around the grains and have rough surfaces which may feel like sandpaper when rubbed. Most quartzites are produced by the metamorphism of quartzose sandstone.

Marble is a nonfoliated metamorphic rock (Fig. 30-15) composed almost entirely of calcite (as well as dolomite). It is produced by the metamorphism of limestone and similar rocks. The rock can be scratched easily with a knife and effervesces briskly in cold, dilute hydrochloric acid. Marbles differ from most limestones in being visibly crystalline and having purer colors. Impurities in the limestones are eliminated during the process of recrystallization.

DISTINCTIONS AMONG ROCKS

In identifying a rock specimen, one should attempt first to place it in the sedimentary, igneous, or metamorphic group. Field relationships may be valuable for this purpose. Identification of a rock outcrop in the field is commonly much easier than the determination of a small chip in the laboratory. For example, stratification in a thick-bedded sandstone may be readily apparent in field exposures and labels it as a sedimentary rock. However, evidence of bedding may be entirely missing in a small specimen taken from one of the layers.

Sedimentary rocks characteristically are layered, contain rounded particles, and may include fossils, mud cracks, ripple marks, or cross-bedding. If a high percentage of quartz is present in a specimen, or if calcite is present, it can be distinguished from an igneous rock. Igneous rocks commonly have distinctive sets of minerals with characteristic interlocking textures. Metamorphic marbles and quartzites likewise have interlocking textures but can be distinguished from igneous rocks because of their compositions. Visibly crystalline marble can generally be distinguished from dense limestone on the basis of grain size. Coarse-grained limestones containing undeformed fossils are readily recognizable. Foliated metamorphic rocks may be distinguished from igneous rocks on the basis of foliation and from layered sedimentary rocks, because this foliation depends upon the parallel orientation of platy elongated minerals, not upon an alternation of various layers or beds. Hornfelses take more skill in recognizing.

The preceding classification is a simplified version of the classification used by geologists. However, exact terminology is unnecessary for the nonprofessional. Emphasis should be placed upon rock origins and upon the information which rocks contain concerning past events on the Earth. For example, identification of a certain rock outcrop as a limestone may be important because it represents part of a former sea floor on which lived and died a whole host of organisms.

EXERCISES AND QUESTIONS FOR CHAPTER 26

1. Pick out three or four sites in your neighborhood where rocks are exposed in some variety. Visit each on a field trip. Make notes on the types of rock that occur and on the order of their occurrence. Collect a speci-

men of each type for testing in the laboratory. Note especially any finds of fossils or of fairly pure mineral deposits.

2. With the aid of a hand lens, a streak plate, a magnet, a nail, a piece of window glass and acid, study a large number of specimens of rocks, minerals, and fossils. Keep notes on how each specimen responds to tests and how each appears under the lens.

3. Make notes on the types of rocks which have been used in five nearby buildings and construction projects.

4. How are unconsolidated sediments changed to firm sedimentary rocks? Why are sediments deposited in layers?

5. Why does a certain type of mineral always crystallize and cleave in the same way?

6. Describe at least one simple test (give two or three if you can) which would readily distinguish between the following:

    (1) Calcite vs. feldspar
    (2) Quartz vs. calcite
    (3) Dark fine-grained limestone vs. basalt
    (4) Granite vs. syenite
    (5) Mica vs. gypsum
    (6) Pyrobole vs. magnetite
    (7) Marble vs. quartzite
    (8) Pyrite vs. gold
    (9) Black limonite vs. black hematite.

7. Discuss reasons why classification is of value in science.

8. Distinguish between foliation and stratification. Give two reasons why foliation may be poorly developed in a rock.

9. Why is it easier to identify many rocks in the field than as specimens in a laboratory?

10. In the blank near each item in the left column, write in the number of the type of rock listed in the right column which would commonly be associated with it. Certain rock types may be used more than once. Others may not be used at all. An occasional item in the left column may have more than one correct answer.

    _____Intrusive igneous rock   1. Gneiss
    _____Product of wind erosion   2. Granite

_____High-silica lava flow

_____Microscopic grains of pyrobole with some feldspar

_____At contact of a limestone with a thick dike

_____Result of nonuniform pressure and metamorphism

_____Unsorted accumulation of boulders, gravel, sand, and mud

_____Cooled very rapidly; no minerals present

_____Composed almost entirely of silica

_____Will float on water

_____Deposited in a sea

_____May once have been a granite

3. Limestone containing brachiopods and crinoids
4. Cross-bedded well-sorted sandstone with frosted grains
5. Pumice
6. Obsidian
7. Quartzite
8. Basalt
9. Felsite
10. Marble
11. Sediments deposited by a glacier
12. Slate

Deformation - breaking of rocks

1 faulting   syncline

2 folding   anticline

CHAPTER 27

Weathering, Mass-Wasting, and Stream Erosion

There rolls the deep where grew the tree.
O earth, what changes hast thou seen!
There where the long street roars, hath been
The stillness of the central sea.

The hills are shadows, and they flow
From form to form, and nothing stands;
They melt like mist, the solid lands,
Like clouds they shape themselves and go.
—TENNYSON: *In Memoriam*

ONE feature of Fig. 27-1 will strike the eye of any observer: the layers of sedimentary rock in the scattered tepees match exactly. How has this come about? Apparently we are looking at what remains of layers deposited originally as continuous beds and later consolidated into rocks. Erosion has slowly removed the volumes of rock which once occupied the spaces now separating the tepees. Perhaps former overlying layers have been entirely removed.

Fig. 27-1 illustrates once more an important geologic concept: the "everlasting hills" are really not everlasting at all. Rocks break up, decay, and crumble; the resulting fragments and dissolved materials move from higher to lower ground; and eventually the sediments are transported from the area by some agent such as running water or wind. Eventual burial in the sea is the fate of most sediments. How such vast quantities of rock can be removed from an area and how the Earth's surface can be sculptured into mountains and valleys is the

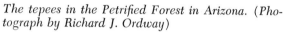

The tepees in the Petrified Forest in Arizona. (Photograph by Richard J. Ordway)

Fig. 27-1.

theme of this chapter. Moving from scene to scene, the traveler often feels frustration as he lets his eyes fall on diverse landscapes—cliffs and valleys and badlands—and gropes vaguely for explanations of how they came to be. The pages that follow tell the story of the formation of such features by *weathering, mass-wasting,* and *stream erosion*.

WEATHERING

From the time someone first bounced a stone off a tender shin, most people have been thoroughly impressed by the hardness of rocks. Rock outcrops in one's local neighborhood show no readily discernible changes during a lifetime, and stone monuments and buildings are accepted as permanent features. Yet the action of the weather in changing shiny iron nails to rust is familiar to all, and careful observation will show that rocks do crumble and decay in buildings and in nature (Fig. 27-2). The weathered surface of a rock may be strikingly different in color from that of a fresh surface. A reddish exterior may hide the true white color of the rock. The outer parts of some rock exposures can be crumbled by the fingers.

A good example of weathering is furnished by two ancient granite monuments transported about seventy years ago from Egypt—one to London and one to New York (Cleopatra's Needle in Central Park). Inscriptions which had remained almost unchanged by 3500 years of exposure to the dry Egyptian climate have become somewhat indis-

Weathering of rocks along cracks (joints). The site is in eastern California near the Nevada border. Note the alluvial fans which have formed where streams flowed from the mountains onto lower ground. This abrupt decrease in velocity caused a stream to drop most of its load of sediment at the mouth of the valley. As sediment piles up in one area, the stream is forced to shift sideways to lower ground on either side. Repetition of this process eventually produces a fan-shaped mass of sediments. (Photograph by Richard J. Ordway)

Fig. 27-2.

tinct in one-fiftieth of that time in London and largely erased in New York, although preservatives were painted over the surfaces (Fig. 27-3).

Weathering is the static part of the general process of erosion (Fig. 27-4); it is a name for all processes which combine to cause the breaking up and chemical alteration of rocks. Two general kinds are recognized: In *chemical weathering* chemical reactions bring about the decay and rotting of rocks. In *mechanical weathering* rocks are reduced to smaller pieces without chemical decomposition. Although one type of weathering may predominate under certain conditions, the two are intimately related, and one aids the other. For example, the breaking of rocks furnishes additional surfaces for attack by chemical action; some chemical reactions result in an increase in volume which causes disintegration. Weathering produces three types of materials:

Cleopatra's Needle in Central Park, New York City. (Courtesy, New York City Department of Parks)

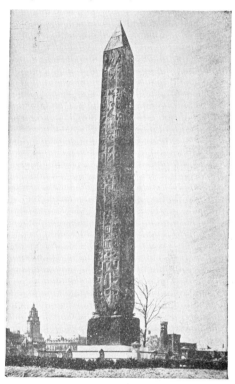

Fig. 27-3.

broken rock and mineral fragments, residual decomposition products, and dissolved substances. The terms *bedrock, mantle,* and *soil* are explained in Fig. 27-5.

Chemical Weathering Warm moist climate, gentle slopes, and abundant vegetation are most effective for chemical weathering. Water is important as a medium in which chemical reactions can oc-

Fig. 27-4.

Bryce Canyon, Utah, and "Queen Victoria." The horizontal sedimentary rocks are cut by systems of vertical cracks which separate the strata into columns. Erosion has worn away the edges of the columns more rapidly than the sides and produced the rounded shapes seen in photographs. (Photograph by Richard J. Ordway)

Fig. 27-5.

Bedrock, mantle, and soil. Mantle may be either transported or residual (accumulated essentially in its present location by the disintegration and decay of bedrock). The bedrock may consist of igneous, sedimentary, or metamorphic rocks.

Bedrock is the solid outer part of the earth's rocky crust. Here it has been exposed by erosion

Soil is the upper part of the mantle which supports rooted vegetation. It may be absent from an area

Loose boulder which might be mistaken for bedrock

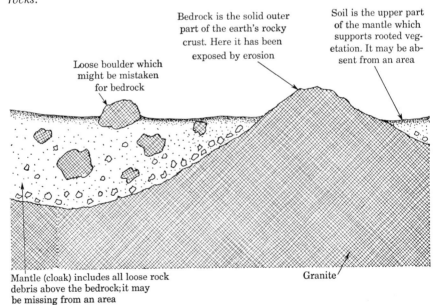

Mantle (cloak) includes all loose rock debris above the bedrock; it may be missing from an area

Granite

ur that take place slowly, if at all, between dry substances. Water combines with carbon dioxide in the air and with the humus of decayed vegetation to form carbonic and humic acids, which can dissolve many rock materials. An increase in temperature speeds up most chemical reactions and causes some which cannot take place at lower temperatures. The commonplace process of rusting involves the chemical union of oxygen and water with iron to form limonite, a hydrous iron oxide group of minerals. The presence of cracks and other openings in rocks is important because they allow penetration by air and water.

Since feldspars, pyroboles, quartz, and mica are estimated to constitute over 90 percent of the minerals of the Earth's crust, the manner in which they tend to weather is important. Feldspars decompose chiefly to clay minerals (hydrous aluminum silicates); pyroboles and black mica may yield clay and hydrous iron oxide; quartz and white mica are highly resistant to chemical weathering.

Mechanical Weathering Freezing and thawing of water confined in rock openings is the most important purely mechanical process involved in the breaking of rocks. On freezing, water expands about 10 percent by volume and exerts a pressure approaching 2000 lb/sq in. A cool moist climate, such as that prevailing at many high altitudes, is most favorable for this process (Fig. 27-6). Much rock decay involves an increase in volume which causes disintegration. The wedging action of rooted vegetation growing in cracks likewise reduces rocks to smaller pieces. Piles of rock debris (talus) at the base of most cliffs (Fig. 27-7), the many "Fallen Rock" zones along highways, and the damage to roads caused by frost heaving testify vividly to the effectiveness of weathering.

Frost heaving is most effective in fine-grained materials in moist regions with frequent frosts. Lenses and layers of ice form at different levels below the surface by drawing up water from below like a blotter. Frost heaves up to 18 inches have been measured. Sometimes the amount of heave has equaled the combined thicknesses of the ice lenses. The same process accounts for the presence of rock fragments in some gardens each spring, even though similar fragments have been tediously removed the year before. Certain areas of the garden are heaved more than others, and this uplifted soil is afterward removed by rains into adjoining lower areas. Rock fragments in the heaved soils remain at or near the surface.

Rocks such as granite disintegrate into their constituent mineral grains in many desert areas. An explanation of this phenomenon was

Fig. 27-6.

The Old Man of the Mountain in Franconia Notch, New Hampshire. The freezing and thawing of water along cracks has been important in shaping this rock outcrop. (Courtesy, New Hampshire Development Commission)

formerly offered somewhat as follows. During the extreme temperature changes which occur between day and night in desert areas individual minerals in a thin zone near the surface of the rock should expand and contract under the alternate heating and cooling. As different minerals swell and shrink at different rates, strains must be set up in the rocks which can cause eventual disintegration. This logical hypothesis has recently been tested in the laboratory. Different rock specimens have been alternately heated and cooled thousands of times at temperature variations greater than those occurring in any desert. Examination of the specimens under a microscope revealed no disrupting effects. Doubt is thus cast upon the importance of such temperature changes in causing rock disintegration directly. Apparently volume changes caused by certain chemical reactions are more important in the breaking up of rocks in such areas. Flaking and

Crater Lake, Oregon. Rock debris (talus piles) accumulates at the foot of a cliff. The geologic history of Crater Lake is discussed on page 680. Note the rounded cross section of the glaciated valley at the left. The small island (Phantom Ship) is composed chiefly of a dike of basaltic material. (Photograph by Richard J. Ordway)

Fig. 27-7.

disintegration are produced, however, by the extreme temperature changes which occur when a forest fire burns an area and is extinguished by a heavy rain.

Soils Soils consist of decomposed rock debris and decayed organic matter (humus) which have been produced by weathering. Thousands of years are normally required for the formation of a thick fertile topsoil from a naked rock outcrop. Abundant humus colors soils dark, whereas the presence of iron oxides imparts yellowish, brownish, or reddish colors. Mature soils commonly have several distinct layers (Fig. 27-8).

Worms are important soil makers. Earthworms extract vegetable matter from the soil by literally eating their way through it. As the soil passes through their bodies, mechanical and chemical modifications occur. In humid temperate regions it has been estimated that earthworms completely work over a soil layer from 6 to 12 inches thick every 50 years. Reflect upon this the next time you pick up a handful of soil from your garden!

Vertical section through a residual soil. Loam is a soil composed of sand, silt, and clay. (Courtesy, Soil Conservation Service)

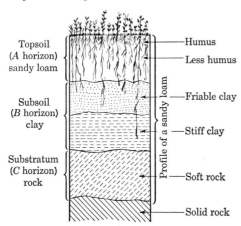

Topsoil
(A horizon)
sandy loam

——Humus

—— Less humus

Subsoil
(B horizon)
clay

——Friable clay

—— Stiff clay

Substratum
(C horizon)
rock

——Soft rock

—— Solid rock

Profile of a sandy loam

Fig. 27-8.

Practical Aspects of Weathering   Without question, the formation of soil is the most important single result of weathering to mankind. In addition, however, many valuable mineral deposits have originated by this process. Either an originally useful mineral is concentrated by removal of waste products, or valuable minerals are produced by weathering and then accumulate. For example, ore deposits of iron, copper, and aluminum have formed in this way.

Knowledge of the manner in which various rocks weather under different climatic conditions should enable a contractor to make wise choices of building stones. In a warm moist climate, a sandstone naturally cemented by calcium carbonate or iron oxide would be unsatisfactory, because the cement would either dissolve or stain the rock with rust spots. As another example, a badly fractured silica-rich sandstone would not be suitable in a cool moist climate, because water that entered the cracks could freeze and disintegrate the rock. On the other hand, a soluble limestone makes an excellent building stone in dry areas.

MASS-WASTING

In mass-wasting, large masses of material move downward as units. It forms an essential process in the general wasting away and leveling of the lands. Gravity is the direct controlling agent of movements, which may be slow or fast. Rock falls, landslides, soil slump, soil creep, mud flows, and slopewash are examples of mass-wasting. Two general types of movement are involved, either of which may be very fast— fast enough to bring death and destruction—or almost imperceptibly slow. One type is represented by the familiar landslide (Fig. 27-9)

Fig. 27-9.

Landslide in Franconia Notch, New Hampshire, in 1948. The main highway through the Notch has been buried by the slide in the foreground. (Courtesy Richard J. Ordway)

in which a mass of bedrock and mantle slides as a unit upon some sort of lubricated surface. The other type is exemplified by the less familiar soil creep in which irregular movement occurs throughout the moving mass. Gradations between these two types are common in nature.

Soil Creep The cloak of loose material above bedrock may move slowly downward along even gentle slopes. A covering mat of vegetation decreases the rate but does not halt the movement. Several kinds of evidence indicate that the mantle is moving downward. Roads, tunnels, and railroad tracks may be shoved out of line; fence posts, monuments, and buildings may be tilted or disrupted by the irregular movements. As the surface part of the mantle moves to lower ground more rapidly than the deeper part, a downslope tilt develops in fence posts and power-line poles which have been sunk for some depth into the loose material. The trunks of many trees are distinctly curved (convex downslope) as the result of a compromise between this downward tilting and their tendency to grow vertically (Fig. 27-10).

Fig. 27-10.

Soil creep. The upper part of the mantle moves slowly downslope, but more rapidly than the lower part. Objects which project downward into the mantle for some distance tend to be tilted.

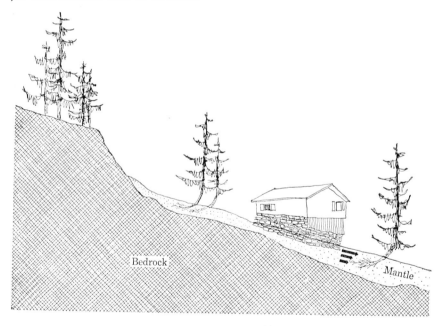

The causes of creep are numerous. Frost heaving tends to push loose pebbles at the surface outward at right angles to the slope. However, when the ice beneath the pebble melts, it falls vertically downward; thus it moves a tiny distance downslope. Weathering produces loose fragments which may fall or roll down the slope. Openings which are formed by the dissolving of soluble materials, by the decay of tree roots, or by the burrowing activities of animals are all eventually filled by downward movement of upslope material. Water adds weight and acts as a lubricant. Constantly repeated, these forces, all of them tiny, combine to move material downslope. Movement at the rate of 1 foot every 5 to 10 years has been measured and may be representative.

Rounded vs. Angular Topography   Topography tends to be rounded in humid areas and angular in arid and semiarid regions (Figs. 27-11

Fig. 27-11.

Angular topography in arid regions. An aerial view of desert mountains which are being buried by alluvial fan material. Islandlike portions project from the stream-laid deposits. South of San Felipe, Lower California. (Courtesy, Spence Air Photos)

and 27-18). In humid temperate zones a thick protective mat of vegetation covers the mantle and prevents gullying. The entire mantle moves slowly downslope, filling in irregularities and hiding differences between resistant and weak rock formations. Furthermore, chemical weathering so weakens the rocks that steep slopes cannot commonly be supported. On the other hand, mechanical weathering predominates in drier areas; rock falls, landslides, and mud flows tend to leave

slopes steep. No creeping mantle exists to mask differences in bedrock resistance by filling in low areas. Resistant rocks stand out as ledges or ridges.

WORK OF RUNNING WATER*

From the atmosphere water falls upon the Earth's surface as rain, snow, hail, and sleet. Some water evaporates or is taken up by plants, some runs off immediately into streams, and the remainder sinks into the ground. Much ground water later emerges at the surface at a lower altitude and becomes runoff. Streams carry excess water from the land to the sea. In doing so they erode valleys and help shape the Earth's surface. They transport rock debris and dissolved materials, and eventually they deposit most of the sediment in the oceans. As lands seem to be higher and more extensive now than they were during most of the Earth's history, stream activity today predominates over other types of erosion such as wind, ice, or marine.

Streams are important to man whether he uses them as sources of drinking water, irrigation, or electric power, as scenic inspiration, or as places in which to fish or swim. Valleys furnish the most convenient courses for many roads and railroads. The location of a number of important cities depended upon the navigability of large rivers. Civilization flourished first on fertile flood plains. Bridges, dams, and reservoirs have to be built. Frequent floods with appalling loss of life and property emphasize the importance of streams to man.

Valleys as a Result of Stream Erosion   With few exceptions, streams have excavated the valleys in which they now flow. Different kinds of evidence indicate that this is so. A branching treelike pattern is common in river systems (Fig. 27-12). Small tributaries enter larger streams at angles which are acute upstream, and this relationship holds true from the tiniest gully to the chief river in the area. Under different conditions, a rectangular stream pattern develops (western part of Fig. 27-19). In general, a definite proportion exists between the size of a valley and the size of the stream flowing in it. Each stream

* Little drops of water,
   Little grains of sand,
Run away together
   And destroy the land.
—ROBERT E. HORTON.

Fig. 27-12.

Soda Canyon, Colorado. This area illustrates the youthful stage in the erosion cycle in a region of flat-lying rocks, dendritic drainage pattern, canyons, plateaus, and mesas. This relief map-model is one of a set of twelve which have been selected to illustrate typical topography studied in geology. (Courtesy, Aero Service Corporation, Philadelphia)

tends to flow on a steep slope near its head and on a gentle slope near its mouth; thus it forms a profile which is concave upward. Commonly, tributaries meet larger streams at just the proper level—not too high, and not too low; this accordance at intersections is maintained throughout the system. The sediments being transported by many rivers are readily observed and indicate that excavation has gone on somewhere upstream. All of this regularity and uniformity appears too great for chance coincidence; most valleys apparently have been shaped by the streams which flow in them. What happens can be traced in the miniature replica of a branching river system that will be produced by spraying water from a garden hose for a few minutes on a pile of loose soil.

Stream Erosion   A stream carries its load of sediments in suspension and in solution and moves larger fragments by rolling them along the bottom. Stream erosion is achieved by abrasive impacts of transported fragments on the beds and sides of channels, by the solvent action of water (relatively small), and by the lifting effect of running water. Without sediment, streams cannot scratch and scour their channels. (Tiny plants can grow on the brink of Niagara Falls, and moss can be seen at the bottom of many clear, vigorous mountain streams.) A sediment-laden river was aptly described by Mark Twain when he characterized the muddy Missouri as "too thick to navigate, but too thin to cultivate." Potholes are produced by stream abrasion (Fig. 27-13).

A stream normally originates as a tiny gully in a depression at the

Fig. 27-13.

A stream bed of limestone honeycombed with potholes, near Boonville, New York. Eddies in the stream whirl gravel and sand around in a small circular area and gradually bore a cylindrical hole in the bedrock. New supplies of gravel and sand replace older pieces as they are worn out. Potholes may form rapidly. One 10 feet deep was observed to form in limestone in 18 months; one 5 feet deep formed in 75 years in granite. Resistance of the rock is only one of the factors involved.

Earth's surface where runoff is concentrated. This miniature valley grows deeper and wider; it becomes longer by headward erosion, because more water generally enters at the head of a valley than at any one place along its sides. At first, water flows down the valley only after rains, but eventually the stream cuts into the surface deeply enough to reach the zone in which all open spaces are filled by ground water (see p. 624). It then becomes permanent, shrinking in size during dry spells and enlarging greatly after heavy rains. Steep slopes, high velocities, great volumes of water, and weak bedrock all increase the erosive capacity of a stream. In its mountainous headward portion, where a stream commonly must transport large boulders, steep slopes are required. However, sediment sizes have decreased near its mouth, and the volume and velocity of the stream have increased. Friction reduction caused by deeper channels more than compensates for the decrease in gradient. Therefore the stream can carry its load on a gentler gradient; its long profile is commonly concave upward.

Base Level   A stream cannot cut downward indefinitely. If a river enters the sea, it may scour its channel a little below sea level in the vicinity of the coast. Headward from its mouth, however, the channel must rise above sea level in order to furnish a slope down which the water can flow. Sea level projected inland as an imaginary surface is thus the deepest approximate level to which a stream can lower its channel; it is called *base level*. Lakes, dams, and resistant rock formations may form local, temporary base levels.

Graded Streams   At any one time a stream has just so much energy for its work of erosion and transportation. Near its head a stream tends to flow on steep slopes and to carry a relatively small load of sediments. Much of its energy is used to saw vertically downward into the Earth's surface. However, as the stream cuts downward, its gradient decreases, whereas the load it carries increases. Thus the rate of down-cutting diminishes because an increasingly larger proportion of the total energy supply is lost in the work of transportation. Increased volumes of water at lower altitudes do not offset this tendency. Eventually an approximately constant balance is reached between the load the stream carries at any one point and the volume and gradient of the stream at that point. Such a stream is said to be *graded*.

After a river has become graded, conditions may change. For example, the load of sediment transported by the river may be increased, or the amount of water available to it may be decreased. In each of these instances, the river would deposit some sediment all along the floor of its channel until it moved on a steeper gradient (the mouth of the river remains at the same altitude) and at the greater velocity thus produced, once more carried a full load; it would again become graded. On the other hand, if the load of a river were decreased, the excess energy thus made available would be applied to lower the channel by downcutting. In this manner, a graded condition would once more be attained. When a stream is graded, minor fluctuations occur through a norm; the stream deposits material at one place and picks up sediment at another. Downcutting continues after the graded condition has been attained, although it then becomes exceedingly slow.

Meanders   Irregularities in the path of a river cause the deepest and swiftest part of the channel to impinge against the outer part of each bend. Deposition takes place in slack water on the inside of a bend and decreases the cross-sectional area of the channel (Fig. 25-9). This causes the stream to undercut the outer and downstream side of the bend. In addition, centrifugal force is greatest on the outer part of the curve. Flat crescent-shaped areas develop on the insides of each bend. They coalesce eventually to form a continuous flood plain, because each bend migrates slowly downstream as well as laterally. The winding sinuous course which develops eventually is called *meandering* (Fig. 27-14).

Experiments with models show that meanders tend to form only in streams with banks consisting of easily eroded sediments. Bank caving produces irregularities in the channel which initiate the formation of the meanders.

Erosion Cycle in a Single Valley   If erosion is not interrupted by some geological change, such as an uplift, a river tends to evolve through a cycle of gradual changes: vigorous youth, powerful maturity, and sluggish old age. These stages are not marked by absolute numbers of years. The time it takes to reach a given point in the sequence depends upon the composition and structure of the rocks, the altitude above sea level, the quantity and distribution of rain, and other factors. The stages are determined by the amount of erosion

Fig. 27-14.

A meandering river and its flood plain. The meander of Crooked Creek, California, in the left foreground shows an undercut outside bank and a gently sloping inside bank. (Courtesy, U.S. Geological Survey)

which a river has already accomplished relative to the amount of work that remains for its drainage area to be reduced to base level.

A youthful stream tends to have a V-shaped cross profile; valley sides are steep, and the channel occupies nearly the entire bottom part of the valley (Fig. 27-15). Falls, rapids, and lakes are common along its course. The stream acts like a saw which cuts vertically downward. Weathering breaks and loosens rock materials along the valley sides, and mass-wasting moves the loose materials downward to the stream channel. Thus a valley is deepened by stream erosion, but it is widened chiefly by mass-wasting. The mature stream is graded and meanders on a flood plain which may contain natural levees (p. 615) and a few oxbow lakes (Fig. 27-15) which develop when a stream in flood cuts across the narrow neck of a meander. Falls and rapids have been largely eliminated, and lateral cutting is now more prominent than

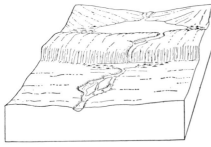

A. In the initial stage a stream has lakes, waterfalls, and rapids.

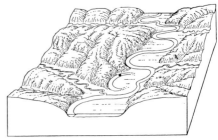

D. Approaching full maturity, the stream has a flood-plain almost wide enough to accommodate its meanders.

B. By middle youth the lakes are gone, but falls and rapids persist along the narrow incised gorge.

E. Full maturity is marked by a broad floodplain and freely developed meanders. L = levee; O = oxbow lake; Y = yazoo stream; A = alluvium; B = bluffs; F = floodplain.

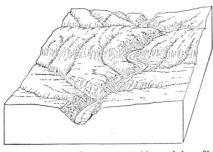

C. Early maturity brings a smoothly graded profile without rapids or falls, but with the beginnings of a floodplain.

Fig. 27-15.

Stages in the life history of a stream. (After E. Raiz. Courtesy, A. N. Strahler, Physical Geography, 1951, John Wiley & Sons, Inc.)

valley deepening. As additional tributaries have developed, the region is well drained. Old age is reached gradually. It is characterized by low, gently sloping valley walls and a very wide flood plain on which the river meanders sluggishly.

Most existing major flood plains originated by sedimentation which filled the entire bottom portions of their valleys (Fig. 27-23). Perhaps this is a direct result of the huge volume of sediment which many rivers had to transport during the recent Ice Age (p. 642).

If uplift occurs, the cycle of erosion begins again. Some natural bridges have formed via stream erosion (Figs. 27-16 and 27-17).

Stream valley and natural bridge. This is the Rainbow Natural Bridge in southeastern Utah. (Courtesy, Union Pacific Railroad)

Fig. 27-16.

A river may be youthful in its upper reaches, mature in its middle portions, and old near its mouth where erosion has continued for the longest period of time. Variations occur if a river passes through rocks of different resistances or through areas which have been affected by crustal movements during the development of the valley (Fig. 27-19).

For example, a wide valley could develop in weak rocks both upstream and downstream from a region underlain by resistant rocks in which the valley is still V-shaped.

Geologists are confident that a valley develops through a sequence of changes somewhat as described above, though the complete cycle takes too long for observation of even a tiny fraction of the total changes involved. Erosion and deposition by running water can of

Formation of a natural bridge by a stream with intrenched meanders.

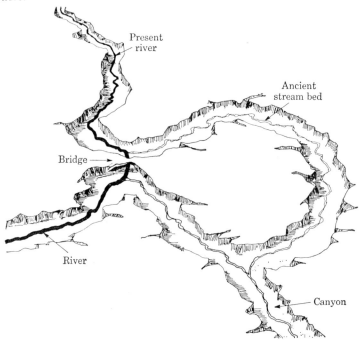

Present river

Ancient stream bed

Bridge

River

Canyon

Fig. 27-17.

course be seen to occur today. Moreover, all stages of the cycle from youth to old age have been discovered at various places on the Earth.

Erosion Cycle in a Region An entire region may develop slowly through stages which can be characterized as youth, maturity, and old age like the stages of a single valley as discussed above.

If uplift of an area of subdued topography should take place rather rapidly (in geologic terms), the youthful stage in the erosion cycle would be featured by broad flat-topped divides between a few

V-shaped valleys (Fig. 27-12). The area is chiefly upland. As the streams enlarge their valleys and become more numerous, the amount of upland decreases, slopes (sides of valleys and mountains) predominate, and the area is mature (Figs. 27-18 and 27-19). As erosion continues and the region is lowered closer to base level, the amount of bottom land becomes greater and the old-age stage is reached.

The land forms which are produced during the erosion cycle are influenced by factors such as the following: differences in rock structures, crustal movements or igneous activity which may occur after initiation of the cycle, variations in original altitude above sea level and distances from the sea, climatic dissimilarities, the length of time involved, and the effects of other erosive agents, such as wind, waves, and ice. The stage in the erosion cycle attained by a single valley may not be the same as that of the entire region. For example, numerous youthful tributary streams may exist in a region which has reached maturity.

Peneplane ("almost-a-plane") is the term for the nearly smooth erosion surface of low relief and low altitude which covers a large area and which develops in late old age. Its surface may be dotted here and there by an occasional small, rounded hill underlain by resistant rock. The peneplane bevels different kinds of rock formations and geologic structures as if a gigantic carpenter's plane had been pushed back and forth across the region. Peneplaned surfaces may subsequently be uplifted and dissected by erosion. Remnants of such surfaces probably exist in various places on the Earth (Fig. 32-3).

Prevention and Control of Soil Erosion Soil is one of man's most important natural resources, an irreplaceable heritage which he has abused terribly in the past and, unfortunately, continues to misuse today. For example, according to some estimates approximately one-half of the total quantity of agricultural land in the United States has lost much of its topsoil in the last two centuries, is in danger of doing so, or has been destroyed. Perhaps 100,000 acres are being lost annually at present. Stated in another way, topsoil in the United States may have averaged about 9 inches in depth before settlement. Today this thickness is estimated at 6 inches. These 6 inches of topsoil stand between us and starvation. Although a number of remarkable soil conditioners have been introduced recently, no economic method is known which produces rich topsoil from infertile mantle. The appalling waste of this

The normal cycle of erosion in a moderately elevated region of essentially uniform, stratified rocks devoid of important structures. Top, region in youth; middle, in maturity; bottom, in old age. A region in typical maturity is one of slopes with a rolling hill-and-valley topography. Drainage is good, relief is at its maximum, and erosion is most effective. Major streams have begun to develop flood plains and meanders.

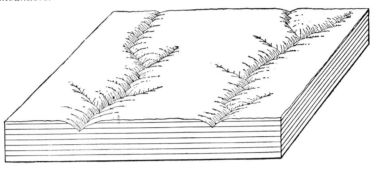

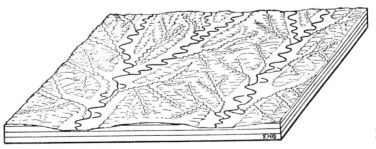

Fig. 27-18.

Fig. 27-19.

Map-model of the Loveland, Colorado, quadrangle. Note the striking contrast in topography between the western (early maturity) and eastern (old age) parts of the area. After erosion had produced a subdued surface over the entire area, uplift and folding occurred in the western section. Rivers were rejuvenated and cut canyons into the mountains. The north-south ridges in the western part are the result of differential erosion on tilted sedimentary rocks of varying resistances; valleys are underlain by easily eroded rocks. The shapes of the ridges indicate the direction of dip of the rocks underlying them. (Courtesy, Aero Service Corporation, Philadelphia)

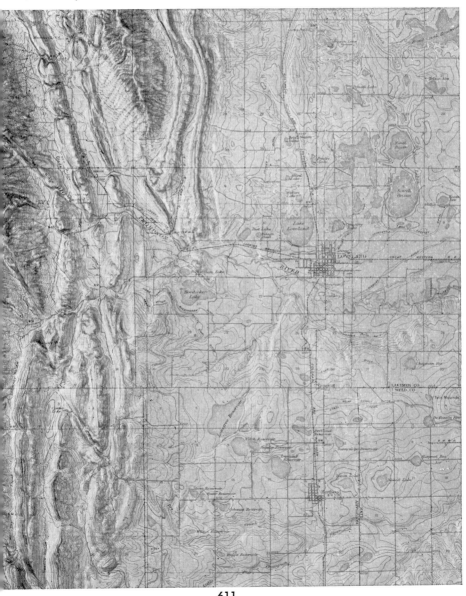

essential material is thus a critical matter and its prevention is of vital concern to us all.

In addition to the direct loss of crop-producing capacity, soil erosion increases the destructiveness of floods and decreases the storage capacity of water in reservoirs. As an illustration, some calculations indicate that about one-half of the water supply reservoirs in the United States will be useless within 100 years because they will be filled by sediment.

A protective mat of vegetation prevents or greatly retards soil erosion by wind and water. Of first importance, therefore, is the restoration or maintenance of such a cover on slopes which have been deforested, overcropped, overgrazed, or burned over. Submarginal soils, especially those on steep slopes, should not be plowed. A double loss occurs when good soil is washed down a slope, changed in the process into an infertile mixture by additions of insufficiently weathered rock debris, and finally dropped on top of fertile soils at lower altitudes.

Fig. 27-20.

A. Eroded farmland with deep gullies formed by the rapid runoff of surface water after heavy rains.—B. The same field several years later, now planted with kudzu, a cloverlike plant that absorbs the rain and holds soil together. Erosion has been halted. (Courtesy, Caterpillar Tractor Co.)

(A)   (B)

Various techniques can be used to prevent or decrease the downward movement of soil along a slope. Drainage may be controlled by a system of ditches or small dams. Small gullies may be healed by the planting of quick-growing vines and shrubs (Fig. 27-20). Row crops may be planted parallel to the contours of a slope, not up and down the incline. Crops planted in any given field may be varied from year to year. Strip cropping (Fig. 27-21) on a slope intersperses areas

Fig. 27-21.

Contour strip cropping on sloping land. (Courtesy, U.S. Soil Conservation Service)

of row crops such as corn with protective strips of thick-growing grains and grasses. Terracing (Fig. 27-22) of a slope permits the tilling of gently sloping or flat areas which are separated by steeply sloping sections that are kept permanently covered by a mat of vegetation or held in place by retaining walls. Materials such as hay or straw can be scattered about between rows of corn or among other crops and prevent much soil erosion. Such mulches have the added advantage of slowing the growth of weeds.

Perhaps the U.S. Conservation Service has best summarized the elements of good practice in this recommendation: Use each acre according to its capabilities; treat each acre according to its needs.

Fig. 27-22.

Terracing of a valley in Japan.

Floods and Flood Control   Streams perform most of their work of erosion, transportation, and deposition during floods. In fact, in the few days of a powerful flood a river may accomplish more in these respects than it does during the rest of the year or perhaps even for several years. Some large rivers have been known to deepen their channels more than 100 feet when flood waters are exceptionally high. Such large rivers flow upon unconsolidated sediments that bury the bedrock floors of their valleys and can erode the bedrock only during floods. As the flood subsides, other sediment is deposited, refilling the bottom part of the channel.

When a river overflows its banks during times of high water, its velocity is checked abruptly beyond the margins of the channel where the water becomes shallow. The sudden decrease in velocity causes deposition; coarser materials are deposited at once along the banks of the channel, and finer sediment is spread over the rest of the flood plain. Numerous repetitions of this process may produce low ridges along each side of the channel. Such ridges are called natural levees (Fig. 27-15). Commonly they rise only a few feet above the flood plain, yet during extensive floods they may form long, low islands which parallel the channel and constitute the only dry land in the floor of the valley.

As flood plains are exceedingly fertile areas for farming and furnish flat land for roads and building purposes, many farms, towns, and cities are located on them, even though they are subject to periodic flood. To prevent floods, people began building artificial levees to confine floodwaters to the river channels. Unfortunately, this construction inaugurated a vicious cycle. During a flood a river carries an extra load of sediment, part of which is normally spread over the flood plain as the flood subsides. If the river is confined to its channel, the extra sediment is deposited on the channel floor instead of the flood plain, and the level of the water is thus raised. The levees subsequently are not adequate everywhere and must be built higher. Such construction provides only temporary protection, because the river continues to build up the floor of its channel by deposition of sediment during each flood. In some valleys, such as the Hwang Ho in China and the Po in Italy, the tops of the levees are above the roofs of houses built on the adjacent flood plains. A break-through under these circumstances is very destructive, and large areas of the flood plain are inundated. The first levees built along the Mississippi River more than 100 years ago were only about 4 feet high and relatively short. Since then, hundreds of miles of levees of increasingly greater heights have been constructed.

Floods are the most disastrous of natural forces to mankind and are becoming increasingly destructive year by year, primarily because of greater use of the flood plain by man. Floods and flood control affect the lives of all citizens today either directly or indirectly. The floods of the Kansas and Missouri Rivers in 1951 and 1952 are estimated together to have caused more than $1\frac{1}{4}$ billion dollars' worth of property damage. According to the U.S. Department of Agriculture, the total average annual damage from floods and sediment in the United States is about 1 billion dollars. This damage may be separated into upstream and downstream parts: upstream areas lie above existing or proposed major flood control structures; downstream areas lie below such structures. More than half of the total flood damage probably takes place in the upstream areas from frequent, small, unpublicized but destructive floods. None of the existing or proposed major flood-control structures aid in preventing these floods. Estimates suggest that more than $60 has been spent on downstream structures for each dollar spent for upstream flood control. Obviously this is not a proper balance. More than two-thirds of the upstream damage is agricultural: damage to crops, roads, and buildings, erosion of good farmland, deposition of unfertile sediment on productive soil, and indirect losses such as delays in planting or marketing.

Flood control is a many-faceted complex problem. A large river system which extends throughout several states is a natural unit and must be treated as a unit—omissions or commissions in one part of the system can affect remote areas vitally. The multiple uses of a stream system must be considered: floods, power, water supply, navigation, irrigation, recreation, sewage disposal, fish, and wildlife. Sometimes these interests conflict; for example, reservoirs need to be kept nearly empty for maximum efficiency in preventing floods, but they need to be full to serve as adequate water supply.

One reason for the more extensive damage caused by recent floods (other than greater construction of property along the flood plain) is the destruction by man of the cover of vegetation which formerly protected slopes throughout the entire drainage area of the river. Forests have been leveled. The plow has knifed through countless acres of land and turned the sod under, thereby exposing the soil to relentless pounding and spattering by the rains. When water falls on slopes which are covered by thick grass and numerous trees, much of it sinks into the ground, and very little runs off immediately—almost none from a forested area. On a slope not held together firmly by a mat of vegetation, much water at once washes down the slope, carrying large quantities of soil with it. Therefore, anything which reduces the amount of immediate runoff after heavy rains and melting snows must help to prevent high waters downstream and deposition of sediment in confined channels and reservoirs. Thus reforestation and soil conservation throughout the entire area drained by a river system appears to constitute a very important portion of a satisfactory long-range solution of the flood problem. Rapid runoff must be halted. Straightening and dredging channels and strengthening levees are temporary expedients. Less valuable areas along the river may be selected as temporary reservoirs to be flooded at times of exceptionally high water in order to lessen the pressure on more valuable areas downstream.

Although reforestation is important in preventing or limiting numerous small upstream floods, it apparently has much less effect in preventing major disastrous downstream floods. Reforestation throughout an entire drainage basin would not "soak up" these major floods before they started. Such floods occurred before man entered the scene and cut down the forests.

A system of dams and reservoirs, therefore, is likewise essential in the control or prevention of floods. If it can prevent the many tributaries which feed a large river from flooding simultaneously, the danger will be averted, and the water can be released from the reservoirs later at times of drought. Yet agitation by the population of a large city for the building of dams and reservoirs upstream may arouse the hostility of the people who live and farm in the upstream areas which would have to be condemned and flooded to make room for the reservoirs. A number of well-informed people believe that the construction of a few large expensive dams across major rivers will provide less storage volume at greater cost than would the building of many small dams across numerous minor streams. Furthermore, water which collects behind the small dams may not flood large areas of valuable land. In a number of instances, further study has shown that the annual income from the area which is to be flooded by a proposed reservoir far exceeds the total benefits to be derived from its construction.

Settlement control should play a vital role in any long-range plan for controlling floods. To keep flood waters entirely confined to a river channel is extremely difficult and expensive. However, if valuable properties could be zoned to higher altitudes or to areas somewhat removed from the river channel, much property damage would be prevented. Dikes could be located far enough from the channel to provide space for overflow in time of floods. Only temporary or less valuable buildings would be permitted in the zone between the dikes and river channel. Somewhat similar zoning regulations could be applied to farm buildings constructed on the flood plain. Such zoning would tend to eliminate the two most important reasons for the construction of many huge dams and reservoirs.

THE BURIED VALLEY—A READING
OF THE RECORD

Geologists made a field study some years ago of an area east of the
Rocky Mountains and uncovered clear traces of a buried valley of the
kind shown in Fig. 27-23 (a few details have been altered). The profile of the hidden bedrock surface indicates that a V-shaped stream

Fig. 27-23.

A V-shaped valley formed by erosion and later filled with sediment.

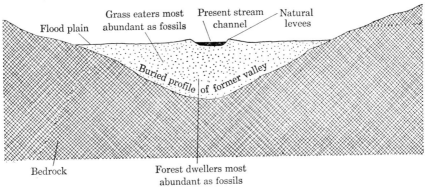

Grass eaters most   Present stream   Natural
Flood plain   abundant as fossils   \ channel   levees

Buried profile of former valley

Bedrock   Forest dwellers most
                    abundant as fossils

valley once existed here. Following the development of the valley,
conditions changed, and its entire lower part was filled by sediment
and thus became a "flood plain of aggradation." What caused this
change? Working out the answer to this question involves the geologist's technique of interpretation.

The method of *multiple working hypotheses* has often been applied
to similar problems successfully. Make a list of every conceivable explanation which might account for the change from erosion to deposition. Of course, the correct explanation may not find a place on the
list. For instance, the following hypotheses do not exhaust all possibilities in the problem under consideration: (1) If the load of the stream
had been increased—perhaps when the stream eroded headward into
an area of weaker rocks more susceptible of rapid erosion—erosion of
the bedrock valley floor would have ceased, and deposition of sediments would have begun. (2) A decrease in gradient would have had
a similar result, as would (3) a decrease in the volume of water. (4) A
dam across the stream below this area (perhaps lava flowed across the

valley) would have caused the filling of the valley by sedimentation. An additional relevant fact was discovered as the mapping of the area moved forward. Fossil remains of forest-dwelling animals were found to be most abundant in the older sedimentary layers found along the bedrock floor of the valley. These turned up in smaller numbers in the younger sediments above. Conversely, many fossil remains of grass-eating animals were discovered in the youngest layers near the top, but these were absent in the oldest layers which had been deposited on the bedrock floor of the valley. It is significant that forested areas require more rainfall than grass-covered regions. Furthermore, evidence from another area suggests that the Rocky Mountains were uplifted approximately at the same time that the change from erosion to deposition occurred in the stream.

These data appear to support hypothesis (3). Apparently this episode of Earth history commenced with a stream which flowed eastward from its source in the moderately high Rockies to the west. The stream was actively deepening the floor of its V-shaped valley and passed through forested areas. Gradually the Rocky Mountains were uplifted until they presented a high barrier to the prevailing westerly winds. As eastward-moving air masses were forced to climb higher and higher to cross the Rockies, increasing quantities of precipitation occurred on the westward side of the mountains (Fig. 22-10). Less and less rain fell on the eastern side. Decreased rainfall east of the mountains thus reduced the volume of water carried by the stream. It began to deposit sediment along the floor of the valley (the countereffect of the increase in gradient was too small to offset this change). As time passed, the area became too dry to support many trees, and they were gradually replaced by grasses. The forest dwellers migrated slowly to other areas and the region became populated by grass-eating creatures.

EXERCISES AND QUESTIONS FOR CHAPTER 27

1. Draw a geologic structure section which shows the kind of bedrock and mantle near your home or college. Study nearby rock outcrops and road cuts for helpful information.

2. Describe the relative roles played by weathering, mass-wasting, and stream erosion in the origin of the Grand Canyon.

3. Why is topography commonly rounded in humid areas and angular in dry areas?

4. Describe topographic and climatic conditions which would favor chemical weathering over mechanical weathering and vice versa.

5. Extensive erosion occurs in a warm humid climate in areas underlain by the following types of rocks: limestone, shale, granite, quartzite, silica-cemented conglomerate, marble, and gneiss. Predict the location of hills and valleys relative to the underlying bedrock—for example, would an area underlain by shale eventually become a hill or a valley?

6. Discuss the development of a stream valley through the youthful, mature, and old age stages of the erosion cycle.

7. A certain river is in the following stages of the erosion cycle from its head to its mouth: (1) youth, (2) maturity, (3) youth, (4) maturity, and (5) old. Give at least two different explanations for the stage of youth in number 3.

8. How will an area in the mature stage of the erosion cycle in a region of folded rocks differ from an area in the youthful stage of the erosion cycle in a region of nearly horizontal sedimentary rocks?

CHAPTER 28

Subsurface Water

Water in the ground beneath the Earth's surface is our most important mineral resource. People living in humid areas with ample supplies of surface water find it difficult to realize that a large percentage of the world's population obtain their water from subsurface supplies. An estimated 30 to 35 billion gallons of ground water* were used each day in the United States in 1950. Probably more than half of all the families in the United States use some ground water. The availability of this water is taken for granted until it is gone. Only then is its true value fully appreciated.

Subsurface water has for thousands of years been a vital need in many areas of the world. Like so many vital matters, the search for it was surrounded with magic and mystery. The superstition of the water diviner's forked stick is still with us, and so is an agelong ignorance that condones the close intimacy of the outhouse and the well in many farming areas, and supports belief in great underground rivers, or in springs occurring on mountain tops. Even educated people are liable to know little more about their water supply than that a turn of the faucet brings forth clear cold water. Yet questions of ground-water supply have gained rather than lost importance in modern civilization, and conservation has become a vital matter that all need to understand.

---

* Ground water and subsurface water are used synonymously here, although technically ground water refers only to water beneath the water table.

THE WATER CYCLE

The oceans are the great reservoirs for the world's water supply. Energy from the sun causes evaporation at the surface; some of the resulting water vapor is carried by the atmosphere over the lands where it may be precipitated or condensed as rain, snow, hail, frost, or dew (Fig. 28-1). Part of this may be evaporated again either directly or indirectly by plant action; part runs off immediately to join streams and lakes; and part sinks downward into open spaces in the mantle or crust. Much of this ground water emerges at the surface again at lower altitudes.

The average annual precipitation in the United States is equivalent to some 30 inches of rainfall. Of this about 22 inches (70 percent) returns directly to the atmosphere by evaporation and the transpiration of vegetation. A field of vigorously growing plants on a summer day probably furnishes nearly as much moisture to the air as is evaporated from the surface of a water body of the same size. The remaining 8 inches is the source of all surface and ground water. This would be an ample supply if distributed uniformly in time and space. Problems arise because too much water or too little water occurs at a certain place at a certain time. These problems are increasing in number and magnitude each year.

Knowledge of the water cycle and of the nature and movement of ground water has developed chiefly within the last 250 years. Ancient Greek mythologists told of huge caverns existing beneath the Earth's surface. The caverns were believed to furnish water for wells and springs and to augment rain water in forming streams. According to ancient physicists, water came from the oceans by flow along subterranean channels, or air in the huge caverns was condensed to water. They theorized that rainfall was insufficient to account for all subsurface water and that rain water could not penetrate deeply into the ground. Such opinions, untested by experiments, were widely held for many hundreds of years. A number of interesting ideas were developed to explain how sea water could lose its salt content and rise to such high levels. For example, the astronomer Kepler thought the Earth acted like an animal: water was taken from the oceans, digested, assimilated, and then given off as de-salted water in springs and wells.

Thus two false assumptions based entirely on opinion held sway for

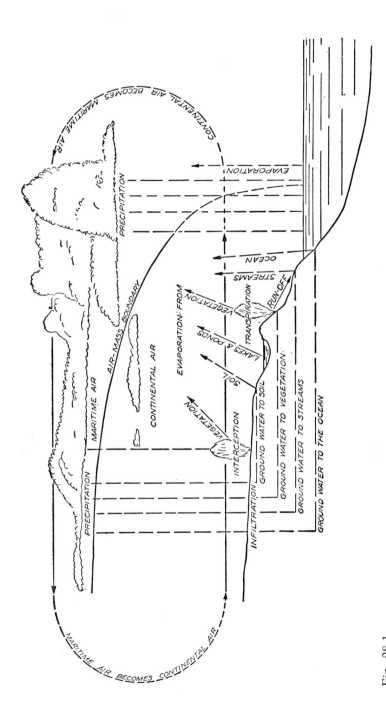

Fig. 28-1.

The hydrologic cycle. (Courtesy, U.S. Dept. of Agriculture)

623

about 2000 years before theory was checked by experiment and found wanting. Such errors certainly underscore the principle that all hypotheses should be checked and checked again with all of the facts that can be obtained from observation and experiments. Near the end of the seventeenth century, experiments were performed to study the origin and nature of ground water. A French scientist (Perrault) measured rainfall in the Seine drainage basin for a period of three years and the volume of water discharged by the river during that time. His results showed that about six times as much rain and snow fell in the drainage area as left it via the Seine River (the life functions of organisms and evaporation use a great deal of water). Halley, another scientist, was among the first to explain the water cycle correctly; he showed experimentally that evaporation from the oceans was sufficient to account for all surface and subsurface water.

DISTRIBUTION OF SUBSURFACE WATER

When water condenses from the atmosphere at the Earth's surface in areas of permeable* rocks or mantle, some of it sinks into openings in the rocks and rock debris (Fig. 24-9). A number of factors determine whether the water runs off, evaporates, or sinks below the surface (p. 600). Below a certain variable depth, which is near the surface in humid regions, all open spaces are saturated with water. The upper surface of this saturated zone is called the *water table* (Fig. 28-2). The water table rises in wet seasons and falls in dry seasons, but the open spaces below it are always filled with water. Between the water table and the Earth's surface is a zone in which open spaces are alternately filled with air and water. In this zone chemical weathering and leaching take place; below this zone cementation of rock particles and precipitation are prominent. Where the water table intersects the

* Permeability is the capacity of a rock to allow a fluid to pass through it, whereas porosity is defined as the percentage of open space in a rock. Such openings are the spaces between individual fragments in a sediment or sedimentary rock (pores), gasbubble holes in some igneous rocks, spaces formed by solution in rocks such as limestone, and cracks of widely different sizes in all kinds of rocks. Angular materials commonly have a greater porosity than spherical ones. As water oozes through a rock, friction is greater in small pores than in large ones because a greater surface area is exposed. Therefore, if other factors are equal, permeability in sedimentary rocks is greatest when large grains are involved. A sand is more permeable than a clay, although clay may have a higher porosity than sand. Igneous and metamorphic rocks commonly have few pore spaces but may be cut by fractures and cracks.

Earth's surface, the result is seepage (Fig. 28-3), a swamp, a spring, a stream, or a lake.

An ordinary well dug or drilled below the water table is actually a tiny pond. If the well is not deep enough, it goes dry during a drought. However, if it is then drilled to a greater depth, it again contains water. Nothing mysterious has occurred. The water table merely fell to a lower level during the dry period. In a similar manner, many shallow lakes or ponds disappear during dry sea-

Fig. 28-2.

The water table in homogeneous rocks or sediments. All open spaces below the water table are filled completely with water. In dry months or years, the water table drops; in wet months or years, it rises. If new supplies of water were not added by occasional rains, the water table would flatten out and approach a level surface. The configuration of the water table in homogeneous materials is a modified replica of surface topography; the distance to the water table tends to increase with increasing altitude. As many impervious materials exist below the Earth's surface, subsurface water does not constitute a vast interconnected underground reservoir.

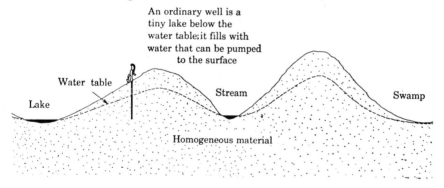

ons. Great industrial demands on large deep wells may cause many shallow domestic wells to go dry in its vicinity. Thus the water table is not a fixed or level surface. In homogeneous rocks in humid regions, it forms a subdued replica of the topography; it is farthest from the surface under hills and nearest the surface in valleys. The water table would eventually level out if new supplies of water did not move downward from the surface.

Estimates indicate that enough water is present beneath the surface in the United States within the outer 100 feet of rocks and mantle to completely cover the whole area to an average depth of approximately 17 feet. For example, if a sandstone formation has a thickness of 100 feet and a 10 percent porosity and is located beneath the water table, it contains the same amount of water as a lake 10 feet deep. Porosities from 5 to 15 percent are considered average in rocks; higher porosities occur in unconsolidated sediments. Unfortunately, a considerable volume of subsurface water is in material with very small pore spaces

Fig. 28-3.

Springs and seepage. A possible structure is shown below. Water sinks through the permeable sandstone to the top of the impermeable shale. It then moves along the surface of the shale to the face of the cliff.

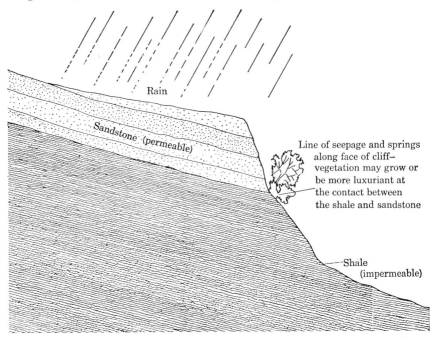

Rain

Sandstone (permeable)

Line of seepage and springs along face of cliff–vegetation may grow or be more luxuriant at the contact between the shale and sandstone

Shale (impermeable)

and cannot be obtained readily. Streams commonly do not become permanent until they have cut below the water table.

Water is a serious problem in many mining operations, and a number of mines have been closed before exhaustion because pumping costs became too great. For example, the rich Los Lamentos mine in cavernous limestone in Mexico was abandoned after two years of constant pumping had failed to lower the water table appreciably

However, water constitutes an entirely different problem in most deep mines (the deepest mine extends about one and three-quarter miles below the surface). At such depths the mines are dry and hot. Water must be brought downward to eliminate dust in drilling operations. Increased pressures at greater depths permit few open spaces to exist in rocks at depths greater than one-half mile or so.

Movement of Subsurface Water   Gravity causes rain to fall and makes water move down slopes into streams. Gravity is likewise the force which causes movement of ground water. Movement from the surface to the water table is dominantly straight down—a slow seepage in which the soil acts as a natural sponge. The surfaces of all openings must be coated with a thin film of water before more water can pass through. When water reaches the saturated zone beneath the water table, it oozes slowly downward and laterally, generally in much the same direction as runoff at the surface. According to Meinzer the rate of movement varies greatly: 420 feet per day is one of the fastest by field test; 1 foot in 10 years is one of the slowest by laboratory test. Less extreme rates range from a few feet per day to a few feet per year. A drop of water may move from the surface through the ground and return to the surface at a lower altitude, and this journey may take a few days or a few centuries; it may cover a few yards or a few hundred miles. Of course what is said here about the water table does not apply generally to impermeable rocks or to confined water.

WELLS

There is a familiar problem in areas in which many inhabitants rely upon individual wells. Why is one successful well 50 feet deep, a neighboring one 30 feet, and two others nearby each more than 100 feet deep? Why do some of these wells go dry and others not? Such questions are not asked purely out of intellectual curiosity. One's interest in the location of wells is sharpened by a drilling cost of $5 per foot or by weeks of hauling water during a dry spell (Figs. 28-4 and 28-5).

Ordinary and Artesian Wells   Prehistoric man dug for water, although he probably began his pursuit of underground water by cleaning out springs. In arid and semiarid areas, people lived only near available supplies of water. The ancient Chinese developed a method of drilling and casing wells. Their manually churned wells are reported to have reached depths of 5000 feet; two generations of workers were necessary to complete the job. The location of wells and the finding of ample water supplies beneath the Earth's surface is of practical value to many persons.

The ordinary well is simply a hole dug or drilled below the water table. A miniature lake forms in the hole, its surface at the water table.

Fig. 28-4.

A perched water body. A local water table may occur above the main water table in an area and cause variation in the depths of successful wells. A lens of impermeable clay is located in permeable sand in the sketch at the left below. The main water table is situated a number of feet below the clay. However, the clay traps any water that enters the ground above it and starts to move downward. Thus a local saturated zone forms above the clay. This perched water table would flatten out if frequent replenishment did not occur. At the right, successful wells on either side of a fault. Water enters the sandstone in adjoining areas where it crops out at the surface.

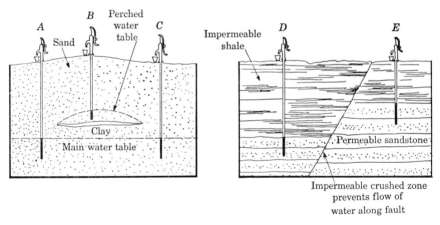

The level of this tiny lake rises in wet seasons and falls in dry seasons.

Popularly, any drilled well may be (mistakenly) called an artesian well. An artesian well, however, is defined correctly as one in which confined water under pressure rises above the local water table (actually above the aquifer which contains it) by its own power (Fig. 28-6). An inclined permeable fracture zone located between impervious rocks may provide the required conditions. Artesian systems are less common in igneous and metamorphic rocks.

The Dakota artesian system is one of the most important in the United States. A permeable sandstone formation with a basinlike structure crops out at the surface in the Black Hills, Big Horn Mountains, and Rocky Mountains. It receives supplies of water at these places. The sandstone beds are overlain by impermeable layers and dip downward from the mountainous areas to underlie parts of Kansas, Nebraska, the Dakotas, Wyoming, and Montana. More than 15,000 wells have been drilled into this formation. Unfortunately, so much

Fig. 28-5.

Well-drilling problems in areas of impermeable rocks. In such rocks circulation of ground water is confined mainly to cracks. A successful well depends upon the more or less chance intersection of an adequate network of cracks and fissures. Openings decrease in size and number with increasing pressures at greater depths. Therefore, it is sometimes more practical to start a second well at a new location than to extend a first unsuccessful one ever deeper. (Width of cracks is greatly exaggerated.)

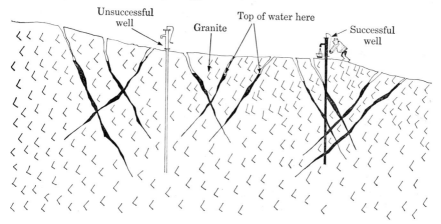

water has been withdrawn from the wells that fresh supplies from the intake areas cannot replace it. Some wells that formerly flowed out at the surface now have to be pumped.

An understanding of the rock formations and structures in an area can produce amazing results in locating ground water. For example, in 1905 in an area where the Dakota artesian system was inadequate to supply the huge demands of a railroad, a geologist was able to predict that a satisfactory aquifer would be encountered at a depth of 3000 feet. After three years of laborious drilling, the aquifer was penetrated within 31 feet of the predicted depth; water flowed from the well at the rate of 400,000 gal/day. Another hole drilled to the same aquifer in 1945 in 50 days had a flow of about 1½ million gal/day.

When an artesian system is first tapped, prodigious quantities of water may be made available. However, in dry areas the annual addition of water to the system from intake areas may be relatively small and the water in an aquifer may be virtually irreplaceable—almost a one-crop resource. If we use the slowly accumulated supply rapidly,

Fig. 28-6.

One type of Artesian system. Necessary conditions are (1) a permeable bed (aquifer), (2) impermeable beds above and below the permeable one, (3) a dip (slant) to the beds steep enough to establish a hydraulic gradient, and (4) exposure of the permeable bed at the surface so that it receives supplies of ground water.—Rain falls on the outcrop of the permeable sandstone which is at a high altitude (at the left in the sketch). Some of this rain sinks into the sandstone and oozes slowly down the bed under the pull of gravity. When the sandstone is tapped by the well, pressure forces water up the hole. In this instance, pressure is sufficient to cause the well to flow.—At the oasis, water has seeped upward along the fractured fault surface. If the water table is located above the permeable bed, no impermeable layer is needed below it.

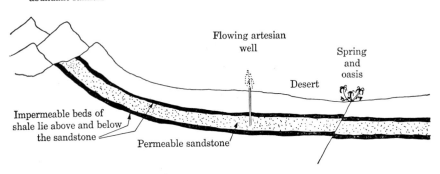

we are like the man inheriting a large sum of money who spends his fortune quickly and recklessly and is poor for the rest of his life. Conservation is necessary to maintain a balance between the natural supply and the total yield; some legislative action has been taken.

The important Illinois-Wisconsin artesian system formerly supplied the city of Chicago with a large portion of its water requirements. Permeable sandstones dip southward toward Chicago from their intake area in Wisconsin. A drop of water is estimated to require about 200 years to travel the several hundred miles from the intake area to the Chicago wells. Under such conditions, Chicagoans were drinking "fossil" water. To find out the rate of movement of ground water in such a system, we put a colored dye down one well. When the water in a second well downdip first shows the color, we register the time and measure the distance between wells to get the rate of travel. Several such measurements made at strategic locations give an average for the entire artesian system.

Oases in desert areas are often the cause of wonder and amazement. Why should vegetation grow in small areas scattered here and there throughout a hot desert of sand and bare rock surfaces? Many oases are located at places where an artesian water system locally cuts the Earth's surface (Fig. 28-6). One is appalled at the thought of the number of desert travelers who have died of thirst only a few hundred feet from water—inaccessible because it was buried beneath the surface.

WATER CONSERVATION

Ground water forms a great reservoir for the storage of water supplies. It commonly extends downward from the water table to depths of 2000 to 3000 feet below the surface. However, much of this water is in impervious beds, the quality is not everywhere desirable, and the supply is not inexhaustible. Conservation must thus be practiced.

In 1950 in the United States, estimates indicate, subsurface water was probably used somewhat as follows: (1) irrigation 63 percent, chiefly in the western states; (2) industrial 17 percent—for example 300 gallons are needed to make a barrel of beer, 10 gallons must be used to refine 1 gallon of gasoline, and one large paper mill uses more water than a city of 50,000 inhabitants; (3) municipal 11 percent; and (4) rural 9 percent. Ground water probably constitutes about one-fifth of all the water used in the United States. Total resources of surface and subsurface water in the United States are enormous. However, shortages exist in some areas and for some special uses. Not all areas have the desired amount (neither too much nor too little) at the desired time. These problems will be aggravated as the population increases and as the per capita use increases. Air conditioning and supplemental irrigation are new uses requiring enormous volumes of water.

Mining vs. Sustained Yield   In some areas water is being withdrawn from the ground much more rapidly than it is being replenished. Water tables have dropped alarmingly and continue to fall in such areas. Both artesian and nonartesian sources are affected. Water is virtually an irreplaceable natural resource in such areas, and its withdrawal from the ground can properly be called mining. For example, water is being mined today in parts of Texas (withdrawals are some twenty times greater than replenishment), Arizona, and California. There are plainly social and political aspects to any decision to mine such stored water—entirely, in part, or not at all. Some defend the mining of water by arguing that certain areas can be developed in no other way and that capital thus accumulated can later be used to find and utilize distant and costly sources of water. However this may be, a minimum prerequisite in such decisions should be an accurate knowledge of the facts involved. If extensive industrial and agricultural development is based upon a definite supply of water, and the supply of water later becomes inadequate, much economic waste and personal hardship result.

Long-term figures are needed. A certain part of Kansas experienced falling water tables for a number of years, enough to suggest that the water was being mined. But subsequent heavy rains raised the water tables higher than they had been twenty years earlier. There is some evidence that most recharge in arid and semiarid areas occurs during an occasional wet year.

If ground water is removed more rapidly than recharge takes place, the Earth's surface may sink as compaction occurs in the aquifer. The permeability of the aquifer may be seriously and permanently damaged. An extreme example is Mexico City. Some 9000 water wells were developed between 1910 and 1952 in unconsolidated materials underlying the city. In some places the surface has subsided as much as 16 feet. Some buildings are sinking into the ground—the former entrance at ground level is now a basement reinforced against collapse. The maximum rate of sinking in 1953 was 20 inches per year. New buildings are located on firmer ground, on piles, or have a floating type of foundation; but the problem remains very serious. Every time a person has a drink of water in Mexico City, they say, the city sinks a little. Withdrawals of oil may likewise cause subsidence.

Withdrawal and Recharge Ground water cannot be conserved simply by non-use. Some of it will drain out of underground reservoirs

Fig. 28-7.

Withdrawal and recharge of ground water. In the area illustrated below, the water table originally was near the surface. A swamp was located in one place, and a shallow domestic well yielded water when pumped. A large industrial concern moved to the area and drilled a deep well for a large water supply. Pumping was almost continuous and resulted in the development of a large cone of depression. The swamp and domestic well dried up.—The problem was solved when the company was persuaded to return its uncontaminated water to the swamp, where it seeped into the ground and raised the level of the water table.

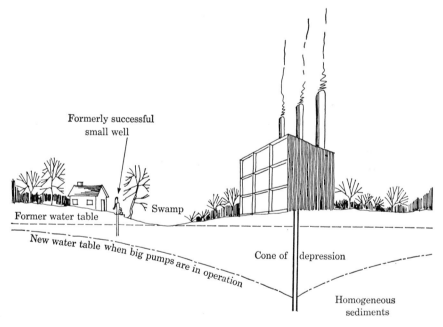

as part of the water cycle. When a well is pumped in homogeneous materials, a cone of depression occurs as the water table is lowered around the wells (Fig. 28-7). A rapid withdrawal, or withdrawal from less permeable aquifers, causes a steep-sided cone of depression. A balance occurs when the recovery by inflow during pumping equals the amount withdrawn. This is considered a safe yield.

Natural recharge occurs in areas of abundant rain and snow, especially where vegetation is present to limit the percentage of runoff. Replenishment of ground water by natural recharge is not uniform throughout an area. Just as there are cones of depression, there are the reverse, water table mounds. The mounds tend to flatten out if new supplies are not continuously added. Lakes and ponds do not cause recharge in humid areas because they themselves are fed by ground water. However, in a dry area the water table is commonly highest beneath a stream channel, and recharge occurs when water occasionally flows down the channel and filters into the unsaturated materials below.

Artificial recharge has been practiced successfully in many areas and is becoming more important in regions in which increased demands are being made upon the water supply. Water may be forced under pressure down a well from which it slowly oozes into adjacent rocks to be added again to the local supply of ground water. Precautions are demanded to avoid contaminating the local water supply (Fig. 28-8).

Contamination of wells. The shallow dug well A was unwisely located downslope from a cesspool C^1 and therefore received contaminated drainage from it. The owner then drilled a deeper well at B. This well tapped layers of soluble limestone inclined toward it from the direction of the lower cesspool C^2. The water dissolved openings in the limestone and flowed, unpurified by slow percolation, to where it was drawn out through well B. The owner of the two wells must either relocate his cesspool or dig a shallow well somewhere near B. (After Longwell, Knopf, and Flint, Physical Geology, John Wiley & Sons, Inc., 1948.

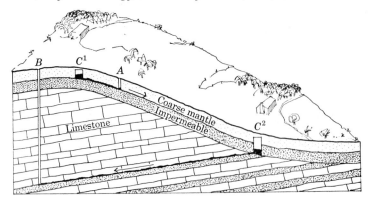

Fig. 28-8.

However, experiments have shown that polluted water can be purified by percolation through rocks and sediments. At one city, the slow lateral filtration of sewage-polluted river water through about 500 feet of sediment purified the water.

A second method of artificial recharge is water spreading. Water spreading can be accomplished by directing waste water into shallow grounds, ditches of permeable rock, or mantle. (Occasional cleaning operations are necessary to prevent clogging.) Stream flow may be regulated by dams to prevent the alternation of times of low water with those of great flow during floods: at such times water rushes through an area and does not have an opportunity to sink into the ground to form storage supplies for future use. Stream flow may also be diverted from place to place.

Increasing Usable Water Supplies The volume of water stored in underground reservoirs is many times greater than the capacity of all surface reservoirs. Usable supplies of water, both surface and subsurface, may be conserved in many ways. Water may be used and re-used with very great savings, circulation being arranged according to purity requirements. Following such a plan, the Fontana steel plant (California) consumes about 1400 gallons of water per ton of steel instead of the 65,000 gallons more commonly consumed elsewhere.

Reclaimed water may be used for some purposes. For example, Bethlehem Steel uses great quantities of water available after wastes from the city of Baltimore have been treated at sewage disposal plants. The arrangement is mutually beneficial: the company gets cheap water and the cost of treating the water is reduced for the city. A similar agreement was made in 1953 between the Texas Company and Amarillo, Texas.

The presence or absence of vegetation has great and controversial effects upon water supplies. Estimates suggest that the water used by waste vegetation in seventeen western states is probably equivalent to $1\frac{1}{2}$ times the annual flow of the Colorado River. How much of this could be saved by destruction of the waste vegetation without causing harmful erosion is uncertain, but the current disagreement concerning the uses of Colorado River water emphasizes the importance of saving even a fraction of this. On a hot summer afternoon in the United States, the amount of water being added to the atmosphere by evaporation and transpiration from all available sources (not just vegetation)

probably exceeds by ten times the maximum flow of the Mississippi.
Contrary to many opinions, forestation does not always increase
usable supplies. Experiments performed in certain areas in Colorado
and California have shown that deforestation has actually increased
the total quantity of surface and subsurface water available in the
area. The amounts used by the growth of vegetation each year are
saved. Snow also falls to the ground rather than collecting on trees and
evaporating. In some tests, usable trees have been removed in strips in a
forest. Snow which reaches the surface in the cut-over strips may be
blown under the trees in the adjoining tree belts. Shade from these
trees causes the snow to melt later in the spring when more of the water
can sink into the ground following the rapid runoff produced by heavy
spring rains. Coniferous forests may be converted to hardwoods, and
dense growths may be thinned to increase snow-water supplies. In the
test basins, as natural reforestation occurred, the total runoff decreased. Of course, care must be taken not to expose the soil to dangerous erosion, but research has given definite indications that careful
manipulation of upland vegetation can increase usable water supplies.
Much research remains to be done in this area.

The Problem of Seabrook Farms   A few years ago Seabrook Farms
in southern New Jersey faced the problem of getting rid of as much as
10 million gallons of water every day, polluted with vegetable scraps.
Except for some dissolved sugar and suspended starch, the Seabrook
farmers removed all foreign matter by filtering and chlorinating the
water. Still, local people objected to the addition of this material to
the local water supply. The farmers then tried to return the water to
the earth in unfarmed acres. They started a spraying operation on an
unused field covered with a sparse red-clover crop. It soon changed
the surface to a sandy soup. Next the sprayers were moved to the
edge of a scrubby white-oak forest. For two days the ground soaked
up water as fast as it was sprayed on. Then 50 inches of water were
poured on in the next 10 hours. Still the earth acted like a sponge and
absorbed all of the water. The forest floor had the capacity to soak
up almost limitless amounts of water, which filtered down through
alternating layers of sand and gravel to some black muck at a depth of
about 200 feet.

Seabrook Farms then solved its water disposal problem by scattering
rotary sprayers strategically through the woods. Their precipitation

averaged more than 50 inches per week and probably made this the wettest forest in the world. Yet the forest seemed no wetter than before except for droplets of water glittering on the leaves. Readings at observational wells have shown an upward movement of the water table, but enough springs have developed at the surface to establish an equilibrium. Pure potable water is flowing out of the woods as fast as the waste water is being pumped in.

In 1956, after six years of increasingly successful operation, the infiltration capacity and permeability of the soil had actually increased. Purification by filtration is complete, and there is no contamination or offensive odor from surface or subsurface waters in the area.

The effect on the growth of vegetation of the tremendous increase in the amount of water received by the forest within the range of each nozzle has been startling, and an important discovery has been made. For years it was thought that water in excess of ground saturation was unusable by plants. However, the amazing junglelike growth of plants —both rates and sizes have increased enormously—seems to disprove this idea. Preliminary experiments with food plants such as peas and potatoes indicate favorable results.

Long Island's Water Supply   Long Island furnishes a good example of intensive use of ground water by many people in a relatively small area. Long Island is separated from the rest of the Atlantic Coastal Plain and forms an island about 115 miles long by 20 miles wide; maximum altitude is 420 feet. The island is underlain by clays, sands, and gravels which dip gently seaward and contain three water-bearing permeable beds (Fig. 32-1). As these beds do not extend to the coast, ground water is supplied to them only by precipitation, which averages 40 inches or more of rainfall per year. An estimated one-third to one-half of this rainfall sinks to the water table. About one-half the water is pumped from the mainland.

Fresh ground water extends for considerable depths below sea level (in open spaces among the sediments) and rests upon the heavier salt water beneath it. Difference in densities is slight. Every foot of ground water above sea level may indicate an extension of approximately 40 feet beneath sea level (Fig. 28-9). For example, if the water table is 20 feet above sea level at one point, fresh water may extend to a depth of 800 feet below sea level at that point. However, if the water table is lowered 1 foot by pumping, the bottom of the ground-water zone

Fig. 28-9.

Fresh vs. salt water on a small island. The area is assumed to be underlain by permeable homogeneous materials. As the area became settled (left), many shallow wells were drilled, and great volumes of water were used. The water table thus fell enough throughout the island to let salt water enter the deep well on the opposite side of the island. The cone of depression commonly does not extend more than a few hundred yards from a well, but measurable lowering of the water table has occurred several miles from a well during heavy pumping in highly permeable sediments.

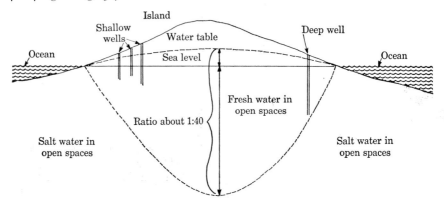

rises 40 feet. Therefore, excessive withdrawal results in contamination by salt water of the deepest wells. This occurred on Long Island. Conservation practices have since corrected this situation. Water spreading is practiced in rural areas and more than 300 recharge wells have been drilled in populated areas.

SUBSURFACE WATER IN SOLUBLE ROCKS

Limestones, marbles, and related rocks are soluble in water which contains carbon dioxide. The carbon dioxide may come from the atmosphere or from decaying organic material. Commonly the rocks are cut by cracks or fractures along which subsurface water can move. As water moves slowly along the cracks, the more soluble parts of the rock are slowly dissolved and the cracks widen. Solution is greatest at the surface, where carbon dioxide in the water is most abundant. Thus the cracks tend to widen near the surface. Where two cracks intersect, a funnel-shaped opening may develop and grow larger. Finally the roof collapses, forming a sink hole (Fig. 28-10). Sinks may be tiny pits or large holes more than a mile in diameter. If floored

Stages of evolution of a karst landscape. Increasing relief and cavern development are followed by decreasing relief and the removal of the limestone mass. Note the sink holes and natural bridge. (Courtesy, A. N. Strahler, Physical Geography, John Wiley & Sons, Inc.)

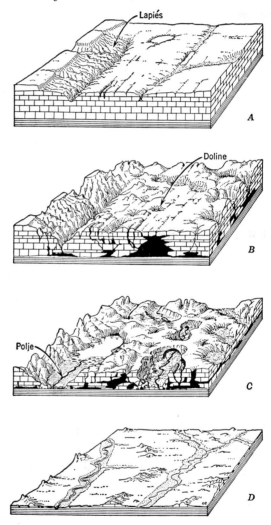

Fig. 28-10.

with impervious material or cut below the water table, sink holes may contain lakes or ponds. They may be circular in outline or quite irregular in shape. Several sinks may coalesce to form a very large one.

Most of the ground water that sinks below the surface in limestone

Fig. 28-11.

Mammoth Hot Springs in Yellowstone National Park, Wyoming. (Courtesy, The Milwaukee Road)

areas tends to move downward and laterally; eventually it joins streams in the deepest valleys of the area. The soluble rocks may be cut by two sets of parallel cracks which intersect at about right angles. Although limestone is commonly dense, individual layers are separated by bedding surfaces along which water can move slowly. Thus a three-dimensional network of cracks and fissures comes into existence to carry ground water through the rocks in the area. The dissolving action of the water along these cracks and bedding planes gradually enlarges them into a series of interconnected passageways; later these enlarge into caves and caverns by continued dissolving and collapse of the roofs. Surface streams may enter such a system and aid in the work of cave formation. Undermined parts of the system may collapse and enlarge the caverns or make holes at the surface. Remnants of such collapsed roofs may form natural bridges (Fig. 28-10).

The dissolving action of water may take place above or below the water table. As the master stream in the area cuts downward, it lowers the water table. Tributary streams follow suit, and many caves lose their underground streams. Beautiful caverns, visited each year by interested tourists, have thus been formed by the slow, unspectacular action of ground water.

Sometimes water containing calcium carbonate solution descends along a crack to the roof of a cave. At this place it partly evaporates and a very little calcium carbonate is precipitated out of solution. Centuries of this process result in iciclelike projections from the roof of the cave (stalactites). Part of the water may fall to the floor and there evaporate a little, thus precipitating more calcium carbonate. Eventually another iciclelike body is formed which grows upward from the floor (stalagmite*). Stalactite and stalagmite may meet, and form a column. Precipitation may occur in layers forming terraces (Fig. 28-11) and many weird shapes.

Calculations suggest that solution in limestones in northern Kentucky is occurring at such a rapid rate as to remove an average of about 1 foot of rock every 2000 years. Solution is much slower in other areas and in other rocks. Nevertheless studies in North Carolina in an area underlain by igneous rocks (diorite) indicate that rock material is probably being removed by solution at the rate of about 1 foot every 28,000 years.

EXERCISES AND QUESTIONS FOR CHAPTER 28

1. Why are deposits around hot springs commonly thicker than those around cold springs?

2. Why are veins of calcite common in limestone?

3. Why does the bulk of natural recharge occur in the spring in humid areas although precipitation is as great or greater in the summer? (Hint: effects of vegetation.)

4. Compare the shapes of the cones of depression which will develop in each of the following: (1) moderate pumping in permeable materials, and (2) rapid pumping in less permeable materials.

5. What is meant by the statement that one drinks "fossil" water from a certain artesian well?

6. What is the source of water supply at your college and/or your home? Is the supply adequate? the quality satisfactory? Can you suggest any improvements?

* It has been said that stalactites and stalagmites have a certain resemblance to "ants in the pants." The "mites" go up and the "tites" come down.

CHAPTER 29

Glaciation

T HE story of the recent Ice Age is one to capture the imagination. It is a gift to us from the combined labors of many geologists who have traced the course of glacier ice that covered almost a third of the Earth's land surface during its maximum extent in the Ice Age. At this time about half of the states in the United States were covered by ice—some completely, others partially. Evidence of the former presence of the ice is abundant, widespread, and clear; it is little affected by geologic forces, such as weathering, erosion, burial, and metamorphism. Approximately 10 percent of the Earth's land surface is still covered by glacier ice, most of it in the Antarctic ice sheet (about 5 million square miles) and the Greenland ice sheet (over 600,000 square miles).

The Ice Age may have begun from 300,000 to 1 million years ago. The magnitude seems to be of this order. Recent evidence (carbon-14: pp. 553-555) indicates that ice covered the northern part of the United States and Canada as recently as 10,000 years ago. During the Ice Age, great changes took place at and below the Earth's surface both in the glaciated areas and outside of them. The changes involved climates, animals and plants, crustal movements, sea water, erosion, and deposition. The Pleistocene (Greek: "most recent") epoch is the name given by geologists to the time in which these changes occurred. It is more or less synonymous with the popular term, Ice Age.

A traveler in the northern part of the United States or in Canada cannot escape a feeling of amazement if he realizes that this vast area was covered by a mass of ice some thousands of years ago. If this con-

cept is new to the traveler, his reaction may be a quick and skeptical
"How do you know?" And indeed the concept of glaciation is almost as
startling now as when it first emerged.

Evidence of Glaciation   Louis Agassiz, a Swiss naturalist (1807-
1873), is often credited with the development of the glacial concept
about a hundred years ago; but a number of Agassiz's contemporaries,
scientists of earlier days, and many observant individuals deserve to
share the credit—as is often true of key principles in science.

The basic idea came from people who lived in areas of existing
glaciers. Erosion and deposition by the ice created features which could
be seen and compared readily with similar features located beyond
the present margins of the glaciers. From the plain hint that glaciers
once extended farther down their valleys than they now do, there
slowly grew a realization that great sheets of ice actually once covered
large parts of the Earth's surface. This idea was accepted after much
argument and discussion.

Agassiz himself was at first skeptical of the concept of widespread
glaciation. He studied existing glaciers and supposedly glaciated areas
with the intention of disproving the whole idea. However, the field
evidence was so convincing that Agassiz became the leading figure
in spreading and developing the glacial concept.

There were rival theories. British geologists had noticed large foreign boulders scattered widely, some at higher altitudes than their
distant sources. They had observed scratched and polished bedrock
surfaces and had studied widespread nonstratified deposits of boulders, gravel, sand, and mud. These were quite unlike the sorted layers
of sand and silt they could see being deposited by streams. Furthermore, these deposits occurred on hilltops as well as in low areas. Such
unusual phenomena called for an unusual answer. Being familiar with
the sea and not with glaciers, they theorized that a great flood had submerged the entire area; icebergs had carried the huge boulders and
had scratched the bedrock surfaces. The unsorted sedimentary deposits, which they termed "drift," had been picked up and dumped by
a great rush of waters—perhaps the Noachian deluge. Similar ideas
had developed in other countries.

But the answer to the question "How do you know?" involves the
fundamental geologic principle that the present is the key to the past.
Glaciers exist. They have been studied, and their characteristic kinds

of erosion and deposition have been identified. Such distinctive features are then sought in areas not now covered by glaciers. If found, they indicate the former presence of ice.

WORLDWIDE EFFECTS OF THE RECENT ICE AGE*

Glaciation has occurred several times during the Earth's geological history; that of the Pleistocene is the most recent and has the clearest

Fig. 29-1.

The extent of glaciation of North America at the maximum of the glacial ages. The details are somewhat generalized because of insufficient information, especially in the north. Boundaries between glacier ice, sea ice, and open sea are conjectural, but are based on modern analogies. Arrows show the general directions of glacier flow. Note the relation of the Ohio and Missouri rivers to former ice margins. (After Longwell, Knopf, and Flint, Physical Geology, John Wiley & Sons, Inc.)

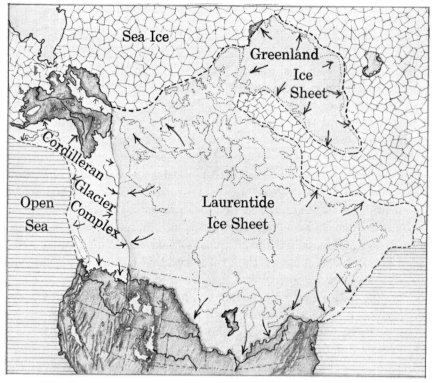

* R. F. Flint, *Glacial Geology and the Pleistocene Epoch,* John Wiley & Sons, New York, 1947, pp. 1-12.

record. Still existing glaciers were much larger during this epoch, and regions which today are without ice were then covered by it. Three huge ice sheets formed more or less simultaneously in the Northern Hemisphere: (1) At its maximum the North American ice sheet covered approximately 5 million square miles and extended southward to Long Island and the channels of the Ohio and Missouri Rivers (Fig. 29-1). (2) The smaller Scandinavian ice sheet once extended from northwestern Europe, through Denmark, to the northern parts of Germany and European Russia. (3) A Siberian ice sheet existed.

Fig. 29-2.

Evidence indicating multiple glaciation: (1) Granite boulders predominate in the older glacier material, whereas boulders of quartzite predominate in the younger glacial material. Evidently the glacier came from two different directions (bedrock in source areas is different) on its two trips to this area. (2) Stumps of trees at the top of the older deposit indicate that sufficient time elapsed between glaciations for soil to develop and a forest to grow. (3) Two V-shaped valleys are shown eroded in the older glacial deposit. These are filled by the younger material. (4) The soil is thickest on the right where the younger material does not rest upon the older. In this location weathering has been producing soil for a longer time: burial under the younger glacial deposit stopped the process elsewhere. (Modified from Leet and Judson)

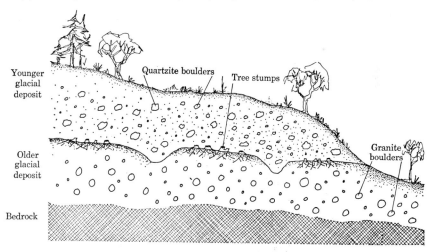

The ice sheets probably advanced and retreated four times during the Pleistocene (Fig. 29-2). As indicated by the record, ice in the Pleistocene was more extensive than today during less than half the total length of time. In other words, more time elapsed between advances of the glaciers (interglacial stages) than occurred while glaciers actually existed on the lands.

Volume Changes in Sea Water   Glacier ice is metamorphosed snow which has fallen as part of the water cycle. Because the total amount of water at the Earth's surface in the Pleistocene was probably about

Fig. 29-3.

Relief map of the Northeastern United States and the Atlantic Coast. The vertical scale is exaggerated (10 times). The continental shelf, continental slope, and ocean basin show clearly. Origin of the submarine canyons which cut the continental slope and head on the continental shelf is controversial. Some rival the Grand Canyon in size. Water is about 600 feet deep at the outer edge of the continental shelf. (Courtesy Aero Service Corporation, Philadelphia)

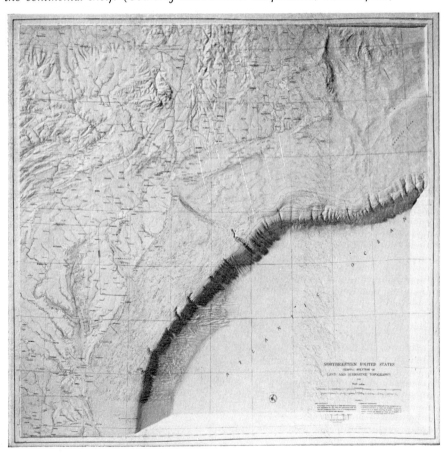

constant, the volume of ocean water must have been decreased by the amount that was frozen on the lands as ice. Thus, sea level probably fluctuated four times during the advances and retreats of glacier ice during the Pleistocene. Sea level may have dropped about 300 feet below its present level during the maximum extent of the glaciers. On the other hand, if all glacier ice on the Earth today were melted, sea level might rise approximately 100-200 feet. Advocates of the atom bombing of Antarctica to melt the ice and uncover its supposed mineral deposits certainly are not extensive dealers in coastal real estate or are unaware of the implications of their suggestion.

Various kinds of geologic evidence show that sea level fluctuated during the Pleistocene, although exact amounts are somewhat uncertain. The channel of the Hudson River can be traced seaward on the Atlantic floor for some 90 miles to a depth of about 240 feet (Fig. 29-3). The channel of the Rhine extends to a depth of approximately 300 feet. Similar figures can be cited for channel continuations of other rivers. Today streams do not excavate their valleys much below sea level. When these channels originated, the level of the oceans was probably about 300 feet lower than it is at present. Insufficient time has elapsed for subsequent burial of the channels by sediments from the lands. Crustal movements, of course, might have depressed land areas after the channels had been eroded. However, the drowned channels on the sea floor have a world-wide distribution and extend to a more or less uniform depth. Therefore, it seems likely that they originated at a time when sea level everywhere was lower than it is today.

Crustal Movements Caused by the Weight of the Ice Sheets   Research has shown convincingly that the Earth's crust sagged beneath the tremendous weight of the ice sheets. The downwarping of the Earth's surface probably occurred simultaneously with a slow plastic flow of rock materials at a depth of a few tens of miles outward from the overloaded glaciated areas (Fig. 29-4). At such depths great pressures and high temperatures presumably permit rocks to be deformed slowly without breaking. Apparently the weight of a growing ice sheet squeezed rock material from beneath it, and the space thus made available permitted the Earth's surface to bend downward. As the ice sheet melted, the crust warped upward, and rock material at depth returned slowly under the glaciated areas. Similar warping of the crust

Fig. 29-4.

Weight of the ice causes the Earth's surface to sag. The vertical scale and amount of sag are greatly exaggerated. The ideas of isostasy and isostatic adjustment are involved. Apparently a balance exists in the outer part of the Earth; if this balance is upset, as it was during the Ice Age when great volumes of water shifted from the oceans to the lands as glaciers, a slow adjustment to restore the balance occurs.

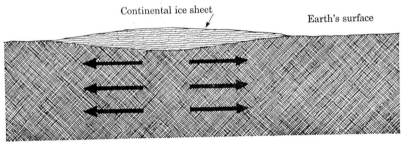

Continental ice sheet

Earth's surface

Slow outward flow of
rocks at a depth of a
few dozen miles causes
the earth's surface
to sag

was probably repeated during each advance and retreat of the ice sheets. Since the ice retreated only recently in terms of geologic time, the Earth's surface is still rising slowly in the glaciated areas.

Evidence of crustal movement as a direct result of glacial loading and unloading is especially well exposed in Scandinavia. The picture is less complete for crustal movements caused by the North American ice sheet, partly because fewer studies have been made. Evidently the weight of the ice caused the Earth's surface to sag several hundreds of feet or more. As the front of the ice sheet retreated toward the north, a number of large lakes formed in this depressed area in the southern part of Canada and northern part of the United States. Upward movement of the surface apparently did not take place immediately. Around the shores of these lakes there formed wave-cut cliffs, beaches, and other features associated with shore lines. The once-level shore lines of these lakes have been bent upward progressively. The greatest uplift has occurred in the north where the center of the ice sheet was formerly located. For example, one previously level shore line (glacial Lake Algonquin) now at an altitude of about 600 feet in Michigan, is 1150 feet above sea level at North Bay on Lake Huron and may rise to about 1500 feet above sea level some 150 miles north of this latitude. Uplift apparently continues today. After the ice front had retreated north of the St. Lawrence Valley, sea water entered this area and spread into the Champlain Valley. Sediments containing marine shells and the bones of whales today occur about 500 feet above sea level at the Vermont-Quebec border.

Pluvial Lakes in Nonglaciated Areas   Climatic changes apparently occurred during the Pleistocene in areas which were not glaciated. Today areas such as Utah and Nevada are semiarid and arid. According to some deductions, they were probably cooler, more moist, and had less evaporation in the past when approximately 5 million square miles of North America were covered by ice. Pluvial (Latin: "of rain") lakes should have been larger and more numerous than they are today. Field workers have checked these deductions and have discovered evidence of many former lakes in the Utah-Nevada area. In fact, Great Salt Lake in Utah occupies a tiny part of former Lake Bonneville, which at one time covered much of the state of Utah. These former lakes also show evidence that they grew and shrank several times, corresponding presumably to advances and retreats of the ice sheets. Similar evidence is being gathered from other parts of the world.

Migrations of Animals and Plants   As the ice sheets gradually advanced, animals and plants probably migrated southward to warmer climates or perished. Fossil reindeer and the woolly mammoth have been found in southern New England, walrus along the Georgia coast, white spruce in Louisiana, and musk oxen in Arkansas and Texas. As the ice fronts retreated, the animals and plants could return to their former habitats. In sediments deposited at any given location, assemblages of fossil animals and plants indicating a cool climate may be found above or below fossil assemblages indicating a warm climate. At one site in Kansas, two groups of fossil rodents were found one above the other in sedimentary deposits. Living relatives of one group exist today only in cooler areas like the northern United States and Canada; living relatives of the other group exist today only in warmer areas like the southwestern United States and Mexico. This evidence suggests that at different times during the Pleistocene, Kansas had climates which were cooler or warmer than its present one. In other words, during one interglacial time the climate was probably milder than it is today. Perhaps glacier ice was less extensive than it is at present, and sea level was higher.

One line of research which should throw much light on Pleistocene history in the future involves study of sediments deposited at great depths on the sea floor. As erosion is not believed possible in this environment, the record furnished by the accumulated sediments should be entirely preserved. Instruments have been devised recently which can extract cores as long as 70 feet from the ocean floors at depths of thousands of feet. These cores have shown alternations of the remains of warm- and cool-water animals. For example, a 50-foot core has been taken from a depth of more than 15,000 feet in the Caribbean Sea. Eleven or twelve shifts between tropical and temperate conditions are indicated by the vertical distribution of the Foraminifera fauna. The Foraminifera lived near the surface of the ocean, but when they died their shells sank to the bottom. The shifts suggest changes in the temperature of the water related to the four major advances and retreats of the Ice Age as well as to various glacial substages.

Summary of Major World-Wide Effects of the Ice Age　　Pleistocene glaciation originated when continents were more extensive and mountainous than they had been for much of the geologic past. At this time temperatures probably dropped (8°C is the estimated decrease in temperate areas), more precipitation occurred as snow, and less snow melted each summer. Three huge ice sheets developed, and many smaller glaciers formed or grew larger in other areas. As the ice sheets grew, the following changes occurred gradually: the volume of sea water became smaller and sea level fell, the crust beneath the ice sheets warped downward, more rain fell in areas beyond the margins of the ice sheets to form large lakes, and animals and plants migrated southward to warmer climates. Next, temperatures rose, the ice sheets dwindled in size, and a corresponding reversal occurred in the changes listed above. The ice sheets probably grew and advanced four times; each advance was followed by a time of glacier shrinkage; minor fluctuations also occurred. During at least one retreat of the ice fronts, less ice than today apparently existed on the Earth's surface. In the glaciated areas, characteristic features of erosion and deposition were formed.

These effects continue today. Glaciers have been retreating almost everywhere during the last 100 years or so, and measurements suggest that sea level has risen some $2\frac{1}{2}$ inches during this same period, presumably in large part because of the melting of glacier ice. The Earth's crust is still moving upward slowly in the glaciated areas. Such changes affect man in many ways. For example, codfish, unknown in the waters around Greenland before 1900, now has become the main diet of the Eskimos living there. With the warmer temperatures, Greenland's population is increasing rapidly. The rise in temperature seems to have been accelerated during the last 30 years or so.

However, these changes follow earlier fluctuations. For example, some areas which were inhabited during the Middle Ages have subsequently been covered by ice. Today the ice is retreating from these areas. Evidently, therefore, climate was milder during the Middle Ages than it is today. Around the beginning of the seventeenth century, temperatures seem to have dropped, and glaciers began to expand. This change has been reversed during the last 100 years or so.

What of the future? Will the present trend to a warmer climate continue? Will coastal areas be gradually flooded as more and more ice melts? Or will temperatures again become lower and glaciers begin to grow and spread outward? These questions have no answers at present.

GLACIERS AND GLACIER ICE

In some areas on the Earth's surface not all of the winter's snowfall melts or evaporates during the succeeding summer. In the polar regions such places occur at every altitude, but in equatorial areas they occur only near the tops of high mountains. Thus each year in certain parts of these areas, the snow piles higher and higher. The weight of each succeeding snowfall and the moisture that is present from melting snow near the surface gradually cause the snow at the bottom of the pile to take on a granular texture similar to that of many snowdrifts during the spring. Each snowflake is changed to a tiny granule of ice. Continued compaction by more snowfalls changes the granular material to solid ice. Commonly this ice is layered, evidence that it was formed from many separate falls of snow. When sufficient ice has piled up on a slope, gravity tends to move it gradually to a lower altitude (Fig. 29-5). Commonly a thickness of 100 feet or more of ice is needed before movement occurs; this depends upon the steepness of

Fig. 29-5.

Nourishment and wastage in the valley glacier. Glacial gouging will be most pronounced in parts of the valley underlain by less resistant or badly fractured rocks. These are sites for future lakes.

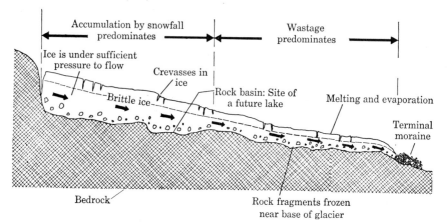

the slope, temperature of the ice, and other factors. Such a moving mass of ice, or one that has moved in the past, is called a glacier.

Among the types of glaciers are valley glaciers (Fig. 29-6) and ice sheets (ice caps are small ice sheets). In mountainous areas, glacier ice moves slowly down valleys previously eroded by streams. Sometimes ice fills the valley from wall to wall. Ice sheets are very broad masses of ice, of continental dimensions, which bury whole areas almost completely—high mountains as well as parts near sea level. Ice caps commonly form on undissected plateau areas high above sea level. Such ice caps may be circular in plan. The weight of the ice causes radial outward flow from the center in the plastic ice near the bottom of the mass. Besides low temperatures, abundant snowfall is needed for glaciers to develop. Northern Siberia is extremely cold, but the small amount of winter snowfall wastes away during the short cool summer, and glacier formation is prevented.

Glacier ice consists of a mass of interlocking grains which can flow under pressure, apparently by more or less continuous changes in the individual particles. Stresses set up by the weight and motion of the ice cause individual ice grains to grow in size, to twist and rotate, and to slide along planes of weakness in the crystals much as a pack of cards slides when pushed by the hand. Perhaps skating illustrates how part of the flow takes place. A skater actually glides on a thin film

Fig. 29-6.

Barnard Glacier, Alaska. Note the formation of medial moraines where tributary glaciers join the main glacier. (Bradford Washburn)

of water which pressure forms momentarily beneath the blades of the skates. When ice changes to water, the volume is reduced; therefore, pressure on ice promotes liquefaction. The water freezes again immediately after the pressure is removed.

Stresses in the glacier ice cause momentary liquefaction, the transfer of water downslope, and immediate freezing. Ice at the bottom of a glacier moves plastically, but the upper part, some 100 feet or more in thickness, is too brittle and rigid to flow under the lower pressure there. It is carried by the flowing ice below. The rate of flow of glacier ice varies from a maximum measured rate of over 100 feet a day to a general average of a few feet or less per day. The surface of a valley glacier moves more rapidly in the center of the valley than along its sides because less friction occurs there. This fact was first determined by placing a straight line of stakes across a valley glacier and measuring the movements of individual stakes.

In 1820 three guides were buried in the ice of a valley glacier beneath a great avalanche of snow. A scientist used his knowledge of the rate of flow to predict that the bodies would require some 35 to 40 years to reach the front end of the glacier. The bodies were recovered in 1861 after they had been carried nearly 2 miles by the ice at the rate of about 8 inches per day.

GLACIAL EROSION AND DEPOSITION

Three four-letter words have been used to indicate the work of glaciers: plow, file, and sled. Perhaps valley glaciers illustrate these functions best. To be effective as a file and thus to polish, scratch, and abrade the surfaces over which it moves, a glacier must have rock pieces frozen into its basal portions. A valley glacier may obtain these rock pieces from the mantle or bedrock over which it moves. In addition, rock materials may slide upon the ice from the valley walls. A glacier resembles a plow by pushing and shoving materials ahead of it.

In arctic areas where some glaciers end at the water's edge in cliffs, the exposed cross sections show that most of the transported rock materials are contained in the basal portions. This illustrates the role of a glacier as a sled. Large blocks of the glacier may break off to form icebergs which later melt and deposit their loads of rock debris far from land in places ordinarily reached by only the finest of materials. The origin of such deposits, composed of fine-grained layered

Glacial boulder showing flattened, polished, and scratched surface. (U.S. Geological Survey)

Fig. 29-7.

sediments which contain occasional large boulders, puzzled geologists for some time.

Stones transported by glaciers were once frozen firmly in the ice, and many of them were dragged under great pressure over solid bed-

Fig. 29-8.

Record of two glaciations. An ancient Precambrian boulder-bearing glacial deposit has been beveled, striated, and polished by the Pleistocene ice sheet. (Photograph by A. P. Coleman)

rock. This abrasion produced polished, scratched, and faceted surfaces on the stones. Later, if the ice melted temporarily around the stones, they would rotate to new positions and receive additional smoothed surfaces (Fig. 29-7). Bedrock surfaces are polished, scratched, and grooved by rock materials frozen solidly into the bottom of the ice (Fig. 29-8).

Fig. 29-9 illustrates why parts of the Ohio and Missouri Rivers mark

Fig. 29-9.

The origin of part of the Ohio River (highly diagrammatic). In some areas, ice flowed from the north or northwest.

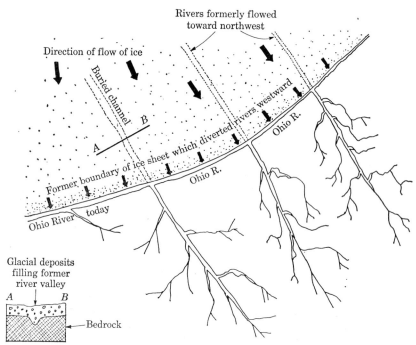

the southernmost boundaries of the North American ice sheet. The Ohio River did not exist before the Pleistocene. Instead, several rivers existed in that area and flowed to the northwest. As the front of the ice sheet advanced from the northeast, the rivers were blocked and turned westward along the margin of the ice sheet to join the Mississippi River. The ice sheet kept the combined waters of these rivers in their new course long enough to erode a channel. When the ice retreated, it filled the old channels with glacial drift. That is why the newly formed Ohio River continued to flow in its new course. A simi-lar explanation accounts for the location of part of the Missouri River. Note the many rivers which flow from the west (unglaciated) into the Missouri in contrast to the few which enter it from the east. Discovery of the abandoned river channels, now filled by glacial drift, has en-abled geologists to decipher this bit of Earth history.

Fig. 29-10.

Yosemite Valley and the Sierra Nevada. The former V-shaped cross section of Yosemite was changed into the present rounded U shape by a valley glacier. Note the even skyline. A peneplane apparently existed in this area in the past before the relatively recent uplift of the Sierra Nevada (tilted upward along the eastern front and downward in the west to form the Great Valley of California). Some of the mountain tops are remnants of this surface. (Fairchild Aerial Surveys)

Valley glaciers change the shapes of the valleys down which they move by widening, deepening, and straightening them. The typical V-shaped cross section of a youthful mountain valley is altered to a steep-sided, flat-floored U-shape (Fig. 29-12). For example, Yosemite Valley in California is estimated to have been deepened some 1500 feet by glacial erosion (Fig. 29-10).

Constricted parts of a valley may be deepened more than wider sections. In addition, if some sections of the bedrock floor of a valley are cut by more cracks than other parts or are underlain by weaker rocks, these areas may be deepened considerably by glacial erosion.

Fig. 29-11.

Convict Lake area along the eastern front of the Sierra Nevada. The lake (altitude 7583 feet above sea level) is located in a basin formerly occupied by a valley glacier which flowed out upon the valley floor for about 1½ miles as shown by the moraines: terminal moraine T, lateral moraines L, L, and recessional moraines R_1, R_2, and R_3. The outlet creek has cut through the moraines on the left. (Fairchild Aerial Surveys)

Fig. 29-12.

Land forms produced by valley glaciers. (After W. M. Davis and A. K. Lobeck; reprinted with permission from A. N. Strahler, Physical Geography, John Wiley & Sons, Inc.)

A. *Before glaciation sets in, the region has smoothly rounded divides and narrow, V-shaped stream valleys.*

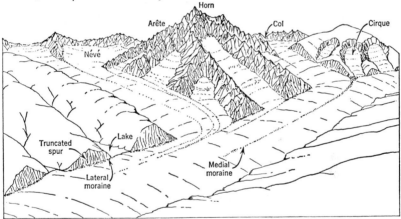

B. *After glaciation has been in progress for thousands of years new erosional forms are developed.*

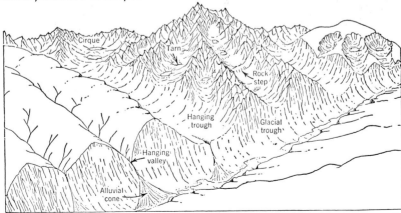

C. *With the disappearance of the ice a system of glacial troughs is exposed.*

The basin-like areas thus formed may become lakes after the ice disappears (Fig. 29-11).

Tributary glaciers contain a small amount of ice relative to the main valley glacier into which they flow. Therefore, they are unable to cut downward as rapidly. When the ice eventually wastes away, such tributaries may be left hanging above the main valley, and beautiful waterfalls may occur at their mouths (Fig. 29-10).

In summary, the typical glaciated valley should be fairly straight, have a U-shaped cross section, head in a great bowl-shaped depression (called a *cirque*), have several rock basin lakes along its course, and possess hanging tributary valleys (Fig. 29-12).

A ridge between two valley glaciers may be reduced to a knife-edge crest as the glaciers erode the valley walls. Three or more valley glaciers working headward toward a mountain peak may shape it into a jagged summit with triangular-shaped cliffed faces like the Matterhorn in the Alps and the Grand Teton in Wyoming (Fig. 29-13).

The Grand Tetons in Wyoming. (Photograph by Richard J. Ordway)

Fig. 29-13.

Glaciers deposit their loads in a number of different ways, each with a characteristic shape and appearance (Fig. 29-14). Rock materials rich in clay may be plastered onto the surface over which the ice is moving and produce low, streamlined hills called *drumlins* (Fig. 29-15). These commonly occur in swarms. New York State alone is estimated to have over 10,000 drumlins (Fig. 29-17). Rock materials may

Fig. 29-14.

Whitewater, Wisconsin: Map-model illustrating the effects of continental glacia-tion. Note the end moraine with kettle holes and lakes, outwash plain, drumlins, and disturbed drainage. (Courtesy Aero Service Corporation, Philadelphia)

be shoved ahead of a glacier to be left at its terminus or may be brought there and dumped as *end moraines* by the moving, melting ice (Fig. 29-11). All of the rock debris carried by a glacier and deposited by it or by streams flowing from it is called *glacial drift*. This may or may not be stratified.

The enormous load of rock debris given to streams by glaciers causes these streams to deposit thick blankets of sediments over the floors of their valleys. This outwash material may extend for hundreds of miles beyond the margins of a great ice sheet and gradually merges

Fig. 29-15.

Airphoto of a Wisconsin drumlin (Photograph by C. C. Bradley. Courtesy, F. T. Thwaites)

with normal stream deposits. Most of the larger rivers in the United States today flow on flood plains which originated in this manner.

The load of rock debris carried by an ice sheet varied in volume from place to place, and the surface over which it rode was commonly irregular. Therefore, the thickness of material deposited by the ice varies from one area to another. This produces a characteristic swell-and-swale or knob-and-kettle type of topography. Kettle holes (Fig. 29-16) are common in many glaciated areas.

Thick ice sheets have less effect on the surfaces over which they move than might be expected. They plow and push mantle rock ahead of them and pick up many blocks of bedrock. This material is left behind as the glaciers waste away. The surfaces over which they moved have been polished, scratched, and grooved. However, an ice sheet tends to modify the shapes of hills and mountains in its path—not to destroy them. Ice sheets have been known to ride over loose material without great disturbance. When the thickness of an ice sheet

Formation of a kettle hole.

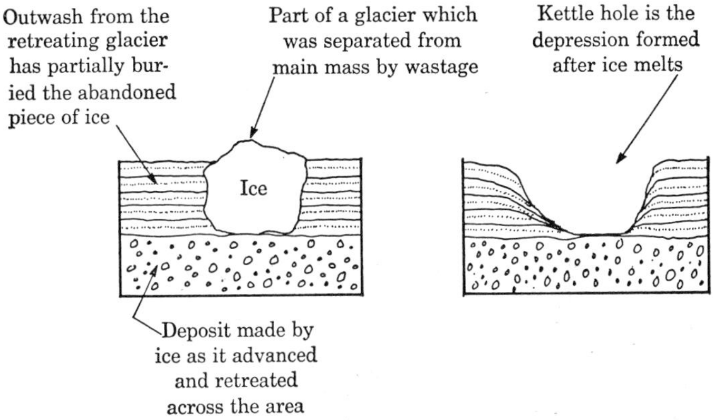

Outwash from the retreating glacier has partially buried the abandoned piece of ice

Part of a glacier which was separated from main mass by wastage

Kettle hole is the depression formed after ice melts

Deposit made by ice as it advanced and retreated across the area

Fig. 29-16.

is reduced beyond certain limits by wastage, brittle ice will extend from top to bottom, and flow will be impossible.

DIRECTION OF ICE MOVEMENT

A valley glacier of the Ice Age of course moved down the valley it occupied. The direction of movement of a great ice sheet is more difficult to determine. Several kinds of evidence can be used.

Striations. Glacial scratches or striations are elongated parallel to the direction of ice movement, but striations can vary greatly in orientation because of highly irregular movements of the ice margins (Fig. 29-8).

Asymmetrical Bedrock Abrasion. Bedrock outcrops over which ice moves may be abraded asymmetrically; that is, smooth gentle slopes face the direction from which the ice came and steep slopes face the opposite direction.

Drumlins. The general trend of the elongated streamlined hills called drumlins is parallel to the direction in which the ice moved (Fig. 29-17). Ideally a drumlin is shaped like an inverted spoon with its steep slope facing the direction from which the ice came.

Fig. 29-17.

Drumlins and glacial lakes south of Lake Ontario in New York. (Reprinted with permission from Monnett and Brown, Principles of Physical Geology, *Ginn and Company)*

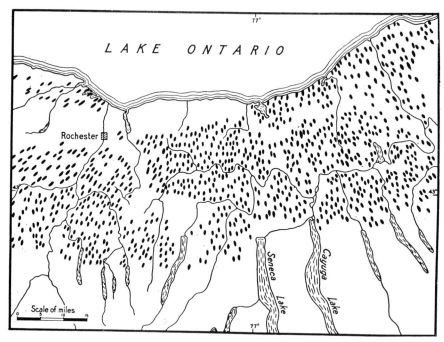

Moraines. Moraines are topographic features composed of glacial drift which have resulted chiefly from direct deposition by the ice. Moraines are of several kinds, and end moraines are of importance in showing direction of ice movement. When an ice sheet is said to advance or retreat, reference is made to the actual position of the front margin of the ice. The forces of nourishment which make the glacier larger oppose the forces of wastage which make it smaller. When wastage exceeds nourishment, the front of the ice sheet recedes. The forward flow of the ice continues, but the rate of backward melting of the front of the ice exceeds that of forward flow. If forward flow and backward wastage exactly balance each other, the front of the ice sheet remains stationary. New supplies of rock debris are brought by the moving ice to this stationary front and dumped there as the ice melts. This material augments that previously shoved ahead of the ice by its snowplow action. A ridge of material (end moraine) thus forms along the margin of the ice sheet. This is oriented approximately perpendicular to the direction of flow of the ice at any one point (Figs. 29-11 and 29-14). Such an end moraine may be pitted by kettle holes and have a great outwash plain of stratified drift extending from it beyond the ice margin. A series of end moraines (a terminal end moraine and one or more recessional ones) may form during the retreat of a glacier.

Indicator Stones and Boulder Trains. Unique rock types may occur as ice-transported boulders. If the boulders and their distant sources have both been located, the direction of movement of the ice in that area has been determined. When the place of origin is known, such transported boulders are called *indicator stones.* Elongated fan-shaped areas which contain numerous ice-transported boulders of a unique kind are known as *boulder trains.* Such boulders were picked up by the ice as it moved over a relatively small source outcrop. Later they were scattered in a fan-shaped area by irregular forward movements of the ice.

In eastern Finland, large areas are covered by glacial drift. In this glacial drift a number of boulders containing copper-bearing minerals were found, but the source of the copper was not known. In the early 1900's someone with imagination plotted the site of each copper-bearing, ice-transported boulder on a map. When this was done, the map showed a fan-shaped area which contained all of the boulders. Although the apex of the fan was buried beneath glacial drift, drilling there in 1910 disclosed one of Finland's most important copper deposits.

A farmer is reported to have found an unusual stone in his fields in Wisconsin one day. He brought the stone home to his wife, who also thought it was pretty and placed it on the mantel. There it remained until the local jeweler purchased it for a dollar. The pretty stone changed hands a number of times and eventually was purchased for several thousand dollars. It proved to be a large diamond. A dozen or so other diamonds, all smaller than the first, have been found in Wisconsin, Michigan, Indiana, and Ohio in ice-transported drift. You can be certain that their locations were plotted on a map. However, the stones are few and the area is large. The source is located somewhere north of the Great Lakes.

ORIGIN OF GLACIATION

In the past, glaciation seems to have occurred only when lands were high. At the present time, the land areas of the Earth apparently are more extensive and higher than they were throughout much of geologic history. Yet extensive glaciation has not occurred every time that lands have been high and widespread. Moreover, glaciers advanced and retreated several times during the Pleistocene while the lands remained high. According to Flint a drop in mean annual temperature at a time when lands are high may bring on a period of glaciation. A rise in the mean annual temperature would cause recession of the glaciers. This seems to furnish the most satisfactory explanation concerning the origin of glaciation at the present time.

What would cause a fluctuation in temperature? The sun is the source of the Earth's heat energy. Variations in the amount of energy received from the sun have been explained by the occasional presence of volcanic dust or carbon dioxide in the atmosphere or by the passage of the Earth through nebula material. Perhaps a better explanation is found in the fact that solar energy is known to fluctuate a maximum of 3 percent. This is not enough to cause glaciation. However, if solar output has varied 3 percent during the brief time interval it has been measured continuously by man (since 1918), it may have fluctuated much more throughout the very long expanse of geologic time. About this we can only speculate.

EXERCISES AND QUESTIONS FOR CHAPTER 29

1. Can sediments transported and deposited by streams commonly be distinguished from those carried and dropped by a glacier? How?

2. Why are smoothed scratched bedrock surfaces in certain areas interpreted as having been produced by glaciation and not by wind or stream?

3. What evidence indicates that certain world-wide changes associated with Pleistocene glaciation probably continue today?

4. Compare and contrast glaciated and nonglaciated mountain valleys.

5. How does glaciation support the concept of isostasy?

6. What evidence supports multiple glaciation during the Pleistocene?

7. Why are many end moraines curved like crescents?

8. What is the evidence that parts of the Missouri and Ohio Rivers have resulted from glaciation?

CHAPTER 30

Volcanoes and Related Phenomena

IN 1943 a Tarascan Indian by the name of Dionisio Polido lived on a farm near the village of Paricutin about 125 miles west of Mexico City. The ground in his cornfield was warmer than that elsewhere in the vicinity. On cold nights Dionisio slept on the warm earth rather than in his hut. One February day, Dionisio sighted a wisp of smoke rising from small openings in the earth in the cornfield. He thought that a fire had started in dry vegetation buried beneath the surface, and he shoveled dirt into the opening to put out the fire. In the following days the wisps of smoke were more numerous, and the ground became warmer.

Fig. 30-1.

Paricutin. (Courtesy, Smithsonian Institution)

Fig. 30-2.

Eruption of steam and volcanic ash from the crater of Vesuvius. A small cone has built up inside the crater. (Courtesy, Italian State Tourist Office)

In the late afternoon of February 20, 1943, the Polidos were working in their fields when the ground before them suddenly belched smoke. Dionisio reported later that the ground thundered and hissed and that water seemed to be running below. Earthquakes had been occurring during each of the preceding eighteen days, and an engineer had predicted that a volcano might come. In panic the Polidos and their neighbors hurried from the cornfield out of which spouted steam, fire, and rocks. That night the whole area was lighted up by molten lava and red-hot cinders erupting every few seconds from the ground. The fragmental debris fell to the surface and piled up around the opening. A volcano was born in Dionisio's cornfield that February day (Fig. 30-1).

In three days the volcanic cone was 170 feet high; at the end of ten weeks it had grown to a height of 1100 feet; and within a year it towered 1400 feet above the surrounding lands. During its growth the volcano erupted flames, smoke, gases, and fragmental material; lava flowed out from its base and flanks. At first, explosions were like the firing of cannon and occurred every few seconds. At night the volcano was described as a flowerpot of fireworks. The surrounding area was buried beneath lava and volcanic debris, and the inhabitants of Paricutin were forced to construct a new village nearby. Seventeen years later the volcano is almost inactive.

Volcanoes consist of two parts: an external hill or mountain which commonly is heaped on the Earth's surface as a conical mass; and the more important internal part consisting of a fissure or cylindrically shaped opening (vent or pipe) or openings which lead from the surface to a source of magma far below (Figs. 30-2 and 30-3). It seems

Fig. 30-3.

Cross section of a volcano. Sketch shows that the volcano was built by explosive eruptions alternating with flows of lava. After a volcano has become large, flows tend to issue from its slopes, not from the crater.

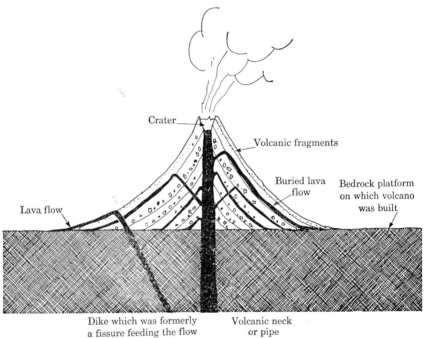

appropriate now to inquire about the possibilities of the birth of a volcano in one's own vicinity. If a volcano originated in a cornfield in Mexico, could one also develop in a similar cornfield in Nebraska, in an apple orchard in New York, or in a tobacco patch in North Carolina? Where do volcanoes occur on the Earth's surface? Why do some erupt violently at sporadic intervals, whereas others sputter harmlessly much of the time? Where do the lava and gases come from? From below the surface, of course, but can one be less vague than that? When will a certain volcano erupt again, and will it be more or less violent than the last time? Let us review in this chapter some conclusions reached by geologists about these questions and the data upon which the conclusions are based.

Paricutin is located in an area that contains thousands of similar volcanoes, several hundred situated within a radius of 75 miles. The history of Paricutin has paralleled that of its many neighbors. In 1759 Jorullo exploded out of cultivated fields about 50 miles southeast of Paricutin and built a cone 1300 feet high before becoming inactive. Other regions have similar stories to tell. In 1538 a new volcano (Monte Nuovo) originated near Naples, Italy, and remained explosively active for about a week. A cone rose some 450 feet, and then operations ceased.

Rock debris and gases may erupt from the sea. In 1831 a volcanic island was built in the Mediterranean, but it was soon eroded below sea level. The three Bogoslov volcanic islands in the Bering Sea formed in 1796, 1883, and 1906.

DISTRIBUTION OF VOLCANOES

Some 500 volcanoes are active now or have erupted during historic times. Thousands of others have been active in the recent geologic past (Fig. 30-4). Erosion has had time to modify them only slightly. These volcanoes tend to be grouped in two great belts, the more pronounced of which rings the Pacific in a "girdle of fire" on the east, north, and west. The other great belt extends from the Alpine-Mediterranean area eastward to the Indonesian states. Many volcanoes have a linear arrangement on a small scale also, apparently because many of them are aligned along crustal fractures. Earthquakes occur most frequently in these same volcanic areas; two-thirds of all earthquakes probably originate in the circum-Pacific belt, one-fifth in the other great belt.

Since volcanoes which originated in historic times have been confined to volcanic areas, probably future volcanoes will likewise be limited to these regions; cornfields in Nebraska and other similar areas have slight chance of being the sites of future volcanic activity. However, a study of geologic history indicates that almost all parts of the Earth's surface have been visited by some kind of igneous activity

Spatter cones in Craters of the Moon in Idaho. These are small piles of volcanic fragments ejected from solidifying lavas by escaping gases. (Photograph by Richard J. Ordway)

Fig. 30-4.

in the past. Perhaps, then, one should conclude that although no area should be considered immune to volcanic action, some places are much more susceptible than others.

VOLCANIC GASES

The explosive activity of a volcano depends upon the amount of gas in the magma beneath it and the manner in which that gas escapes (Fig. 30-5). Without gas, no explosion can occur. In a fluid magma (low silica or very hot) the gas may be able to escape readily without creating great pressures. The eruptive action of a volcano may change during its lifetime because the compositions, temperatures, and amounts of the dissolved gases and magma are all variable factors. Furthermore, if the magma moves upward through calcareous rocks like limestone, it may enhance its explosive power by melting the limestone and obtaining an abundant supply of carbon dioxide gas. In addition, the heat of the igneous material may change ground water into steam.

Although uncontaminated samples of volcanic gases are difficult to obtain for chemical analysis, steam is far the most abundant material given off. Other gases include carbon dioxide, nitrogen, sulfur dioxide, hydrogen, carbon monoxide, chlorine, and fluorine.

Heavy rains are commonly associated with volcanic eruptions. The precipitation has two immediate sources: huge quantities of water vapor in the form of steam may be erupted and then condense; and air above the volcano may be blown violently upward causing con-

Powerful eruption of Lassen Peak, California, May 22, 1915. The volcanic cloud was 8 miles high. The photograph was taken from a point 50 miles away. This is the only active volcano in the United States excluding Alaska and Hawaii. (Courtesy, Myers and Loomis)

Fig. 30-5.

densation of much of the moisture in it. Torrents of water sometimes pour down on loose fragments resting on steep volcanic slopes and result in disastrous mud flows.

VOLCANIC TOPOGRAPHY

Characteristically, volcanoes have conical shapes, consist of layers of volcanic materials that dip outward from the center, and possess craters at their tops (Fig. 30-6). Eruptions throw masses of molten lava and rock fragments high into the air because volcanic vents commonly are vertical. The bulk of the material falls around the opening and forms a cone. In a single eruption large pieces fall first and smaller particles later, thus producing a crude stratification. Successive eruptions vary in magnitude, and there are corresponding changes in the sizes of the fragments thrown out. Between explosions, lava may flow

Recently formed cinder cones and a lava flow. The lava flow emerged from the base of a cone and spread out; it is about 5 miles long. The site is about 40 miles southeast of the Grand Canyon, Arizona. (Fairchild Aerial Surveys)

Fig. 30-6.

down the surface of the volcano from its top or, more frequently as it grows larger, from openings on its flanks or near its base. The continuous upward movement of volcanic debris from the central opening during an eruption prevents most of the material from falling back directly into this central opening and results in the formation of a crater at the top. When the explosions cease, some material falls into

Fig. 30-7.

Shiprock, New Mexico. This volcanic neck and radiating dikes are the only remnants of a once-majestic volcano. The neck extends more than 1000 feet above the surrounding countryside. (Spence Air Photos)

the crater and other debris slumps in from the sides. Some volcanoes consist chiefly of erupted fragments and are steep-sided; others have been built largely by the piling up of flow after flow of fluid lava around a central vent. The latter are the "shield" volcanoes—large dome-shaped masses like Mauna Loa in the Hawaiian Islands, which rise about 30,000 feet above the floor of the ocean, nearly 14,000 feet above sea level. Most volcanoes are a combination of these two types.

Fig. 30-8.

Devil's Tower, Wyoming. According to one hypothesis, this structure is a volcanic neck. The towerlike, erosion-resistant mass of igneous rock stands about 700 feet above its surroundings. Note the excellent columnar jointing which forms under certain conditions when igneous rocks cool and shrink. The columns average about 10 feet across. (Photograph by N. H. Darton, U.S. Geological Survey)

A number of volcanoes are strengthened by a system of vertical dikes which lead radially outward from the central vent (Figs. 30-7 and 30-8).

DORMANT OR EXTINCT?

A volcano may be active, dormant, or extinct. The distinction between a dormant and extinct volcano is difficult or impossible to determine in terms of human lifetimes. Vesuvius near Naples, Italy, furnishes an instructive illustration (Fig. 30-9). It is situated on the remnants of an ancient volcano called Monte Somma. Monte Somma, with its forest-clad slopes and fertile soil, was believed to be an extinct volcano by the Romans—Vesuvius was not yet in existence. However, in A.D. 79, following several years of frequent earthquakes, Somma exploded mightily, blew off much of its top, and buried two towns, Pompeii and Herculaneum, lying between it and the sea. Little

Vesuvius and Naples. (Courtesy, Italian State Tourist Office)

Fig. 30-9.

lava was extruded at this time, but enormous volumes of debris and gases were hurled high into the air by the powerful eruptions. Gases killed many of the population. Others were buried beneath falling debris or under huge mud flows which formed during the accompanying torrential rains and moved rapidly down Somma's steep slopes. The buried towns were forgotten until their accidental discovery and subsequent excavation that began during the eighteenth century. Molds had formed of many of the victims, some in restful poses and others in the act of fleeing. A number of casts have been made from these molds. Vesuvius, which now exceeds 4000 feet in altitude, has since been built in the huge hole which formed at the top of Monte Somma during this eruption.

In the seventeenth century, following a long period of dormancy during which its crater had become overgrown, Vesuvius was again believed to be extinct. However, in 1631 it erupted, and thousands of people were killed. Since that time Vesuvius has been almost constantly active.

Crater Lake   Crater Lake in Oregon lies on the crest of the Cascade Range amid the great volcanic mountains of the Pacific northwest. This is one of the world's most scenic spots—actually as beautiful as Oregonians and others say it is. Its geologic history illustrates some of the events which may take place during the life of a volcano.

Crater Lake (Figs. 27-7 and 30-10) is circular in outline, about 5 miles in diameter, and completely enclosed by cliffs, which rise from 500 to 2000 feet above the surface of the water (altitude about 6000

Crater Lake, Oregon (see also Fig. 27-7.) Wizard Island is a symmetrical cinder cone. Piles of talus and snow (the picture was taken in August) can be seen at the left. The dark object immediately to the left of Wizard Island is a vertical dike, one of several exposed in the crater walls and radiating outward from the center. In the upper right is a lava flow (a large dark mass) which filled in a rounded U-shaped glaciated valley. (Photograph by Richard J. Ordway)

Fig. 30-10.

feet above sea level). At its deepest the water is some 2000 feet deep. The top of a small cone-shaped hill occurs as an island in the lake. Thus Crater Lake occupies a huge circular depression located at the top of a mountain. The mountain is interpreted as the stump of a once-majestic volcano. How was this "sermon" deciphered, and what happened to the top of the volcano?

Bedrock is exposed in the cliffs which tower above the lake. It consists of volcanic debris and former lava flows in layers that everywhere dip away from the lake. Glacial deposits are interbedded with the volcanic rocks, and U-shaped valleys can be seen in cross section where they have been truncated by the crater walls. Evidently a radial glacial system existed when the volcano was much higher, perhaps resembling that now present on nearby Mt. Rainier. If the dips of the volcanic strata are projected toward the center of the lake and upward, they suggest that this beheaded volcano once towered approximately 12,000 feet above sea level. However, the top was south of the present lake center.

The geologic story of Crater Lake is told in several chapters (Fig. 30-11). First, eruptions of volcanic debris and outpourings of lava (predominant) piled material higher and higher around a central vent until a huge volcano resulted. The bottom part of the volcano formed on a relatively smooth surface about 6000 feet above sea level; when full grown, the top of the volcano extended another 6000 feet or so above this platform. Glaciers developed, moved down the slopes of the mountain, and produced features typical of glacial erosion and deposition. Following completion of the volcano, there probably occurred a long period of repose during which gas pressure increased within the volcano; this was chapter two. Chapter three was spectacular and probably brief. It included violent eruptions which blanketed the surrounding countryside with volcanic debris. During these outbursts, the entire top of the mountain disappeared. Measurements show that some 17 cubic miles of rock materials have vanished from the upper parts of the volcano. Where did they go? Careful mapping has located only part of the 17 cubic miles; a large volume is still missing. Therefore, some geologists believe that the great depression formed partly by collapse of the central section of the volcano and partly by "blowing its top." Outward movements of magma may have occurred at a depth which left the top of the volcano unsupported, and it collapsed.

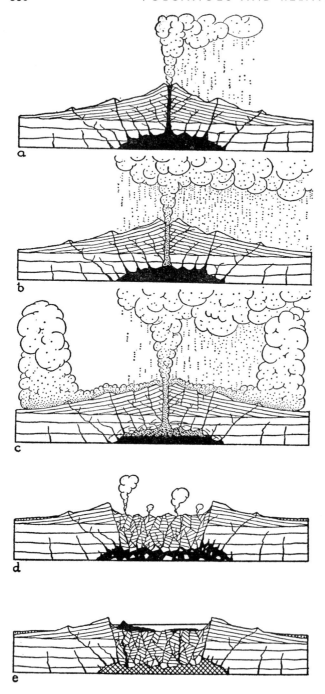

Recent weak renewal of volcanic activity has resulted in the formation of a small volcanic cone within the huge opening (the *caldera*). The top of this cone today forms Wizard Island. Rain and melting snow have produced the present lake. The income and outgo of water seem to have struck a balance, and the level of the lake is about constant. Carbon-14 tests of the age of trees buried by the climatic eruptions indicate that the explosions took place about 6500 years ago.

Lassen Peak in California, a steep-sided cone rising a mile or so above its surroundings, is the most recently active volcano in the United States (Fig. 30-5). From 1914 to 1917 several powerful eruptions occurred, and gases still escape feebly from the volcano. Previous to 1914, Lassen Peak had been inactive for hundreds of years.

DIKES, SILLS, AND BATHOLITHS

Intrusive igneous rock bodies are classified chiefly on the basis of their shapes and relationships to surrounding rocks (Fig. 30-12). Dikes and sills are tabular-shaped masses which formed when magma was squeezed by pressure into cracks or weak zones in rocks. They are shaped like sheets of plywood—two large dimensions and one small. They may be quite large and extend for miles or be very small. If the magma squeezed between two layers in a pile of stratified rocks, it formed a sill; if it cut across the layers or squeezed into a crack in nonstratified rocks, it formed a dike (Fig. 30-13). The intrusive rocks may be more or less resistant to erosion than the materials they intruded. A batholith (p. 686) is a huge intrusive igneous rock body which becomes larger at increasing depths. Identification of a certain rock out-

Fig. 30-11.

*The evolution of Crater Lake. (See opposite page)—a. Beginning of culminating eruptions. Magma is high in the conduit and there is a mild eruption of pumice.
—b. Activity increases in violence. Showers of pumice are more voluminous and the ejecta are larger. The magma level lowers to the top of the feeding chamber.
—c. Activity approaches the climax. There is a combination of vertically directed explosions and glowing avalanches (nuées ardentes). The chamber is being emptied rapidly and the roof is beginning to fracture and founder. Magma is also being drained from the chamber through fissures at depth.—d. Collapse of the cone as a jumble of enormous blocks, some of which are shown sinking through the magma. Fumaroles appear on the caldera floor.—e. Crater Lake today. Post-collapse eruptions have formed the cone of Wizard Island and probably have covered parts of the lake bottom with lava. Magma in the chamber is largely crystallized.*

Types of igneous intrusives. A laccolith resembles a sill, for the magma is squeezed between rock layers. However, the laccolith is lens-shaped and domes the rocks above it. A stock is a small batholith.

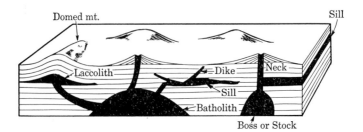

Fig. 30-12.

crop as part of an intrusive igneous rock body indicates that the following events have occurred: (1) the rock was once hot molten magma, (2) the igneous rock is younger than the surrounding rocks into which it intruded, and (3) erosion has removed the rocks which once covered this outcrop.

Mount Moran and vertical dike in the Grand Tetons, Wyoming. (Photograph by Richard J. Ordway)

Fig. 30-13

RECOGNITION OF IGNEOUS ROCKS

That some rocks had hardened from a previous molten state was recognized by certain men long ago. They observed lava flowing copiously down volcanic slopes and watched as it cooled into hard slaggy rock. Accounts of such flows (Fig. 30-6) in different parts of the Earth appear in ancient writings and in present-day newspapers and periodicals year after year. The lava streams may bury tens of square miles of the Earth's surface in the vicinity and overwhelm villages and towns in their paths. Volcanic activity is one aspect of nature that forces mankind to recognize it.

Establishing the igneous origin of rocks no longer connected with active volcanoes was much more difficult and the theory has been generally accepted for only about a century and a half. In fact, knowledge that rocks have formed at different times and in different ways in the past has become common only during the past 150 years or so. This discovery was fundamental; the development of geology could not come until it had been made. The manner in which the discovery came about is typical of the origin of many concepts in science. There came first a long period of groping and fumbling during which isolated glimpses of insight into the true nature of rocks by a few gifted men fell on barren ground. As an example, certain fundamental principles concerning the origin and history of sedimentary rocks, such as the law of original horizontality, were developed by Steno in the seventeenth century but remained little known and unaccepted for the next 100 years.

A bitter controversy existed between two factions, the Neptunists and Plutonists, for a generation and a half during the last part of the eighteenth century and the first part of the nineteenth century. Each group went to extremes; too little attention was paid to unbiased observations by some of the participants, although the Neptunists were more guilty than the Plutonists in these respects.

The Neptunists were led by Werner, a German teacher of geology, who believed that the Earth had been entirely covered by ocean water early in its history. From this universal sea were precipitated rocks such as granite, basalt, gneiss, and slate. These primitive rocks were supposed to have been universal, although their thicknesses were thought to vary from one location to another. As the volume of marine water decreased, other rocks formed. Tilted layers were deposited on the precipitous flanks of mountains which were emerging as islands in this universal sea. Werner had the ability to inspire and stimulate his students. He awakened in them an ardent interest in geology, and his eloquent lectures convinced them of the accuracy of his ideas.

Here is an illustration of the manner in which field observations were sometimes distorted to fit preconceived ideas. Part of the evidence cited by Werner involved a nearby outcrop in which basalt (a buried lava flow) supposedly could be seen to alter downward into shale and sandstone, apparent proof according to the Neptunists that all had been precipitated from solution. A geologist today would explain this apparent gradation as a partial metamorphism of the sediments by the basaltic material. Werner tried to develop geological theories which could be applied to the entire Earth. Unfortunately, his field observations were limited to the natural phenomena in one small area.

The Scottish geologist Hutton was the leader of the Plutonists— who favored a concept of the igneous origin of basalt and granite. His methods stand out in decided contrast to those of Werner. Hutton spent his life making careful observations in the field. His concepts developed inductively from the mass of data he accumulated. Some of the evidence given by Hutton for the concept that basalt was formerly molten are included in Fig. 30-14, which considers a few methods by

The distinction between a sill and a buried lava flow. In the sketch, a series of sedimentary strata contain a buried lava flow of basalt and a felsite sill. The sill can be distinguished from the flow thus: (1) The sill has altered both its upper and lower contacts; the flow has baked only the rocks beneath it.—(2) Blocks of the overlying rock (conglomerate) have fallen into the felsite; on the other hand, boulders of basalt are found in the first stratum to be deposited above the flow.—(3) Tongues of felsite have intruded the enclosing rocks.

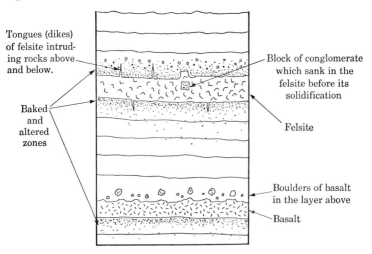

Tongues (dikes) of felsite intruding rocks above and below.

Block of conglomerate which sank in the felsite before its solidification

Baked and altered zones

Felsite

Boulders of basalt in the layer above

Basalt

Fig. 30-14.

which a buried lava flow (Fig. 24-7) may be distinguished from a sill. Hutton was so impressed by the intrusive nature of many igneous rock bodies that he thought a number of buried lava flows were of an intrusive nature.

That coarse-grained igneous rocks, such as some granites, were once molten is indicated by several types of evidence. Microscopic examination shows that certain types of minerals are present, that the grains interlock, and that the minerals crystallized in a definite order. Similar features can be seen in rocks found on volcanoes, except that individual mineral grains in the granite are larger. Is this merely a coincidence? In studying the margins of a granite batholith in the field, geologists have noted that the granite commonly grades into fine-grained rocks along its outer boundaries that are identical with the ones on the volcanic slope. Beyond the margins of the granite are rocks that have been metamorphosed; the effects of the alteration fade out gradually from the granite mass. In addition, thin tongues of the granite extend outward from the main body as dikes or sills.

However, other granite bodies are known which show gradations from unquestioned granite in their central portions, into rocks which look like granite yet show traces of sedimentary structures such as stratification, into metamorphic rocks, and finally into sedimentary rocks. Exposures of this type suggest another origin for granite (granitization).

Thus, geologists today are not in agreement concerning the origin of many granite masses, and another controversy exists. Meanwhile more general agreement does exist concerning the origin of basaltic magma (p. 686). One group of geologists, called the "soaks," maintain that granite is a metamorphic rock which formed by replacement (much as wood is petrified) when emanations from below transformed rocks in the Earth's crust into granite. On the other hand, the magmatists contend that granite has crystallized from magma as an igneous rock. Most geologists are agreed that granite has formed in both ways and that the chief problems lie in determining which manner of origin is the more common and how each process operates. The source of the emanations is quite mysterious; yet the source of the granitic magma is also uncertain.

One problem involves the discovery that granites are far more voluminous than all other kinds of intrusive igneous rocks and that basalts have a similar position among the extrusive group. This is anomalous in the eyes of many geologists because they believe that the extrusive igneous rocks should correspond in composition to the intrusive group. But basaltic magma is much more fluid than granitic magma, and basalt may be the most abundant extrusive rock because its magma commonly remains fluid long enough to reach the surface. On the other hand, granitic magma may be too viscous for the extrusive equivalents of granite to be abundant.

There is another explanation for the predominance of granite among the intrusive igneous rocks: Huge volumes of granitic magma may have originated by the melting of sedimentary rocks which closely resemble granite in chemical composition. Thick accumulations of such sediments are associated with the great mountain belts of the Earth and seem to have been buried far below the surface during times of mountain building (p. 736). Granitic batholiths are located only in the cores of such mountainous areas. Perhaps they formed in this manner.

A major problem for the magmatists involves the emplacement of granitic batholiths. No adequate explanation has been found to account for the manner in which huge volumes of pre-existing rocks were subsequently displaced by the granite. How did the granite bodies find or make room for themselves? If the batholiths have been formed by the metamorphism of the pre-existing rocks in place, the space problem may be largely eliminated, although other difficulties remain.

Another solution for the origin of granitic magma (magmatic differentiation) is discussed just below. Its chief limitation is that of volume. Have large quantities of granitic magma been produced in this manner?

ORIGIN OF BASALTIC MAGMA

Several decades ago geologists were quite confident that they knew how magma originated. They believed that the Earth had once been molten, that the outer part had cooled and crystallized to form a relatively thin crust, and that the entire interior of the Earth still consisted of fluid material. Weak zones or cracks in the crust permitted the molten material to move upward and at times to pour outward on the Earth's surface. It was commonly held that the Earth was still cooling off; geologists could point to the recent Ice Age as apparent confirmation. Data accumulated since this time have shown this concept to be erroneous, and geologists are now much less certain concerning the source and manner of origin of magma. Episodes of ancient glaciations have been deciphered from the rocks; temperatures on the Earth apparently have fluctuated and have not steadily become lower. In addition, study of earthquake waves seems to show that the entire outer part of the Earth is solid, and that this surrounds a central core about 4300 miles in diameter. The discovery of radioactivity and the heat produced from radioactive elements has cast doubt upon the concept that the Earth is slowly cooling off.

Magma originates beneath the Earth's surface, but details concerning the exact manner of its origin are highly conjectural. The hypothesis discussed briefly below fits a number of the facts connected with igneous phenomena and is acceptable to some geologists. But other geologists consider aspects of it inadequate and perhaps erroneous.

According to this hypothesis, all magma was originally solid material similar to basalt and gabbro in chemical composition (low in its silica content, high in iron, calcium, and magnesium). Part of the supporting evidence consists of basaltic extrusions at the Earth's surface at numerous times in the past, in different parts of the world, and in enormous volumes. An example is the Deccan basalt of western India. Geologic mapping has shown that these rocks, previous to their present eroded state, formerly covered an area nearly 500,000 square miles in extent to a maximum thickness approaching 2 miles. Lava flow after lava flow, averaging about 15 feet in thickness, once emerged from fissures in the Earth's crust, piled one on top of the other, and spread widely over vast areas. Manifestly a very large source of this fluid basaltic material must exist somewhere below the crust. Since similar flows have occurred from time to time in many parts of the Earth, a world-wide layer of low-silica rock somewhat like basalt is assumed to exist at a depth of a few tens of miles below the Earth's surface. Evidence obtained by a study of earthquake waves substantiates this assumption.

Pressures and temperatures in existence at a depth of a few tens of miles below the Earth's surface must now be considered. Measurements in wells and mines in the outer 5 miles of the Earth's crust show that temperatures increase downward an average of approximately $1°F$ every 60 feet. Hot springs, geysers, and volcanic phenomena also show that temperatures rise with increasing depth. If the average increase in temperature is continued downward to the postulated world-wide basaltic layer, this material should be above its melting point. Since for most solids, melting necessitates expansion, and as pressures at the depth of the basaltic rocks are very great, probably melting cannot occur. Therefore, a world-wide layer of solid basaltic material may exist at a depth of a few tens of miles at temperatures above its melting point. If in some way the pressure should be reduced on this layer, expansion could take place. The basaltic material should then melt and begin moving upward to zones of lesser pressure. The reduction in pressure conceivably might be brought about by several factors: great cracks in the Earth's crust may develop in earthquake areas, the wearing down of a mountainous region by erosion may lighten the crustal load sufficiently, or part of the crust may be bent upward by crustal movements. The intimate association of earthquakes and volcanoes may be explained in this way.

Dissolved gases may aid in the upward movement of the magma, which is less dense than the surrounding rocks, just as when a warm bottle of coke is uncorked, release of pressure permits dissolved carbon dioxide gas to expand and carry some of the liquid out of the bottle with it. Furthermore, the weight of the crust pressing down on either side of a weak zone may be sufficient to force magma upward through it, just as in the winter when cracks occur in ice which covers a lake, the weight of the ice pushing downward on each side of the crack forces water up the crack and onto the surface. The upward-moving magma may cool and harden before it reaches the Earth's surface, thereby producing intrusive igneous rocks.

Magmatic Differentiation   Many magmas and lavas are not similar to basalt in chemical composition; continuous gradations exist between low-silica material that hardens to basalt or gabbro and high-silica material that produces granite when it cools slowly. According to one hypothesis most magmas were once basaltic; some of the original low-silica material later changed to the other kinds through a process called magmatic differentiation. Imagine that a large volume of low-silica basaltic magma moves upward through a weak zone in the crust. Its upward movement stops several thousand feet below the surface. Here the top and outer margins of the basaltic mass cool first. As is explained in Fig. 30-15, the percentage of silica in the magma near the top of the igneous reservoir may have gradually increased until eventually the molten matter became granitic in composition. At any stage in this process, part of the magma may resume its upward movement. If the resurgent magma comes from the upper portions of the igneous chamber after crystallization has been going on for some time, its

Fig. 30-15.

Magmatic differentiation.

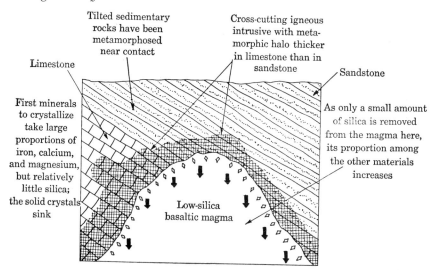

Tilted sedimentary rocks have been metamorphosed near contact

Cross-cutting igneous intrusive with metamorphic halo thicker in limestone than in sandstone

Limestone

Sandstone

First minerals to crystallize take large proportions of iron, calcium, and magnesium, but relatively little silica; the solid crystals sink

As only a small amount of silica is removed from the magma here, its proportion among the other materials increases

Low-silica basaltic magma

silica content will be higher than that of the original basaltic material. Therefore, any gradation between a high- and low-silica magma is theoretically possible.

Presumably the first-formed low-silica minerals sink in the molten matter until they are melted or come to rest on the floor of the igneous chamber. Therefore, an intrusive igneous body, such as a thick sill, theoretically should show a crudely layered structure. Lower-silica minerals should be concentrated at the bottom; higher-silica minerals should be more abundant at the top. The Palisades along the Hudson River in New York is a well-known sill which illustrates this phenomenon. The concept of magmatic differentiation grew out of studies of similar structures. Furthermore, field study has shown that, in a series of intrusive or extrusive igneous masses in an area, the lower-silica members tend to be older than the higher-silica ones. This general order of intrusion or extrusion likewise supports the concept of magmatic differentiation.

Origin of Some Primary Ore Deposits Gases and rare elements such as gold and copper that are dissolved in the magma do not enter into the growth of the rock-forming minerals. As the volume of magma shrinks by crystallization, these materials concentrate in the dwindling portion that remains. The gases may produce sufficient pressure to cause volcanic explosions. Magma which contains dissolved gas occupies less space than the same materials after they separate into free gas and solid mineral particles. Near the end of the process of crystallization, pressure may force the gases and rare elements dissolved in them to leave the igneous chamber and to move along zones of weakness toward the surface. Such fluids may begin their journey upward as liquids, or as gases which later become liquids. Water is their chief constituent. The hot water solutions rise into zones of lower pressures and temperatures where they can no longer hold in solution all of the dissolved materials. The substances in solution are precipitated, perhaps along fissures to form veins of ore minerals. Many ore deposits (primary) are believed to have formed in this way. Such deposits represent tremendous concentrations of materials once widely dispersed. According to this theory, magma is the parent of all such ore deposits.

This concept of the origin of ore deposits developed partly from studies made at volcanoes. During observations, cracks were filled by minerals such as galena and hematite which were deposited from gases that carried lead, iron, sulfur, and other elements in solution.

MANKIND AND VOLCANOES

Although volcanic eruptions have killed millions of people—thousands in single violent explosions in populated areas—and have destroyed much valuable property, people stubbornly continue to live in volcanic areas. Java, with numerous active volcanoes, has one of the highest population densities in the world. For one thing, volcanic soils are highly fertile. In addition, climatic conditions vary with altitude on the slopes of some towering volcanoes, and a wide variation in the type of cultivated crop is possible.

Scientists are studying volcanoes in an attempt to learn enough about them to be able to make approximate predictions of future volcanic activity. Volcanic eruptions are commonly preceded by earthquakes and by a rise in the temperature of gases given off by the volcano. Instruments which can measure these factors aid in the prediction of future eruptions. In addition, a number of simple principles may be utilized. For example, an eruption that follows a long period of quiet during which gas pressure has had time to increase is more apt to be violent than one that follows a relatively short dormancy.

GEYSERS, FUMAROLES, AND HOT SPRINGS

Volcanoes and intrusive igneous material may give off hot gases which produce a number of interesting phenomena as they emerge from openings in the ground. Geysers, fumaroles, and some hot springs originate in this manner. Steam is the chief gas involved. Some of the steam has a magmatic source, but much more probably originates by vaporization of ground water upon contact with upward-moving hot magmatic gases. Not all hot springs are related directly to igneous activity: ground water has percolated downward considerable distances to zones of higher temperature, and later the heated waters may rise along a fault or other channelway and emerge at the Earth's surface.

Fumaroles are holes or fissures in the ground from which issue steam and other gases. For example, carbon dioxide is given off copiously in Death Gulch in Yellowstone National Park. Since the colorless and odorless gas is heavier than air, on windless days it collects in low areas near the fumaroles. Animals which wander into these low areas may suffocate before they can get out. Grizzly bears have been killed in this way in Death Gulch.

Hot springs and fumaroles are of practical importance to man. In a number of areas, hot springs have been used for many years as laundries and as baths. A hotel at Kilauea volcano (Hawaii) is heated by a hot-water radiator system that uses natural steam obtained from holes drilled nearby. Schools and other public buildings in Iceland are heated by natural steam. Farmers near Naples, Italy, use fumaroles to warm certain plants so that they will sprout sooner. In the crater of one volcano, a farmer is reported to use a hot-water irrigation system and to rotate his planting and harvesting in such a manner that he produces vegetable crops throughout the year. Several fumarole fields have been utilized as sources of steam for the generation of electricity.

Geysers (Fig. 30-16) are hot springs which occasionally erupt columns of hot water and steam. Most geysers occur in three areas: Yellowstone National Park, New Zealand, and Iceland. Geysers hold a great deal of interest for many people. On a small scale they illustrate some of the spectacular effects of volcanic activity. Old Faithful

Grotto Geyser in Yellowstone National Park, Wyoming. (Photograph by Richard J. Ordway)

Fig. 30-16.

in Yellowstone National Park (Fig. 30-17) is justly famous as the tourist's friend. An average of approximately 66 minutes elapses between eruptions that throw thousands of gallons of hot water higher than 100 feet into the air. Old Faithful has been performing at these intervals winter and summer since its discovery by white men in 1871. Other geysers have since become extinct and new ones are being formed. Several thousand geysers, hot springs, and fumaroles exist in Yellowstone National Park. Some geysers are transformed into hot springs during the wet season, just as certain hot springs become fumaroles during dry seasons.

The action of a geyser probably depends upon the relationship between the boiling point of water and pressure. An increase in pressure raises the boiling point; a decrease lowers it. Familiar examples are the ease with which water in a radiator boils at high altitudes (low pressure allows a low boiling point) and the short time interval in which foods can be made edible in a pressure cooker (high pressure produces a high boiling point). Thrifty housewives know that the temperature of boiling water in an open dish cannot be raised by increasing the heat under its container; increased heat merely causes the water to evaporate more rapidly while it remains at the same temperature.

Below the geyser vent a series of interconnected fissures and open-

Fig. 30-17.

)ld Faithful in Yellowstone National 'ark at sunset. (Photograph by Richard . Ordway)

ngs are filled with hot water, chiefly ordinary ground water (Fig. 0-18). Heat is supplied by steam rising from below. At first the steam s assimilated, and the temperature of the water rises until it boils. lowever, since pressure increases downward from the surface, the oiling point is reached only at higher and higher temperatures at reater depths. For example, water may boil at 212°F at the surface nd at 290°F some 200 feet below the surface. If the passageways are ortuous enough to prevent convection, water in the geyser tube will verywhere be heated to its boiling point. When all of the water in he geyser tube is boiling (at different temperatures at different epths), steam must accumulate. When sufficient steam has accumuted, its expansive force causes overflow at the surface and the consequent upward movement of water throughout the system. This upard movement transports water into zones of lower pressures where

Fig. 30-18.

The origin of geysers. (After Day and Allen. Courtesy, The Carnegie Institution of Washington)

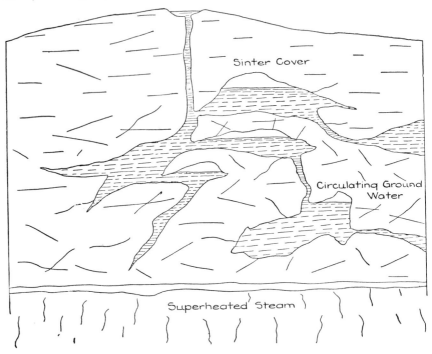

it can boil at lower temperatures. It flashes instantaneously into steam and erupts.

EXERCISES AND QUESTIONS FOR CHAPTER 30

1. Why are volcanoes shaped like cones? Why does a crater occur at the top?

2. How can a sill be distinguished from a buried lava flow?

3. Sedimentary rocks and igneous rocks are in contact along a surface which is nearly vertical. Describe possible criteria which would distinguish a fault contact from an intrusive contact.

4. You find an outcrop of coarse-grained intrusive igneous rock. Describe the geologic events which have occurred in this area. Be complete.

5. Do fossils ever occur in igneous rocks?

6. How does a vein differ from a dike?

7. How is the eruption of a geyser explained by some geologists?

CHAPTER 31

Rocks Bend, Break, and Flow

ABUNDANT evidence indicates that powerful forces have acted upon the Earth's crust many times in the geologic past and are acting upon it today (p. 530). Parts of the crust have been squeezed together or have been stretched apart; areas have been uplifted and depressed; movements have been slow or fast, large or small. Depending upon conditions of pressure, temperature, composition, solutions, and time, rocks have reacted to these forces by cracking, faulting, folding, and warping, or by developing a foliation (metamorphism). Countless times the earth has shivered in earthquakes. These aspects of diastrophism are discussed below.

FOLDS

Most of us think of rocks as hard, brittle substances incapable of any change of shape without fracturing. Yet even at the Earth's surface, rocks have been known to bend a little without breaking. For example, in some monuments, limestone slabs, supported only at their ends, have sagged slightly under their own weight in a few hundred years. Under powerful confining pressures in laboratory experiments, certain kinds of rocks have been made to flow plastically (i.e., to change shape by slow continuous movement without breaking). When crustal forces act slowly, layered rocks under great pressure tend to be

696

deformed by folding (Fig. 31-1). In contrast to warps, folds commonly show a pairing of crests and troughs, more uniformity of structure, and a greater amount of bending.

Folding in layered rocks may take place by plastic flow, by microscopic fracturing and slipping, and by the sliding of one layer over another. Any one stratum slides upward toward an anticlinal crest over the bed lying beneath it. What happens can be illustrated if a package of file cards is bent by pushing inward on the ends. The top layer slides the greatest distance. As this mechanism is a very important one, folding is confined chiefly to stratified rocks. Major folds

Heaven's Fold, Montana. Highly inclined folded strata exposed in a mountain 2000 feet high. (Photograph by Chapman for U.S. Geological Survey)

Fig. 31-1.

result from the compression of an area by powerful forces which act more or less parallel to the Earth's surface. Crustal shortening occurs in the affected area.

Upfolds forming arches are called *anticlines* (Fig. 25-9), and downfolds forming troughs are termed *synclines*. Following prolonged erosion, a syncline may form the crest of a mountain and an anticline underlie a valley. Anticlines and synclines, the two most common kinds of folds, tend to occur together like waves on a lake surface (Fig. 31-2).

Folds vary in scale from tiny ones measured in fractions of an inch to huge ones several miles across. Folds may be upright and symmetri-

Fig. 31-2.

Structure sections through the folded mountainous region west of Harrisburg, Pennsylvania. The origin of a zigzag or loop-shaped mountain is shown. Peters, Cove, and Second Mountains have their present locations because resistant rocks (Pocono) form part of a syncline with a nonhorizontal axis; the axis dips or plunges down toward the upper right side of the sketch. If the axes of a series of folds are horizontal, parallel ridges and valleys result. (Drawn by A. K. Lobeck)

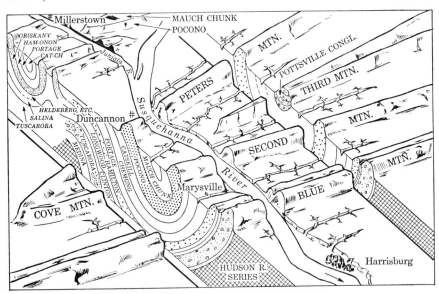

cal, or one side may be steeper than the other. The crest of a fold (axis) may be horizontal or may plunge downward. Smaller folds can be seen in their entirety in a single outcrop. However, the structure of a large fold or dome can sometimes be determined only by mapping and matching outcrops scattered over many square miles (Fig. 31-3). Strike and dip (Fig. 31-4) show the orientation of a layered structure.

FAULTS

Rocks tend to break or rupture rather than fold when crustal forces are applied relatively rapidly, when confining pressure is insufficient for plastic flow, or when rocks are of a type resistant to flow. A fault is a fracture in rocks along which one side has moved relative to the other (Fig. 25-10); formerly contiguous points along the crack are

Fig. 31-3.

The Dakota Black Hills consist of a broad, flat-topped dome deeply eroded to expose a core of crystalline rock. (Reprinted with permission from A. N. Strahler, Physical Geography, 1951, John Wiley & Sons, Inc.)

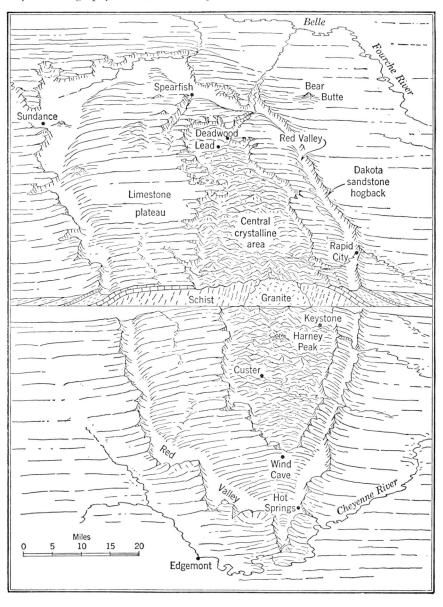

*Strike and dip. Strike is the direction of a
horizontal line in the plane of the bedding.
Dip is the angle between the horizontal and
the plane of the bedding. Strike and dip are
always measured at right angles to each
other.*

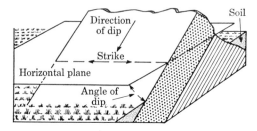

Fig. 31-4.

offset by the movement (Figs. 31-5 and 31-6). Like folds, faults may
be measured in inches, yards, or miles; they may be visible in a single
outcrop or require careful mapping over large areas for detection.
The two most common kinds of faults, normal and reverse, were
originally defined by miners (Fig. 31-7). Two additional faults are
shown in Fig. 31-8.

The word "apparent" in the definition of a normal or reverse fault
should be stressed. For example, although the hanging-wall side of a
normal fault may seem to have dropped, the actual movement may
have been quite different: (1) Both sides may have moved downward,
the hanging-wall block moving a greater distance. (2) Each block

*Normal fault showing displacement of several feet. Small
step faults occur on each side of it. Near Lomita, California.*

Fig. 31-5.

may have moved upward, the foot-wall block covering the greater distance. (3) The hanging-wall block may have remained motionless while the foot-wall block moved upward.

Reverse fault showing displacement of several feet. The dark bands are shale; the rest of the rock is sandstone. Near Whittier, California. (Photograph by M. R. Huberty)

Fig. 31-6.

The development of a large fault undoubtedly requires much time. Movements of thousands of feet along some fault surfaces probably are the end results of a number of smaller movements each involving a few tens of feet at the most; each quick movement perhaps caused an earthquake. The bending of pipes and casing in drill holes by crustal movements in a California oil field has shown that faulting can also occur slowly and gradually without earthquakes. Fault surfaces commonly are curved. Movement along fault surfaces may be

Fig. 31-7.

Normal fault. In the sketch, mining operations are proceeding downward along the fault surface. The miners walk along the foot-wall side of the fault; the other side hangs over their heads. In a normal fault, the hanging-wall side apparently moved downward. Miners found that this was the common kind of fault they encountered. The opposite direction of movement along the fault surface is called a reverse fault. Commonly normal faults are caused by tensional (pulling apart) forces—formerly contiguous rocks have been separated so that a gap exists between their offset edges (e.g., points A and B above). Reverse faults commonly result from compression which produces an overlap—CD in the insert. In each fault, erosion has worn down the uplifted side.

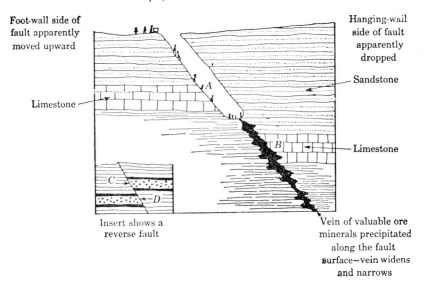

Foot-wall side of fault apparently moved upward

Limestone

Hanging-wall side of fault apparently dropped

Sandstone

Limestone

Insert shows a reverse fault

Vein of valuable ore minerals precipitated along the fault surface—vein widens and narrows

sideways as well as vertical, or any combination of the two. Such faults are given special names by geologists.

UNCONFORMITIES

An unconformity records a significant story about Earth history. Sediments are conformable when they accumulate layer upon layer without important delay or change occurring during deposition. As

Faults near Las Vegas, Nevada. Fault A occurs on Frenchman Mountain and is a low-angle normal fault. Note the steep dip of the Paleozoic strata. In B, the fault surface is about vertical and the terms normal and reverse do not apply. This would be described as a high-angle fault with the western (distant) side upthrown. Note that the faults have been recognized because the strata have been offset. It is easy to see why deserts appeal to geologists (during the cooler months). Such faults would probably be buried by mantle and vegetation in more humid areas. (Photograph by Richard J. Ordway)

(A)

Fig. 31-8.

(B)

Fig. 31-9.

Unconformity. After layers 1 through 7 had been deposited as shown in the sketch below, erosion proceeded to remove layers 7, 6, 5, and 4 from the area. During this interval of erosion, beds 8, 9, and 10 were deposited in an adjoining area. Bed 11 was deposited when sedimentation began again in this area. Thus, the unconformity below shows a local gap in the geologic record represented elsewhere by beds 4 through 10. There are two causes for the break: (1) erosion that has removed rocks which had formed earlier, and (2) nondeposition in this area while erosion was going on.

Strata are numbered
  in chronological
  order-number 1
  is the oldest rock
  exposed here

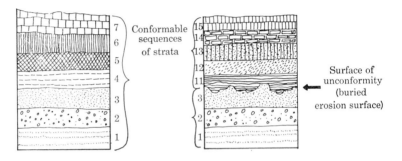

Fig. 31-10.

Striking unconformity. Horizontal sands and gravels rest upon tilted and eroded shales (Cenozoic). (After G. W. Stose, U.S. Geological Survey)

strata pile up, fossils may be buried with them; thus they record information concerning events of their times. However, conditions may change in an area—perhaps an uplift occurs; deposition then ceases, and erosion begins. Tiny valleys are carved out of the recent products of sedimentation; these grow larger and become more numerous. In a later age the Earth's crust may again subside, and the process of deposition supplant that of erosion in this location. The new strata are said to be *unconformable* upon the older ones beneath them. An unconformity, therefore, involves a break in the geologic record; a surface of unconformity is commonly a buried surface of erosion (Fig. 31-9). Crustal movements, such as folding or faulting, may occur during the

Fig. 31-11.

Geologic history determined from a structure section. Events occurred in the following chronological order: (1) The conglomerate was deposited first.— (2) A fault cut across the conglomerate. As the layers cannot be matched on opposite sides of the fault, its type cannot be determined.—(3) A basalt dike was intruded into the conglomerate and across the fault. If the fault had come after the dike, the dike would be offset by it.—(4) Erosion occurred.—(5) Sandstone was deposited on the erosion surface forming an unconformity.— (6) and (7) (The order of the next two events cannot be determined) a. A granite dike was intruded into the conglomerate and sandstone. b. A normal fault intersected the conglomerate and sandstone.—(8) Erosion occurred at the surface. A small valley has developed along the fault surface because erosion has proceeded more rapidly in the crushed-rock zone along the fault.

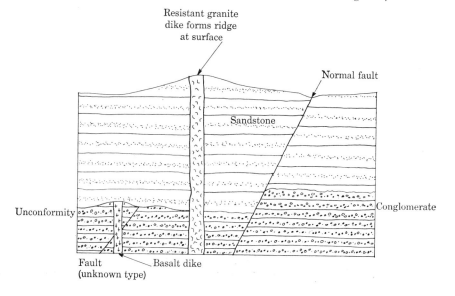

Resistant granite
dike forms ridge
at surface

Normal fault

Sandstone

Conglomerate

Unconformity

Fault
(unknown type)

Basalt dike

time interval represented by an unconformity. Older rocks beneath the surface of an unconformity are thus deformed, whereas younger rocks above this surface are not (Figs. 31-10 and 25-2). The lost time intervals represented by unconformities in the geologic record are both numerous and long.

Part of the fascination of geology lies in the attempt to interpret from rock outcrops the sequence of events which occurred long ago in an area. Fig. 31-11 illustrates the geological version (structure section) of a challenging jigsaw puzzle.

HIDDEN DEPOSITS

Fig. 31-12 illustrates a simplified version of a practical problem frequently encountered in mining. A horizontal series of sedimentary

Fig. 31-12.

Ore deposit cut off by a fault. Two signs show this to be a normal fault: (1) matching strata and (2) drag folds which formed as the edges of the layers were bent by movement along the fault surface. Drag folds bend toward each other on opposite sides of the fault surface in both normal and reverse faults.

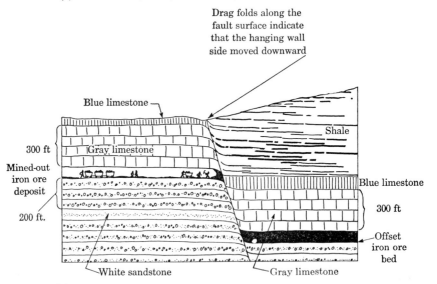

rocks contains a valuable iron ore deposit which is being mined far below the surface. Work has proceeded from a shaft located off the diagram to the left. The mine has proved to be a rich one. However, one day the miners find that the ore body ends. Since the deposit stops abruptly, it may have been truncated by a fault. If so, is the offset part upward along the fault surface or downward? How far has it moved? Exploratory drilling, especially in the wrong directions, is expensive. A hurried call goes out to the company geologist who has previously studied the rocks in the area. Following a careful inspection, the geologist is able to state that the missing bed will be found some 350 feet down the fault surface. Work proceeds and the geologist is proved correct. How was this seemingly mysterious estimate made? Note that the ore deposit occurs among a number of different kinds of rock layers, many of which can be recognized and matched. For example, the iron-ore bed occurs 200 feet stratigraphically above a white sandstone but 300 feet below a blue limestone containing distinctive fossils. Thus identification of the bed exposed in the mine on the opposite side of the fault surface indicates whether the offset ore deposit is above or below, and about how far.

Fault surfaces may be polished, scratched, or grooved (*slickensides*) by friction between the moving blocks. The grooves are parallel to the direction of movement. If a finger is rubbed along some fault sur-

Fig. 31.—13.

Discovery of a hidden ore deposit. The outcrops of conglomerate in the valley provide the key clue to the anticlinal structure. The following geological events are recorded by the structure section: (1) Origin of the older sedimentary rocks and the ore body.—(2) Folding.—(3) Erosion.—(4) Deposition of horizontal beds of sandstone which probably once covered the entire area.—(5) Erosion to the present surface.

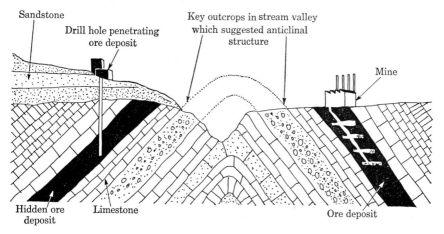

Sandstone

Drill hole penetrating ore deposit

Key outcrops in stream valley which suggested anticlinal structure

Mine

Hidden ore deposit

Limestone

Ore deposit

faces, a smoothness can be detected in the direction of the last movement along the fault. The reverse direction feels rough.

Faults are common in mining areas. If several faults intersect mutually, the ingenuity of the mining geologist is particularly tested. *Drag folds* provide an additional method to locate a stratum offset by faulting (Fig. 31-12).

Fig. 31-14.

An ore deposit predicted on the basis of surface outcrops. Most of the sedimentary rocks shown below are insoluble in water, and the mineralized zone is lean along the fault in them. However, limestone is readily soluble in water. The geologist who found the outcrop of limestone hoped that it had been replaced by the ore minerals along the fault to form a rich deposit. The drill hole proved his hypothesis correct. Another ore deposit occurs on the foot-wall side of the fault in the offset part of the limestone.

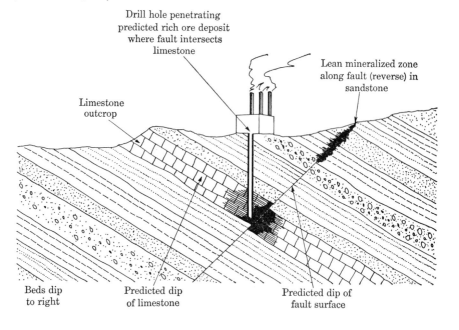

As someone once said, geologists cannot see into the ground any farther than anyone else. Yet a knowledge of geologic structures permits shrewd interpretations of subsurface conditions (Figs. 31-13 and 31-14). An understanding of geological conditions has more than once proved important in international politics (Fig. 31-15).

Geology plays an important role in the search for oil. Four prerequisites are necessary for petroleum to accumulate in commercial quantities in an area: (1) A source bed in which the oil originates. Commonly this is a marine shale which was once a black mud, rich in organic compounds. (2) A permeable reservoir rock in which the oil can accumulate after it has left the source bed. Openings in the source beds tend to be so small that oil cannot pass through them fast enough

Fig. 31-15.

Geology in international politics. France possessed the iron-ore outcrops before the war of 1870 but lost them during diplomatic negotiations following the war. However, when the deposits later became more important and their structure was better understood, it was found that the bulk of the iron-ore deposit (Lorraine iron ores) still belonged to France because of its westward dip. The sketch is highly diagrammatic.

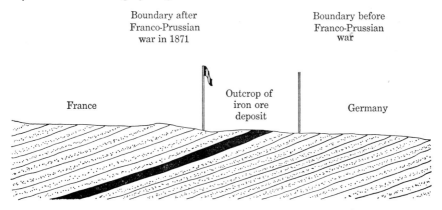

to be profitable. (3) A nonpermeable layer above the reservoir bed. (4) A favorable structure. Prerequisites three and four function to trap and concentrate the oil (Fig. 31-16). The task of the geologist is the location of promising structures in regions where rocks are favorable for the occurrence of the three other necessary conditions. Drilling a hole is then the only known method of determining whether or not oil is present in the structure.

Although the United States is fortunate enough to have large reserves of many minerals, it is not self-sufficient. For example, during World War II the United States supplemented its supplies of some 65 minerals—coal, iron, and salt alone were not imported. Many vital materials must be transported long distances by ships. Stockpiling these strategic materials during peacetime is essential. Such stockpiles have been aptly described as "canned manpower and transportation."

The world has exploited its minerals at a tremendous rate during the twentieth century. As an illustration, from 1937 to 1947 as much petroleum was used as during all previous history. Reserves which

Fig. 31-16.

Favorable structure for oil. Anticlinal structures are easier to locate than other types of structural traps. Oil and gas occur commonly in tiny openings in solid-appearing rocks and sediments.

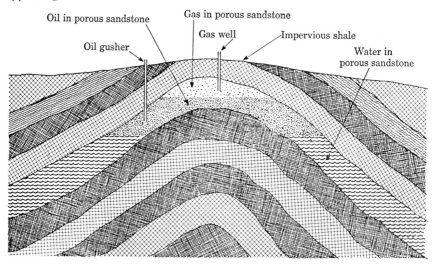

once seemed almost limitless, now look quite small, and will appear even smaller in the future. Wise conservation of these reserves is imperative. The world's demand for energy and minerals seems destined to increase tremendously in the future. Geology will play a vital role in the discovery and exploitation of these natural resources.

EARTHQUAKES

An earthquake is a shaking, trembling, vibratory motion of the Earth's crust. Approximately one-half of the several hundred natural earthquakes which occur every day are strong enough to be felt by local populations. Sensitive machines (seismographs) detect the other half. Locally even the passage of a railroad train or heavy truck may cause rocks to tremble. Earthquakes have terrified mankind for thousands of years. For many the term evokes a picture of death and devastation—huge waves racing across the oceans to overwhelm the coasts, villages buried by landslides, fissures opening and spouting water, rivers and springs going dry, all amid the rumble of earth sounds. Earthquakes have relatively little destructive effect on nature herself and affect man chiefly in an indirect manner by causing destructive "tidal waves," landslides, fires, broken water mains, and diseases produced by contaminated water supplies. The opening and closing of fissures in earthquakes is not so common as is popularly believed, but it grips the imagination. In 1948 in Japan a woman working in a rice paddy sank to her neck in a fissure that opened beneath her and was crushed when it closed. During the 1950 earthquake in Assam four men and a mule are reported to have perished in a similar manner. In the center of the earthquake area, people, rocks, and small buildings are said to have been "tossed into the air like peas on an enormous kettle drum."

Besides their destructive effects, earthquakes furnish much information about the Earth's interior. Artificial earthquakes are sometimes brought about by man-made explosions to further the search for oil beneath the Earth's surface.

Many earthquakes originate beneath the floors of the oceans. Their most destructive effect is the powerful "tidal wave" (a misnomer: tides do not cause them) which they may produce. Some of these waves originate when part of the ocean floor drops suddenly along a fault, and the overlying water is disturbed violently all the way to the surface. The waves may cross the ocean at speeds up to 500 mi/hr; some rise 40 feet in height and measure more than 100 miles from crest to crest. When such waves strike land, they pile up and move inland as a great destructive flood of water. Recent study indicates that such waves may cause more erosion during their sporadic occurrences than do ordinary waves which function continuously.

Great loss of life has accompanied some earthquakes. For example, in the 1923 Japanese catastrophe, approximately 140,000 persons were killed and property damage was estimated at 3 billion dollars.

Cause of Earthquakes   Research has shown that most major earthquakes are apparently caused by quick movements of the Earth's crust along fault surfaces (Fig. 31-17). Although many earthquakes originate within the outer 30 miles of the Earth's spherical body, ap-

*Elastic rebound theory. A, B, and C are blocks
of the Earth's crust. A is unaffected by
stresses. B shows bending in response to vertical stresses which have been applied slowly.
In C the strain has been relieved by a sudden
movement along the fault surface. The rocks
on opposite sides of the break vibrate or tremble for a time after their abrupt movement,
and waves are created which cause the earth
to shake.*

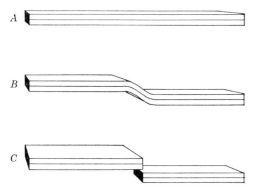

Fig. 31-17.

Fig. 31-18.

*Road offset along the San Andreas Fault. During the 1906 California
earthquake, the road was offset horizontally a distance of 20 feet. The
broken surface indicates the fault. Near Point Reyes. (After G. K. Gilbert,
U.S. Geological Survey)*

parently some are created by disturbances that are located about 400 miles below the surface.

The San Andreas fault in California is approximately vertical, passes near San Francisco, and can be traced for many tens of miles both northwest and southeast of the city. In April, 1906, abrupt horizontal movement occurred along approximately 270 miles of this fault. Roads and fences along the line of the fault were offset as much as 21 feet (Fig. 31-18). Careful measurements which span several decades seem to show that land west of the San Andreas fault is moving northward and that land on the east side of the fault is moving southward. The total movement seems to be about 2 inches a year. No sooner has relief from this bending been afforded by the sudden movement that causes an earthquake than stresses begin to accumulate for another quick movement sometime in the future. In some places, valleys trending across the San Andreas fault have been offset 150 feet. Presumably this represents the total effect of several earthquakes similar to the one in 1906 after the valleys had been formed by erosion.

THE INTERIOR OF THE EARTH

Earthquake waves seem to indicate that the Earth has a central core about 4300 miles in diameter which differs from the outer part of the Earth surrounding it (Fig. 31-19). Two types of evidence suggest that the specific gravity of the core is high: (1) The specific gravity of the Earth as a whole (5.5) is about double the average specific gravity of rocks found in the Earth's crust (2.7 to 3.0); (2) the magnitude of the Earth's equatorial bulge implies the existence of a heavy core. If the Earth had a uniform specific gravity of about 5.6 beneath a thin surface shell of lighter rocks, the equatorial bulge should be much larger. As was suggested in discussing meteors (p. 393), this core may be composed chiefly of iron and nickel.

MOUNTAINS

Mountains are large isolated land masses which project conspicuously above their surroundings (Figs. 31-20 and 31-21). Diastrophism, igneous activity, and erosion—these are three phases of their origin. The simplest type of mountain is the volcano, the mountain of accumulation. Products of volcanism heap up quietly or explosively about an opening that leads downward to a magma reservoir. As the volcano grows larger, it is attacked ever more vigorously by erosion; its shape at any one time is a compromise between the push from below and erosion at the surface.

The Earth's interior. The shadow zone is a belt about 2750 miles wide (about 40 degrees) which extends around the Earth. It begins at 103 degrees from the place of origin of the earth-quake and extends to 143 degrees from that place. The location of the shadow zone shifts with the location of the earth-quake. It thus suggests the presence of a spherical core inside the Earth. The outer part of the core may be fluid. Evidence: One of the two types of waves that pass through the Earth cannot pass through fluids; it seems not to pass through the Earth's core. The other type of wave does pass through the core but is deflected. Further deflections of this wave suggest that the inner part of the core may be solid. To consider the thickness of the crust of the Earth—perhaps 20 to 25 miles thick beneath the continents—and relate it to the length of the Earth's 4000-mile radius, imagine that the radius is sub-divided into four 1000-mile segments. If the outer segment is again subdivided into ten 100-mile-thick units, the crust proves to be very thin relative to the size of the Earth as a whole.

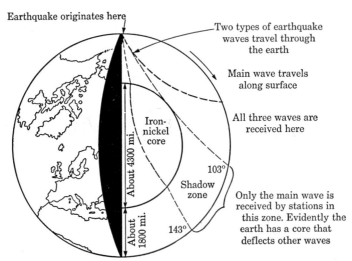

Earthquake originates here

Two types of earthquake waves travel through the earth

Main wave travels along surface

All three waves are received here

Iron-nickel core

About 4300 mi.

103°

Shadow zone

About 1800 mi.   143°

Only the main wave is received by stations in this zone. Evidently the earth has a core that deflects other waves

Fig. 31-19.

All other types of mountains have originated because part of the Earth's crust was uplifted and subsequently sculptured by erosion into isolated mountainous remnants. The Catskill Mountains in New York furnish a good example. They consist of nearly horizontal sedimentary rocks that were elevated by crustal movements to form a large plateau. Erosion then cut into the plateau, isolated the part in New York, and made it mountainous.

"How old is that mountain?" is a common question, and one often hard to answer simply. We can tell the age of the rocks making up the mountain, and this yields one answer. However, the mountain did not exist then. If "age" refers to a time in the past when diastrophic movements folded, faulted, and uplifted the entire region, a second and different answer is required, but the present mountain had not yet

Fig. 31-20.

Structure section through the United States, approximately along the 39th parallel—Washington, D.C., to San Francisco. (Adapted from A. K. Lobeck)

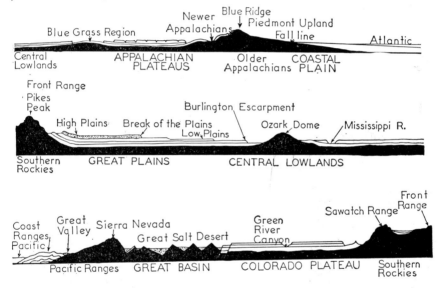

been formed. If "age of the mountain" refers to a time when erosion had proceeded far enough to separate a high land mass into isolated remnants, a third answer is called for. A correct reply manifestly should be an explanation involving all these factors.

Parts of the crust may be elevated along great fractures to form fault block mountains (Fig. 31.20). For example, the Sierra Nevada in California forms part of a large block of the Earth's crust which has been tilted up on the east to form the mountains and tilted down on the west to form the Great Valley of California. Other examples of this type of mountain are found in the Basin and Range Province centering in Nevada.

Compression may wrinkle the crust into huge folds similar to those that form part of the Appalachian Mountains. On the other hand, the

Relief map of North America. (Courtesy, U.S. Geological Survey)

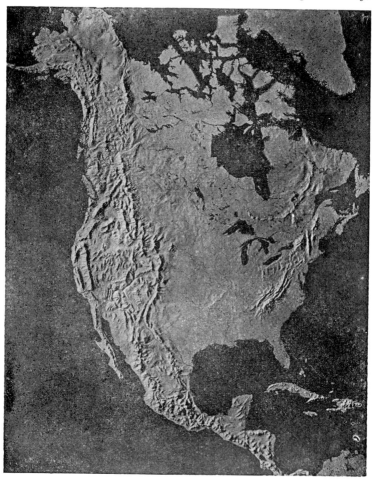

Fig. 31-21.

Earth's crust may be warped upward in the form of a dome (Fig. 31-3).

Still other mountains—great chains like the Appalachians, Rockies, Andes, Alps, and Himalayas—have been called complex because their origins have involved long periods of sedimentation, crustal compression, metamorphism, vulcanism, uplift, and erosion (p. 724).

EXERCISES AND QUESTIONS FOR CHAPTER 31

1. Continue the sandstone layer to the fault in such a manner that it shows a drag fold produced by a reverse fault.

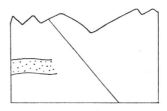

2. Draw a structure section which shows that the following events have occurred in the geologic history of a certain area:

   (1) Sandstone formed
   (2) Folding produced anticlines and synclines
   (3) Basalt dike formed
   (4) A normal fault occurred
   (5) Erosion continued for a long time
   (6) Conglomerate formed
   (7) A granite dike formed
   (8) Erosion occurred

3. Develop two reasons why an unconformity involves a break in the geologic record.

4. A vein of calcite is seen in rocks. The surfaces of the calcite and of the rock on either side of the vein contain many parallel scratches and grooves. Describe the probable origin of these features.

5. Describe two different types of evidence which indicate that faulting has occurred in an area.

6. What conditions favor rock deformation by folding? by faulting?

7. What causes an earthquake?

8. List in chronological order from earliest to latest the events that have occurred in the geologic history of this area. Be certain that you under-

stand the evidence showing that a given geologic event must have occurred before, at the same time as, or after another geologic event. (The
information given in the structure section is not enough to date all the
geologic events precisely.)

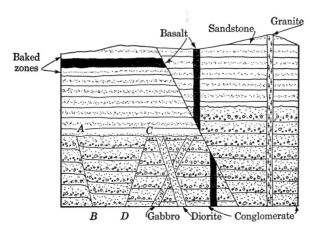

CHAPTER 32

Appalachian Mountain Geology

The evolutionary development of the Appalachian Mountains from the beginning of the Paleozoic era to the present is a telling illustration of physical geologic history. The succession of events in the Appalachian Mountains forms a pattern which has been repeated with variations in most of the complex mountain chains on the Earth.

GEOLOGIC SETTING

The central part of North America forms a huge tract of comparatively low, topographically subdued country which stretches from the Gulf of Mexico northward into the Arctic (Fig. 31-21). Part of it is covered by water; the Great Lakes and Hudson Bay are examples. This entire area has been called the Central Stable Region because it forms the nucleus of North America and has been relatively undeformed during the Paleozoic, Mesozoic, and Cenozoic eras. Precambrian igneous and metamorphic rocks are exposed at the Earth's surface or can be found at comparatively shallow depths below it throughout the region. To the north and east in Canada and the Adirondacks, Precambrian rocks crop out at the surface; to the south and west in the United States, they are buried beneath a cover of nearly flat-lying Paleozoic (chiefly marine) and younger sedimentary rocks (Cenozoic strata are predominantly nonmarine). The geologic history of the Precambrian in this area and elsewhere on the Earth has been exceedingly long and varied. A succession of events such as the following has been repeated several times: (1) A long period of sedimentation took place accompanied at times by huge outpourings of lava; great thicknesses of such rocks accumulated. (2) Following this came a time of mountain building when diastrophic forces buckled and twisted the Earth's crust, and huge volumes of granitic rocks originated. (3) A long period of relative quiet followed, during which erosion slowly peneplaned the rocks in the area.

The deciphering and correlation of Precambrian events is extremely difficult because fossils are almost entirely lacking. Precambrian rocks are chiefly igneous and metamorphic, although thick sequences of undeformed sedimentary rocks are known and have preserved in them such features as cross-bedding, ripple marks, and mud cracks. The oldest rocks dated by radioactive methods are intrusive into metamorphic rocks which, therefore, must be still older. Furthermore, some of these metamorphic rocks contain faint structures that are relics from their original sedimentary origin. Thus, metamorphic rocks are the oldest known. Yet they originated by metamorphism of sedimentary rocks which had formed by the erosion of still older rocks, no traces of which have yet been discovered. It follows that familiar geological processes, such as erosion, sedimentation, igneous activity, diastrophism, and metamorphism have been taking place since the very beginning of that part of Earth history which is recorded in rocks.

Elongated mountain systems have formed around the margins of the Central Stable Region during the Paleozoic, Mesozoic, and Cenozoic eras. The Appalachian and Ouachita systems formed during the Paleozoic era and are located to the east and south of the Central Stable Region. The Rocky Mountain system of Mesozoic-Cenozoic age is situated to the southwest and west. To the north and northeast on the outer borders of Greenland and Ellesmere Land are additional and less well-known mountain systems. Thus the geologic setting of the Appalachians in North America is that of a former mobile belt of the Earth's crust which was located along one margin of a relatively stationary continental nucleus.

PHYSIOGRAPHIC SUBDIVISIONS OF THE APPALACHIAN MOUNTAINS

The Appalachian Mountains form an elongated belt that trends northeastward from Alabama for hundreds of miles into the State of New York and beyond (Fig. 31-21). The central part of the Appalachians consists of conspicuous parallel ridges interspersed with valleys which trend northeastward in large sweeping curves and exhibit numerous sharp hairpin turns. Both east and west of the parallel ridges, the topography is more irregular. To the southeast across the trend of the Appalachians, rock deformation by folds, faults, and metamorphism becomes more pronounced. Throughout its extent the mountainous belt parallels the margin of the Atlantic Ocean and can be subdivided into four units on the basis of topography, rocks, and rock structures. Between these four subdivisions and the Atlantic Ocean lies the Coastal Plain, a nearly featureless lowland underlain by geologically youthful, unconsolidated sedimentary layers that dip gently to the east. From the Coastal Plain westward across the Appalachians, the four subdivisions are: the Piedmont, Blue Ridge, Valley and Ridge, and the Appalachian Plateaus (Figs. 32-1 and 31-20).

The Piedmont This subdivision forms foothills (the name in French signifies "foot of the mountain") along the eastern margin of the Appalachian Mountains and is underlain by igneous and metamorphic rocks. Near the mountains the Piedmont consists of hilly country with summits that rise 1000 to 1200 feet above sea level. The surface of the Piedmont gradually decreases in altitude toward the Atlantic where it disappears beneath the Coastal Plain sediments. The Piedmont is widest and best-developed in the south.

The Coastal Plain and Piedmont intersect along a northeast-southwest line (The Fall Line). In crossing the Fall Line (Fig. 32-1) eastward-flowing streams shift from the resistant rocks of the Piedmont to the weaker materials of the Coastal Plain. In such locations, more extensive erosion has taken place in the unconsolidated sediments; falls and rapids exist upstream (west) of the Fall Line. Ships can navigate as far westward as the Fall Line along a number of rivers which flow over the Coastal Plain. Philadelphia, Baltimore, Washington, Augusta, and other cities were originally located along the Fall Line for this

Fig. 32-1.

Subdivisions of the Appalachian Mountains. Valley and Ridge is considered a better term than Newer Appalachians. Note how rivers such as the Susquehanna cut across the folded structure and ridges. Evidently the rivers developed their courses at a time in the past when these structures could not influence them. Perhaps at this time the structures were buried by younger sediments, subsequently removed by erosion, or part of a peneplaned surface. (Drawn by E. J. Raisz. From International Geological Congress Guidebook No. 7)

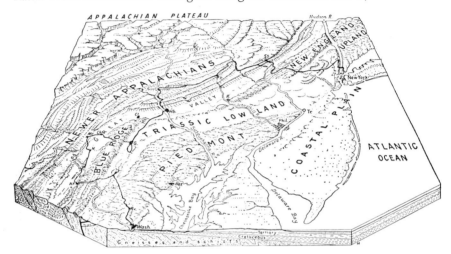

reason. In addition, water power is available in the zone of falls and rapids upstream from the Fall Line.

The Blue Ridge   The Blue Ridge forms a nearly continuous chain of mountains that extends from the Highlands of the Hudson River (part of the New England Upland in Fig. 32-1) southwestward into the Great Smokies and beyond. The mountainous area is widest in the south, where it contains the highest peaks in the United States east of the Mississippi River. Igneous and metamorphic rocks underlie this area and are cut by many large thrust faults that dip to the southeast. Until recently it had been assumed that the badly deformed rocks which underlie both the Piedmont and the Blue Ridge were almost entirely Precambrian in age. Now a substantial portion is thought to consist of rocks that formed during the Paleozoic era and were metamorphosed before its end.

The Valley and Ridge   The northeastward-trending, nearly parallel, even-crested ridges and intervening valleys of the Valley and

Ridge are situated northwest of the Blue Ridge; they disappear beneath the younger rocks of the Coastal Plain in Alabama and have a restricted width north of Pennsylvania. Some of the ridges rise 3000 to 4000 feet above sea level. The Shawangunk Mountains in New York form the northernmost part of this subdivision. The folded and faulted sedimentary rocks underlying this area were deposited during the Paleozoic era. Folds are gentle along the northwest margin of the Valley and Ridge but are steeper and even overturned to the northwest along the opposite side (southeast). Thrust faults (Fig. 32-2) and overturned folds are more abundant to the south.

Great thrust fault exposed in Muddy Mountains near Las Vegas, Nevada. A thrust fault can be defined as a low-angle large-scale reverse fault. Movement along the fault surface as a result of compression measures several miles. The lighter-colored rocks are chiefly sandstones of Mesozoic age. Above these rocks are the darker-colored Paleozoic strata, which are predominantly limestone. This illustration is an exception to the principle of superposition—here older rocks rest upon younger rocks. The Paleozoic strata formed first and the Mesozoic beds piled on top of them; then faulting and erosion (the hanging wall of Paleozoic rocks once covered the whole area) brought about the present conditions. Note that in a dry climate, limestone is a resistant rock. (Photograph by Richard J. Ordway)

Fig. 32-2.

The Appalachian Plateaus   The westernmost subdivision of the Appalachian Mountains is underlain by nearly horizontal Paleozoic sedimentary rocks. The Cumberland and Allegheny Plateaus and the

Catskill Mountains are part of it. Its eastern boundary is distinctly marked by steep slopes. The surface of the Plateau in places rises 3000 to 4000 feet above sea level and in some areas has been so dissected by erosion that it forms mountains. The Plateau is widest along that part of the Appalachians which extends from New York to Tennessee.

EVOLUTIONARY CHARACTER OF THE APPALACHIAN MOUNTAINS

The long geological history of the Appalachian Mountains falls into three phases, each of which merged into the next and formed part of a continuous evolutionary development:

(1) The geosynclinal phase lasted throughout most of the Paleozoic era and included the Taconian and Acadian times of mountain building.

(2) The diastrophic phase includes at least three times of mountain building which occurred during the early, middle, and later portions of the Paleozoic era: these are the Taconian, Acadian, and Appalachian *orogenies* (Greek: "birth of mountains").

(3) The post-diastrophic phase includes the events of the Mesozoic and Cenozoic eras which involve erosion, peneplanation, and uplift.

The Geosynclinal Phase   Sediments deposited during the Paleozoic era in North America show that it was formerly quite different from today in its physical appearance and biological inhabitants. At the beginning of the Paleozoic era, no Appalachian Mountains existed. Rather, the zone in which the Appalachian Mountains now are located was then the site of an elongated trough in the Earth's crust called the *Appalachian geosyncline.* This is thought to have subsided slowly during most of the Paleozoic era; occasional upward movements and times of quiet interrupted the sinking. Shallow seas commonly covered the trough or advanced and retreated slowly along it. Geographically, this elongated belt once extended from Alabama northeastward to Newfoundland. Thus, it paralleled the present coast line of the Atlantic Ocean but was located some distance west of it. Sediments were carried by rivers and spread out along the floor of the shallow sea. As the floor of the sea subsided, room was made available for the deposition of additional sediments. Deposition and subsidence continued during most of the Paleozoic era, and an exceedingly thick pile of sediments accumulated. Perhaps the maximum thickness approached 40,000 feet, although the average may have been half of this amount. Such an elongated, subsiding, sediment-collecting belt—commonly the site of a future great mountain chain—is called a *geosyncline*. (Some geologists now recognize many kinds of geosynclines.)

Two additional geosynclines were in existence in North America during the Paleozoic era. One (the Cordilleran geosyncline) extended in a north-south direction more or less parallel to the present Pacific coast line but was situated a considerable distance east of it. In part it coincided with the location of the present Rocky Mountains; in part it was somewhat west of them. The other geosyncline (Ouachita) extended in an east-west direction along the southern margin of the continent and may at times have joined the southern part of the Appalachian geosyncline. The Ouachita and Arbuckle Mountains in Arkansas and Oklahoma were one part of this geosyncline.

Recognition of the geosynclinal concept developed from a study of Paleozoic sedimentary rocks in the eastern part of North America. American geologists originated the concept in the latter half of the nineteenth century, and the Appalachian geosyncline was used by them as the type example. They discovered the physiographic subdivisions and rock structures just described. They measured the total thickness of Paleozoic sedimentary rocks in the Appalachian Mountains and found it to be several times greater than the total thickness of Paleozoic strata westward in the area of the Mississippi Valley (Fig. 32-3A). Furthermore, sedimentation was found to have taken place more continuously in the Appalachian geosyncline than in the interior of the continent.

This great thickness of marine Paleozoic sedimentary rocks does not mean that the sea covering the Appalachian geosyncline was once about 8 miles deep and that it was gradually made shallower by the deposition of sediments. Features associated with shallow water deposition (coarse sediments, cross-bedding, ripple marks, and mud cracks) are found here and there in the pile of strata and indicate that the floor of the sea was covered much of the time by relatively shallow water. Therefore, it was postulated that the first step in the evolutionary development of a great mountain system might involve the origin of a geosyncline and its slow subsidence in the very area out of which the mountains would subsequently emerge. Similar belts of thick sedimentary accumulations have since been found in other great mountain

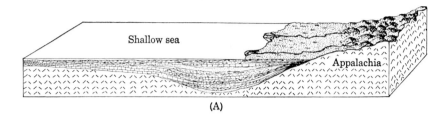

(A)

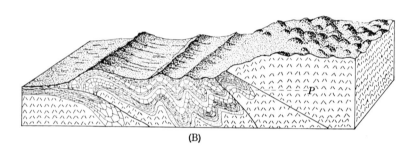

(B)

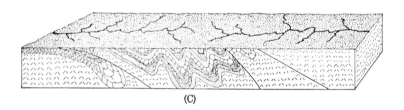

(C)

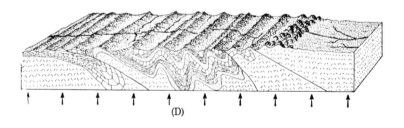

(D)

chains like the Rockies, Andes, Alps, and Himalayas. Why great mountain chains have developed out of areas which were once sea floors is still one of the great mysteries of geology.

Source of Sediments Deposited in the Appalachian Geosyncline

Many of the Paleozoic sedimentary rocks in the Valley and Ridge and the Plateau division grade from coarse to fine as they are traced from east to west. Deposition of the coarsest material in the east seems to indicate that a source area for the sedimentary materials was located east of the geosyncline (Fig. 32-3A). Furthermore, lack of much sediment coming from the Central Stable Region suggests that it was not affected by crustal movements of great magnitude during the Paleozoic and that it never was uplifted far above sea level.

The source area to the east has been named Appalachia, but its nature and geographic extent are not known. Formerly it was believed to have been a continuous highland mass which bordered the Appalachian geosyncline on the east. Thus it would have occupied what is now the Piedmont and Coastal Plain areas and the eastern margin of the Atlantic Ocean. The volume of sediments deposited in the Appalachian geosyncline is so large that the source area must have been enormous—or, more likely, was subjected to repeated uplifts. At present, some geologists prefer to assume that Appalachia was a chain of volcanic islands something like the present Japanese Islands off the

Fig. 32-3.

Four stages in the evolution of the present Appalachians. (See opposite page) The view is toward north, each block is about 200 miles long, and the vertical scale is exaggerated:—A. The inner division of the geosyncline receiving sediments from a former land on the east. The exact nature of the source area, Appalachia, is uncertain.—B. Folding and thrust faulting of the rocks in the geosyncline during the Appalachian orogeny. The form and height of the surface are entirely hypothetical; it is not known how much uplift resulted directly from the folding or to what extent erosion kept pace with the uplift. After several geologic periods had elapsed, the region was worn to a peneplane, indicated by the broken line at P.—C. General appearance of the peneplaned Appalachian region near the close of the Mesozoic era. The eastern part of the region was submerged and received a veneer of coastal-plain sediments; possibly this veneer covered much of the folded belt and has been removed by erosion.—D. During Cenozoic time the region was warped up, as indicated by arrows at the bottom of the block. Belts of weak sedimentary rock were eroded faster than the resistant strata, which therefore make the present ridges. (After Longwell, Knopf, and Flint, Physical Geology, 1948, John Wiley & Sons, Inc.)

coast of China. Whatever its former shape and extent, it has since been destroyed by erosion and subsidence.

Inner and Outer Divisions of the Appalachian Geosyncline   Recent discoveries indicate a subdivision of the original Appalachian geosyncline into Inner and Outer Divisions. The present Blue Ridge probably marks the approximate boundary between these two troughs in the early and middle parts of the Paleozoic era. The eastern Outer Division corresponds in geographic location to the present Piedmont and Atlantic Coastal area. Much volcanic material accumulated in it. Orogenies affected it three times during the Paleozoic era: Taconian, Acadian, and Appalachian. However, it apparently ceased to exist as a trough after the Acadian orogeny in the mid-Paleozoic.

The western Inner Division corresponds in location to the Valley and Ridge and the Plateau divisions. Shales, sandstones, conglomerates, and limestones piled up to great thicknesses in it. The Inner Division was not deformed until the Appalachian orogeny in the late Paleozoic. Higher land probably separated these two subsiding troughs during most of the first half of the Paleozoic era.

The reason for the change to Inner and Outer divisions follows: The source area, Appalachia, as originally defined was believed to be made of Precambrian rocks. However, recent field studies have shown some of the igneous and metamorphic rocks of the Blue Ridge and Piedmont divisions to be of Paleozoic age, not Precambrian. Therefore, the existence of a trough (Outer Division) in which deposition, igneous activity, and metamorphism occurred seems demonstrated.

The Paleozoic Record in the Appalachian Geosyncline   The character and volume of sediments deposited in the Inner Division of the Appalachian geosyncline during any one interval in the Paleozoic era furnish information concerning the source area for the sediments to the east. A succession of uplifts followed by periods of erosion and two times of mountain building (Taconian and Acadian) are recorded by the Paleozoic rocks.

The oldest Cambrian sediments deposited in the Inner Division trough were predominantly coarse detrital ones like sand and gravel. Sediments deposited on top of these as the Cambrian period advanced tended to become finer grained, and limestone formed near the end of the Cambrian. The rocks suggest that the source area was rugged at the beginning of the Cambrian and was gradually worn down by erosion during the period. When lands are high, streams and rivers can flow swiftly and carry large loads of coarse sediments. When lands are low, little sediment is transported, and materials accumulating on the floor of a nearby sea may consist chiefly of calcium carbonate in the form of shell fragments or precipitated matter. Later this consolidates to form limestone.

Sediments deposited in the Inner Division trough during the succeeding period (Ordovician) reversed the size gradations that occurred during the Cambrian. The oldest Ordovician rocks are chiefly shale and limestone and apparently show that nearby lands did not extend far above sea level. Younger Ordovician sedimentary rocks are coarser grained and very thick, thus indicating that the source area was uplifted before the end of the period. However, unconformities have been found between Ordovician and younger rocks at various places from Pennsylvania to Newfoundland (Fig. 32-4). These record the occurrence of the Taconian orogeny which chiefly affected the Outer Division of the Appalachian geosyncline. Intensity of the de-

Fig. 32-4.

Structure section through part of southeastern New York. Late Ordovician strata were folded during the Taconian orogeny and eroded before the Silurian strata were deposited unconformably upon them. The Silurian strata were deformed at a later time (Appalachian orogeny). The dip of the Devonian rocks in Slide Mt. has been exaggerated.

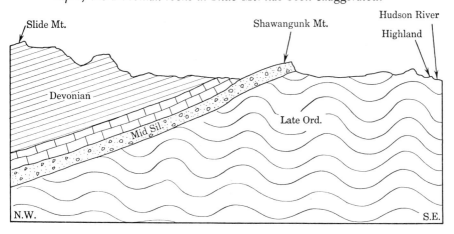

formation decreases toward the northwest. Horizontal compression of this type tends to shorten the Earth's crust and produces folds, thrust faults, and an elongated mountainous area. This Ordovician interval of mountain building is named the Taconian, because rocks which now form part of the Taconic Mountains (the New York–Massachusetts border) may have been shoved to the northwest along a major thrust fault at that time.

Mountains produced by the Taconian orogeny influenced the character of the sediments deposited in the Inner Division during the next geological period (Silurian). The oldest Silurian rocks are chiefly conglomerates and sandstones. These imply a mountainous area to the east during the time of their formation. Younger Silurian rocks are finer grained, and the very youngest are chiefly limestone. Evidently erosion gradually reduced the rugged lands to the east to low-lying areas before the end of the period.

The geologic history of the succeeding period (Devonian) in the Appalachian geosyncline in many ways parallels that of the Ordovician. The oldest Devonian sedimentary rocks are chiefly limestone. Younger Devonian rocks contain many sandstones and conglomerates and are exceedingly thick. The Catskill Mountains in New York have been carved by erosion from these rocks. Uplift of the source area to the east is again recorded. Furthermore, unconformities have been found in the Canadian Maritime provinces (land of Acadia), although none have been found south of New England. These structures show that Devonian and older rocks located chiefly in the Outer Division along the Appalachian geosyncline were crumpled and folded during the Acadian orogeny. Granitic masses abundant in the White Mountains of New Hampshire, in Mount Katahdin in Maine, and in Nova Scotia were formed at this time.

During the remaining periods in the Paleozoic era (Mississippian, Pennsylvanian, and Permian) the western Inner Division of the Appalachian geosyncline was kept nearly filled with sediments. The source area to the east apparently was uplifted several times, because alternations of coarse and fine sediments were deposited in the geosyncline. Of course, other explanations are possible for such alternations. For example, if rainfall is increased, rivers will flow more rapidly and carry coarser sediments. However, if very large volumes of coarse sediments accumulate, uplift of the source area probably has taken place. During the Pennsylvanian period, large swampy areas formed in parts of the geosyncline and the continental interior south and west of it. As the swampy areas subsided, thick piles of vegetation accumulated. Later these changed to coal. Apparently at no other time in the history of the Earth were conditions so favorable for the formation of coal on such a large scale.

Near the end of the era, the sedimentary rocks which had been deposited in the geosyncline were crushed and deformed by powerful compressive forces in a major orogeny (Fig. 32-3B) that marked the end of the Appalachian geosyncline. Compression during this Appalachian orogeny may have been applied several times rather than just once. Thrust faults, folds overturned to the northwest, and metamorphism are best developed along the eastern margin of the area formerly occupied by the Appalachian geosyncline. Diastrophic effects everywhere fade out to the northwest where rocks in the Appalachian Plateaus are today nearly horizontal and undisturbed. A chain of lofty mountains (but not the present Appalachians) apparently stretched about 2000 miles from Alabama to Newfoundland. All of the rock structures (folds, faults, and metamorphism) now found in the Valley and Ridge subdivisions south of New York and Pennsylvania apparently formed during this orogeny. Northeast of this area, however, the effects of the earlier Taconian and Acadian movements are difficult to separate from those produced by the Appalachian orogeny.

Large batholiths of granitic rocks may have formed during and after the compression. These are now located in the Blue Ridge and Piedmont. However, the time of their formation is uncertain. Recent radioactive dates indicate that some formed during the Taconian orogeny.

The Appalachians: Post-Diastrophic Phase   The chain of mountains produced during the Appalachian orogeny was subsequently reduced in altitude by erosion (Fig. 32-3C). Before the first part of the Mesozoic era had ended, apparently the entire area was worn down until only stumps of the mountains remained.

Three steps are traceable though they did not leave conspicuous results throughout the entire area: (1) During the Triassic period, a series of uplifts and downward movements occurred along a number of large normal faults at several locations in the eastern part of North America (the Palisades disturbance—no compression). (2) Erosion reduced the area again to a fairly smooth surface near sea level (the Fall Zone peneplane). (3) This erosion surface was then warped upward to form a domed, plateaulike area which was subsequently worn down to another (the Schooley) peneplane (Fig. 32-3C).

During the latter part of the Cenozoic era, the Schooley peneplane was gradually arched upward until its highest portions projected 3000 to 4000 feet above sea level (Fig. 32-3D). Erosion continued during and following the uplift. Weaker rocks were removed relatively rapidly; lowlands developed and became larger in areas underlain by such rocks. Where the Earth's crust was formed of uplifted resistant rocks, however, erosion proceeded more slowly. For this reason, northeast-southwest-trending ridges and mountains were produced as erosion carved away the weaker rocks that flanked them. The tops of some of the mountains in the Valley and Ridge subdivision are remnants of the Schooley surface. They are particularly well displayed in Pennsylvania (Fig. 31-2). This uplift of the Schooley peneplane apparently was complex and involved more than one time of uplift followed by a quiet interval; however, geologists differ on the exact number and magnitude of these movements.

Thus the present-day Appalachians did not form until the Schooley peneplane was elevated high above sea level and subsequently sculptured by erosion. However, the rocks which form the mountains and the rock structures associated with them originated long before the latter part of the Cenozoic era. The northern portions of the Applachians were covered by ice during the Pleistocene, and their topography was modified by glacial erosion and deposition.

The mobile belt (Ouachita geosyncline) along the southern margin of the Central Stable Region was likewise compressed and folded near the end of the Paleozoic era. The diastrophism that produced the rock structures of the Rocky Mountains did not occur until the latter part of the Mesozoic era and the first part of the Cenozoic.

THE OROGENIC CYCLE

Complex mountain systems seem to share a number of sequential steps in their development, although details vary considerably from one system to the next: (1) A necessary initial phase appears to be the formation of a geosyncline, its subsidence over a long period of time, and the accumulation of a thick belt of sediments. (2) Eventually the sedimentary rocks in the geosyncline are compressed by powerful crustal forces which act chiefly in a horizontal direction. (3)

During or shortly after the folding and faulting, huge batholiths of granitic rocks originate. (4) Next, a long period of crustal quiet occurs during which erosion produces a peneplane. (5) Subsequently the entire region is arched upward and dissected by erosion. Weaker rocks are removed at a relatively rapid rate; areas underlain by resistant rocks are isolated to form mountains.

Explaining the Orogenic Cycle: The Convection Current Hypothesis

The origin of the horizontal forces that have squeezed and crumpled geosynclines and the causes of the other events which have commonly occurred in the history of most great mountain systems are mysterious and have been the subject of much speculation on the part of geologists. One explanation, the *convection current hypothesis*, exemplifies the thinking in this field.

Any hypothesis is based upon assumptions. Naturally assumptions are chosen which have a factual basis and seem reasonable, but if they are not correct the entire hypothesis will be invalid. The convection circulation hypothesis depends on certain assumptions about the nature of the Earth's interior, which is assumed to consist of three distinct parts: (1) a core about 4300 miles in diameter, (2) a "crust" (sial and sima) which may average 18 to 25 miles in thickness but be double this amount beneath great mountainous areas, and (3) a thick shell of more or less uniform material called the mantle which is located between the crust and the core. The crust is divided into an upper portion called *sial* (silicon and aluminum) which resembles granite in chemical composition and a lower portion called *sima* (silicon and magnesium) which resembles basalt in chemical composition. Oxygen is abundant in both the sial and sima. The granitic rocks in the sial weigh less than the dark heavy basaltic rocks beneath them.

It is postulated that some parts of the core attain a higher temperature at times than do adjoining parts. Is this heat residual? Is it of radioactive origin? Or does it come from some other source? These questions are left unanswered. In addition, very slow plastic movement is assumed to occur in the mantle. (Some scientists argue that this is not possible.)

According to this hypothesis, the part of the mantle immediately above a very hot section of the core should tend to rise. Surrounding parts of the mantle would then move laterally toward this point, thereby setting up a gigantic, exceedingly gradual convection current

(Fig. 32-5). As the upward-moving current meets the Earth's crust, it divides, and moves laterally. If two such currents meet, they may sink and drag the crust down in that area. Clever and carefully scaled

Mountain building and convection circulation (highly diagrammatic). A. At the beginning of the cycle slowly rising warm currents spread beneath the crust, cool, and descend.—B. The convectional system reaches its maximum speed and the crust is highly compressed. The lightweight granitic rocks of the crust are dragged deep into the mantle. Mountains which result at this time are subsequently eroded to a peneplane as the currents gradually slow down.—C. At the end of the cycle, convection ceases, and the part of the crust which had been pulled downward tends to "float" back up as the subcrustal forces weaken. A mountain belt is formed when this uplifted peneplane is subsequently carved into isolated topographic units by erosion. (After Griggs)

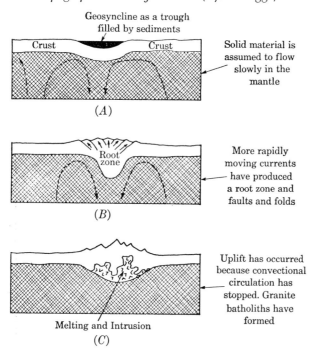

Geosyncline as a trough
filled by sediments

Crust   Crust

Solid material is
assumed to flow
slowly in the
mantle

(A)

Root
zone

More rapidly
moving currents
have produced
a root zone and
faults and folds

(B)

Uplift has occurred
because convectional
circulation has
stopped. Granite
batholiths have
formed

Melting and Intrusion

(C)   Fig. 32-5.

models have been made by geologists in which the convection currents are produced by a rotating drum in a tank of glycerin. Floating at the surface of the liquid is a mixture of sawdust and oil that simulates the strength and thickness of the crust. These models show that a trough develops where the downward moving parts of the currents meet. Perhaps the trough illustrates the formation of a geosyncline.

Convection currents, if they exist, may act cyclically. Perhaps a long initial phase of slow movement is followed by a shorter period in which currents move more rapidly. At this time very hot material would be rising and relatively cool material sinking. This in turn may be succeeded by another long period during which the currents gradually slow down. At the Earth's surface the cycle might be manifested by (1) the formation of the geosyncline and its long slow subsidence, (2) the relatively brief period of orogeny which compresses the geosyncline, and (3) a long period of crustal quiet during which peneplanation occurs.

Isostasy in the Earth's Crust The Earth's crust is known to have a lower specific gravity than that of the mantle. In addition, a balance (isostasy) probably exists among various large segments of the crust. Consider, as an example, the iceberg. About nine-tenths of the ice is below the surface. Suppose we want to make our iceberg 10 feet higher. It will not be enough to add 10 feet of ice at the top. The bottom of the ice will simply sink down about 9 feet; the surface will project only 1 foot higher. If we compare the continents to floating icebergs, they "float" or stand high because they are made of lightweight material, and the sial, like the submerged part of the iceberg, seems to be thicker under mountainous areas as a support for the higher altitude of the Earth's surface (Fig. 32-6). The lightweight granitic rocks which form the continents appear to be almost entirely absent from the floors of the oceans. If this supposed condition of balance is upset, as it appears to have been during the Pleistocene by the formation of huge ice sheets (pp. 647-649), the Earth's crust should move to compensate for overburdening or unloading.

According to the convection current hypothesis, a great "root zone" of lightweight crustal rocks forms below the geosyncline. Crustal balance is upset, and the lightweight rocks tend to rise. However, they are prevented from rising by the downward drag of the convection currents. Peneplanation of the original mountains may occur at this time. As the currents gradually slow down and finally stop, the thickened zone of lightweight crustal rocks should move slowly upward. Perhaps this corresponds to the uparching which commonly has occurred after peneplanation in the history of many complex mountain

Fig. 32-6.

Isostasy in a highly schematic sketch. Columns A, B, and C have equal cross sections. The specific gravity of sial is less than that of sima. The columns would all weigh the same although their lengths vary. The short column A is composed of heavy sima and mantle. A high proportion of lightweight sial is present in B, the longest column.—If the columns were extended equal distances to A', B', and C', their weights would still be equivalent, since material at this depth is believed to be homogeneous in a horizontal direction.—Deflections of earthquake waves show that the Mohorovičić discontinuity (Moho) occurs at the base of the Earth's crust. The crust seems to average about 20 to 25 miles in thickness beneath the continents but may be nearly double this beneath large mountain belts. Beneath the oceans, the Earth's crust may be as thin as $2\frac{1}{2}$ to 3 miles in places.—This thinness has inspired a project termed the "Mohole"—a proposal to drill a hole from a ship at the surface of the ocean. After descending through some 3 miles of water and penetrating $\frac{1}{2}$ mile or so of sediments, the drilling could extend through the $2\frac{1}{2}$ or 3 miles of crust and through the Moho into the mantle. Investigations are now under way to determine if such a project is feasible.*

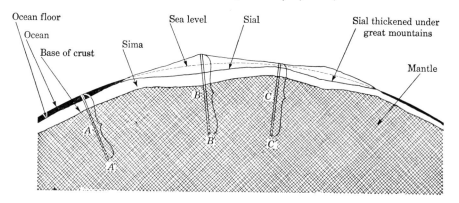

systems. A crude analogy is the reaction of a rubber ball that is held beneath the surface of a body of water and then released.

The Evidence of Granitic Batholiths   The location of large granitic batholiths in the cores of complex mountain systems may be explained as follows. The sial (upper part of the crust) approximates granite in chemical composition. In laboratory experiments, granitic rocks melt at a lower temperature than basaltic ones. Therefore, if convection currents thicken the sial and drag it far below the surface at the time of geosynclinal compression, the sial should melt. On the other hand, temperatures might not be high enough to melt the sima which underlies the sial. The molten material would form granitic magma which

* In April 1961 in the Pacific Ocean near Guadalupe Island, in water nearly 12,000 feet deep, the drilling barge CUSS I pulled up sample cores of sediments and rocks from depths as great as 600 feet below the ocean floor.

might move upward to squeeze into deformed rocks in the mountainous area.

Critique of Hypotheses Although the convection hypothesis offers an ingenious explanation for some aspects of mountain building, it has a number of deficiencies. Probably the most serious is the question: Is convection possible?

The Taconian and Acadian orogenies seem of the same approximate magnitude as the Appalachian orogeny. Perhaps three convections cycles are involved in the geologic history of the Appalachians. Evidence suggests that an orogeny may consist of a series of movements spaced over a long period of time which affect first one and then another part of the mobile belt involved. In fact, some geologists have suggested that a hypothesis of almost continuous deformation during an orogeny fits the facts about as well as the concept of an orogeny consisting of a series of episodes of deformation. If so, perhaps the convection hypothesis can be modified to account for this.

However, other hypotheses also seem inadequate. It seems best to conclude that the cause of complex mountain building is still virtually unknown or at least highly speculative. The possibilities are so vast that we are like the blind men describing the elephant: one felt the trunk and declared an elephant was like a tree; another touched the tail and likened an elephant to a rope; the third touched its side and announced that an elephant was like a wall.

EXERCISES AND QUESTIONS FOR CHAPTER 32

1. What problems are involved in answering a question such as: How old is that mountain?

2. Describe the subdivisions of the Appalachian Mountains.

3. What has been the geologic relationship between some geosynclines and great mountain belts?

4. What is meant by an orogeny?

5. What major events have occurred in the geologic history of most great mountain belts?

6. How does the convection current hypothesis attempt to explain each of the following: (1) origin of granitic batholiths; (2) origin of compressive forces which fold and fault the rocks in the geosyncline during an orogeny; and (3) uplift of the entire region following peneplanation?

CHAPTER 33

The Fossil Record

So far we have dealt with the inanimate side of the Earth's long and eventful past—the advances and retreats of ancient seas, volcanic eruptions, the formation of great mountain ranges, the constant wasting away of higher land masses by the persistent forces of erosion, and the growth and shrinkage of glacier ice. With the entrance of life on this scene, the Earth's history takes on a new focus of interest. Our subject is the countless multitude of animals and plants— huge and tiny, spectacular and commonplace, marine and nonmarine —that lived and died during the immensity of geologic time stretching back from the present to that shadowy reach when life itself first arose.

Fig. 33-1.

Uncovering a fossil cephalopod. (Courtesy, Geological Survey of Canada)

The former existence of these organisms is recorded by fossils found in rocks.

Whether the history is physical or biological, its keynote is unending, leisurely change—changes that are imperceptible to untrained eyes during lifetimes measured in terms of a few scores of years, but whose cumulative effect has been very great. These changes of course continue at the present time. Valleys grow deeper, glaciers shrink, the Earth's crust moves, new types of animals and plants arise. Although the kinds, conditions, and rates of change have not been constant throughout the past, geologists are confident that the techniques and concepts developed through their observations of present-day changes can be applied to deciphering the rest of the Earth's history.

For convenience, geologists have subdivided the long, detailed account of past events into several major units (eras), each of which includes a number of smaller units (periods) in much the same manner as books consist of chapters. Most of the pages of the first long volume are missing, tattered, or scattered widely around the world. However, less ancient portions of the geologic record tend to become more legible and detailed. In this respect the Earth's history parallels the story of man. Life forms a fascinating part of Earth history and is an important factor in its subdivision and deciphering. The rocks hold the record of life in its detail in the form of fossils.

FOSSILS

A fossil (Latin: "something dug up") is the recognizable remains or trace of organisms preserved from prehistoric times (Fig. 33-1). Fossils provide a record of past life which is at best fragmentary. Consider the multitude of organisms in existence at any one time. A very small fraction of these will subsequently become fossilized, and only a tiny proportion of the fossilized forms will eventually be exposed by erosion at the Earth's surface and be discovered by man (Fig. 24-2). However, museums testify that fossils have been found in remarkable numbers and in astonishingly good condition.

Two factors are favorable for the preservation of organisms as fossils: one is the possession of hard parts, such as shells and bones; the other is quick burial of the remains to prevent destruction by scavengers and decay. Obviously, animals like worms and jellyfish have much less chance for preservation than animals like clams and oysters. Yet the possession of hard parts by no means guarantees fossilization in the future. Until late in the 1800's, huge herds of buffalo roamed the prairies of the western United States. Today the buffalo have all but vanished, and hardly a trace remains of their former presence. Their carcasses were not covered rapidly by sedimentation following death. Scavengers and bacteria quickly destroyed the flesh, and the hard parts soon weathered to dust.

The quick burial necessary for preservation of organic remains may occur in a number of ways. The sea floor is the environment in which the greatest number of organisms become fossilized. This was especially true in much of the past when ocean water covered larger portions of the Earth's surface than it does at present. Countless animals with hard parts lived on sandy or muddy bottoms. After death, the shells of these organisms accumulated on the sea floor and were covered rapidly by sediments. In addition, many living animals were buried by sudden shifts of sediments during storms at sea. As a result, some marine sedimentary rocks are extremely fossiliferous. (Such fossil-bearing beds should be seen in the field for a true appreciation of the significance of fossils to geology.)

Falls of volcanic ash may also bury organic remains quickly. Much less frequently, lava flows overwhelm and solidify around organisms before their destruction by the heat. A mold in the lava indicates the former presence of the animal or plant and provides an exception to the general rule that igneous rocks do not contain fossils. For example, the mold of a rhinoceros was discovered a few years ago in Oregon. The shape indicated that the animal was dead and that its bloated carcass probably floated in a pond of water when it was buried by a flow of lava. The water chilled the lava quickly enough to preserve a mold. Animals have likewise been buried rapidly when they were trapped in peat bogs and asphalt pits. At the famous La Brea asphalt pit in Los Angeles (Fig. 33-2), oil seeped out of the ground, collected in a pool at the surface, and changed to a sticky tar as its more volatile constituents evaporated. Animals venturing on this smooth, solid-looking surface were quickly trapped. Scavengers were attracted to the pool by cries of distress and were also mired. Excavations in the asphalt have uncovered the bones of horses, camels, elephants, giant bison, antelope, great ground sloths, vultures, saber-toothed tigers, bears, lions, and wolves. Such large collections of carnivorous animals from one location are unusual.

Fig. 33-2.

The La Brea tar pits. As oil seeped from the ground, the more volatile portions distilled away and left a sticky residue. Here Pleistocene birds and beasts of prey gather around victims mired in the pits, only to find themselves trapped. We see great vultures, saber-toothed cats, the dire wolf, horses.

Fossilization Fossilization may occur in several ways: preservation of an entire organism, preservation of the hard parts alone, petrifaction, and the formation of impressions, molds, casts, and carbon residues.

Preservation Entire The entire animal may be preserved without change. This is rare and occurs only for organisms that lived recently (in terms of geologic time). Everyone has heard accounts of how hunters occasionally find woolly mammoths preserved in the permanently frozen ground of Siberia. For example, one woolly mammoth was discovered in the bank of a stream by a Russian hunter. Sudden, violent death seemed indicated by the presence of unswallowed food in its mouth, a broken hip, and clotted blood in its chest. Perhaps the scene can be reconstructed: The animal browsed along a high river bank, moved too near the edge, caused a landslide, and was killed and buried during the resulting fall of dirt and debris. Later the loose material froze solid, and the mammoth remained in cold storage until the river undercut its bank and exposed it. When discovered, some of the animal's flesh was still red and was eaten by wild dogs. A baby mammoth, preserved in a similar manner, was found in Alaska recently.

Organisms may also be preserved unchanged in antiseptic oil seeps. Skeletons of rhinoceroses have been found in oil seeps in Poland with some flesh, skin, and hair still attached to the bones.

Preservation of Hard Parts More commonly the flesh and soft tissues disappear soon after death, and only the hard parts of animals are preserved unchanged. To date, more than 45,000 pairs of tusks of the woolly mammoth have been sold from Siberia as ivory. Of course the flesh and soft parts of these huge beasts were found preserved in only a few cases. The shells of many marine animals have been kept intact in the sediments in which they were buried on the sea floor. Hard parts may be preserved unchanged for millions of years.

Petrifaction Still more commonly the bones and shells of animals are changed into a stony substance and thus preserved. Porous bone structures may be filled by mineral matter, or organic materials may actually be replaced little by little by such substances as silica, calcium carbonate, and iron oxide (Fig. 33-3). Replacement is often complete to the tiniest detail of structure.

Impressions, Molds, Casts, Footprints These terms are nearly self-explanatory. Impressions may be formed and preserved in the sand and mud in which animals are buried (Fig. 24-10). Again, a shelled animal, say one of the snail-like gastropods, may die, be buried in sediments, and lose its soft internal parts by decay. A cast of this animal forms subsequently if mineral matter or sediments fill the interior of the shell and harden before the shell itself is dissolved (Fig. 33-4).

Remarkable lifelike molds of insects turn up in amber. The insects were trapped and buried in the sticky resin of conifer trees, which later hardened and fossilized as amber. The insects decayed and disappeared, but the hollow molds that remain in the amber faithfully reproduce the delicate hairlike appendages.

Footprints or trails may form if an animal crosses an area of soft mud or sand that is subsequently baked and hardened by the sun's rays and then buried by additional sediments (Figs. 24-1 and 26-9).

Carbon Residues Organic materials are composed largely of carbon, hydrogen, and oxygen. The hydrogen and oxygen volatilize and disappear soon after the death of an organism, but a thin film of carbon may be left to record the former presence of the animal or plant. If an impression has been formed by the organism, the carbon covers that impression (Fig. 33-5). Even animals without hard parts have been preserved in this manner as "carbon copies."

Fossils and Ancient Geography Fossils are essential in determining the past locations of lands and seas because they commonly distinguish marine from nonmarine sedimentary rocks. Careful mapping of rock

The Petrified Forest in Arizona. The organic material which once made up these logs has been entirely replaced by silica. The logs occur in stream-deposited sedimentary rocks of early Mesozoic age. Apparently the trees, something like the present pines, grew upstream and were floated down as logs to be buried in sand bars and along the banks of the ancient river. During and after petrifaction, sediments accumulated to a great thickness on top of the layers with abundant logs. Uplift and erosion has subsequently exposed the zone with petrified logs. A few millions of years ago the logs were probably still buried; a few millions of years in the future (or sooner) all traces of the logs will probably be gone. (Photograph by Richard J. Ordway)

Fig. 33-3.

Fig. 33-4.

Fossil cephalopods. At any one time the animal lived in the opening at the large end of the coiled shell. It secreted a "floor" (septum) across its shell. As the animal grew bigger, it made the shell longer; eventually it moved forward and secreted another septum. This process was repeated many times. The septa thus produced are diagnostic of the cephalopod and distinguish it from gastropods which have a similar appearance. The septa are not visible on the exterior of the shell. This type of cephalopod (ammonite: complex septa) was abundant during the Mesozoic era. (Courtesy, Ward's Natural Science Establishment, Inc.)

Fig. 33-5.

Fossil fish from Cenozoic shales in southwestern Wyoming. Shale represents mud which was formerly deposited in a large fresh-water lake. The carbonaceous residue makes the fish stand out prominently from the rest of the rock. The body has been flattened by compaction of the sedimentary material. (After Veatch, U.S. Geological Survey, Prof. Paper 56)

formations and the matching (correlation) of various strata enable the geologist to work out past distributions of land and sea. Such evidence shows that North America and the other continents were partly submerged by extensive shallow seas a number of times in the past. In fact, apparently one half of North America was flooded by ocean water during one interval in its geologic history.

Fossils indicate that North and South America were separated several times in the past by a water barrier in the vicinity of the present Isthmus of Panama. Fossils likewise seem to show that a land bridge once connected Siberia and Alaska in the Bering Strait area. Evidence consists of the sudden appearance in North America of elephants and other animals after they had lived and developed for a long period of time in Eurasia. In other words, fossils from rocks of similar age in Siberia and Alaska would be quite similar if they had formed when the lands were connected and the animals could wander back and forth without difficulty. A drop in sea level of less than 200 feet would create such a land bridge today. Similar evidence indicates that Great Britain formerly had a land connection with the European coast.

The direction from which the sea flooded an area can sometimes be determined. For example, modern marine shells differ considerably along the Atlantic and Pacific coasts because a land barrier exists. One study in the Panama area had the following results: several hundred species of shell-bearing invertebrates were collected on the Atlantic side, and a similar number of species were found on the Pacific side. However, only 2 dozen or so were common to both sides. Evidence such as this has led geologists to conclude that identical species are restricted to certain faunal realms even though fauna throughout the world have similar characteristics at any one interval in geologic time. Therefore, a comparison of fossil types aids geologists in determining the direction from which the interior of a continent was once flooded.

Interpretation of Former Climates   Most animals and plants of today are restricted to certain climates and types of environment. Did ancient relatives of these organisms exist under similar climatic restrictions? It is true that animals and plants adapt themselves to widely different environments; yet whole assemblages of animals and plants seem to have strong climatic implications. For example, large reptiles and amphibia live today only in areas where temperatures do not drop below freezing. Ancient large reptiles and amphibia probably existed under similar climatic conditions. Fossil palms and crocodiles found in the Dakotas imply that at one time the climate in that region was warmer than it is now.

Recently in Kansas the fossilized remains of nine wild pigs, all facing the same direction, were found in cross-bedded sandstone. Cross-bedded sand may be deposited by streams, but it seems unlikely that the nine skeletons would be oriented in the same direction in stream-laid sediments. Furthermore, the cross-bedding resembles more closely that formed in sands by wind in dry areas today. Perhaps the group of pigs was crossing a semidesert area when they were caught in a sudden sand storm. They turned tail to the wind as do modern cattle and horses and were suffocated and buried beneath shifting sands.

What interpretation might a geologist of the future give to the following facts? A long drought occurred in Argentina from 1827 to 1832. During this time vegetation died, many streams disappeared, and cattle and wild horses perished by the thousands in low-lying areas to which they had migrated in search of water. Heavy rains followed these exceptionally dry years and caused floods which buried many of the skeletons under a blanket of sand and mud. A geologist studying the strata in this area at some time in the future should discover thick, widespread layers of sedimentary rock containing abundant fossilized remains of horses and cattle. On the other hand, thinner layers above and below these beds would contain relatively few fossils. Could he interpret correctly the "sermon" thus recorded in the rocks? Can geologists today reconstruct past events accurately from records and clues they find in the rocks? The answer appears to be yes, even though the stories may be incomplete or imperfectly known.

EVOLUTION

Evolution (Latin: "an unrolling") is the concept that all existing types of animals and plants have developed from previously living types by slow orderly changes which, in general, have produced more complex organisms from more simple. The kinds of changes that produce new types are familiar to us all. Consider the varieties of dogs existing today. They have all originated by selective breeding, most of it during the last few centuries, from common ancestral stock. The great variations in other domesticated animals—horse, cow, and chicken—and the diversity of cultivated plants underscore the ability of organisms to change type. A theory of evolution is accepted almost unanimously by all who have examined the evidence bearing on it, even though the exact mechanisms whereby evolution occurs in nature are not fully understood.

The central themes in the current explanation of evolution (modified considerably from Darwin's original proposal) include the following:

(1) All organisms tend to produce more offspring than can survive within limitations set by amounts of food and space available.

(2) Because of this overpopulation, a competition for the means of existence occurs, in which some organisms perish without reproducing themselves, or reproduce in inferior numbers.

(3) Although offspring tend to inherit the characteristics of their parents, they vary in many minor ways. No two individuals are exactly alike. From time to time, notable changes show up in offspring, produced apparently in the reproductive cells by a a process of *gene mutation.*

(4) Changes caused by gene mutations are transmitted to the next generation of offspring.

(5) Some of the changes produced by gene mutations are advantageous in a given environment, whereas some handicap the offspring. If the variation results in organisms which are better adapted to their environment, they will tend to live longer and produce more offspring than their less fortunate relatives. The interaction of these factors eventually produces changed individuals that are remarkably fitted for survival under the conditions in which they exist.

(6) If the environment changes, or if the organisms move to a different environment, they may not survive under the new conditions unless their mutations produce a new and better-adapted type from the original stock. Environments have changed many times in geologic history and animals and plants have evolved into many diverse forms, as one or another mutated form was favored.

Note that according to current ideas of evolution, the individual does not pass on the qualities he has acquired to his offspring, but only those he has inherited. The modern giraffe has a long neck, but not because its ancestors stretched for foliage high in the air in times of food shortage. A child may develop powerful muscles, but not because his father exercised diligently and passed powerful muscles on to his children. What is thought to have happened is more nearly this: sudden change in germinal material (gene mutation) created a few antelope that varied from their parents by having unusually long necks. These antelope-giraffes were better able to survive periods of food shortage than their relatives with short necks. The long-necked antelope-giraffes produced offspring who inherited the long necks of the parents because gene mutations are transmittable to future generations; and among these, those with the very longest necks thrived best. Thus antelope-giraffes with short necks became scarce, whereas long-necked antelope-giraffes increased in number. The food shortage did not cause the gene mutations which produced long necks, but it did act as a selective factor that eliminated giraffes without long necks (natural selection). Perhaps gene mutations producing long necks had occurred in the antelope-giraffe species a number of times in the past when food was abundant. As there would be no advantage for long necks at such times, a breed of long-necked giraffes could not become established.

An impressive body of data supports this concept of evolution. "Ontogeny recapitulates phylogeny" is an erudite phrase asserting that the life history of the individual (ontogeny) tends to go quickly through the stages (recapitulate) of the evolutionary history of the race (phylogeny). Often this recapitulation is incomplete and imperfect. As an illustration, the tadpole stage of the frog seems to imply descent from a fishlike ancestor. Vestigial structures, such as the vermiform appendix and ear muscles in man, seem to indicate their derivation from an ancestor who found them useful. Dozens of such vestigial structures have been recognized in the human body. Blood tests, taxonomy, and the geographic distribution of animals and plants furnish additional evidence supporting the concept of evolution.

But perhaps the most convincing data attesting to the evolutionary changes that have occurred in the millions of years since life appeared on Earth are offered in fossil sequences found in rock layers. The horse sequence furnishes a classic example (Fig. 25-12). The rhinoceros, elephant, and camel are other animals which developed from small unspecialized ancestors that have left their record in the rocks.

GEOLOGIC CHRONOLOGY

The Earth's long record of physical and biological changes would be hard to survey if we could not subdivide it into convenient units. The whole range of geologic history can be divided into four major units called eras: Precambrian, Paleozoic, Mesozoic, and Cenozoic. In turn, each era is composed of a number of smaller units known as

Table 33-1   GEOLOGIC CHRONOLOGY

Era	Period or Epoch	Characteristic Life	Physical Events (North America)
CENOZOIC ERA The Age of Mammals— subdivided into 6 epochs Probably began 63 ± 2 million years ago	Pleistocene Pliocene Miocene Oligocene Eocene Paleocene	Man appears. Some mammals become extinct after culmination. Animals and plants essentially modern. Mammals widespread and abundant. Some ancient mammals become extinct; first anthropoids appear. Mammals become dominant; all modern groups represented. Mammals first become varied.	Ice Age. Cascade and Coast Ranges uplift and erosion. Sediments deposited in interior.
MESOZOIC ERA The Age of Reptiles— subdivided into 3 periods Probably began 230 ± 10 million years ago	Cretaceous Jurassic Triassic	Extinction of dinosaurs, many forms of reptiles, and other organisms after culmination of many forms; modern flowering plants appear. Dinosaurs abundant; first birds; reptiles dominate life in sea. First dinosaurs and mammals; amphibians culminate.	——Rocky Mountains—— (Laramide orogeny). Sierra Nevada; Rocky Mountain geosyncline formed. Palisades disturbance.
PALEOZOIC ERA The Age of Invertebrates—subdivided into 7 periods Probably began 600 ± 50 million years ago	Permian Pennsylvanian Mississippian Devonian Silurian Ordovician Cambrian	Extinction of some groups; finback reptiles appear. First reptiles; amphibians varied; first insects. Amphibians become more abundant; vegetation becomes luxurious. Age of Fish; lungfish; first amphibians; first forests. First vertebrates (fish). First abundant fossils. Nearly all the invertebrates are represented. Trilobites and brachiopods dominate.	Appalachian orogeny (exact date uncertain). Coal-forming swamps widespread. Widespread shallow seas on continent; limestone forms. Acadian orogeny. Taconian orogeny. Appalachian and Cordilleran geosynclines in existence.
PRECAMBRIAN Subdivisions not clear: sometimes subdivided into Archeozoic and Proterozoic eras; oldest rocks dated so far appear to be about 3 to 4 billion years old		Record of life very scanty; algae (primitive plants) in existence. Limestones and graphite deposits may have had organic source.	Glaciation. Sequences of sedimentation, igneous activity, deformation, and erosion repeated several times.

periods. We can think of the eras as four volumes of a multivolume book. The periods are like the several chapters which make up a single volume. Volumes and chapters vary greatly in length, and the number of chapters in a volume is far from uniform (Table 33-1).

Pronounced changes in both the physical and fossil records separate the eras of geologic time. The influence of the prevalent forms of life in this subdivision is shown by the names of the eras: Paleozoic means "ancient life," Mesozoic "medieval life," and Cenozoic "recent life." The Precambrian era includes all Earth history which precedes the oldest period (Cambrian) of the Paleozoic era. Precambrian is sometimes divided by geologists into two or more eras (Archeozoic and Proterozoic) and eventually may be divided into several of them. It encompasses an estimated five-sixths or more of all geologic time.

A number of geologists believe that natural physical breaks (unconformities) separate the eras and that these may be recognizable throughout the world. Smaller breaks are thought to separate the periods. Times of great mountain building (orogenies) have occurred at irregularly spaced intervals in the past. At such intervals, crustal movements deform rocks, elevate lands, and restrict seas, perhaps in part by deepening the ocean basins. Erosion thus predominates everywhere on the lands; no permanent records are formed which are later accessible to man, and older records are destroyed. Climatic changes caused by such mountain building may speed up evolutionary development somewhat because organisms must adapt themselves successfully to changed environments or perish. Restricted seas crowd shallow-water marine animals into smaller areas where many perish. If erosion finally succeeds in wearing down the continents or if subsidence takes place, seas again may encroach upon the lands. Sediments deposited in such shallow seas may be preserved as permanent records. These sediments rest unconformably upon the underlying rocks and contain distinctly different types of fossils from those in the older rocks beneath. Thus great biological changes tend to correspond to great physical changes on the Earth. Whether such changes have recognizable world-wide effects is disputed. Numerous minor unconformities, which have affected different areas at different times, make it difficult to find unconformities that match throughout the world— if such exist. At any rate, geographic locations (chiefly in western Europe and Great Britain) where geologists first carried out their studies, and the rocks of certain breaks and periods, have had a great influence on geologic chronology. If rocks had been studied first in other areas (e.g., China or Africa) a quite different chronology would probably have been proposed.

EVOLUTIONARY DEVELOPMENT
OF THE VERTEBRATES

Beginning of the Fossil Record   In most areas Cambrian strata are separated by an unconformity from underlying older rocks. Fossils are practically lacking in Precambrian rocks beneath the unconformity, even in unmetamorphosed sedimentary layers. Although direct fossil evidence in the Precambrian is extremely scanty, the record does include deposits formed by simple single-celled plants of a type which still live today (calcareous algae), a few reported sponge spicules, and some wormlike trails. Indirect evidence of the existence of life in the Precambrian is furnished by huge volumes of calcareous materials in ancient limestones and marbles, of carbon in graphite deposits, and of enormous Precambrian sedimentary iron ore deposits. Such deposits may owe their origin to the accumulation of organic materials or to the functions of living organisms which cause their precipitation.

Paleozoic Forms   Many of the Cambrian strata above this major unconformity are abundantly fossiliferous. Furthermore, the creatures who left fossils possessed highly organized systems; they were not simple forms. Nearly every phylum except that of the vertebrates had representatives living at the beginning of the Paleozoic era. In fact, if, as one theory holds, life has evolved from a one-cell initial stage to present-day complex organisms, more than half of the evolutionary development is estimated to have taken place before Cambrian time.

Animals with hard parts predominate among fossils collected from Cambrian rocks. Trilobites are the most abundant forms, and brachiopods are numerous (Figs. 33-6, 33-7 and 33-8). Thus, the fossil record suggests that trilobites, brachiopods, and other creatures with hard parts constituted about the only forms of life in existence at that time.

But now an exciting fossil discovery in Cambrian rocks in British Columbia indicates that soft-bodied forms were also abundant. About 130 species of animals have been described from this location. Sponges, jellyfish, worms, and shrimplike animals are preserved as thin films of carbon along bedding surfaces.

Fig. 33-6.

Restoration of Middle Silurian sea bottom in the Niagara region. The model shows typical forms of crinoids, straight-shelled cephalopods, trilobites, brachiopods, and cystoids. (Prepared by George and Paul Marchand under the direction of Irving G. Reimann. Courtesy, Buffalo Museum of Science)

Rarely indeed are such soft-bodied creatures fossilized. How did it happen in the British Columbia site? Perhaps the rocks were once fine black muds containing much organic matter which collected in a quiet depression on the sea bottom in that area about 500 million years ago. As poisonous sulfide gases produced in the mud bubbled to the surface, they killed swimming organisms which sank and were buried. Scavengers avoided this part of the sea floor because of the poisonous gases and lack of oxygen. The organisms were preserved because waves and currents were not effective in the depression. This fossil discovery, one of the most important ever made, suggests the countless numbers of soft-bodied forms which once populated Cambrian seas.

The fossil discovery described above may explain the great difference between the fossil content of Cambrian and Precambrian rocks.

The advanced stage of development attained by Cambrian forms implies complex ancestors and a long period of evolution in the Precambrian. But no record of such forms has been found. Why? One hypothesis suggests that such ancestors did exist but had no hard parts and were not preserved as fossils. The unconformity between Cambrian and Precambrian rocks represents a long interval in most areas —for which no record has been found—perhaps a million years or more. During this gap in the geologic record, animals may have developed external shells and hard parts which could later be preserved as fossils. However, Cambrian sedimentary rocks do seem to pass conformably downward into Precambrian strata in some areas, and the absence of Precambrian fossils in them is mysterious.

Geologists can only guess at the appearance of early Paleozoic lands. Fossil trees have not been found in rocks older than the Devonian. However, it seems likely that plants more complex than algae were present during the first part of the Paleozoic era and perhaps in the Precambrian, because animals are directly or indirectly dependent upon the plant kingdom for food. Devonian plants were complex forms which imply a long previous period of evolution. Early Paleozoic plants may have been restricted to the water. Vegetation flourished during the latter part of the Paleozoic era (Fig. 33-9).

Primitive types of fishes, found as scattered bony plates and scales

Fig. 33-7.

Restoration of life on a shallow sea floor in the Devonian. A sharklike fish is swimming toward a large coiled cephalopod that is moving about among several different kinds of sponges growing on the bottom. (Prepared by George and Paul Marchand under the direction of Irving G. Reimann. Courtesy, Buffalo Museum of Science)

in Ordovician rocks, constitute the first vertebrate fossil remains known. A real "missing link" in the evolutionary sequence is awaited between the invertebrates and vertebrates. According to theory vertebrates probably evolved from the simpler invertebrates, but the evidence has not been found as yet, and no agreement exists among the experts concerning the most likely invertebrate ancestor.

Trilobites. (Courtesy, Smithsonian Institution)

Fig. 33-8.

However, many succeeding steps in the evolutionary history of the vertebrates seem to be shown clearly by fossils found in Paleozoic and younger rocks. The order of increasing complexity among the five classes of vertebrates follows: fish (simplest), amphibians, reptiles, and birds and mammals (most complex). This sequence parallels their first appearances in the geologic record: the oldest fossil fish are found in rocks which formed in the Ordovician period; amphibians

Fig. 33-9.

A Late Paleozoic (Pennsylvanian) landscape showing characteristic animals and plants. Fin-backed reptiles and the giant dragonfly among scale trees. (Courtesy, Peabody Museum, Yale University)

first became part of the fossil record in the Devonian; reptiles have not been encountered in rocks that formed before the Pennsylvanian period; and mammals and birds are not found in Paleozoic rocks— they appeared in the Mesozoic era, although they were not prominent in the life of that time. Future fossil discoveries may, of course, produce older representatives of each class, although this appears unlikely in some instances. These parallel sequences—the order of first appearance and of increasing complexity—suggest convincingly that evolutionary development has taken place. The first appearance of a member of one of the vertebrate classes is followed up by a fossil record showing that a few unspecialized ancestral forms spread out widely, were adapted to different environments, and developed numerous new types. Each group of animals has tended to spread, diverge, and specialize until it attained a maximum development. This culmination has been followed by a decline and the eventual extinction of many forms. Study of the record suggests that conservative, unspecialized forms persist longest on the Earth in each of the phyla and that highly specialized forms become extinct rather rapidly. So far as is known, evolutionary development is not reversible, and evolution has been succinctly termed a one-way road. But the road winds and detours; and it has many dead-end branches.

Fish Fossil fish are uncommon in rocks formed before the Devonian period, which is sometimes called the Age of Fish because of this initial abundance. Fish become more plentiful as fossils in succeeding

756

periods, though true bony fish have not been encountered in rocks that formed before the Permian.

Among the diverse kinds of fish existing in the Devonian was one group, the lungfish, which had special evolutionary significance. Although lungfish are rare today, once they were more numerous and varied. Two general types of lungfish lived at that time; they can be called the weak-finned and stout-finned groups. A few members of the weak-finned group (*Dipnoi*) still live today in areas that annually undergo long dry spells. Apparently the type has experienced relatively little change in the 300–350 million years which may have elapsed since the Devonian. These lungfish, which have been found in Africa, Australia, and South America, have a swimming bladder opening into the throat so that it can be used as a crude lung. Such lungfish have been known to live out of water for more than a year.

Until recently, the stout-finned group of lungfish (lobe-finned crossopterygians) was believed to have become extinct during the Mesozoic era. However, several living members of the coelacanths, a branch of the crossopterygians, have been found in the past few years. These fish are being studied carefully, because they may be able to supply much information about the soft parts and organs of their ancestors which did not fossilize readily. The fins, a distinguishing feature of this group, have fleshy middle sections with supporting bone structures that resemble very primitive limbs. Results of autopsies, however, have been reported recently. They indicate that the fins of the coelacanths are not closely allied to the limbs of amphibians and that the coelacanths were not the direct ancestors of the amphibians. Coelacanths apparently should be regarded as "the fish that time forgot"; they have undergone remarkably little change since the Devonian.

Amphibians   Short-legged, sprawling amphibians apparently evolved from the stout-finned lungfish during the Devonian period. Convincing evidence supports this evolutionary step. A comparison of the skeletal structures and teeth of the first amphibians with corresponding features possessed by the stout-finned lungfish shows too much similarity for mere coincidence. The evolutionary development of swimming bladder into lung appears to be an adaptation to recurrent conditions of dryness. As the amount of water diminished in an area during its annual dry spell, continuous water bodies may have been reduced to isolated pools of stagnant water. Many fish would die under these circumstances. According to the modern theory, however, if gene mutations had previously produced a few fish with stronger fins and more efficient air-breathing apparatus, such fish might be able to flop from a waterless depression to a nearby pool of water. The mating of such survivors would produce offspring with the characteristics of their parents. Perhaps the amphibians evolved from the stout-finned lungfish in such a manner, with occasional detours into unproductive forms.

Fossils found in younger Paleozoic rocks (Fig. 33-9) show that the amphibians became more diverse as they gradually migrated into other areas and became adapted to different environments. As a class, the amphibians culminated late in the Paleozoic era and then declined.

Descent from fishlike ancestors is likewise strongly suggested by the life cycle of living amphibians. Members of this class of vertebrates still return to the water to lay their eggs. These hatch into youthful, appendageless, fishlike forms which breathe by means of gills. Later in life, limbs grow and lungs develop.

The question has been asked: Why do simple forms of life still exist today if the evolutionary trend has been in general from the simple to the complex? For example, why have not all fish evolved into amphibians? This question seems to ask, "Why are there any fish left?" and the answer is not far to seek. So long as the waters of the Earth furnish abundant means of fish life, there will be abundant forms of fish life there. Fish no doubt continue to develop forms even better adapted to life in this and that environment in the water. But why does not a new form of amphibian crawl onto the land and start a new race of land-living forms? There is nothing in the theory of gene mutations to deny this possibility, and yet the opportunity will never again be what it was for the first lung fish that flopped out upon a

Fig. 33-10.

A Mesozoic (Jurassic) landscape showing characteristic animals and plants. The neck of Brontosaurus arches over Stegosaurus with his ridge of plates, while Allosaurus grazes. (From a painting by Rudolph Zallinger. Courtesy, Peabody Museum, Yale University)

land where no other vertebrate had its range. Today so ill-adapted a land creature would hardly be in the competition. The first creature to produce the needed mutations for land forms gave its descendants a head start that is not easily overcome. Fish today lack both the opportunity and the necessary organic structures, such as primitive lungs and stout fins, to initiate such an evolutionary change.

Reptiles   The oldest fossil reptiles have been found in sedimentary rocks which formed during the Pennsylvanian period. Evidence indicating that the stem reptiles (cotylosaurs) evolved from a type of amphibian (labyrinthodonts) is clear and convincing. Many similarities in skeletal structures have been observed in the fossil representatives which have been found of each group in Pennsylvanian rocks. Transitional forms have been discovered which fit so nicely between reptiles and amphibians that some paleontologists classify them as reptiles, but others classify them as amphibians. From the stem reptiles came the turtles, certain huge marine reptiles, the flying reptiles, mammal-like reptiles (therapsids), the fin-backs, the ancestral stock of the dinosaurs and birds (thecodonts), and other forms. The fin-backs (Fig. 33-9) were unique in their possession of spines that projected upward from the vertebral column and attained a maximum length of about 3 feet. Membranous material probably connected the spines in life, but their function is uncertain. The group became extinct in the Permian at a time when it had no known enemies. Apparently the fin-backs furnish an example of overspecialization which led to rapid extinction.

Fossils taken from Mesozoic rocks, the Age of Reptiles (Fig. 33-11), make spectacular exhibits in museums. Reptiles were present during

Fig. 33-11.

A Late Mesozoic landscape in Wyoming. We see rhinoceros-like Triceratops, the terrible Tyrannosaurus, a flying reptile, and spike-armored and duck-billed dinosaurs. (Courtesy, Peabody Museum, Yale University)

the latter part of the Paleozoic era and exist today, but they culminated in numbers, varieties, and evolutionary development during the Mesozoic era, when they dominated land, sea, and air. The dinosaurs (Greek: "terrible lizards") were confined to the lands and varied in bulk from the size of a rooster to ponderous giants that approached a length of 85 feet and a weight of 50 tons.

The greatest meat-eater of all times undoubtedly was *Tyrannosaurus rex*, who lived near the end of the era. This creature had two powerful hind legs armed with claws 6 to 8 inches long, a powerful tail, short neck, two tiny forelegs, and a skull which measured 4 feet in length and 3 feet in width. It was armed with jaws that contained recurved teeth as long as 6 inches. This carnivorous monster may have reached a length of 50 feet, walked with his head about 20 feet above the ground, and weighed as much as 10 tons. However, he lived in the latter part of the Mesozoic era and was quite different from the first carnivorous dinosaurs that appeared early in the Mesozoic. They had fairly long necks in proportion to their small sizes and forefeet which were more nearly equal in size to the hindlegs. A dinosaur (*Allosaurus*) that lived during the middle part of the era showed an evolutionary development between the first primitive flesh-eating dinosaurs and the highly specialized *Tyrannosaurus*.

Certain plant-eating dinosaurs, such as *Brontosaurus*, carried a huge body on four elephantlike legs; they had long tails, very long necks, and small heads. If these animals had walked head to tail as in a circus parade, 60 to 70 of them would have spanned a mile. Imagine four of these incredible creatures lined up in this manner on a football field. The tail of the first would project beyond one goal post, and the head of the fourth would extend beyond the other! Probably such heavy creatures lived in swampy areas to take advantage of the buoyant effect of the water in moving about. The combination of such a hulk with the tiny head seems grotesque, indeed ridiculous. Keeping the huge stomach filled was probably difficult even if the animal ate almost continuously and possessed a slow body metabolism. Fortunately, the tiny head with its 2-ounce brain would hardly have the means to worry.

Brachiosaurus was the real giant. Perhaps he attained a length of 80 feet, much of it neck. This animal probably could have peered over the top of a three-story building. Stop a moment, look out of your window, and imagine the size of a dinosaur that could perform this feat! The nostrils of *Brachiosaurus* were located on a sort of bump on the top of the head; evidently the animal, including the head, could remain submerged in water and could breathe as long as the top of his bump projected above water.

Other types of dinosaurs lived during the Mesozoic era: the duck-billed, plated, armored, and horned varieties (Fig. 33-11). The seas were dominated by several huge reptiles (Fig. 33-12) and the air by

Fig. 33-12A.

Mesozoic life. Carnivorous marine reptiles (Mosasaur). This type may have attained a length of 75 feet. (From painting by C. R. Knight. Copyright American Museum of Natural History)

others. One of the batlike flying reptiles had wings that measured 26 feet from tip to tip. Its lightweight body was about the size of a goose. Apparently the creature was particularly well adapted for soaring long distances over water because most of its fossilized remains have been found in marine sediments which seem to have been deposited far from land.

At the end of the Mesozoic era, the dinosaurs, flying reptiles, some of the large marine reptiles, the toothed birds, and other forms of life became extinct. This interval in geologic history has been picturesquely called by Walther "the time of the great dying when the hosts

Fig. 33-12B.

Mesozoic life. Flying reptiles. (From a painting by C. Astori. Courtesy, American Museum of Natural History)

Fig. 33-13.

The first known birds, two small dinosaurs, and a number of flying reptiles (ptero-saurs). The trees are cycads. Mesozoic (Jurassic). (From a painting by C. R. Knight. Copyright, Chicago Natural History Museum)

were tried in the balance and found wanting." Many of the forms which became extinct, like *Tyrannosaurus rex*, appeared to be at their zenith point of development: they were not decadent creatures ready for extinction. Several hypotheses attempt to explain these mysterious disappearances, but none is very satisfactory. Some disease may have caused the "great dying," or perhaps a climatic change took place to which these forms could not become adapted. It has been suggested that high temperatures produced sterility in the huge reptiles. According to another hypothesis, mammals may have developed a fondness for dinosaur eggs and reduced the reptile population by consuming the eggs they left in unguarded nests.

Birds The oldest bird fossils have been found in Jurassic rocks and constitute a convincing link between later birds and their reptilian ancestors. Fossils show that this first bird (*Archaeopteryx*, Fig. 33-13)

763

(A)

(B)

Fig. 33-14.

Two Cenozoic mammals: A. A Woolly mammoth. Common inhabitants of Eurasia and North America near the close of the Pleistocene. (Chicago Natural History Museum)—B. Restoration of Baluchitherium. This hornless rhinoceros lived in central Asia during the middle part of the Cenozoic era. (American Museum of Natural History)

was about the size of a crow, had feathers, and could fly. But *Archaeopteryx* had three features retained from its reptilian predecessors: (1) jaws set with true teeth, (2) three claws on each wing, and (3) a long tail on which the feathers were arranged pinnately instead of in a fan shape as in modern birds.

Evidently the toothed birds and the flying reptiles each evolved from the ancestral stock of the dinosaurs. However, the toothed birds apparently did not evolve directly from the flying reptiles. More modern ancestors of present-day birds had evolved from the toothed birds before their extinction late in the Mesozoic era. Fossils of birds are relatively rare.

Mammals   Although the first mammals apparently had evolved from reptiles (therapsids) before the middle of the Mesozoic, they remained inconspicuous throughout the remainder of the era. Mammals assumed their present dominant role in the biological world during the Cenozoic era (Age of Mammals). Four major trends occurred in the mammalian evolution of the Cenozoic—an increase in size and brain power, and a specialization of feet and teeth. The horse series set forth in Fig. 25-12 is a classic illustration of these specializations.

Some mammals became efficient carnivores, like the lion, tiger, and wolf; others took to the oceans, like the whale and the porpoise; still others developed the ability to run rapidly like the horse and the antelope. Some forms became extremely specialized and then extinct. The ability of a group of animals to adapt and evolve seems greatest early in its history.

During the Cenozoic era, North America was the home of many animals (Figs. 33-2 and 33-14) which are no longer associated with it. The woolly mammoth, the mastodon, and the rhinoceros have vanished from the continent, as have the hippopotamus, camel, giant pig, giant ground sloth, giant bison, and saber-toothed tiger.

MAN

Man is classified as a primate (Latin: "first"), a group of mammals considered to be of foremost importance in the animal kingdom by the biologist (Linnaeus) who named them. It includes the gorilla, chimpanzee, and monkey. Data supporting this classification are fur-

nished by studies of man's skeletal structures, muscles, organs, embryo-
logical development, vestigial organs, and blood tests—and the fossil
record. Among the primates, man seems most closely akin to the gorilla
and chimpanzee. An outstanding primate characteristic is a large, well-
developed brain. The average cranial capacity of man (1350 cc—
normal variation 1050 to 1800 cc) is about 2½ times that of an adult
gorilla (550 cc—normal variation 300 to 650 cc). A comparison of the
skull of a man with that of a gorilla (Fig. 33-15) shows similarities—

Fig. 33-15.

*Skulls of man and gorilla cut longitudinally to show comparative size of the
brain case. The gorilla skull shows a prominent eyebrow ridge above the orbit,
the sagittal crest on the top, a low facial angle, and no chin. (Courtesy, Peabody
Museum, Yale University)*

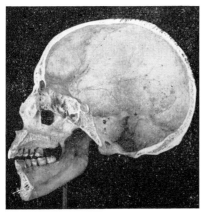 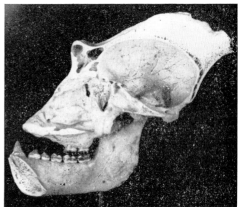

and the following relatively minor differences: the thicker skull of the
gorilla exhibits a protruding mouth with projecting canine teeth, no
chin, a prominent eyebrow ridge, low sloping forehead, and a saggital
crest.

Primate fossils, particularly those of man, are not common, and the
paleontological record of the entire group is fragmentary. Primates
tend to inhabit forested areas in which quick burial following death
occurs infrequently, and fossilization is rare. Early man's intelligence
was his chief advantage over the animals with whom he had to com-
pete. In speed, strength, and ability to withstand cold or heat, he was
inferior to many of his contemporaries. When man began to bury his
dead and dwell in caves, fossilization occurred more frequently.

Fossil evidence of the primates is confined to the Cenozoic era, and that of man to the Pleistocene. Man's culture has been subdivided into three main phases: the Stone Age, the Bronze Age, and the Iron Age. At first, stones were used as tools and weapons by man as he found them (eoliths); next they were shaped by chipping alone (paleoliths); and finally they were ground and polished as well as chipped (neoliths). Next, man used implements made of metal. The three cultures were not attained simultaneously throughout the world. For example, the culture of certain primitive tribes today is still that of the Stone Age.

Early man evidently did not consider sanitation a problem. Refuse collected in great amounts around favored camp sites such as caves which were used in succession by different tribes. For example, about 70 feet of crudely layered refuse accumulated at a cave in Palestine. It represents a number of cultures belonging to the Stone and Bronze ages and is one of the most complete records yet found. Apparently the dumping areas of early man were always located within easy tossing range of his dwelling. The smells which permeated such camp sites must have been robust indeed!

Four types of early man discussed below suffice to illustrate the fossil record; dozens of additional discoveries are omitted. The peoples represented by such finds have commonly been named for the localities in which they were found. Many of the discoveries are very fragmentary. Part of a jaw and a limb bone, a few teeth, or bits of a shattered skull furnish the only evidence now available for the former existence of many of these types. Reconstructions and interpretations made on such limited data should be flexible enough to allow for future evidence. Many of the discoveries have been classified as different genera and species and have been given different names. This may have complicated the evolutionary picture unnecessarily and obscured relationships. Perhaps a much wider range of variation should be expected within a genus or species.

Pithecanthropus Erectus (Java Ape-Man) A widely publicized discovery of a human fossil was made in Java in 1891. It consisted of part of a skull and several bones belonging to a primitive type of man subsequently named *Pithecanthropus erectus* (Greek: "ape-man"). Several additional finds of skull caps and other bones suggest that this creature was a primitive human type with characteristics of both man and ape (Fig. 33-16). Although the brain cases outlined by these skulls are smaller than those of modern man, they are nearly double the cranial capacity of a great ape. The receding chin and forehead, the heavy brow ridges, and the protruding mouth are apelike. How-

Fig. 33-16.

Skulls of Pithecanthropus *(left),* Neanderthal *(middle), and Cro-Magnon (right). (Courtesy, American Museum of Natural History)*

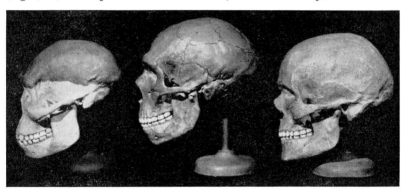

ever, the large brain, teeth, and erect posture (shown by the shape of the leg bones) indicate that the creature was a primitive human type. Associated mammalian fossils indicate a mid-Pleistocene age for this discovery.

Near Peking, China, fossil fragments have been found of a few dozen individuals of a type similar to the Java ape-man. The remains are chiefly skulls and jaws, and each skull has been fractured in a manner which suggests cannibalism. Apparently fire was used by this type of man; numerous flint tools were found associated with the fossil remains. Later discoveries in other areas suggest that several pithe-canthropoid types lived at various times during the Pleistocene, some before *Pithecanthropus erectus,* others later. The older pithecanthropoids may have been larger than present-day man.

Neanderthal Man   This prehistoric type of man lived during the latter part of the Pleistocene in Europe, western Asia, and along the northern coast of Africa. According to fairly abundant fossil remains, Neanderthal man had a short stocky body, a receding chin and forehead, and heavy brow ridges (Fig. 33-16). The big toe was offset against the others in an apelike manner. The brain was as large as modern man's, but apparently smaller in the parts devoted to thinking. Neanderthal man used fire, buried his dead, was a good hunter, and made stone implements with considerable skill. Apparently Neanderthal man was not the direct ancestor of modern man and became extinct.

Cro-Magnon Man   At some time during the last glacial age, a modern type of man came to southern Europe. Many skeletons show that these individuals were tall and straight, with high foreheads, prominent chins, and modern-size brain cases (Fig. 33-16). The Cro-Magnons appear to be the direct ancestors of the present southern Europeans; therefore, they probably did not become extinct as a number of earlier types seem to have done. The Cro-Magnons used fire, were good hunters, buried their dead, made excellent stone implements, and possessed clothing and ornaments. In combination with the numerous multicolored paintings found on the walls of caves, these show a well-developed art and culture. Evidence that the Cro-Magnons were good hunters is supplied by the report that the bones of about 100,000 horses have been found in piles around one camp site in France.

Australopithecus ("Southern Ape")   The first specimen of this group was discovered in South Africa in 1924, and a rather large number of similar fossils have since been found. The dating and classification of *Australopithecus* have been controversial. Apparently a typical representative of *Australopithecus* was short, probably not over five feet tall, with a very small brain (cranial capacity seems to have ranged from 450 to 700 cc) and large teeth and jaws. However, he walked in an erect manner and had features of dentition, skull, and pelvis which apparently allied him more closely to man than to apes. The oldest fossils of *Australopithecus* seem to antedate those of *Pithecanthropus*. Therefore, it has been proposed that *Australopithecus* or a similar type was the ancestor of *Pithecanthropus*, who in turn was the ancestor of more modern types of man, who in their turn were the ancestors of the Cro-Magnons and modern man. *Australopithecus* subsequently became extinct, but some types persisted longer than others.

Early Man in North America   The history of early man in the Americas is still quite uncertain but seems to involve only the last part of the Pleistocene epoch. Apparently he came from the Old World (via

Siberia?) before the extinction of certain types of elephant, camel, horse, and bison, because his stone implements and some human bones are associated with them. Carbon-14 data indicate that man arrived in North America some 20,000 to 30,000 years ago or earlier.

Tentative Conclusions on the Origin of Man   The fossil record and other evidence indicate that man evolved from the primate group of mammals, although many details are lacking. Mammals in turn seem to have reached their present state via a progression that leads backward in time through the reptiles, amphibians, and fish to the invertebrates. Apparently man and the great apes had a common ancestor during the latter part of the Cenozoic era from which each subsequently diverged. This much is generally accepted today. However, controversy and uncertainty beset many aspects of man's development.

Until recently it was rather generally assumed that man had evolved from this common ancestor in an undeviating progressive development from primitive to modern types. Likewise, the most primitive types (i.e., unlike modern types) of fossil men were thought to have been the oldest and most brutal ones. These ideas led to a search for a series of "missing links" which, when found, would determine the places of all fossil men in this progression. Recent evidence throws doubt on the validity of these assumptions. For example, certain modern types of fossil men are now known to have lived long before other types of a more primitive nature. Since the soft parts have not been fossilized, the appearance of fossil types is largely guesswork.

The common ancestor believed to link the great apes and man has been commonly pictured as much more apelike than manlike. Perhaps this is not correct. Certain primitive fossil men such as the Neanderthals may represent specializations away from a more modern ancestral stock.

Fossils of man illustrate an important principle in evolutionary development. Evolutionary changes apparently do not take place little by little with each part of an organism changing at the same rate. In other words, a transitional stage midway between an ancestral species and a descendant species would not be midway in the development of all of its features. More probably, there would be a number of midway organisms with various combinations of more advanced and more primitive features. For example, in man the limbs apparently reached their present stage of evolutionary development before the brain, skull, and teeth.

Unfortunately, many details concerning man's evolutionary history are still shrouded in the mists of antiquity and the fogs of too few fossil remains. His (and her) present position of dominance in the biologic world on the Earth comes only at the end of a long succession of changes. Apparently man has succeeded to a position formerly held in turn by other mammals, reptiles, amphibians, fish, and invertebrates during an immensity of time that is nearly beyond comprehension.

EXERCISES AND QUESTIONS FOR CHAPTER 33

1. Describe an efficient method of obtaining undamaged silicified fossils from a limestone.

2. Describe some of the ways in which fossils form.

3. Describe several different types of fossils which would give useful information about the environment in which they lived.

4. Describe some of the key ideas involved in evolution.

5. What criteria have geologists used in subdividing the geologic record into eras and periods?

6. What implication does the fossil record of the Cambrian have for the Precambrian?

7. Describe important evolutionary steps in the origin of the vertebrates.

8. Which came first the chicken or the egg? Is the following statement probably correct: The first bird hatched from an egg laid by a reptile?

9. If evolutionary development has generally proceeded from the simple to the complex, why are there any simple forms left?

10. Why are certain organisms today called "living fossils"?

SELECTED LABORATORY AND DEMONSTRATION EXPERIMENTS

EXPERIMENT 1 (CHAPTER 1)

Estimation of Numerical Quantities*

Materials: Steel ball or wooden block, wooden splint or straight piece of glass tubing.

Apparatus: Meter sticks, graduated cylinders (25 ml, 50 ml, 100 ml), weight sets (standard masses), spring balances, interval timers, closed glass tube containing glycerin and a steel ball, battery jar, large funnel.

A variety of measuring devices such as meter sticks, graduated cylinders, weight sets, etc. are assembled in one room and may be examined and handled by the student only in this room. In an adjoining laboratory the student estimates the lengths, areas, and masses of objects, time intervals, velocities, etc. The student may return as often as he wishes to the room containing the measuring devices but none of these may be brought into the laboratory. The student reports his estimates of the following:

Length of a small object (splint, piece of glass tubing, etc.).
Height of the room.
Area of a desk top.
Volume of a battery jar.
Mass of an object (steel ball, wooden block, etc.).
Time required to empty a large funnel of water.
Rate of fall of ball in the glycerin-filled tube.

EXPERIMENT 2 (CHAPTER 1)

Measurement, Significant Figures

Materials: Steel ball, wooden block, stone, liquid unknowns.

Apparatus: Micrometer caliper, vernier caliper, platform balance, graduated cylinder, burette, pipette, hydrometers.

A. Density of an Irregular Object. Weigh an irregular stone. Determine its volume by immersion in water in a graduated cylinder. Calculate the density, retaining an appropriate number of significant figures in the answer.

---

* The authors are indebted to Dr. Floyd W. Parker for this experiment.

B. Density of a Geometrical Object. 1. Measure the thickness of a rectangular wooden block by means of a vernier caliper. Measure its length and width. Calculate its volume, retaining in the answer an appropriate number of significant figures.

2. Measure the diameter of a steel ball by means of a micrometer caliper. Calculate its volume, retaining an appropriate number of significant figures.

C. Density of an Unknown Liquid. 1. Fill a pipette to the calibration mark with a liquid unknown. Discharge the contents of the pipette into a weighed beaker. From the weight and volume calculate the density of the liquid. Retain an appropriate number of significant figures.

2. Release a measured volume of liquid unknown from a burette into a weighed beaker. Reweigh. Calculate the density of the liquid. Retain an appropriate number of significant figures.

D. Specific Gravity of a Liquid. Float a hydrometer on a liquid unknown which is contained in a graduated cylinder. Note the point at which the liquid surface crosses the specific gravity scale of the hydrometer. Read the specific gravity and record an appropriate number of significant figures.

What is the difference between density and specific gravity?

EXPERIMENT 3 (CHAPTER 2)

Simple Machines

Materials: String.
Apparatus: Inclined plane and car, spring balance, weight set, meter stick, pulleys, wheel and axle, lever (balanced meter stick).

A. The Inclined Plane. Determine the force (spring balance) needed to pull a car (of known weight) uniformly up an inclined plane. Measure the length of the plane and its height. Make similar measurements for different inclinations of the plane. Calculate the mechanical advantage, velocity ratio, and efficiency of the machine.

B. The Pulley. Determine the force (spring balance) required to raise a weight slowly and uniformly by means of a system of pulleys. Measure the distances moved by the effort (spring balance) and resistance (weight). Calculate the mechanical advantage, velocity ratio and efficiency of the system.

C. The Wheel and Axle. Determine the force (spring balance) which must be applied to the wheel in order to lift a weight suspended from the axle (or wheel of smaller diameter). Measure the distances moved by the effort (spring balance) and resistance (weight). Calculate the mechanical advantage, velocity ratio and efficiency.

D. The Lever. Attach weights to a lever and adjust their positions until a state of equilibrium is established. Record the values of weights, their distances from the fulcrum, and the sense (clockwise or counterclockwise) in which they tend to cause rotation. Calculate the various moments of force and show that the sum of the clockwise moments equals that of the counterclockwise moments.

EXPERIMENT 4 (CHAPTER 4)

Local Value of Gravitational Acceleration

Materials: String, pendulum bob.
Apparatus: Stop watch, meter stick.

The time elapsing during one complete (small angle) swing of a pendulum is:

$$T = 2\pi \sqrt{\frac{l}{g}}$$

$T = \text{time (sec)}$

$l = \text{length of pendulum (cm)}$

$g = \text{gravitational acceleration}$

Measure the length of a pendulum. Time ten consecutive swings and calculate the time required for one swing. Repeat the above procedure using at least four more different pendulum lengths.

Make a table of the values obtained above and calculate the square of the time interval in each case, recording as follows:

Length of Pendulum	Time Period (sec)	Square of Time Period

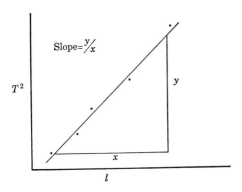

Plot on the y axis of a graph values of the square of the time and on the x axis values of the length of the pendulum. Draw the best straight line through the points thus plotted. Measure the slope of this straight line. Calculate the value of g from the relation

$$g = \frac{4\pi^2}{\text{slope}}$$

Retain in your result an appropriate number of significant figures and label with correct units.

EXPERIMENT 5 (CHAPTER 6)

Boyle's Law

    Materials: Mercury.
    Apparatus: J tube, meter stick, barometer.

Record the value of the barometric pressure. Pour enough mercury into a J tube so that it rises into the vertical portion of the closed tube. Measure the distance (cm) from the table top to the top of the meniscus of the mercury column (1) in the closed tube and (2) in the open tube. To the difference between readings 2 and 1 add the barometric pressure reading (express in cm of mercury). This result is the pressure of the air trapped in the closed tube.

Measure the distance from the table top to the top of the air column in the *closed* tube (3). The difference between 3 and 1 (in cm) is the length of the column of air. If this length were multiplied by the cross-sectional area of the glass tubing the volume of the entrapped air would be obtained.

Pour more mercury into the open tube. Repeat measurements 1 and 2 as above (3 is the same in each case). Record the value of the pressure of the air in the enclosed space and the length of the air column. Repeat the procedure of adding more mercury and making the measurements as described until at least five values of pressure and length of air column are obtained.

Show that Boyle's law $P_1V_1 = P_2V_2$ may be rewritten $P_1H_1 = P_2H_2$ (H_1 and H_2 are the lengths of the column of trapped air) provided the cross-sectional area of the glass tubing is uniform. Why?

Plot corresponding values of P and H on a graph.

Make a table showing that the values obtained by multiplying the pressure of the gas by the length of the enclosed air column are (nearly) constant.

EXPERIMENT 6 (CHAPTERS 6 and 7)

Atomic Weight of an Element (Method of Dulong and Petit)

    Materials: Lead shot, nickel shot.
    Apparatus: Calorimeter, thermometer, boiler, towel, Bunsen burner, test tube, platform balance.

Weigh about 40 gm of metallic unknown (nickel or lead shot) in a test tube, recording the value to the nearest 0.1 gm. Immerse the *test tube* in a boiler (beaker of water) so that all the metal in the test tube is beneath the level of the water in the boiler. Continue to boil the water for at least 15 min. In the meantime weigh a calorimeter cup to the nearest 0.1 gm and pour into it about 75 gm of water. Reweigh. (CAUTION: Keep the calorimeter several feet away from the nearest Bunsen burner.) Place a thermometer in the water and record the temperature to the nearest 0.1° after about 5 minutes.

With the aid of a towel remove from the boiler the test tube containing the metal. Immediately pour the heated metal into the water in the calorimeter. Stir the water and record to the nearest 0.1° the highest temperature reached.

Calculate the specific heat of the metal by means of the equation:

$$M_m \cdot S_m (100 - T_2) = M_{H_2O} \cdot (T_2 - T_1) + M_c \cdot S_c (T_2 - T_1)$$

where the symbols are

Masses: M_m = metal; M_{H_2O} = water; M_c = calorimeter
Specific Heats: S_m = metal; S_c = calorimeter (aluminum = 0.22)
Temperatures: T_2 = final temperature of water, calorimeter and metal; T_1 = initial temperature of water and calorimeter

According to the method of Dulong and Petit, the atomic weights of certain elements may be obtained by dividing 6.4 by the specific heats of the elements:

$$\text{Atomic weight} = \frac{6.4}{\text{specific heat}}$$

Calculate the atomic weight of your metal from the value of its specific heat.

EXPERIMENT 7 (CHAPTER 7)

Chemical Reactions

Materials: Mercuric oxide, splint, mossy zinc, hydrochloric acid, cupric oxide, marble chips, lime water, ammonium chloride, calcium hydroxide, phenolphthalein solution.

Apparatus: Test tubes, gas bottles, Erlenmeyer flask, 2-hole rubber stopper, thistle tube, Pyrex test tube, 1-hole rubber stopper, Florence flask, medicine dropper, glass nozzle, pneumatic trough, candle.

A. Oxygen—A Supporter of Combustion. Put 2 gm of red mercuric oxide in a Pyrex test tube. Heat strongly for several minutes. Thrust a glowing splint into the test tube. Result? What do you observe on the cooler, upper portion of the test tube? Write the equation for the chemical reaction.

B. *Hydrogen—A Combustible Gas.* Place about 10 gm of mossy zinc in an Erlenmeyer flask. Fit the flask with a 2-hole stopper carrying a thistle tube and delivery tube. Pour hydrochloric acid into the Erlenmeyer flask until the liquid covers the end of the thistle tube. (Why?) Write the equation for the reaction which takes place.

Collect two test tubes of the gas by downward displacement of water. Remove one of the test tubes, hold it in a towel, turn it mouth up and light it. Result? Remove the other test tube; hold it mouth down and light it. Result? How do you account for the difference?

Pass the delivery tube from the hydrogen generator into a horizontally inclined test tube containing near its closed end 1 gm of cupric oxide. Heat the cupric oxide. Results? Explain. Write the equation for the chemical reaction. (Caution: Keep the burner away from the mouth of the test tube)

C. *Carbon Dioxide—A Noncombustible Gas.* Place about 10 gm marble chips ($CaCO_3$) in a generator like the one used above in B. Cover the marble chips with dilute hydrochloric acid. Write the equation for the chemical reaction.

Collect a bottle of carbon dioxide by upward displacement of air. Pour the contents of the bottle over a lighted candle. Result? Bubble the gas from the generator through a test tube half-full of lime water ($Ca(OH)_2$). Result? Explain. Bubble your breath through a test tube containing lime-water. Result? Explain.

D. *Ammonia—A Highly Water-Soluble Gas.* Place about 10 gm ammonium chloride and an equal amount of calcium hydroxide (slaked lime) in a Pyrex test tube fitted with a delivery tube. Heat the test tube. Fill a Florence flask with ammonia by downward displacement of air. Write the equation for the reaction.

Insert into the neck of the ammonia-filled Florence flask a rubber stopper with a nozzle and medicine dropper of water. Place the lower end of the nozzle tube near the bottom of a beaker of water containing a few drops of phenolphthalein indicator. Squeeze the bulb of the medicine dropper so as to squirt a few drops of water into the flask of ammonia gas. Result? Explain.

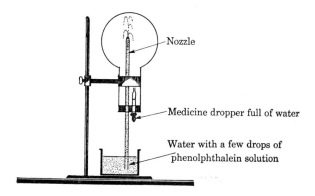

Nozzle

Medicine dropper full of water

Water with a few drops of phenolphthalein solution

EXPERIMENT 8 (CHAPTER 7)

Distillation

Materials: Boiling chips, silver nitrate solution, dilute nitric acid, salt solution (NaCl), ammonium hydroxide, phenolphthalein solution.

Apparatus: Distilling flask, thermometer, Liebig condenser, cork stoppers, cork borer, rubber tubing.

Assemble a distillation apparatus consisting of a distilling flask fitted with a thermometer and a water-jacketed condenser. Pour tap water into the distilling flask until it is about ⅓ full. Add a few boiling chips. Insert the thermometer in the flask. Turn on the cold water so it will circulate through the jacket of the condenser. Heat the water in the distilling flask. Distill at the rate of about a drop per second. Record the boiling temperature of the water. Read the barometric pressure. From a table showing the variation of boiling point of water with changing atmospheric pressure, determine the correct boiling point of water for the observed barometric pressure. What correction, if any, should be applied to temperature readings of your thermometer near the boiling point of water?

Add 2 ml of silver nitrate solution to a few milliliters of dilute salt (sodium chloride) solution. Result? Add several milliliters of nitric acid. Result? This is the test commonly used to identify the presence of a chloride. This test will be used in the next section to determine whether salt may be separated from water by distillation.

Pour salt water into the distilling flask until it is one third full. Heat the solution; distill several milliliters of the liquid. Is the boiling temperature of a salt solution the same as that of water? What effect do dissolved substances (such as NaCl) have on the boiling point of a solvent (such as water)?

Test the distillate for a chloride as described above. Result? Explain.

Add a few drops of colorless phenolphthalein solution to a few milliliters of dilute ammonium hydroxide. Result? Phenolphthalein is an "indicator" which is a red color in the presence of a base and colorless in the presence of an acid. The color of the indicator will be used to determine whether ammonia is separated from water by means of distillation.

Wash out the distilling flask; rinse with a small amount of ammonium hydroxide. Pour ammonium hydroxide into the flask until it is ⅓ full. Heat the flask and distill several milliliters. Add a few drops of phenolphthalein to the distillate. Result? What do you conclude about the effectiveness of distillation in removing from water such impurities as ammonia?

EXPERIMENT 9 (CHAPTER 8)

The Spectrometer (Instructor Demonstration)

Materials: Dilute potassium permanganate solution.

Apparatus: University model prism spectrometer, electric arc lamp, transformer for exciting Geissler tubes (He, N_2), mounted glass prism.

A. Describe the function of each of the parts of a spectrometer.

B. *Continuous Spectra.* Disperse the light from an electric arc by means of a mounted glass prism. Result? Explain.

C. *Line and Band Emission Spectra.* Excite a helium-filled Geissler tube by means of a transformer. Observe in a prism spectrometer the line spectrum when this helium tube is used as a light source. How could helium be identified by these lines? Excite a nitrogen-filled Geissler tube. How does this spectrum differ from that of helium? Why?

D. *Absorption Spectra: 1. The Solar Spectrum—Fraunhofer Lines.* On a bright sunny day, reflect a beam of sunlight into the vertical slit of a spectrometer by means of a mirror. Observe the narrow dark absorption lines or Fraunhofer lines.

2. *Absorption by Solutions.* Place between a light bulb and the spectroscope a dilute potassium permanganate solution. If the concentration is correct, 3 or 4 absorption bands will be observed in the yellow and green region of the spectrum. (If the solution is too concentrated, a large section of the spectrum will be blacked out; if too dilute, no absorption bands will be observed.)

EXPERIMENT 10 (CHAPTER 10)

Electric Currents I: Cells or Batteries

Materials: Metal strips of copper, zinc, lead; dilute sulfuric acid, zinc sulfate solution, copper sulfate solution, ammonium chloride solution, copper wires.

Apparatus: Voltmeter (range 1–6 volts), rectifier, beaker, clay cup.

A. *Cells.* Place a strip of zinc metal and one of copper in a dilute sulfuric acid solution. Attach a wire from each of the metal strips (electrodes) to the terminals of the voltmeter. The metal strips must be kept separated. Why? What is indicated if the needle of the voltmeter moves off scale? How can you tell in advance by consulting an electrochemical series table, which of the metal strips should be attached to the negative terminal of the voltmeter?

Keep the circuit closed several minutes. What happens? Explain.

Place a strip of zinc metal in a zinc sulfate solution in a beaker. Place a strip of copper metal in a copper sulfate solution in a porous clay cup. Put the clay cup into the center of the beaker containing the zinc sulfate solution. Attach wires between the metal strips (electrodes) and the voltmeter. Result? Keep the circuit closed several minutes. Result? Explain.

B. *Series Connection of Cells.* Attach the positive terminal of your battery to the negative of your neighbor's battery. Connect the free ends of the two batteries to the terminals of a voltmeter. How does the reading compare with that from a single cell? Explain.

C. *The Dry Cell.* Place a strip of zinc metal and a carbon rod in a beaker containing ammonium chloride solution. Attach wires from each of the electrodes to the appropriate terminals of a voltmeter. How does the conventional dry cell differ from the above cell?

D. *The Storage Cell.* Place two lead electrodes in a dilute sulfuric acid solution. Attach copper wires from these electrodes to the DC (direct current) terminals of a rectifier. Adjust the voltage until bubbles form on the electrodes. Allow the current to pass for about 5 minutes. Disconnect the wires from the rectifier and attach them to the voltmeter. Result? How does the commercial storage cell differ from the above?

EXPERIMENT 11 (CHAPTER 10)

Electric Currents II: The Dynamo, Thermoelectricity, Photovoltaic Effect

Apparatus: Coil of wire, bar magnet, galvanometer, DC and AC generators, thermo-element, photovoltaic cell, induction coil, rectifier.

A. *Electricity from Magnetism.* Attach the free ends of a coil of copper wire to the terminals of a galvanometer. Move a bar magnet through the center of the coil. Result? Reverse the direction of motion of the bar magnet. Result? How are electric currents produced by means of magnets in the modern dynamo or electric generator?

Examine a DC generator. What structural feature distinguishes this type of generator? Why is the current flow unidirectional?

Examine an AC (alternating current) generator. What structural feature distinguishes it? Why does the direction of the current alternate as the armature rotates?

B. *Thermoelectricity.* Connect a thermo-element (two different metal strips which have been welded together) to a galvanometer by means of copper wires. Heat the metal junction with a Bunsen flame. Result? Explain.

C. *Photovoltaic Effect.* Attach the terminals of a photovoltaic cell to a galvanometer. Cover the face of the cell so as to exclude light. Result? Uncover the cell and move it nearer the window or toward another light source. Result? Explain.

D. *The Induction Coil.* Attach wires to the terminals of the secondary windings of an induction coil. Bend them so the bare ends are separated only a few centimeters. For the input voltage to the induction coil use a rectifier or other DC source of 4-6 volts. Turn on the DC source. Result?

Describe the construction of an induction coil and explain how it operates. What are some of its uses?

EXPERIMENT 12 (CHAPTER 11)

Discharge Tubes: Behavior of Electron Beams
(Instructor Demonstration)

Apparatus: Crookes tubes, induction coil, X-ray tube, oscilloscope tube, TV tube.

A. Luminescence and Straight-Line Propagation. Attach wires from the secondary terminals of an induction coil to the terminals of a Crookes tube, one end of which is coated with a luminescent material. Explain the glow which results when the induction coil is turned on.

Move an object such as a metal cross into the path between the negative electrode (cathode) and luminescent end of the tube. Result? Explain.

B. Magnetic Fields. Attach to an induction coil a Crookes tube used to show magnetic effects. Note the path of the electron beam as outlined on the luminescent plate when the induction coil is turned on. Bring the north pole of a bar magnet above the beam. Result? Reverse the ends of the magnet. Result? How do you account for the magnetic effect of an electron beam?

C. Inertial Properties. Attach to an induction coil a Crookes tube containing a track and paddle wheel. Explain the movement of the paddle wheel when the induction coil is turned on. Reverse the direction of current flow. Result?

D. The X-Ray Tube. Examine an X-ray tube. How does it resemble a Crookes tube and in what respects does it differ?

E. The TV Tube. How may a Crookes tube be modified to serve as a TV tube? an oscilloscope tube?

EXPERIMENT 13 (CHAPTER 12)

Radioactivity

Materials: Radioactive sources such as a radium button, I^{131} (10 microcurie source)* as KI in a water solution.

Apparatus: Electroscope, Wilson cloud chamber, Geiger counter with voltage indicator.

DETECTION OF RADIOACTIVITY

A. Discharge of an Electroscope. Charge an electroscope. Bring a radioactive source near it. Result? Explain.

B. The Geiger Counter. 1. Describe the construction of a Geiger counter tube. What happens when ionizing radiation enters the sensitive portion of the tube?

* May be purchased from Atomic Research Laboratory, 10717 Venice Ave., Los Angeles 34, Calif.

2. With a radioactive source in a fixed position relative to the Geiger tube determine the number of counts per minute at different voltages.* Plot on graph paper the number of counts per minute against voltage. What is the relation of the plateau to the normal operating voltage of the tube?

3. Remove all known radioactive samples from the vicinity of the counter. With the voltage of the Geiger counter set at the proper point on the plateau, record the number of counts received per minute. What is the name given to this count which is observed even when all known radioactive sources have been removed?

4. Using a radioactive source which gives about 500 counts per minute (c/min), take five 1-minute counts. (Position of source must not be changed.) Counting of radioactive disintegrations should be regarded as a statistical phenomenon. Explain.

5. Take readings of the numbers of counts obtained from a radioactive source located at varying distances from the counter. Result?

6. Place a radioactive I^{131} source near enough to a Geiger tube to obtain a count of about 200 c/min with the tube shield open. Close the shield. Result? How do you account for the difference?

THE TRACER TECHNIQUE

By means of a Geiger counter record the number of c/min emitted by a solution containing a few microcuries of I^{131} (carrier added). The sample should be positioned with relation to the counter tube in such a manner that later the test tube may be put in exactly the same place. Add the smallest amount of $AgNO_3$ solution that will completely precipitate all the iodine (iodide) in the I^{131} solution. Centrifuge the solution. Decant the liquid. Wash the precipitate with 1 milliliter H_2O. Recentrifuge. Remove the supernatant liquid with a dropper whose end has been drawn out into a narrow nozzle. Add the washings to the main body of the liquid. Place the test tubes in the same position as the solution when it was counted before precipitation. Test the activity of the liquid (counts per minute) and of the precipitate. Explain the results. Explain what is meant by a tracer.

All manipulations in the above experiment should be carried out on a tray the bottom of which is covered with blotting paper. CAUTION: Avoid spilling any of the radioactive iodine solution.

* The operating voltage will be about 75 volts above the voltage at which the first counts are registered. Beyond the plateau region the count rate may rise sharply. Should this happen, decrease the voltage immediately lest the tube be permanently damaged.

BIBLIOGRAPHY

CHEMISTRY AND PHYSICS

Anthony, H. D., *Science and Its Background*, Macmillan, 1948.
Bell, A. E., *Christian Huygens and the Development of Science in the Seventeenth Century*, Edward Arnold, 1947.
Bendick, Jeanne, *How Much and How Many*, Whittlesey House, 1947.
Boyle, Robert, *The Sceptical Chymist*, Dutton, 1911.
Bragg, Sir William, *Concerning the Nature of Things*, G. Bell, 1932.
————, *Electricity*, Macmillan, 1936.
Brown, G. Burniston, *Science, Its Method and Its Philosophy*, George Allen & Unwin, 1950.
Buckley, H., *A Short History of Physics*, 2d ed., Van Nostrand, 1929.
Cajori, Florian, *A History of Physics*, Macmillan, 1929.
Caldin, E. F., *The Power and Limits of Science*, Chapman and Hall, 1949.
Cohen, I. Bernard, (Ed.), *Benjamin Franklin's Experiments, A New Edition of Franklin's Experiments and Observations on Electricity*, Harvard University Press, 1941.
Cohen, M. R., and I. E. Drabkin, *A Source Book of Greek Science*, McGraw-Hill, 1948.
Conant, James B., *Robert Boyle's Experiments in Pneumatics*, Harvard University Press, 1950.
————, *Science and Common Sense*, Yale University Press, 1951.
————, *The Overthrow of the Phlogiston Theory*, Harvard University Press, 1950.
Cooper, Lane, *Aristotle, Galileo and the Tower of Pisa*, Cornell University Press, 1935.
Crew, Henry, *The Rise of Modern Physics*, Williams & Wilkins, 1935.
Curie, E., *Madame Curie*, Doubleday, 1937.
Dampier, William Cecil, *A History of Science and Its Relations with Philosophy and Religion*, Macmillan, 1936.
Eidinoff, Maxwell L., and H. Ruchlis, *Atomics for the Millions*, McGraw-Hill, 1947.
Farber, Edward, *The Evolution of Chemistry*, Ronald Press, 1952.
Frank, Philip, *Modern Science and Its Philosophy*, Harvard University Press, 1949.
Fraser, Charles G., *Half Hours with Great Scientists (The Story of Physics)*, Reinhold, 1948.
Freeman, Ira, *Modern Introductory Physics*, McGraw-Hill, 1949.

French, Sidney J., *Torch and Crucible*, Princeton University Press, 1941.

Hart, Ivor B., *James Watt and the History of Steam Power*, H. Schuman, 1949.

———, *Makers of Science*, Oxford University Press, 1924.

———, *The Mechanical Investigations of Leonardo da Vinci*, Open Court, 1925.

Hecht, Selig, *Explaining the Atom*, Viking Press, 1947.

Hodgins, Eric, and F. A. Magoun, *Behemoth, The Story of Power*, Doubleday Doran, 1932.

Hoffman, Banesh, *The Strange Story of the Quantum*, Harper, 1947.

Hogben, Lancelot, *Science for the Citizen*, Knopf, 1938.

Holmyard, Eric J., *Makers of Chemistry*, Oxford, 1931.

Holton, Gerald, *Introduction to Concepts and Theories in Physical Science*, Addison-Wesley, 1952.

Jaffe, Bernard, *Crucibles*, Simon & Schuster, 1930.

Jeans, Sir James, *An Introduction to the Kinetic Theory of Gases*, Cambridge University Press, 1946.

Knedler, John W. (Ed.), *Masterworks of Science*, Doubleday, 1949.

Kolin, Alexander, *Physics, Its Laws, Ideas and Methods*, McGraw-Hill, 1950.

Ladenburg, Albert, *Histoire du développement de la chimie depuis Lavoisier jusqu'à nos jours*, Colson, 1911.

Lapp, R. E., and H. L. Andrews, *Nuclear Radiation Physics*, 2d ed., Prentice-Hall, 1954.

Larsen, Egon (Lehrburger), *An American in Europe: the Life of Benjamin Thompson, Count Rumford*, Rider, 1953.

Leicester, Henry M., and Herbert S. Klickstein, A *Source Book in Chemistry*, McGraw-Hill, 1952.

Lemon, H. B., *From Galileo to the Nuclear Age*, University of Chicago Press, 1946.

Luhr, Overton, *Physics Tells Why*, Ronald Press, 1943.

Mach, Ernst, *History and Root of the Principle of Conservation of Energy*, Open Court, 1911.

———, *The Science of Mechanics*, Open Court, 1942.

Magie, W. F., *A Source Book in Physics*, McGraw-Hill, 1935.

McKie, Douglas, *Antoine Lavoisier*, Henry Schuman, 1952.

———, and Niels H. Heathcote, *The Discovery of Specific and Latent Heats*, Edward Arnold, 1935.

Mees, C. E. Kenneth, *The Path of Science*, Wiley, 1946.

Meggers, William F., "Measurement by Mercury," *Scientific American* 179: 49 (Aug. 1948).

Miller, Dayton C., *The Science of Musical Sounds*, Macmillan, 1937.

Moody, Ernest A., and Marshall Claggett, (Ed.), *The Medieval Science of Weights*, University of Wisconsin Press, 1952.

More, Louis Trenchard, *Isaac Newton, A Biography*, Scribner, 1934.

———, *The Life and Works of the Honorable Robert Boyle*, Oxford, 1944.

Moreau, Henri, "The Genesis of the Metric System and the Work of the International Bureau of Weights and Measures," *Journal of Chemical Education* 30:3 (Jan. 1953).

National Council of Teachers of Mathematics Twentieth Yearbook, *The Metric System of Weights and Measures*, Bureau of Publications, Teachers College, Columbia University, 1948.

Newton, Sir Isaac, *Opticks*, Dover Publications, 1952.

Ornstein, Martha, *The Role of Scientific Societies in the Seventeenth Century*, University of Chicago Press, 1928.

Partington, J. R., *A Short History of Chemistry*, Macmillan, 1949.

Phin, John, *The Seven Follies of Science*, Van Nostrand, 1912.

Pledge, H. T., *Science Since 1500*, Ministry of Education, Science Museum, Great Britain.

Read, John, *Humor and Humanism in Chemistry*, G. Bell & Sons, 1947.

————, *Prelude to Chemistry*, Macmillan, 1937.

Roller, Duane, *The Early Development of the Concepts of Temperature and Heat*, Harvard University Press, 1950.

Skilling, Hugh H., *Exploring Electricity*, Ronald Press, 1948.

Solomon, Arthur K., *Why Smash Atoms*, Harvard University Press, 1946.

Spiers, I. H. B. and A. G. H. (translators), *The Physical Treatises of Pascal*, Columbia University Press, 1937.

Stillman, John M., *The Story of Early Chemistry*, D. Appleton & Co., 1924.

Stimson, Dorothy, *Scientists and Amateurs*, Henry Schuman, 1948.

Sullivan, J. W. N., *Isaac Newton*, Macmillan, 1938.

Taylor, F. Sherwood, *Galileo and the Freedom of Thought*, Watts & Co., 1938.

————, *The Alchemists*, Henry Schuman, 1949.

————, *The March of Mind*, Macmillan, 1939.

Taylor, Lloyd W., *Physics, the Pioneer Science*, Houghton Mifflin, 1941.

Thompson, J. A., *Count Rumford of Massachusetts*, Farrar & Rhinehart, 1935.

Tyndall, John, *Heat a Mode of Motion*, Appleton-Century, 1909.

Weeks, Mary E., *The Discovery of the Elements*, Journal of Chemical Education, 1945.

White, Harvey E., *Classical and Modern Physics*, Van Nostrand, 1940.

————, *Modern College Physics*, Van Nostrand, 1948.

Whittaker, Sir Edmund T., *History of the Theory of Aether and Electricity*, Thomas Nelson & Sons, 1951.

Wightman, William P. D., *The Growth of Scientific Ideas*, Yale University Press, 1951.

Wolf, Abraham, *A History of Science and Technology in the 18th Century*, Macmillan, 1939.

————, *A History of Science and Technology in the 16th and 17th Century*, Allen & Unwin, 1950.

Wood, Alexander, *Joule and the Study of Energy*, G. Bell & Sons, 1925.

ASTRONOMY

Abetti, Giorgio, *The History of Astronomy*, Henry Schuman, 1952.

Baker, Robert H., *Astronomy*, 7th ed., Van Nostrand, 1959.

———, *Introducing the Constellations*, Viking Press, 1957.

———, *An Introduction to Astronomy*, 5th ed., Van Nostrand, 1957.

Baldwin, Ralph B., *The Face of the Moon*, University of Chicago Press, 1949.

Barton, William H., Jr., and Joseph Maron Joseph, *Starcraft*, Whittlesey House, 1938.

Bok, Bart J. and Priscilla F., *The Milky Way*, 3d ed., Harvard University Press, 1957.

Bonestell, Chesley, and Willy Ley, *The Conquest of Space*, Viking Press, 1950.

Couderc, Paul, *The Expansion of the Universe*, Macmillan, 1952.

Doig, Peter A., *A Concise History of Astronomy*, Chapman & Hall, 1950.

Gamow, George, *The Creation of the Universe*, Viking Press, 1952.

Haber, Heinz, *Man in Space*, Bobbs-Merrill, 1953.

Harsanyi, Zsolt, *The Star Gazer*, translated by Paul Tabor, Putnam's, 1939.

Hoyle, Fred, *Frontiers of Astronomy*, Harper, 1955.

Jeans, Sir James, *The Universe Around Us*, Macmillan, 1944.

King, Henry C., *The History of the Telescope*, Sky Publishing Corp., 1955.

Krogdahl, Wasley S., *The Astronomical Universe*, Macmillan, 1952.

Kuipfer, Gerard P. (Ed.), *The Earth as a Planet*, University of Chicago Press, 1955.

———, *The Sun*, University of Chicago Press, 1954.

Larousse Encyclopedia of Astronomy, first English language ed., Putnam, 1959.

Ley, Willy, *Rockets, Missiles, and Space Travel*, Viking Press, 1957.

Mehlin, Theodore G., *Astronomy*, Wiley, 1959.

Nininger, Harvey H., *Our Stone-pelted Planet*, Houghton Mifflin, 1933.

Payne-Gaposchkin, Cecilia, *An Introduction to Astronomy*, Prentice-Hall, 1954.

Pfeiffer, J., *The Changing Universe*, Random House, 1956.

Rey, Hans A., *The Stars, A New Way to See Them*, Houghton Mifflin, 1952.

Richardson, Robert S., *Exploring Mars*, McGraw-Hill, 1954.

Russell, Henry N., *Astronomy*, Vols. 1 and 2, Ginn, 1945.

Ryan, Cornelius (Ed.), *Conquest of the Moon*, Viking Press, 1953.

Shapley, Harlow, *The Inner Metagalaxy*, Yale University Press, 1957.

Shapley, Harlow, *Of Stars and Men*, Beacon, 1958.

———, and Helen E. Howarth (Eds.), *Source Book in Astronomy*, Mc-Graw-Hill, 1929.

Sidgwick, John B., *William Herschel, Explorer of the Heavens*, Faber & Faber, 1953.

———, *The Heavens Above*, Oxford University Press, 1948.

Skilling, William T., and Robert S. Richardson, *A Brief Text in Astronomy*, 2d ed., Holt, 1959.

Struve, Otto, Beverly Lynds, and Helen Pillans, *Elementary Astronomy*, Oxford University Press, 1959.

Urey, Harold C., *The Planets*, Yale University Press, 1952.

Vaucouleurs, Gerard de, *The Planet Mars*, translated by Patrick Moore, Faber & Faber, 1950.

Watson, Fletcher G., *Between the Planets*, Harvard University Press, 1956.

Williams, Lou, *A Dipper Full of Stars*, Follett Publishing Company, 1950.

Woodbury, David O., *The Glass Giant of Palomar*, Dodd Mead, 1948.

Wright, Helen, *Palomar*, Macmillan, 1952.

METEOROLOGY

Blair, Thomas A., *Weather Elements*, 4th ed., Prentice-Hall, 1957.

Flora, Snowden D., *Tornadoes of the United States*, University of Oklahoma Press, 1953.

Grant, H. D., *Cloud and Weather Atlas*, Coward-McCann, 1944.

Halpine, Charles G., *A Pilot's Meteorology*, 2d ed., Van Nostrand, 1953.

————, and H. H. Taylor, *A Mariner's Meteorology*, Van Nostrand, 1956.

Haynes, B. C., *Meteorology for Pilots*, Government Printing Office, Washington, D.C., 1943.

————, *Techniques of Observing the Weather*, Wiley, 1947.

Koeppe, Clarence E., and George C. De Long, *Weather and Climate*, McGraw-Hill, 1958.

Krick, Irving P., and Roscoe Fleming, *Sun, Sea, and Sky*, Lippincott, 1954.

Lehr, P. E., R. W. Burnett, and H. S. Zim, *Weather*, Simon & Schuster, 1957.

Malone, Thomas F. (Ed.), *Compendium of Meteorology*, American Meteorological Society, Boston, Mass., 1951.

Mudge, Robert W., *Meteorology for Pilots*, McGraw-Hill, 1945.

Neuberger, Hans H., and F. Briscoes Stephens, *Weather and Man*, Prentice-Hall, 1948.

Petterssen, Sverre, *Introduction to Meteorology*, 2d ed., McGraw-Hill, 1958.

Stetson, Harlan T., *Sunspots in Action*, Ronald Press, 1947.

Tannehill, Ivan R., *Hurricanes: Their Nature and History*, 5th ed., Princeton University Press, 1944.

Taylor, George F., *Elementary Meteorology*, Prentice-Hall, 1954.

Trewartha, Glenn T., *An Introduction to Climate*, 3d ed., McGraw-Hill, 1954.

GEOLOGY

Ayres, Eugene, and C. A. Scarlott, *Energy Sources—The Wealth of the World*, McGraw-Hill, 1952.

Bateman, A. M., *The Formation of Mineral Deposits*, Wiley, 1951.

Carson, Rachel L., *The Sea Around Us*, Oxford University Press, 1951.

Cloos, Hans, *Conversation with the Earth*, Knopf, 1953.

Colbert, Edwin H., *The Dinosaur Book*, 2d ed., McGraw-Hill, 1951.

————, *Evolution of the Vertebrates*, Wiley, 1955.

Coleman, Satis N., *Volcanoes New and Old*, John Day, 1946.

Dake, C. L., and J. S. Brown, *Interpretation of Topographic and Geologic Maps*, McGraw-Hill, 1925.

Dunbar, Carl O., *Historical Geology*, John Wiley and Sons, Inc., 1949.

Engeln, Oscar D. von, and Kenneth Caster, *Geology*, McGraw-Hill, 1952.

Fenton, Carroll L. and Mildred A., *Giants of Geology*, Doubleday, 1952.

————, *The Rock Book*, Doubleday, 1940.

————, *The Fossil Book*, Doubleday, 1958.

Flint, Richard F., *Glacial and Pleistocene Geology*, Wiley, 1957.

Garrels, Robert, *A Textbook of Geology*, Harper, 1951.

Gilluly, James, A. C. Waters, and A. O. Woodford, *Principles of Geology*, W. H. Freeman and Company, 2d ed., 1959.

Holmes, Arthur, *Principles of Physical Geology*, Ronald Press, 1945.

Hough, Jack L., *Geology of the Great Lakes*, University of Illinois Press, 1958.

Hurley, Patrick M., *How Old Is the Earth?*, Anchor Books, 1959.

Jaggar, Thomas A., *Volcanoes Declare War*, Honolulu, Paradise of the Pacific, Ltd., 1945.

Jean, F. C., E. C. Harrah, F. L. Hermon, and S. R. Powers, *Man and His Biological World*, revised ed., Ginn, 1952.

King, Philip B., *The Evolution of North America*, Princeton University Press, 1959.

Kuenen, Ph. H., *Marine Geology*, Wiley, 1950.

Lahee, Frederick H., *Field Geology*, 5th ed., McGraw-Hill, 1952.

Leet, L. Don, and Sheldon Judson, *Physical Geology*, Prentice-Hall, 2d ed., 1958.

Lobeck, A. K., *Geomorphology*, McGraw-Hill, 1939.

————, *Things Maps Don't Tell Us*, Macmillan, 1956.

Longwell, C. R., and R. F. Flint, *Introduction to Physical Geology*, Wiley, 1955.

Mather, Kirtley F., and Shirley L. Mason (Eds.), *A Source Book in Geology*, McGraw-Hill, 1939.

Miller, W. J., *An Introduction to Physical Geology*, 5th ed., Van Nostrand, 1949.

Monnett, V. E., and H. E. Brown, *The Principles of Physical Geology*, Ginn, 1950.

Moody, P. A., *Introduction to Evolution*, Harper, 1953.

Moore, R. G., *An Introduction to Historical Geology*, McGraw-Hill, 2d ed., 1958.

Moore, Ruth, *The Earth We Live On*, Knopf, 1956.

————, *Man, Time, and Fossils*, Knopf, 1953.

America's Wonderlands, The National Parks, National Geographic Society, Washington, D. C., 1959.

Parson, R. L., *Conserving American Resources*, Prentice-Hall, 1956.

Pirsson, L. V., and A. Knopf, *Rocks and Rock Minerals*, 3d ed., Wiley, 1947.

The Planet Earth (A Scientific American Book), Simon and Schuster, 1957.

Riley, Charles M., *Our Mineral Resources*, Wiley, 1959.

Shepard, Francis P., *The Earth Beneath the Sea*, Johns Hopkins Press, 1959.
Shepard, F. P., *Submarine Geology*, Harper, 1948.
Shimer, H. W., and R. R. Shrock, *Index Fossils of North America*, Wiley, 1944.
Shimer, John A., *This Sculptured Earth: The Landscape of America*, Columbia University Press, 1959.
Soil: The Yearbook of Agriculture 1957, U.S. Dept. of Agriculture, 1957.
Stamp, Lawrence D., *The Earth's Crust*, Crown Publishers, 1951.
Stirton, R. A., *Time, Life, and Man: The Fossil Record*, Wiley, 1959.
Strahler, A. N., *Physical Geography*, Wiley, 1951.
Thornbury, W. D., *Principles of Geomorphology*, Wiley, 1954.
Trefethen, Joseph W., *Geology for Engineers*, 2d ed., Van Nostrand, 1959.
Water: The Yearbook of Agriculture 1955, U.S. Dept. of Agriculture, 1955.
Williams, Howel, *Crater Lake: The Story of Its Origin*, University of California Press, 1951.
Zumberge, James H., *Elements of Geology*, Wiley, 1958.

SUGGESTED FILMS IN EARTH SCIENCE

Sources of Information:

1. *Educator's Guide to Free Films*, Educator's Progress Service, Randolph, Wisc.
2. *Educational Film Guide*, H. W. Wilson Company, 950 University Avenue, New York 52, N.Y.

A World Is Born
A is for Atom
Birth of an Oil Field
Birth of the Soil
Clean Waters
Energy from the Sun
Exploring Our Universe
Free Horizons
Geyser Melodies
Ground Water
In the Beginning
Krakatoa
Lead from Mine to Metal
Mountain Building

Pipeline to the Clouds
Prospecting for Petroleum
Raindrops and Soil Erosion
Riches of the Earth
Solar Family
Sulfur
The Earth in Motion
The Earth Our Planet
The Fossil Story
The Work of Rivers
Volcanoes in Action
Wearing Away of the Land
Weather
The Depths of Space
How We Explore Space

PERIODICALS

American Journal of Physics, published by American Institute of Physics, Prince and Lemon Streets, Lancaster, Pa.
Earth Science, published bimonthly by Earth Science Publishing Company, Box 1357, Chicago 90, Illinois.
Journal of Chemical Education, published by Division of Chemical Educa-

tion of the American Chemical Society, 20th and Northampton Streets, Easton, Pa.

Natural History, published by American Museum of Natural History, New York 24, N.Y. (includes *The Sky Reporter*).

Science, published weekly by American Association for Advancement of Science, 1515 Massachusetts Avenue, N.W., Washington 5, D.C.

Science Digest, published by Science Digest, Inc., 200 East Ontario Street, Chicago 11, Illinois.

Science News Letter, published weekly by Science Service, Inc., 1719 N. Street, N.W., Washington 6, D.C.

Scientific American, published by Scientific American, Inc., 415 Madison Avenue, New York 17, N.Y.

Sky and Telescope, published by Sky Publishing Corporation, Harvard College Observatory, Cambridge 38, Mass.

The Observer's Handbook for 19—, published annually by the Royal Astronomical Society of Canada, 252 College Street, Toronto 2B, Ontario, Canada.

APPENDIX

Length

1 inch = 2.54 cm
1 meter = 3.28 ft = 1.09 yd
1 angstrom unit (Å) = 10^{-8} cm

Area

1 acre = 43,560 sq ft

Volume

1 pint = 16 fluid oz (U.S.)
1 ml = 0.034 fluid oz (U.S.)
1 ml = 1.000027 cc
1 liter = 0.264 gal (U.S.)

Mass

1 pound = 453.6 gm
1 kilogram = 2.2 lb

Speed

60 mi/hr = 88 ft/sec

Pressure

1 atmosphere = 14.7 lb/sq in.
1 atmosphere = 76 cm Hg
1 atmosphere = 1013.2 millibars

Work and Energy

1 calorie = 4.19 joules
1 joule = 10^7 ergs
1 erg = 1 dyne cm
1 foot pound = 1.35 joules
1 electron volt = 1.60×10^{-12} erg

Force

1 gram = 980 dynes
1 pound = 32 poundals
= 16 oz (avoirdupois)
1 newton = 10^5 dynes

Power

1 horse power = 33,000 ft lb/min

TABLE OF CONSTANTS

Avogadro's number	6.02×10^{23}
Charge of the electron	4.80×10^{-10} E.S.U.
Gravitational constant	6.67×10^{-8} (cgs unit)
Planck's constant	6.62×10^{-27} erg sec
Standard temperature and pressure	0°C and 760 mm of mercury
Velocity of light (in vacuo)	186,000 mi/sec or 3×10^{10} cm/sec
Velocity of sound (at 0°C)	1090 ft/sec

ATOMIC WEIGHTS AND ATOMIC NUMBERS

Element	Symbol	Atomic Number	Atomic Weight*
Actinium	Ac	89	227
Aluminum	Al	13	26.98
Americium	Am	95	[243]
Antimony	Sb	51	121.76
Argon	Ar	18	39.944
Arsenic	As	33	74.91
Astatine	At	85	[210]
Barium	Ba	56	137.36
Berkelium	Bk	97	[249]
Beryllium	Be	4	9.013
Bismuth	Bi	83	209.00
Boron	B	5	10.82
Bromine	Br	35	79.916
Cadmium	Cd	48	112.41
Calcium	Ca	20	40.08
Californium	Cf	98	[249]
Carbon	C	6	12.011
Cerium	Ce	58	140.13
Cesium	Cs	55	132.91
Chlorine	Cl	17	35.457
Chromium	Cr	24	52.01
Cobalt	Co	27	58.94
Copper	Cu	29	63.54
Curium	Cm	96	[245]
Dysprosium	Dy	66	162.51
Erbium	Er	68	167.27
Europium	Eu	63	152.0
Fluorine	F	9	19.00
Francium	Fr	87	[223]
Gadolinium	Gd	64	157.26
Gallium	Ga	31	69.72
Germanium	Ge	32	72.60
Gold	Au	79	197.0
Hafnium	Hf	72	178.50
Helium	He	2	4.003
Holmium	Ho	67	164.94
Hydrogen	H	1	1.0080
Indium	In	49	114.82
Iodine	I	53	126.91
Iridium	Ir	77	192.2
Iron	Fe	26	55.85
Krypton	Kr	36	83.80

* A value given in brackets denotes the mass number of the isotope of longest known half-life.

Element	Symbol	Atomic Number	Atomic Weight*
Lanthanum	La	57	138.92
Lead	Pb	82	207.21
Lithium	Li	3	6.940
Lutetium	Lu	71	174.99
Magnesium	Mg	12	24.32
Manganese	Mn	25	54.94
Mendelevium	Mv	101	[256]
Mercury	Hg	80	200.61
Molybdenum	Mo	42	95.95
Neodymium	Nd	60	144.27
Neon	Ne	10	20.183
Neptunium	Np	93	[237]
Nickel	Ni	28	58.71
Niobium (Columbium)	Nb	41	92.91
Nitrogen	N	7	14.008
Osmium	Os	76	190.2
Oxygen	O	8	16.0000
Palladium	Pd	46	106.7
Phosphorus	P	15	30.975
Platinum	Pt	78	195.09
Plutonium	Pu	94	[242]
Polonium	Po	84	210
Potassium	K	19	39.100
Praseodymium	Pr	59	140.92
Promethium	Pm	61	[145]
Protactinium	Pa	91	231
Radium	Ra	88	226.05
Radon	Rn	86	222
Rhenium	Re	75	186.22
Rhodium	Rh	45	102.91
Rubidium	Rb	37	85.48
Ruthenium	Ru	44	101.1
Samarium	Sm	62	150.35
Scandium	Sc	21	44.96
Selenium	Se	34	78.96
Silicon	Si	14	28.09
Silver	Ag	47	107.880
Sodium	Na	11	22.991*
Strontium	Sr	38	87.63
Sulfur	S	16	32.066†
Tantalum	Ta	73	180.95

† Because of the natural variations in the relative abundance of the isotopes of sulfur the atomic weight of this element has a range of ±0.003.

ATOMIC WEIGHTS AND ATOMIC NUMBERS (continued)

Element	Symbol	Atomic Number	Atomic Weight*
Technetium	Tc	43	[99]
Tellurium	Te	52	127.61
Terbium	Tb	65	158.93
Thallium	Tl	81	204.39
Thorium	Th	90	232.05
Thulium	Tm	69	168.94
Tin	Sn	50	118.70
Titanium	Ti	22	47.90
Tungsten	W	74	183.86
Uranium	U	92	238.07
Vanadium	V	23	50.95
Xenon	Xe	54	131.30
Ytterbium	Yb	70	173.04
Yttrium	Y	39	88.92
Zinc	Zn	30	65.38
Zirconium	Zr	40	91.22

TABLE OF VALENCES OF COMMON IONS

Name of Ion	Symbol	Valence	Name of Ion	Symbol	Valence
Ammonium	NH_4^+	+1	Acetate	$C_2H_3O_2^-$	−1
Hydrogen	H^+	+1	Bicarbonate	HCO_3^-	−1
Potassium	K^+	+1	Bisulfate	HSO_4^-	−1
Silver	Ag^+	+1	Bromide	Br^-	−1
Sodium	Na^+	+1	Chloride	Cl^-	−1
Barium	Ba^{++}	+2	Fluoride	F^-	−1
Calcium	Ca^{++}	+2	Hydroxide	OH^-	−1
Copper (cupric)	Cu^{++}	+2	Iodide	I^-	−1
			Nitrate	NO_3^-	−1
Iron (ferrous)	Fe^{++}	+2	Nitrite	NO_2^-	−1
Lead (plumbous)	Pb^{++}	+2	Thiocyanate	CNS^-	−1
			Carbonate	$CO_3^=$	−2
Magnesium	Mg^{++}	+2	Chromate	$CrO_4^=$	−2
Mercury (mercuric)	Hg^{++}	+2	Oxalate	$C_2O_4^=$	−2
			Oxide	$O^=$	−2
Tin (stannous)	Sn^{++}	+2	Silicate	$SiO_3^=$	−2
Zinc	Zn^{++}	+2	Sulfate	$SO_4^=$	−2
Aluminum	Al^{+++}	+3	Sulfide	$S^=$	−2
Iron (ferric)	Fe^{+++}	+3	Sulfite	$SO_3^=$	−2
Lead (plumbic)	Pb^{++++}	+4	Arsenate	$AsO_4^\equiv$	−3
Tin (stannic)	Sn^{++++}	+4	Phosphate	$PO_4^\equiv$	−3

FORMULA WRITING SHEET I

VALENCES OF POSITIVE IONS

	Silver Ag^+	Sodium Na^+	Calcium Ca^{++}	Aluminum Al^{+++}	Magnesium Mg^{++}
Nitrate NO_3^-					
Carbonate $CO_3^=$					
Phosphate $PO_4^{\equiv}$					
Sulfide $S^=$					
Chloride Cl^-					
Sulfate $SO_4^=$					
Hydroxide OH^-					
Sulfite $SO_3^=$					
Chromate $CrO_4^=$					
Bromide Br^-					

VALENCES OF NEGATIVE IONS

FORMULA WRITING SHEET II

VALENCES OF POSITIVE IONS

	Potassium K^+	Cupric Cu^{++}	Ferric Fe^{+++}	Zinc Zn^{++}	Ammonium NH_4^+
Nitrate NO_3^-					
Carbonate $CO_3^=$					
Phosphate $PO_4^{\equiv}$					
Sulfide $S^=$					
Chloride Cl^-					
Sulfate $SO_4^=$					
Hydroxide OH^-					
Sulfite $SO_3^=$					
Chromate $CrO_4^=$					
Bromide Br^-					

VALENCES OF NEGATIVE IONS

URANIUM DISINTEGRATION SERIES

Name of Element	Atomic Number	Atomic Weight	Radiation	Symbol of Element Resulting from Radiation Emission
Uranium I	92	238	alpha $_2$He	Th^{234}
Uranium X$_1$	90	234	beta	$_{91}$U^{234} Pa
Uranium X$_2$	91 92	234 234	beta $_{-1}e^0$	$_{92}$—
Uranium II	92 90	234 230	alpha	—
Ionium	—	—	alpha	—
Radium	—	—	alpha	—
Radon	—	—	alpha	—
Radium A	—	—	alpha	—
Radium B	—	—	beta	—
Radium C	—	—	beta	—
Radium C^1	—	—	alpha	—
Radium D	—	—	beta	—
Radium E	—	—	beta	—
Radium F	—	—	alpha	—
Radium G (stable lead isotope)	82	206	—	Pb^{206}

The student is to supply the appropriate atomic numbers and atomic weights and to fill in the symbol of the resulting element when the previous element has emitted the radiation indicated.

When Uranium I emits an alpha particle it loses 2 protons, which decreases the atomic number to 90, and 2 neutrons, a total of 4 nucleons. Hence the atomic weight decreases by four units. The element of atomic number 90 is thorium. It is the 234 isotope of thorium.

$$_iX^1 + beta\,(_{-1}e^0) = _2X^1$$

$$_4X^4 + alpha\,(_2He^4) = _2X^0$$

ANSWERS TO PROBLEMS

Chapter 1

1. 29.9 in. *2.* 242 km. *3.* 28.4 kg. *4.* 28.4 gm. *5.* 59 gm. *6.* 7.35 cc. *7.* 587 $\times 10^{10}$mi/yr.

Chapter 2

1. 100 lb. *2.* 60 lb. *3.* 16.7 lb. *4.* 126 lb. *5.* 66.7 lb. *6.* 62 lb.

Review

1. Specific gravity $= 2.78$. *2.* 28 liters.

Chapter 3

1. m/sec. *2.* (a) 247.5 mi. (b) 66 ft/sec. *3.* 2400 lb. *4.* 2000 poundals. *5.* 320 poundals.

Review

1. 16.7 lb. *2.* 111 lb. M.A. $= 6.75$.

Chapter 4

1. (a) ft/sec. (b) g in meters/sec^2, d in meters. (c) meters. *2.* (a) 160 ft/sec. (b) 320 ft/sec. *3.* (a) 2.5×10^6 (or 25×10^5). (b) 1.37×10^{-8} (or 13.7×10^{-9}). *4.* 4.94×10^{19}. *5.* 1.5×10^8. *6.* 1.35×10^{26} molecules. *7.* 5×10^{-9} cm^2. *8.* 6.23×10^{18} electrons. *9.* 2.67×10^{-3} dynes.

Review

1. 40 newtons. *2.* 93 gm. *3.* 503.

Chapter 5

1. 252 calories. *2.* 144×10^6 ft lb. *3.* 387,200 ft poundals. *4.* 725,000 ft lb. *5.* 96.0 kg m; 0.420 hp. *6.* 2551 gm cm. *7.* 27.5°. *8.* 37°C. *9.* $-40°$.

Review

1. 352 ft. *2.* 2.66. *3.* 20,000 dynes.

Chapter 6

1. 1026 millibars. *2.* 9.61 liters. *3.* 151.5°C. *4.* 111 cm of Hg.

5. $PV = NRT$

$$\frac{P}{T} = \frac{NR}{V}$$

If the mass of gas and its volume are constant,

$\frac{NR}{V}$ may be replaced by k.

$$\frac{P}{T} = k$$

1038 mm of Hg.

Review

1. 4.31×10^{-14} ergs. 2. 384 in/sec².

Chapter 7

1. $NaCl = 58.5$ $Al_2(SO_4)_3 = 342$
   $NaHCO_3 = 84$ $Ca_3(PO_4)_2 = 310$
   $NaOH = 40$ $C_2H_5OH = 46$
   $CaCO_3 = 100$ $HNO_3 = 63$
2. (a) $2H_2 + O_2 \rightarrow 2H_2O$.
   (b) $N_2 + 3H_2 \rightarrow 2NH_3$.
   (c) $CaCO_3 + 2HCl \rightarrow CaCl_2 + H_2O + CO_2\uparrow$.
   (d) $2Al + 3H_2SO_4 \rightarrow Al_2(SO_4)_3 + 3H_2\uparrow$.
   (e) $MgCl_2 + 2AgNO_3 \rightarrow 2AgCl\downarrow + Mg(NO_3)_2$.
   (f) $BaCl_2 + K_2CrO_4 \rightarrow BaCrO_4\downarrow + 2KCl$.
   (g) $2Na_3AsO_4 + 3Ca(NO_3)_2 \rightarrow Ca_3(AsO_4)_2\downarrow + 6NaNO_3$.
   (h) $2NaBr + 2H_2SO_4 \rightarrow Na_2SO_4 + Br_2 + SO_2\uparrow + 2H_2O$.
3. (a) $2AgNO_3 + CaCl_2 \rightarrow 2AgCl\downarrow + Ca(NO_3)_2$.
   (b) $3BaCl_2 + Al_2(SO_4)_3 \rightarrow 3BaSO_4\downarrow + 2AlCl_3$.
   (c) $2NH_4I + Ca(OH)_2 \rightarrow CaI_2 + 2NH_3\uparrow + 2H_2O$.
4. (a) 11 lb. (b) 12 gm. 5. (a) 14.3% C. (b) 22.2% N. (c) 14.8% H_2O.

Review

1. 150 lb. 2. 5.6 sec.

Chapter 8

1. 5.1×10^{14} vps. (waves/sec). 2. 300 Å, ultraviolet. 3. Station WABC. Frequency 770 kc. Wave length = 389 meters.

Review

1. 256 ft/sec. 2. 176°F., 353° absolute. 3. 17.3 liters.

Chapter 9

1. 2.68×10^{19} molecules. 2. 21/100,000.

Review

1. 33.3 liters. 2. 83.2 gm. 3. 12,500 ft lb.

Chapter 10

1. 0.33 ampere. 2. 15 ohms. 3. 0.101 gm. 4. 3.2×10^{-3} ohms. 469 amperes.

Review

1. 8.3 sec. *2.* 43.8 = molecular weight, heavier, 1.5 times. *3.* 15.7.

Chapter 11

Review

1. 400 poundals; 12.5 lb. *2.* 2.13 ft.

Chapter 12

1. 3.12×10^6 atoms. *2.* 2.07 mev.

Review

1. 357 lb. *2.* $X = 2/9(F - 32)$. *3.* Hydrogen effuses 4.7 times as fast as CO_2.

Chapter 13

1. 1.99×10^{-4} ergs.

Review

1. 1410 ft. *2.* 56.3 lb. *3.* 9×10^7 ft poundals. *4.* 24 ohms.

Chapter 14

Review

1. Weight in water 213 gm; specific gravity 2.70. *2.* 750 poundals. *3.* 384 ft/sec. 2304 ft. *4.* 64.7. *5.* 4.7 hp. *6.* (*a*) Balanced equation: $Cu + 4HNO_3 \rightarrow Cu(NO_3)_2 + 2NO_2 \uparrow + 2H_2O$. (*b*) 149 gm.

Index

An asterisk (*) following a page number indicates an illustration